The Raman Effect

IN TWO VOLUMES

Volume 2: Applications

Sir Chandrasekhara Raman

1888-1970

THE RAMAN EFFECT

IN TWO VOLUMES

Volume 2: Applications

Edited by A. Anderson

University of Waterloo
Waterloo, Ontario, Canada

MARCEL DEKKER, INC., New York 1973

MARCEL DEKKER, INC.
95 *Madison Avenue, New York, New York* 10016

LIBRARY OF CONGRESS CATALOG CARD NUMBER 77-134788
ISBN 0-8247-1015-0

PRINTED IN THE UNITED STATES OF AMERICA

Preface

> The universality of the phenomenon, the convenience of the experimental technique, and the simplicity of the spectra obtained enable the effect to be used as an experimental aid to the solution of a wide range of problems in physics and chemistry. Indeed, it may be said that it is this fact which constitutes the principal significance of the effect. The frequency-differences determined from the spectra, the width and character of the lines appearing in them, and the intensity and state of polarization of the scattered radiations enable us to obtain an insight into the ultimate structure of the scattering substance.

These words, taken verbatim from Sir C. V. Raman's Nobel Lecture delivered at Stockholm in 1930, are, astonishingly, just as relevant today as 40 years ago. They indicate clearly the insight and perception of the discoverer of the Raman effect, but during most of this period such claims would have been greeted with skepticism, because infrared spectroscopy had proved more convenient and useful for most problems. In recent years, however, Raman spectroscopy has enjoyed a spectacular resurgence in popularity and has attracted many new research workers and students. This "Raman Renaissance," as it has been aptly named, has embraced the disciplines of both physics and chemistry, and although the prime motivator of the revival has been the dramatic experimental advantages afforded by the laser, the many new discoveries have also stimulated intensive theoretical activities.

The aim of this book is to provide a basic coverage of the theoretical and experimental principles of Raman spectroscopy and discussions of some of its important applications in physics and chemistry. It is hoped that it will prove useful to students and research workers entering this exciting field or related areas, and to those in other subjects, where Raman results are providing complementary information to that obtained from different techniques.

The three main problems encountered in the compilation of any multi-authored volume appear to be those of meeting a common deadline, reaching a uniform level of presentation, and avoiding serious overlap. A few comments on each of these, as they affected this book, may be in order. There have been some inevitable delays in obtaining manuscripts from some authors, but fortunately these occurred at a time when there appeared to be a slight slackening of pace in the sometimes frantic activity in this field. The authors were, of course, aware of the dangers of obsolescence in a rapidly developing area, and have tried to emphasize those aspects they believe to have more than transient value. Each author was asked to write at a level suitable for a "typical graduate student," and was reminded that readers would be from the disciplines of physics or chemistry. Nevertheless, some differences in depth of coverage and amount of rigor are inevitable, considering the variety of backgrounds and nationalities represented. Contributors were encouraged to provide references when their own coverage of a particular topic was cursory, and to insert descriptive physical interpretations into long detailed theoretical developments, to minimize these problems. From the chapter outlines submitted by the authors, changes to avoid major regions of overlap were suggested. In a few instances, minor duplications occurred, although usually at different levels or from different viewpoints. Retention of these was preferred to making further changes and possibly breaking the continuity of a particular author's contribution.

I would like to express my thanks to all the authors for their cooperation and efforts during the preparation of this book. I am also grateful to several of my colleagues at the University of Waterloo: Drs. Bruce Torrie, Don Irish, Neil Isenor, and Mike Hutley, for reading several chapters and making valuable suggestions, and Miss Sylvia MacQuarrie for her skilful secretarial help.

Waterloo, Ontario, Canada A. ANDERSON

Contributors to Volume 2

J. A. KONINGSTEIN, Carleton University, Ottawa, Canada

O. S. MORTENSEN, University of Copenhagen, Copenhagen, Denmark

RODRIGUE SAVOIE, Department of Chemistry, Université Laval, Quebec, Canada

R. STUART TOBIAS, Department of Chemistry, Purdue University, West Lafayette, Indiana

ALFONS WEBER, Physics Department, Fordham University, Bronx, New York

G. R. WILKINSON, Department of Physics, King's College, University of London, U. K.

Contents

Contents of Volume 1

The Raman Effect

IN TWO VOLUMES

Volume 2: Applications

CHAPTER 7

Applications to Inorganic Chemistry

R. STUART TOBIAS

DEPARTMENT OF CHEMISTRY
PURDUE UNIVERSITY
WEST LAFAYETTE, INDIANA

I. INTRODUCTION

A. Historical

The inorganic chemist normally makes spectroscopic studies on a compound to obtain information about the molecular or ionic structure and the chemical bonding between atoms. After a long period of quiescence, Raman spectroscopy has emerged as a very useful technique for these studies. Some indication of this is given by the number of articles reviewing various aspects of this topic which have appeared recently (*1–4*). In addition, there are several more general works (*5,6*) and reviews (*7–10a*) to which the reader is referred.

As long as 35 years ago, Raman scattering of inorganic compounds was studied by spectroscopists; however, their work made only a few significant contributions to our knowledge of molecular structure and chemical bonding. For example, the Raman spectrum of boron trifluoride, BF_3, suggested that it had a trigonal planar (point group D_{3h}) structure (*11*), but this first was established definitely by the electron diffraction study of Lévy and Brockway (*12*). Raman spectroscopy could demonstrate that the carbonate ion, CO_3^{-2}, maintained the trigonal planar structure in solution (*13*), but the ion had been known to have this structure in crystals for more than 20 years since the first X-ray investigation of calcite ($CaCO_3$) by Bragg (*14*). Intense Raman scattering assignable only to mercury–mercury bond stretching was observed with aqueous solutions containing mercury (I) salts (*15*) in what was actually the first application of Raman spectroscopy to the study of metal–metal bonding in complexes. Nevertheless, electrochemical cell measurements had shown more than 35 years earlier that univalent mercury had to exist in aqueous solutions as the dimer ion Hg_2^{+2} (*16*), and X-ray structure determinations of the halides also had shown the presence of the mercury–mercury bonds in crystals (*17*). It is interesting to note that Raman spectra again are proving useful in the study of metal–metal bonding in coordination compounds (*18*). Perhaps the most significant contribution of these early studies was in defining the structure of simple ions in aqueous solution, an area in which Raman spectroscopy reigns virtually supreme even today.

The analysis of the vibrations of ions and molecules with even moderately complex structures necessitated the development of simplified mathematical approaches, i.e., the Wilson *FG* matrix method (*19*). For most inorganic chemists, detailed normal coordinate analyses of the vibrations of polyatomic molecules only became feasible after the development of high speed digital computers and the appropriate programs for normal coordinate calculations (*20*). In some respects, the ease with which vibrational analyses now can be made is a mixed blessing. To deal with large molecules of low symmetry, the inorganic chemist normally must use some simplified force field to reduce the number of force constants to be determined. In many cases these fields are such poor approximations to reality that the potential energy distributions and consequently the detailed descriptions of the normal coordinates are virtually meaningless.

B. Raman versus Infrared Spectroscopy

Since the early 1950's, infrared spectroscopy has been used routinely by preparative inorganic chemists. Several comprehensive surveys of these applications have appeared (*21–24*). In spite of its widespread use, there are certain deficiencies which have limited the contributions of infrared spectroscopy in inorganic chemistry. It has been necessary to study many compounds as microcrystalline powders because of the lack of suitable solvents with low infrared absorption. In addition, until quite recently equipment for the study of low frequency vibrations, i.e., those lower than 650 cm^{-1}, was not generally available.

Chemists again began to apply Raman spectroscopy following the development of photoelectric instruments, particularly the Cary 81 in the United States and the Hilger in England. For many compounds these instruments made it possible to obtain a Raman spectrum with little more effort than an infrared or proton magnetic resonance spectrum. However, it has been the development of the laser excited spectrophotometer, particularly by Cary, Spex, and Jarrell-Ash in the United States and by CODERG in France, which has aroused special interest. In the field of transition metal chemistry which has grown so rapidly in the past 15 years, Raman spectroscopy now is beginning to make a contribution. In the past, the absorption of these compounds in the visible region of the spectrum often has precluded their study with instruments using mercury arc excitation. With irradiation at the 6328 Å line of a He–Ne laser, spectra can be obtained for many compounds for which previously only very poor spectra, or, indeed, no spectrum at all could be obtained. While mercury arc excitation together with a high speed monochromator still is very useful in inorganic chemistry particularly for intensity measurements, it is likely that in the future the well-equipped laboratory will also employ two or more laser sources, e.g., He–Ne or Kr^+ and Ar^+ so that blue, green, and red exciting radiation all will be available.

It is always valuable, of course, to have both the Raman and infrared spectra of a compound especially in the case of structures with appreciable symmetry. The selection rules differ, and it is often impossible to obtain all of the fundamental frequencies from one kind of spectrum alone. In addition, water is an excellent solvent for Raman spectroscopy, since it scatters very weakly. With moderately concentrated solutions, it is often possible to obtain spectra up to 3100 cm^{-1} which show no significant solvent background. Low frequency vibrations also can be studied easily with Raman spectroscopy. With relatively little care in sample preparation, aqueous solution spectra can be obtained down to 150 cm^{-1}. With pure liquids, Raman lines very close to the exciting frequency can be observed. With microcrystalline powders, the ability to study low frequency vibrations depends very much on the monochromator design. With double grating instruments, it is usually possible to obtain spectra to within 100 cm^{-1} of the exciting frequency without using special techniques. To observe smaller Raman shifts, it is usually necessary to employ narrow slits or sharp-cutting interference filters to attenuate the intense light at the exciting frequency which otherwise is reflected from the crystal faces directly into the monochromator. The advantage of Raman spectroscopy in studying the low frequency vibrations which are more important in inorganic than in organic chemistry has now been reduced somewhat with the advent of commercial far infrared spectrometers which make it possible to obtain spectra to ca. 33 cm^{-1}.

For studies on chemical equilibria in solution, Raman has an advantage over infrared spectroscopy. Concentrations of solutes can be measured more accurately from Raman intensities as a rule than from infrared intensities.

C. Structure Determination

The main application of Raman spectroscopy in inorganic chemistry will be to the problem of structure, i.e., symmetry determination. Since infrared spectroscopy has been used extensively in the assignment of structures to inorganic compounds, it seems worthwhile to end this introduction with a summary of the applications of these two techniques.

In qualitative studies of structure, Raman and infrared spectroscopy both share many of the same strong and weak points. For a given structure, the number of infrared and Raman active fundamentals may be predicted easily from simple group theoretical considerations (*25*). Additionally, on the basis of the state of polarization of the Raman scattering, it is possible to recognize totally symmetric modes. Spectra predicted for reasonable alternative structures then can be compared with the observed spectrum. With simple molecules, this is often all that is necessary to determine the symmetry of the structure. With larger, more complicated molecules, this frequently is not possible. With most inorganic compounds where all of the atoms are moderately heavy, e.g., masses greater than 15 amu, the fundamental frequencies usually will be lower than 1200 cm^{-1} unless especially strong, multiple bonds are involved. Often when only single bonds are present, all of the Raman scattering occurs within a few hundred wavenumbers of the exciting frequency. The likelihood that two or more vibrations will be accidentally degenerate is great in such cases, and consequently the numbers of Raman lines and infrared bands observed are frequently fewer than predicted on the basis of the correct structure.

With infrared spectra of complicated molecules, it is often difficult to separate the more intense overtone and combination bands from the fundamentals. This makes vibrational assignments particularly difficult. With Raman spectra, this is rarely a problem, because the overtones and combinations are low in intensity and not normally observed when recording the fundamentals.

In some cases, the problem of assigning vibrations is simplified because groups of atoms vibrate almost as entities in certain of the normal modes. Such group frequencies are well known in cyano and carbonyl complexes of metals; and normal coordinate analyses of the vibrations of metal ammines (*26,31*), $M(NH_3)_n$, and methyl derivatives, $M(CH_3)_n$ (*27,31*), have confirmed that the high frequency vibrations involve motions primarily localized in the NH_3 or CH_3^- groups, while in the low frequency vibrations the ammine and methyl groups behave approximately as masses of 17 and 15, respectively.

One additional difficulty which arises often in the study of inorganic compounds is caused by the low Raman and infrared intensities of vibrations. This factor and the problem of accidental degeneracy are responsible for the number of observed Raman lines and infrared bands frequently being fewer than the number predicted. Very often when a given vibration is both Raman and infrared active, the intensities will be found to be qualitatively complementary. As an example, the low frequency infrared active vibrations of heavy-metal ammines which involve primarily metal-nitrogen bond stretching often have such low infrared intensities that the fundamentals cannot be observed (*28–31*). With these compounds, the Raman active metal-nitrogen stretching vibrations give fairly intense scattering, so the characteristics of these bonds can be studied. On the other hand, most metal fluorides involve very polar metal-fluoride bonds. The dipole moment changes greatly in the infrared active metal-fluorine stretching vibrations leading to very high infrared intensities. The molecular polarizability varies little during the Raman active stretching modes, and the Raman intensity may be too low to be measured (*32*). Because of this intensity problem, it is important to have the Raman as well as the infrared spectra even for molecules of low symmetry where most if not all fundamentals are infrared active.

Finally, as previously noted, the group frequency concept can be used just as well with Raman as with infrared spectra. It is to be expected that depolarization ratio data will prove useful in identifying inorganic group frequencies, but such data are almost entirely lacking at the present time. It should also be noted that the group frequencies which have very high infrared intensities making them easily recognizable in a spectrum may have very low Raman intensities. In addition, the conditions which lead to useful group frequencies must be kept in mind. In an infrared spectrum, the C—O stretch of metal carbonyls is recognized easily because of its high intensity. The carbon–oxygen bond is much stronger than the carbon–metal bond, so little coupling occurs, and some of the normal modes of the metal carbonyls involve mainly simple C—O bond stretching. These usually appear in the range 1900 to 2100 cm^{-1} (*33*) compared to 2143 cm^{-1} in gaseous carbon monoxide (*34*). Thus coordination of carbon monoxide to a metal only perturbs the $C\equiv O$ stretching vibration slightly. In, for example, a metal–peroxo complex, it is much less reasonable to expect only a slightly perturbed $O—O^{-2}$ stretch to occur. The metal–oxygen and oxygen–oxygen bonds may be of almost comparable strength, and it becomes very difficult to predict even qualitatively the nature of the normal modes.

II. EXPERIMENTAL PROCEDURES

A. Introduction

The first problem the chemist faces when he wants the Raman spectrum of a compound is to determine how best to prepare the sample. If the compound is a solid, should it be studied as a single crystal, a microcrystalline powder, a mull, an alkali halide disc, a melt, or perhaps as a solution? What can be done to minimize the Rayleigh and Tyndall scattering (described here collectively as background) of solutions which will improve the signal to noise ratio? What are the best solvents to use? Is the compound thermally stable so that the spectrum can be obtained with no further precautions, or must it be cooled to a low temperature to prevent decomposition? If the compound is sensitive to the atmosphere and must be handled on a vacuum line, how can it be transferred to a suitable Raman cell? What, if anything, can be done if the compound is observed to photolyze or fluoresce in the exciting beam? What are the best conditions for studying a colored solution which absorbs to some extent at the exciting frequency? How can correct values of the Raman intensity be measured for determination of equilibrium constants and studies on chemical bonding? How can reliable depolarization ratios be determined? In this section, various techniques which are useful in obtaining Raman spectra of inorganic compounds are outlined.

This discussion will be limited to the procedure for obtaining spectra from liquids or from single crystals or powders, since almost all of the samples which will be of interest to the inorganic chemist fall into one of these categories. With excitation of the spectra by a mercury arc, fairly standard patterns of sample cells have evolved. In most cases these are easily constructed. In the case of instruments using laser excitation, many different sampling techniques have been employed. Many helpful discussions of sampling techniques have appeared in *Raman Newsletter* (*34a*). Because the laser beam may be reflected repeatedly within the sample cell or the incident beam may be focused to provide a very high energy density in a small sample volume, these cells generally require a higher degree of precision in their manufacture.

B. Sample Cells

1. Liquid Cells

Standard Raman cells for use with both mercury arc and laser excitation together with some useful variations are illustrated in Fig. 1. The cylindrical cells can be fabricated easily, and Pyrex glass is satisfactory for most purposes. The window should be optically flat and fused on. In some cases it may be desirable to make cells from fused silica (e.g. Suprasil, Engelhard Industries, Inc., Hillside, N.J.) to minimize interference from fluorescence of the glass. The cell length and diameter are governed by the geometry of the instrument. When only small amounts of samples are available, a cell can be constructed of heavy-wall capillary tubing if it is desirable to maintain a larger diameter, although scattering from the glass will cause increased background. A light pipe, Fig. 1(b), can also be used to mate a

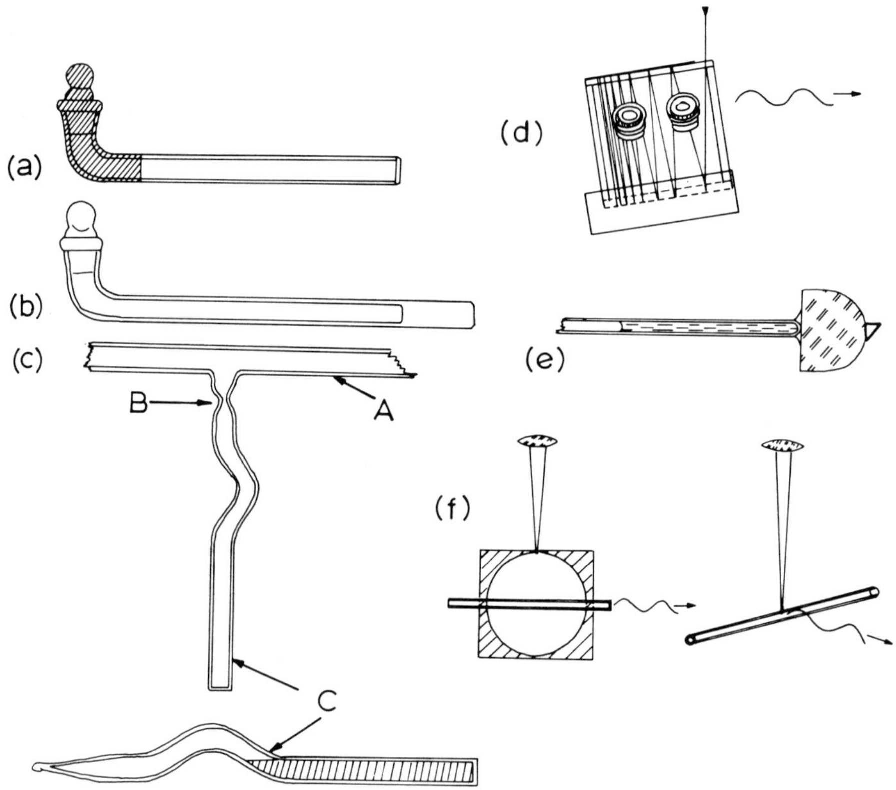

Fig. 1. Liquid Cells (a) Standard Cell; (b) Cell with Light Pipe; (c) Cell for use with a Vacuum Line, A-manifold, B-pinch seal, C-cell; (d) Multireflection Liquid Cell for Laser Excitation; (e) Capillary Cell for 180° Laser Excitation; (f) Capillary Cells for 90° Laser Excitation.

small volume cell to the transfer optics, and this is especially useful when the front part of the cell is shielded from the exciting light source. For samples which must be handled on a vacuum line, a cell is easily sealed to the manifold, Fig. 1(c), so that the sample can be condensed directly into the cell. To minimize reflections from the back of the cells, they can be painted with flat black lacquer. Cells like 1(a) and 1(c) may be used with laser excitation by focusing the beam at a point near the window. A relatively simple multipass liquid cell which uses external plane mirrors has been described by Tunnicliff and Jones (*35*). With laser excitation, simple multipass cells using externally deposited dielectric mirrors, Fig. 1(d), are quite useful, especially for dilute solutions.

The 0.7 mm diameter × 6 cm capillary cells used with the micro attachment for the Toronto arc Cary 81 and also for the laser version, Fig. 1(e), can be made easily too. Precision capillary tubing is available from Jencon Ltd., Hemel Hempstead, England. Similar cells can be used with laser excitation and other monochromators by focusing the laser beam at the entrance to a spherical cavity containing the cell (*36*), by using a spherical bulb at the end of the capillary to collimate the laser beam (*37*), or simply by focusing the beam to a diffraction limited point within the capillary; see Fig. 1(f). With the Cary instrument, distortions in the window at the end of the cell are minimized by using a drop of glycerol to make contact with the hemispherical lens. In many cases where adequate sample is available, it may be convenient to use larger cells, and Pyrex cylinders 2 mm to 7 mm in diameter have been reported to be satisfactory (*2*) giving spectra lower in intensity compared to the standard cell by factors of two and six, respectively.

Since most cylindrical cells for mercury arc excitation use reflection at both the air-glass interface as well as at the glass-sample interface to transmit Raman scattering to the monochromator, it is essential to keep the outside surface of the cells clean and free from scratches. Wiping the cell with isopropanol will remove fingerprints and leave a suitably clean surface.

2. Constant Temperature Liquid Cells

For studies on chemical equilibria, it is usually desirable to hold the solution at a constant temperature. The standard liquid cell can be provided with a jacket as illustrated in Fig. 2. Water is pumped from a thermostat through the jacket, and with this arrangement temperatures in the range 0 to 45° can be maintained. Often thermally unstable compounds which decompose at the ambient temperature of a Toronto arc light furnace (up to ca. 45°) can be studied at 0°. The inside of the water jacket must be kept very clean, and a bubble trap inserted in the water line will minimize the formation of air bubbles which cause high background scattering. A very elegant design for a thermostated cell has been described by Walrafen (*38*). Small multireflection cells used with laser excitation are best set into a metal block provided with passages through which water can be circulated as illustrated in Fig. 2(b).

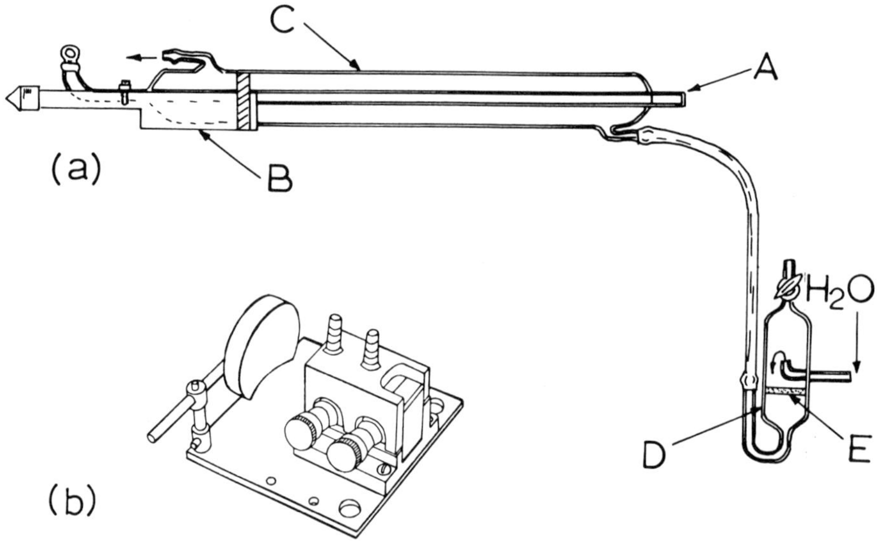

Fig. 2. Jacketed Liquid Cells. (a) Arc excitation: *A*-cell; *B*-metal holder; *C*-water jacket; *D*-bubble trap; *E*-glass frit; (b) Laser Excitation: multi-reflection cell equipped with a copper water jacket designed by Dr. R. P. Cooney in the author's laboratory.

3. Low Temperature Liquid Cells

Studies of thermally unstable compounds and of solutions in low boiling solvents like ammonia require cells which can be maintained at low temperatures. Several different designs for low temperature cells have been described (*39–43c*). The design illustrated in Fig. 3 is a relatively simple one and similar to that used by Craig and Overend (*39*). The Raman cell *A* is cooled by a stream of nitrogen or helium adjusted to the desired temperature. The bulb *F* can be filled on the vacuum line and its contents tipped into the cooled Raman cell. A small version of this apparatus can be used to cool samples contained in capillary tubes as illustrated in Fig. 3(b).

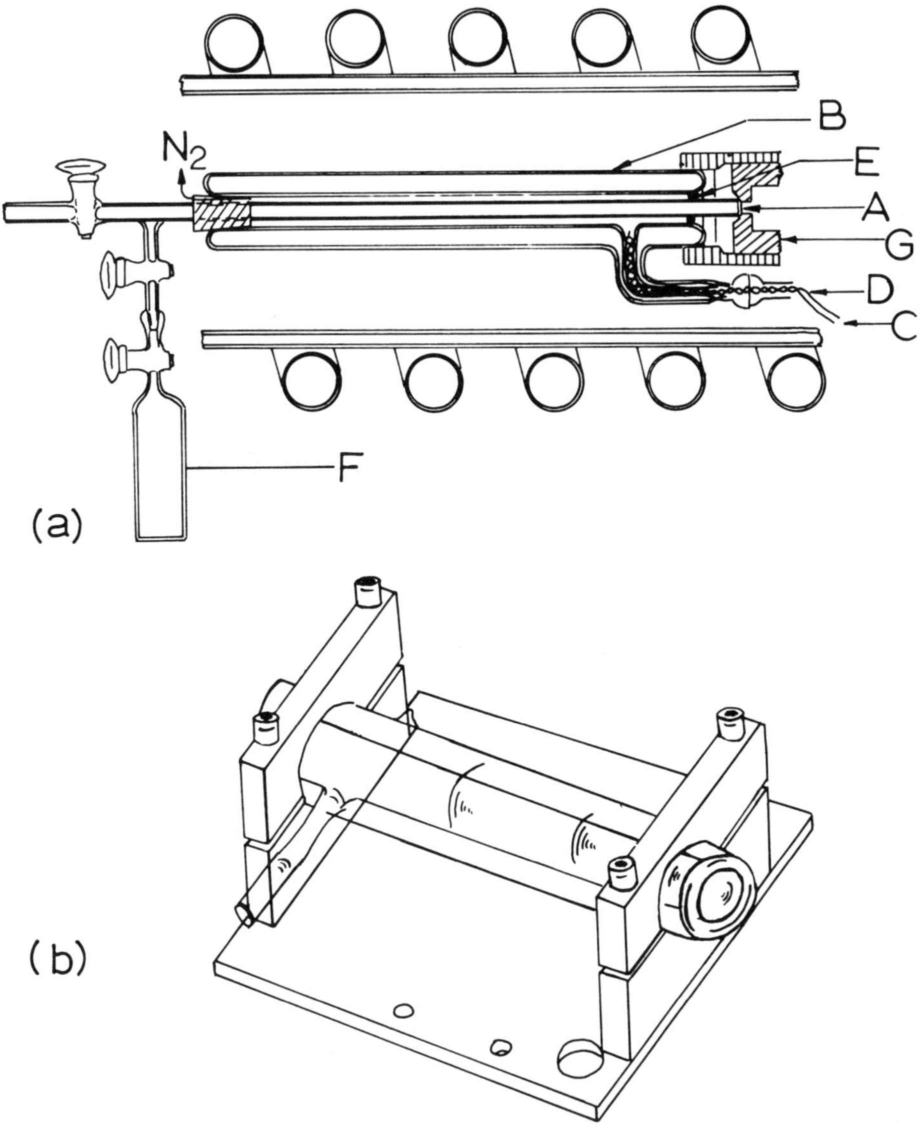

Fig. 3. Simple Low Temperature Cells. (a) Reprinted from Ref. (35), p. 1561, by permission of *Spectrochim. Acta*; *A*-cell, *B*-vacuum jacket, *C*-thermocouple, *D*-cold nitrogen inlet, *E*-silicone rubber "O" ring, *F*-sample bulb, *G*-spectrophotometer for optics. (b) Miniature version used in the author's laboratory to cool capillary sample tubes used with laser excitation.

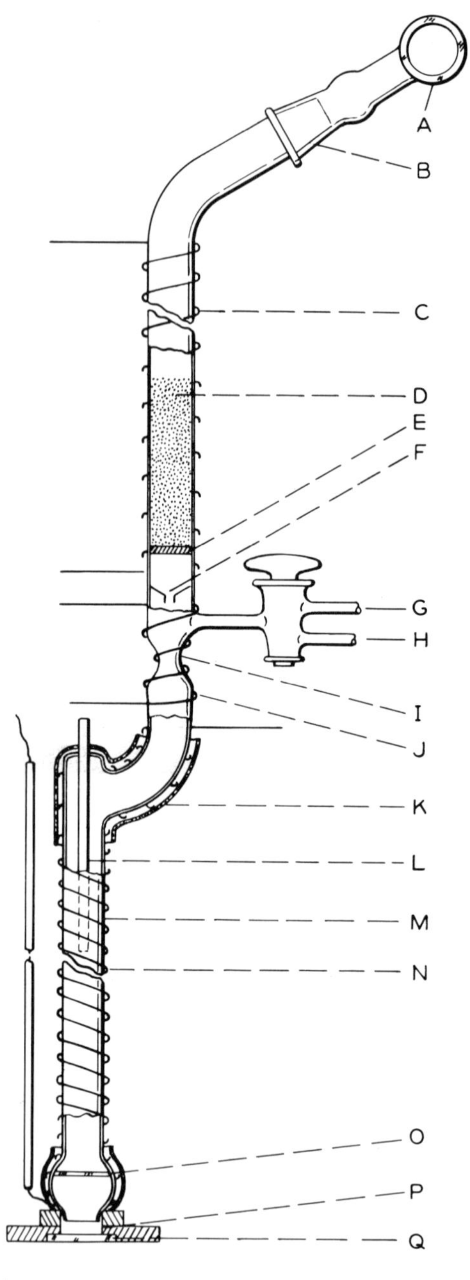

Fig. 4. Simple High Temperature Cell. Reprinted from Ref. (*44*), p. 1765, by permission of *J. Chem. Phys.; A*-vacuum manifold, *B*-joint, *C*-heater winding, *D*-solid compound, *E*-glass frit, *F*-funnel, *G*-dry gas inlet, *H*-to vacuum to effect sample transfer, *I*-pinch seal, *J*-heater, *K*-insulation, *L*-thermocouple well, *M*-cell, *N*-heater winding, *O*-optical flat, *P*-transite base, *Q*-optical flat.

4. High Temperature Cells

Cells which employ resistance heating can be used up to ca. 700° and are easily fabricated from Pyrex or Vycor. These have been described by several workers (*44–47*), and the cell used by Irish and Young (*44*) is shown in Fig. 4. The cells are similar in design to the low temperature cells in that an unsilvered dewar is used to isolate the Raman cell thermally. A Nichrome heater can be wound directly on the cell. Woodward et al. (*47*) were able to operate at 190° by blowing heated air over the cell.

For temperatures up to ca. 1100°, radio frequency induction heated cells have proved satisfactory. Walrafen has described the construction of this apparatus and used it in a study of molten sulfates (*48*).

5. Cells for Acidic Fluoride Solutions

Fluoride complexing of metal ions has been studied by many techniques. Ordinary glass cells would be etched rapidly by aqueous acidic fluoride solutions and consequently are unsuitable. Cells made from halocarbon

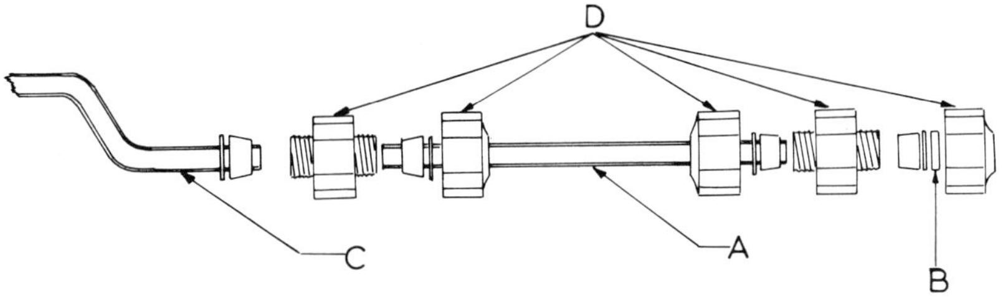

Fig. 5. Cell for Aqueous Fluoride Solutions. Reprinted from Ref. (*49*), p. 2064, by permission of *J. Inorg. Nuclear Chem.*; *A*-sapphire tubing cell body; *B*-optically flat sapphire window, *C*-Kel F tubing, *D*-3/8 in. standard Swagelok fittings.

resin, e.g., polychlorotrifluoroethylene (KelF, 3M Company), or sapphire tubing with a sapphire window have proved satisfactory (*49*). A cell similar to that of Selig, Quarterman, and Hyman is illustrated in Fig. 5. Shamir and Hyman (*50*) have used a cell similar to this except 0.75 inch o.d. polychlorotrifluoroethylene extruded tubing was used for the cell itself in place of sapphire. A sapphire window was attached at one end and a plastic valve at the other using split ring fittings. Areghi and Evans have described another type of cell for corrosive liquids (*51*).

6. Cells for Crystalline Samples

Many types of cells for crystalline powders have been suggested (*52–58*). With both mercury arc and laser excitation, it sometimes is possible to obtain a spectrum from a powder which simply has been tapped into a straight liquid cell. Usually, however, such a sample is too opaque to permit the exciting light to reach an appreciable portion of the sample or the scattered light to reach the monochromator. To provide thinner sample layers for Toronto arc excitation, various types of conical cells

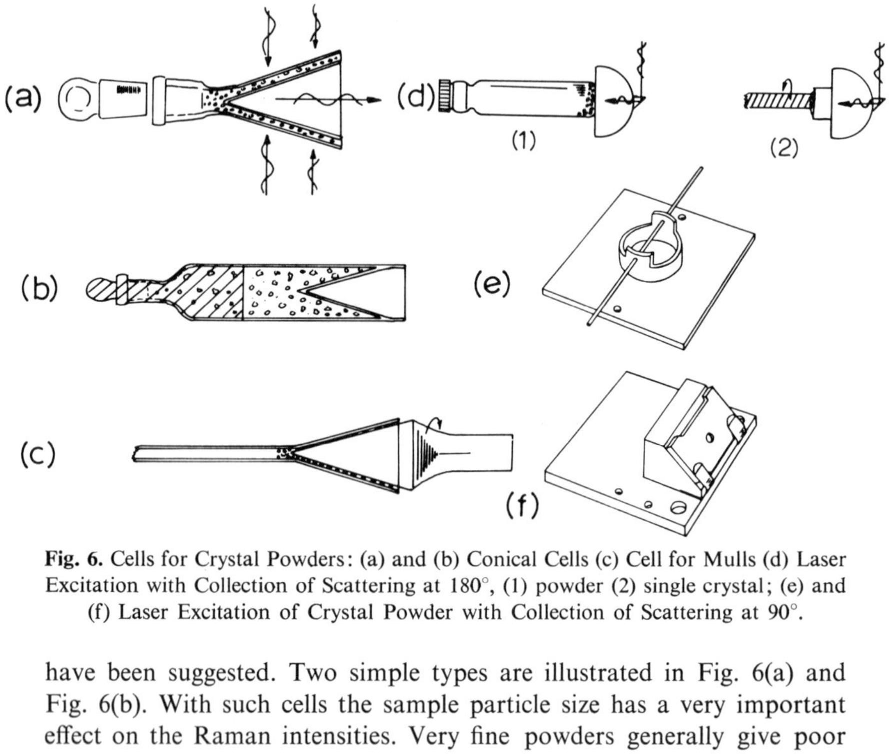

Fig. 6. Cells for Crystal Powders: (a) and (b) Conical Cells (c) Cell for Mulls (d) Laser Excitation with Collection of Scattering at 180°, (1) powder (2) single crystal; (e) and (f) Laser Excitation of Crystal Powder with Collection of Scattering at 90°.

have been suggested. Two simple types are illustrated in Fig. 6(a) and Fig. 6(b). With such cells the sample particle size has a very important effect on the Raman intensities. Very fine powders generally give poor spectra. In general, if the filled tube is illuminated from the side and viewed from the base of the cone, some light must be seen to pass through the sample. If this is not the case, it is extremely unlikely that any Raman scattering will be detectable. Ferraro et al. (*59*) have made a detailed study of the effect of sample tube shape, crystal size, sample thickness, and sample position for the Toronto arc Cary 81 spectrophotometer.

For samples which prove to be particularly opaque, it may be possible to obtain a spectrum on a mull spread as a very thin layer over the inside of a glass cone, and this cell is illustrated in Fig. 6(c). Such a cell has been used recently to obtain spectra of metal ammine complexes (*31*).

With the back scattering arrangement of the laser Cary 81 (*61*), Fig. 6(d), quite good spectra often can be obtained by placing a slug of powder ca. 5 mm long in a liquid capillary cell. When more sample is available, this can be compacted in the bottom of a small vial which is placed in contact with the hemispherical lens. With single crystals, a face is placed against the lens. With laser excitation and collection of the scattered light at 90°, the simple arrangement illustrated in Fig. 6(e) similar to that used for X-ray powder diffractometers generally yields good spectra. The transillumination technique with the sample in a capillary, Fig. 6(f), generally gives a lower background. Because a laser beam can be focused to a diffraction limited point, the examination of single crystals is simplified greatly. The crystal may be mounted and aligned with a normal X-ray diffraction goniometer.

It is also possible to compress powders into pellets if good spectra cannot be obtained with the techniques described above. These can be illuminated from the back and the scattered radiation collected in the forward direction, i.e., at 0° (*60*) or the back scattering can be collected at 180°. This latter technique is employed with the laser excited Cary 81 instrument (*61*).

When powder spectra are recorded without using filters to attenuate the light at the exciting frequency which is reflected into the monochromator, grating ghosts are often quite noticeable and should not be mistaken for fundamentals. With the gratings of the arc Cary 81, these are usually observed at ca. 90, 145 and 170 cm^{-1} with a single slit. With the laser 81, grating ghosts appear at 13, 16.5, 20.0, 23, and 59.4 cm^{-1} with a single slit and at 2903.3 cm^{-1} with single and double slits.

With very fine powders, it sometimes is possible to obtain qualitative polarization data using Polaroid cylinders together with Toronto arc illumination. Normally the reflections from the crystal faces destroy the idealized geometrical relation between source, sample, and monochromator, however, and make this impossible.

C. Sample Preparation

1. Neat Liquids

The purification of pure liquid compounds rarely causes much trouble, and these can be distilled directly into the Raman cell. If it is not convenient to distill the liquid, it may be possible to filter it through a membrane filter such as those supplied by the Gelman Instrument Corp., Ann Arbor, Mich. or the Millipore Corp., Bedford, Mass. These filters are supplied in many different types with pore sizes as small as ~ 4000 Å and with stability against attack by many different reagents. Pressure, e.g., of nitrogen, may be used to force the liquid through the filter directly into the cell, or the filter may be used with a suction flask. In the latter case, the necessity of transferring the solution from flask to cell increases the chance of contamination by dust. This increases the background, particularly near the exciting line.

2. Solutions

a. *Clarification*

Solutions are best clarified by passing them through a membrane filter. Aqueous electrolyte solutions in particular are likely to be quite turbid, and filtration is necessary to reduce the background in the study of low frequency vibrations. This can be accomplished by passing the solutions several times through the fine-pore membrane filters. Filters are available which are fairly resistant to aqueous acids and bases up to ~ 6 *M* concentrations. More corrosive liquids can be filtered through glass frits or in extreme cases through sintered platinum filters.

b. *Choice of a Solvent*

As noted earlier, water and deuterium oxide are almost ideal solvents for Raman spectroscopy. For compounds soluble in organic solvents, carbon tetrachloride and carbon disulfide make a useful pair of solvents just as in infrared spectroscopy, although both scatter strongly in the region of 800 cm^{-1}. A complete Raman spectrum can be obtained with CS_2, $CHCl_3$, and C_2Cl_4; and the spectra of these solvents are illustrated in Fig. 7. Figure 8, taken from the paper of Jones et al. (*62*) shows the regions where several solvents obscure Raman and infrared spectra.

c. *Colored Solutions*

Generally, it is advisable to excite the spectra with radiation which is not absorbed by the sample. With absorbing samples, there is always the danger of photolysis or of the dissipation of the absorbed energy by fluorescence giving a very intense background. When the sample does absorb, the determination of the optimal solute concentration becomes important. At low concentrations of the absorbing scatterer, the scattered

Mulls also are prepared in the usual way, and Raman spectra of Nujol and a Halocarbon oil are illustrated in Fig. 9.

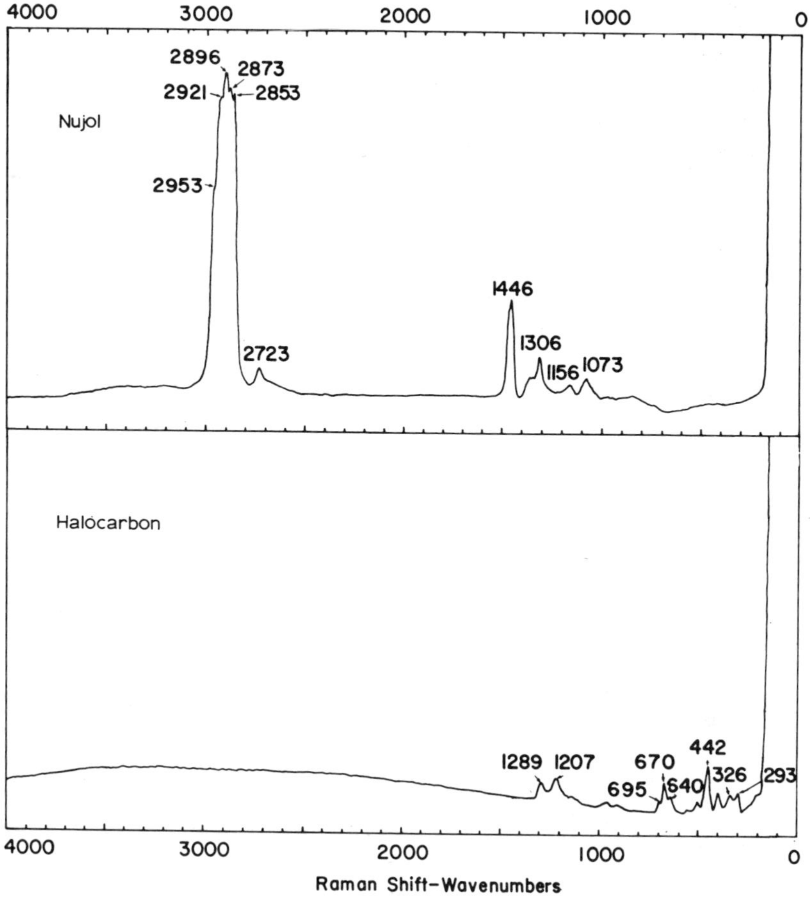

Fig. 9. Raman spectra of mulling agents: Nujol and Halocarbon oil.

D. Intensity Measurements

1. Introduction

There are two areas where the measurement of Raman intensities has played an important part in the study of the properties of inorganic compounds. Studies of chemical equilibria in solution require intensity measurements as a function of the overall system stoichiometry to determine the concentrations of solute species, i.e., for quantitative analysis. Absolute intensity values are required for the calculation of the components of the derived polarizability tensor and deductions from these about the properties of the chemical bonds in the molecule.

The measurement of Raman intensities can be an exceedingly difficult problem experimentally. Values are generally referred to a standard intensity, and the A_1 mode of carbon tetrachloride (459 cm^{-1}) is most often used. For this purpose both external and internal standards have been employed.

Numerous papers have been published on the factors which influence observed Raman intensities (*65–71*). Most of these effects depend upon the characteristics of the particular spectrophotometer used and have been discussed in most detail for the Toronto arc excited Cary 81 spectrophotometer. Among the factors which must be taken into account with liquid samples are the following:

1. The absorbance of the sample. Usually this factor is eliminated by exciting the spectrum in a region where the sample does not absorb.
2. The variation in sensitivity of the photomultiplier detector as a function of frequency.
3. The variation of the monochromator transmission as a function of frequency.
4. The effect of the sample refractive index on the effective sample volume seen by the monochromator.
5. The convergence error resulting from the fact that the light exciting the spectrum is not strictly perpendicular to the viewing axis.
6. Effects associated with the condensed state. These range from the internal field effect, known from infrared spectroscopy, which describes the intensity change from gaseous to liquid state to specific solvent-solute interactions in the case of solutions.
7. The effect of recorder response and scan rate. These factors have particularly marked effects on line shapes, but within fairly wide limits they affect the integrated intensities to a lesser extent.

Errors caused by factors 4 and 5 are usually negligible when using laser excitation.

2. External Standards

In general it is best to avoid the use of external standards whenever possible because of the uncertainty in the corrections and the difficulty in applying them. Nevertheless, in order to consider the effects of these various factors, the use of an external standard will be considered briefly.

Bernstein and Allen (*65*) and Schrotter and Bernstein (*71*) have discussed the following equation for corrections of observed intensities to a standard intensity referred to the CCl_4 459 cm^{-1} line, $S_A^{CCl_4}$.

$$S_A^{CCl_4} = \frac{I_A^{\Delta\nu}}{I_{CCl_4}^{459}} \cdot \left(\frac{1-\rho_{CCl_4}^{459}}{1-\rho_{obs}}\right) \cdot \frac{n^2}{n_{CCl_4}{}^2} \cdot \frac{\sigma_{459}}{\sigma_{\Delta\nu}} \cdot \frac{(M/d)_A}{(M/d)_{CCl_4}} \cdot \frac{\Delta\nu}{459} \cdot \left(\frac{\nu-459}{\nu-\Delta\nu}\right)^4 \cdot \frac{(1-e^{-1.44\Delta\nu/T})}{(1-e^{-1.44\times 459/T})} \qquad (2)$$

In this expression $I_A^{\Delta\nu}$ is the observed intensity at the shift $\Delta\nu$; $I_{CCl_4}^{459}$ is the reference line intensity; $\rho_{CCl_4}^{459}$ is the measured depolarization ratio of the 459 cm^{-1} CCl_4 line and ρ_{obs} is the observed sample depolarization ratio; n and n_{CCl_4} are the refractive indices of sample and of CCl_4, respectively; σ_{459} and $\sigma_{\Delta\nu}$ are the spectrometer spectral sensitivities at the two frequencies, 459 and $\Delta\nu$ cm^{-1}; M/d gives the molar volumes where M is the molecular weight and d is the density, ν is the exciting frequency, and T is the absolute temperature. The term containing $1/(1-\rho)$ corrects for the convergence error, the term containing $1/n^2$ corrects for changes in the effective sample volume with refractive index, the sigma terms take into account the variation of the spectrometer sensitivity as a function of frequency, and the (M/d) term corrects for changes in the number of scattering molecules per unit volume. The remaining terms follow from the standard theoretical expression for Raman scattering.

In order to calculate the standard line intensity, it is necessary to measure the sample intensity, the sample depolarization ratio, the sample refractive index, the intensity of the CCl_4 line, and the depolarization ratio for this line. The spectrometer spectral sensitivity can be obtained as a function of frequency by illuminating the monochromator with diffuse light reflected from a standard tungsten lamp by a MgO surface. Alternatively, a curve of σ versus frequency may be constructed by calculating values with Eq. (2) at several frequencies using the known values of the absolute intensity of a secondary standard, e.g., $CHCl_3$ (*65,71*).

3. Internal Standards

Internal standards can be used for most purposes where it is desirable to report intensities independent of instrumental effects. They are especially helpful when cells are used which lead much light into the monochromator by internal reflection, since this complicates the corrections for changes in sample refractive index. Tunnicliff and Jones (*72*) have discussed their use in quantitative analysis. For studies on organic compounds, Jones et al. (*62*) have suggested the use of an "apparent Raman scattering coefficient" $K_A^{CCl_4}$.

$$K_A^{CCl_4} = \frac{I_A^{\Delta\nu}}{I_S^{\Delta\nu_s}} \cdot \frac{\sigma_{\Delta\nu s}}{\sigma_{\Delta\nu}} \cdot \frac{g_S}{g_A} \cdot \frac{N_S}{N_A} \cdot \beta \cdot 100 \tag{3}$$

Again $I_A^{\Delta\nu}$ is the observed intensity at the shift $\Delta\nu$, $I_S^{\Delta\nu_s}$ is the intensity of the reference line at $\Delta\nu_S$, the σ's have the same meaning as in Eq. (2), g_A and g_S refer to the spectrophotometer amplifier settings for sample and standard respectively, N_A and N_S are the mole fractions of sample and reference respectively, and β is a factor to convert from a secondary intensity standard, *S*, to the CCl_4 scale.

For pure liquids which are miscible with CCl_4 as, for example, many organometallic compounds, a small amount of CCl_4 can be added to serve as the internal standard. With solutions in organic solvents, it is often possible to use a solvent line as a secondary standard. Table 1

TABLE 1

Conversion Constants, β, for Several Secondary Solvent References[a]

Compound	Raman Frequency (cm^{-1})	β
CCl_4	459	1.00
CS_2	656	1.90
$CHCl_3$	668	0.70
	366	0.66
	262	0.72
CH_2Cl_2	700	0.46
	283	0.33
C_2Cl_4	1571	1.07
CH_3CN	2250	0.36

[a] Reprinted from Ref. (62), p. 1828, by permission of the American Chemical Society.

taken from the work of Jones et al. (*62*) lists β values for several common solvents. It should be noted that this β term cannot take into account any specific solvent–solute interactions, and the solvent should be chosen to minimize these.

The use of the perchlorate line at ca. 930 cm^{-1} arising from the totally symmetric breathing mode of ClO_4^- was examined by Chantry and Plane (*73*) as an internal standard for aqueous solutions. Since perchlorate generally forms no complexes with metal ions in aqueous solution, its intensity is unaffected by even the presence of high concentrations of multivalent cations; and this reference has been used in most work involving aqueous solutions. For aqueous systems, it is convenient to use an equation analogous to Eq. (3) with concentrations expressed in terms of molarity, M.

$$K_A^{ClO_4^-} = \frac{I_A^{\Delta\nu}}{I_{ClO_4^-}^{930}} \cdot \frac{\sigma_{930}}{\sigma_{\Delta\nu}} \cdot \frac{g_{ClO_4^-}}{g_A} \cdot \frac{M_{ClO_4^-}}{M_A} \tag{4}$$

4. INTENSITIES IN THE STUDY OF CHEMICAL EQUILIBRIA

Equilibrium studies provide a particularly simple example of the use of intensity measurements. In the determination of the equilibrium constant for a reaction of the general type (5) assuming ideal solution behavior,

$$M + L \leftrightharpoons ML \tag{5}$$

all that is necessary is to measure the concentration of one species as a function of the system stoichiometry. For example the intensity of a line assigned to a vibration of ML measured relative to some internal reference can be followed as the total stoichiometric concentrations of M and L in the system are varied. The reference concentration is held constant and this often is fixed so the same amplifier gain can be used in scanning the reference and ML signals, i.e., $g_S/g_A = 1$. The ratio $\sigma_{\Delta\nu_s}/\sigma_{\Delta\nu}$ is constant for all of the measurements, and rearrangement of Eq. (4) gives

$$\frac{I_A^{\Delta\nu}}{I_S^{\Delta\nu_s}} = \frac{K_A^S}{M_S} \cdot \frac{\sigma_{\Delta\nu}}{\sigma_{\Delta\nu_s}} \cdot M_A = J \cdot M_A \tag{6}$$

The proportionality constant J, sometimes called the specific or relative molar intensity, can be evaluated by "swamping" one reagent, e.g., by adding a large excess of L to a solution of M so that essentially all M is converted to the complex ML. Raman data for chemical equilibria can be analyzed by any of the mathematical methods (*74*) appropriate to absorption spectroscopy with the molar intensities, J, replacing the molar absorptivities.

5. Determination of Depolarization Ratios

Laser spectrophotometers have the advantage that the source is almost perfectly polarized, and so highly accurate values of the depolarization ratio, ρ, can be obtained. With mercury arc excitation and cylindrical cells, cylinders of polaroid are usually employed to provide axially and crossed polarized light (*75*). The apparent depolarization ratios, ρ_{obs}, thus obtained are usually considerably larger than the true values, primarily because of the oblique illumination of the sample tube obtained with mercury arcs, i.e., because of the convergence error. While this can be corrected largely by introducing transverse baffles along the sample cell, this results in a very great decrease in the intensity of irradiation and consequently in the Raman intensities. With many inorganic samples, particularly aqueous solutions, it becomes impossible to measure a spectrum with a properly baffled tube, and it is necessary to correct the observed depolarization values. This also is required with some laser instruments employing capillary cells or when using optics which collect over a large solid angle.

Koningstein and Bernstein (*76*) have derived a relationship for this purpose.

$$\rho_{obs} = T\cdot\rho_{true}\left(1-\frac{\sin^2\theta}{n^2}\right)+\frac{T\sin^2\theta}{n^2} \tag{7}$$

Here θ is an averaged angle of incidence, T is a transmission factor taking into account both the polaroids and the monochromator optics, and n is the sample refractive index. The two unknown parameters θ and T are calculated from measurements on lines of known polarization. These are usually obtained with molecules or ions belonging to one of the cubic point groups where ρ_{true} is 0 for totally symmetric modes and 0.857 for all others.

For constant refractive index and instrument parameters, Eq. (7) reduces to a linear relation between ρ_{obs} and ρ_{true}, and the correction becomes equivalent to that suggested by Edsall and Wilson (*75*). They constructed calibration curves by fitting straight lines to plots of ρ_{obs}

versus ρ_{true}, again using lines of known polarization. Miles, Glass, and Tobias (*77*) used an empirical expression

$$\rho_{\text{true}} = \frac{I_{\parallel} - \alpha I_{\perp}}{I_{\perp} - \beta I_{\parallel}} \tag{8}$$

to correct depolarization data for solutes in aqueous solution. The $I_{\parallel}$ and $I_{\perp}$ refer to integrated intensities with cylindrical polaroids transmitting light with the electric vector parallel and perpendicular, respectively, to the axis of the cylindrical Raman sample tube, and measurements on ClO_4^- were used to evaluate α and β. In a more thorough study, Tobias, Sprague, and Glass (*78*) found that β was approximately zero for several different solutions using CCl_4 or ClO_4^- as internal standards, and the correction becomes equivalent to the graphical procedure of Edsall and Wilson.

III. INTERPRETATION OF RAMAN SPECTRA FOR INORGANIC COMPOUNDS

A. Small Molecules and Ions

Many of the studies of the vibrations of simple inorganic molecules and ions now include Raman as well as infrared spectra. Frequently, this has led to revisions of earlier assignments and provided adequate data for normal coordinate analyses. Since earlier studies of the vibrations of inorganic compounds have been considered by Nakamoto (1962) (*23*) and Siebert (1966) (*22*) and the low frequency metal–ligand vibrations have been reviewed by Adams (1967) (*21*), this discussion will concentrate on giving some idea of the variety and scope of current applications of Raman spectroscopy to the study of the structures of small molecules. Because of the very rapid growth in these applications in the past few years, it is not possible to review all work in the space available here.

There are several types of investigation where Raman spectroscopy has proved particularly helpful. First, it has been used to study simple ions which are distorted readily by the influence of lattice forces but which can be studied in aqueous solution. Raman spectra have been used extensively to study the stereochemistry of molecules where ligands occupy nonequivalent coordination sites, e.g., in the trigonal bipyramidal phosphorus compounds with mixed ligands, PX_nY_{5-n}. The stereochemistry of compounds where variable coordination numbers occur is followed easily by Raman spectroscopy. For example, pure liquid PCl_5 has a 5 coordinate phosphorus atom, while phosphorus is 4 and 6 coordinate in the solid compound which is $[PCl_4]^+[PCl_6]^-$. Because more fundamentals are usually Raman active than are infrared active with highly symmetric structures, e.g. tetrahedral and octahedral, Raman spectra are somewhat more useful for the examination of such structures.

1. Noble Gas Compounds

Raman spectra proved to be particularly helpful in the assignment of structures to the noble gas fluorides and have been used extensively by the groups at Oak Ridge and Argonne National Laboratories. Much of this work has been reviewed by Hyman (*79*).

The Raman spectrum of gaseous XeF_2 shows only one line at 515 cm^{-1} assigned to ν_s(Xe—F) which shifts to 497 cm^{-1} upon crystallization (*80*). In this chapter, ν_s will be used to describe symmetric stretching vibrations, ν_{as} antisymmetric stretches, δ deformations of bond angles, and ρ for rocking vibrations of groups such as CH_3 and NH_3. The two remaining fundamentals ν_{as}(Xe—F) and δ(F—Xe—F) expected for a linear molecule ($D_{\infty h}$) are observed in the infrared at 558 and 213.2 cm^{-1} confirming the linearity of XeF_2 (*81*). The corresponding fundamentals for the analogous molecule KrF_2 are observed at 449, 558, and 232.6 cm^{-1} (*82*).

The XeF_4 molecule exhibits three fundamentals in the Raman spectrum obtained with single crystals, ν_s(Xe—F) 543, ν_{as}(Xe—F) 502, and δ(F—Xe—F) 235 cm^{-1} (*83*). The Raman data for XeF_4 together with the infrared spectrum confirm the square planar (D_{4h}) structure. With HF solutions of XeF_4, ν_s(Xe—F) increases to 553 cm^{-1}. The force constant for Xe—F bond stretching is 3.00 mdyne/Å compared to 2.85 mdyne/Å for XeF_2.

Raman and infrared spectra of solid, liquid and gaseous XeF_6 have been studied very carefully in attempts to determine whether the molecule has full cubic symmetry or whether it is slightly distorted (*84,85*). The vapor shows three lines as expected for an octahedral molecule at 609 ν_s(Xe—F), 520 ν_{as}(Xe—F), and 206 (?) cm^{-1} δ(F—Xe—F), but the highest frequency polarized line is broad. This is not characteristic of octahedral molecules and suggests some distortion which is now supported by recent electron diffraction measurements (*86*). Dissolved in HF, XeF_6 gives three lines for Xe—F stretching at 660, 620, and 600 cm^{-1} (*87*), and three lines are also reported for the solid at 655, 635, and 582 cm^{-1}

(*88*). The similarity of the spectrum of the solid at 40° and the liquid at 54°C (*84*) suggests that the clusters of four molecules known to exist in the solid persist in the liquid near the melting point.

Partial hydrolysis of XeF_6 yields $XeOF_4$ which has a spectrum very similar to that of the square pyramidal molecule (C_{4v}) BrF_5, and the same structure (**I**) was assigned to $XeOF_4$ by analogy (*89–92*). The

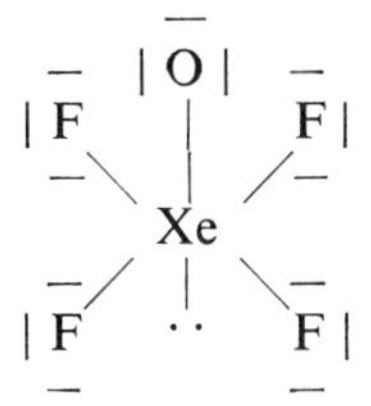

(**I**)

fundamental ν(Xe—O) is observed at 926 cm^{-1} with the gaseous compound. Comparison of the Raman spectrum of pure liquid $XeOF_4$ and solutions in anhydrous HF with solutions to which water had been added gave no evidence for any further hydrolysis by reaction (*9*) to XeO_2F_2(*91*).

$$XeOF_4 + H_2O \leftrightarrow XeO_2F_2 + 2HF \qquad (9)$$

2. Halogens and Their Compounds

The polyatomic halogen and inter-halogen ions have been studied by several groups because of the interest in the nature of the bonding in these anions and their relation to isostructural noble gas fluorides. Since the ions are brightly colored, it has been necessary to use helium or rubidium lamps or more recently helium–neon lasers to excite the spectra. Data for a number of linear triatomic anions are given in Table 2. In all of these ions, the heavier halogen is located in the center. In general, the spectra have been obtained with crystals containing large alkali metal or tetramethylammonium ions. The halogen–halogen bonds in these anions are quite weak, and this is reflected in the stretching frequencies and the corresponding force constants which are approximately half of the values for the same bonds in diatomic halogen or interhalogen molecules (*96*). The stretch–stretch interaction constant is unusually large averaging about 36% of the stretching force constant. The potential well for the central atom appears to be very flat with respect to the principal axis (*97*), and the ions distort easily under the influence of the crystal lattice. The chlorine difluoride anion, ClF_2^- (**II**), was isolated as the NO^+ salt for

TABLE 2

Linear Triatomic Halogen and Interhalogen Anions, $D_{\infty h}$ and $C_{\infty v}$[a]

Ion	State[b]	ν_1	ν_2	ν_3	References
ClF_2^-	xtal	476	—	661	(*93*)
Cl_3^-	xtal, soln	268	165	242	(*94*)
Br_3^-	xtal, soln	162	—	196	(*94,95,96*)
$BrCl_2^-$	xtal, soln	273	—	305	(*96*)
ICl_2^-	xtal, soln	254	138	226	(*96,97*)
IBr_2^-	xtal, soln	160	98	171	(*97, 98*)
$BrICl^-$	xtal, soln	230	128	174	(*97*)
I_3^-	xtal, soln	111	69	143	(*97,98*)

[a] For the XY_2 ions, only ν_1 is Raman active; for XYZ ions all three fundamentals are Raman active. Where available, the missing fundamentals have been added from infrared spectra. (ν_1-sym stretch, ν_2-degenerate def., ν_3-asym stretch.)

[b] In the tables which follow, the nature of the sample will be indicated by xtal = crystalline powder, mull = powder run as mull, soln = solution in an organic solvent, aq = aqueous solution, liq = neat liquid.

which the spectra are consistent with the linear $D_{\infty h}$ structure and also as the rubidium and cesium salts where the anion is slightly distorted (*93*).

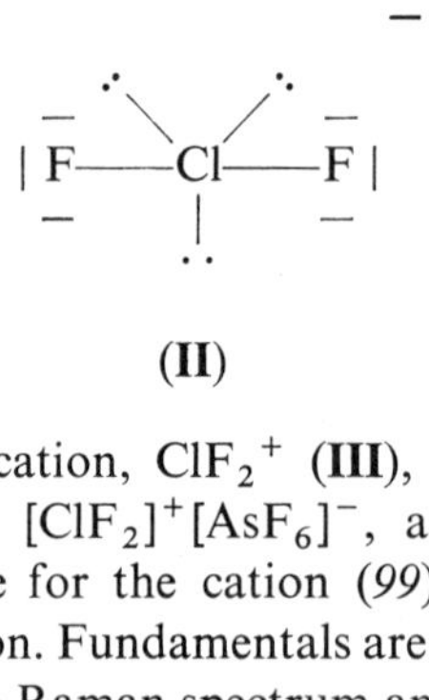

(II)

The chlorine difluoride cation, ClF_2^+ (**III**), has been isolated as the hexafluoroarsenate salt in $[ClF_2]^+[AsF_6]^-$, and the spectra confirm the angular (C_{2v}) structure for the cation (*99*) in contrast to the $D_{\infty h}$ structure for the ClF_2^- anion. Fundamentals are observed at 811 ν_s(Cl—F) and 544 δ(F—Cl—F) in the Raman spectrum and at 818 cm^{-1} ν_{as}(Cl—F)

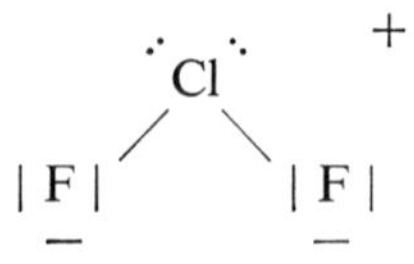

(III)

in the infrared. Comparison with the corresponding fundamentals of ClF_2^-, ν_s(Cl—F) = 476 cm^{-1}, shows the great stiffening in the bonds which occurs in going from anion to cation.

Person also has studied the spectrum of square planar ICl_4^- (*96*) which has quite weak iodine–chlorine bonds similar to those in ICl_2^-. In acetonitrile solutions containing Cl_2:Cl^- mole ratios of 3, Evans and Lo (*94*) observed a broad, intense band at 482 cm^{-1} in addition to the spectrum of Cl_3^-. This additional line is presumably the totally symmetric stretch of an L shaped Cl_5^- ion. For Br_5^-, the corresponding value is 257 cm^{-1} (*95*).

Iodine oxide pentafluoride, IOF_5, has been studied because of its relation to the noble gas compound $XeOF_4$. Raman active fundamentals for this distorted octahedral (C_{4v}) molecule are observed at 927 ν(I—O); 680, 640 ν_s(I—F), and 710 cm^{-1} ν_{as}(I—F) (*100*). Begun and coworkers (*100*) have also reinvestigated the Raman spectra of the interhalogens IF_5 and BrF_5 and determined the spectrum for ClF_5 which was shown to have the same square pyramidal structure as the other pentafluorides. Spectra have been reported for $[ICl_3]_2$ (*101*), one of the first examples of a planar X_2Y_6 molecule to be studied, and qualitative assignments were made for all nine Raman active fundamentals. The octahedral cation IF_6^+ was found to be present in the compound $IF_7 \cdot AsF_5$ prepared by Christe and Sawodny (*102*) which has the ionic structure $[IF_6]^+[AsF_6]^-$. The Raman spectrum shows in addition to the three lines expected for the octahedral AsF_6^- anion at 683, 581, and 377 cm^{-1} three lines assigned to the octahedral IF_6^+ cation ν_s(I—F) 708, ν_{as}(I—F) 738, and δ(F—I—F) 340 cm^{-1}. The force constants for IF_6^+ were compared with those for the isoelectronic molecule TeF_6 and ion SbF_6^-. The anion IF_6^- was isolated as the cesium salt (*103*). It has two more electrons than IF_6^+, is isoelectronic with XeF_6, and the vibrational spectra indicate that it has less than full cubic symmetry in the crystal.

3. Oxygen, Sulfur, Selenium, and Tellurium Compounds

Shamir, Binenboym, and Claassen (*104*) have observed the stretching frequency of O_2^+ at 1858 cm^{-1} in crystals of $O_2[AsF_6]$ and $O_2[SbF_6]$ and compared the value with those of O_2 and O_2^- (*104*). Smith and Leroi (*105*) have reinvestigated the Raman spectrum of carbon suboxide C_3O_2 **(IV)**, a symmetric linear pentaatomic molecule, ($D_{\infty h}$) in the solid, liquid, and gaseous states

O=C=C=C=O

(IV)

The solid undergoes a phase transition at 115±5°K, and the Raman spectrum changes from eight lines characteristic of the low temperature modification to three lines for the high temperature form of the solid. Apparently a crystallographic center of symmetry is lost upon cooling to the low temperature form. Raman and infrared spectra of carbon subsulfide, C_3S_2, in CS_2 solution were determined (*106*), and they show that this molecule also has the linear structure. The ν_s(C═C) is assigned to a very strong, polarized line at 458 cm^{-1}.

Thionyl fluoride, SOF_2, a pyramidal molecule (C_s), has been reinvestigated both as a liquid and a gas (*107*), and fundamentals are observed at 1307.5 ν(S═O), 803.7, 715.5, 527.8, 398.6, and 379.5 cm^{-1}. Long and Bailey have studied the donor–acceptor complexes formed between $SOCl_2$ and $AlCl_3$ (*108*). The complex $SOCl_2 \cdot AlCl_3$ was isolated and ν(S═O) was found to be 1108 cm^{-1}, 121 cm^{-1} lower than that in pure thionyl chloride. This decrease reflects the weakening in the S—O bond as oxygen lone pair electrons are donated (**V**) to form the bond to the aluminum trichloride molecule. A second adduct $SOCl_2 \cdot 2AlCl_3$ was isolated, but its spectrum is essentially a superposition of spectra for the

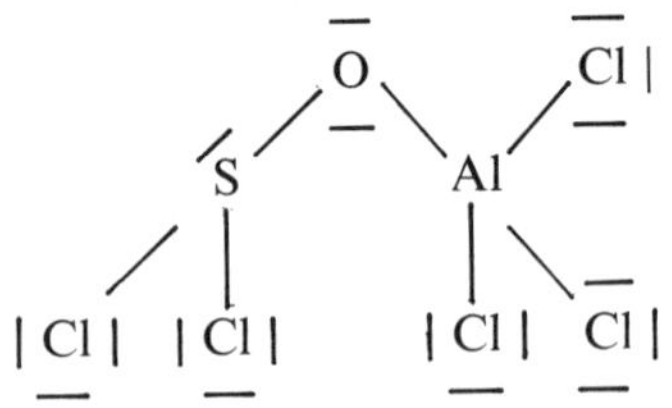

(**V**)

1:1 complex and $AlCl_3$ indicating only a weak interaction occurs with the second $AlCl_3$ molecule.

Two groups have studied the tetrahedral molecule SeO_2F_2 (C_{2v}) (*109,110*) recently, and the spectrum is similar to that of CrO_2F_2 (*111*). A comparison has also been made with the vibrational frequencies of the related molecules SO_2F_2 and SO_2FCl (*112*).

Griffiths investigated the Raman spectra of $ClSF_5$ and F_3CSF_5 (*113*) with six-coordinate sulfur and compared the spectra to that of the parent molecule SF_6. All of these molecules involve, basically, octahedral coordination about sulfur, and $ClSF_5$ was shown to have the expected C_{4v} symmetry. The skeletal vibrations of F_3CSF_5 also obey the C_{4v} selection rules indicating that the barrier for rotation of the trifluoromethyl group with respect to the SF_5 group is probably very small. The related hexafluoride TeF_6 has been studied by Abramowitz and Lewin (*114*).

The Raman spectrum of the unstable molecular form of sulfur S_6 has been obtained using He—Ne laser excitation (*115,116*). In solution, a rapid conversion $4S_6 \rightarrow 3S_8$ is observed, but the spectrum of the hexamer could be obtained with powders. The highest totally symmetric stretching frequency is almost the same for S_6 (471 solid, 476 solution) as for the stable molecular form S_8, 470 cm^{-1}.

The monohalides of sulfur and selenium, S_2X_2 and Se_2X_2, have been studied using He—Ne laser excitation (*117*). The compounds are deeply colored and highly reactive, and earlier reports of their spectra appear to contain spurious frequencies. The spectra indicate low symmetry, and the molecules probably have the C_2 gauche structure.

Stable adducts TeX_2L_2 of tellurium dihalides where L = thiourea and substituted thioureas have been examined (*118*). These molecules have two lone pairs of electrons localized on the tellurium atom. These pairs would be expected to occupy the two axial positions of an octahedron giving square planar complexes (**VI**). Both the *cis* and *trans* isomers are observed, and for the *trans* complexes the symmetric X–Te–X stretching frequencies are Cl = 245, Br = 150, I = 110 cm^{-1}.

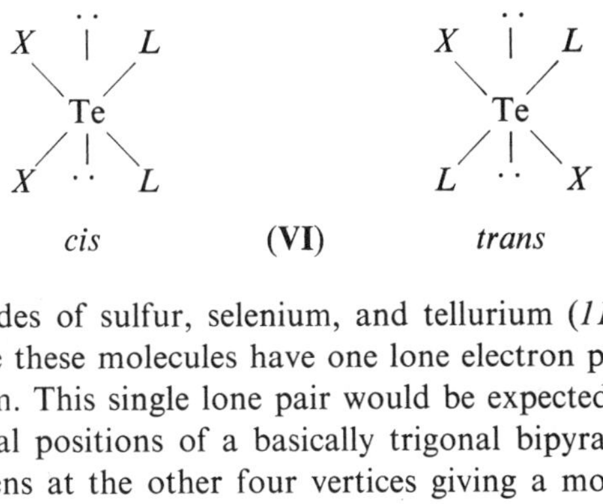

cis (**VI**) *trans*

The tetrahalides of sulfur, selenium, and tellurium (*119,120*) also are interesting since these molecules have one lone electron pair localized on the central atom. This single lone pair would be expected to occupy one of the equatorial positions of a basically trigonal bipyramidal structure with the halogens at the other four vertices giving a molecule with C_{2v} symmetry. Spectra of the vapors are in accord with this structure; however the interpretation of solid state spectra is less clear. The Raman spectra of the solid compounds are somewhat similar to the spectra of the pyramidal (C_{3v}) Group VB compounds, e.g., PX_3, AsX_3, and SbX_3 (*123*). While it was suggested that the sulfur, selenium, and tellurium tetrahalides were ionic compounds $[MX_3]^+X^-$, it is not possible to reconcile completely the observed spectra with the existence of only a pyramidal MX_3 cation. The Raman spectra of solid $SeCl_4$, $TeCl_4$, and $TeBr_4$ determined by laser excitation using pellets are all similar, first suggesting that all three compounds have similar structures (*120*). Hayward and Hendra also found three chalcogen-halogen stretching frequencies rather than the four expected for a XY_4 molecule with symmetry C_{2v} or the two for a XY_3^+ pyramidal cation with symmetry C_{3v}, and they concluded that the covalent C_{2v} structure is in best accord with the vibrational spectra, i.e., the molecular structure is basically the same in both the solid and vapor.

A knowledge of the structure of the hexahalogeno compounds of tetravalent selenium and tellurium also is of considerable interest to the chemist. These molecules have fourteen valence electrons about the central atom, and consequently a distorted octahedral structure is expected on the basis of the simple model of electron pair repulsions. Also, these compounds should be structurally analogous to XeF_6. Their spectra, however, are consistent with full cubic symmetry indicating that the lone pair of electrons is in an orbital mainly derived from a Se or Te *s* orbital. Thus $SeCl_6^{-2}$ and $TeCl_6^{-2}$ show three Raman frequencies at 280, 242, 162 and 289, 247, 139 cm^{-1}, respectively (acetonitrile solution) (*121*). For $TeCl_6^{-2}$, ν_1 also has been reported to have the value 301 cm^{-1}, and the frequencies of $TeBr_6^{-2}$ were observed to be 166 ν_1, 151 ν_2, and 73 ν_3 (*124*).

Raman spectra have been obtained with the methyl derivatives of sulfur, selenium, and tellurium, $(CH_3)_2Se$ and $(CH_3)_2Te$, as well as the deuterated compounds (*122*). The internal vibrations of the methyl groups were studied carefully, and the skeletal frequencies also were assigned: ν_s(S—C) 691, ν_{as}(S—C) 742, δ(C—S—C) 284; ν_s(Se—C) 588, ν_{as}(Se—C) 602, δ(C—Se—C) 237 cm^{-1}. With dimethyltellurium, only a single frequency is observed for ν(Te—C) at 526 cm^{-1} suggesting accidental degeneracy for the two skeletal stretching modes of the molecule with the heaviest central atom. For $(CH_3)_2Te$, δ(C—Te—C) is 198 cm^{-1}. The similarity of the spectrum of the tellurium compound to those of the sulfur and selenium analogues which are known to have C_{2v} effective symmetry indicates that $(CH_3)_2Te$ also has this structure. Spectra recently have been reported for the dialkyldisulfides (*126*).

4. Nitrogen, Phosphorus, Arsenic, and Antimony Compounds

The stable isomer of N_2F_2 has been studied by both King and Overend (*127*) and by Shamir and Hyman (*128*). The appearance of 3 Raman and

3 infrared active fundamentals is in accord only with the planar *trans* structure (C_{2h}) (**VIII**). In the Raman spectrum of the solid, the following

cis (**VII**) *trans* (**VIII**)

fundamentals are observed: ν(N=N) 1522, ν(N—F) 1010, δ(N=N—F) 600 cm^{-1}. The "active" form of N_2F_2, i.e., the *cis* isomer (**VII**), also has been investigated (*129*), and as expected all 6 fundamentals are Raman active. The following three frequencies of the *cis* isomer may be compared with the Raman active fundamentals of the *trans* isomer given above: ν(N=N) 1525, ν(N—F) 896, δ(N=N—F) 341 cm^{-1}. The spectrum of tetrafluorohydrazine, N_2F_4, has been reported over the temperature range -80 to -150°C (*130*). Two isomers with C_2 and C_{2h} symmetry appear to be present.

The spectrum of liquid F_2CN_2 (bp -91°) is consistent only with the diazirine (**IX**) and not with the diazomethane (**X**) type of structure (*131*).

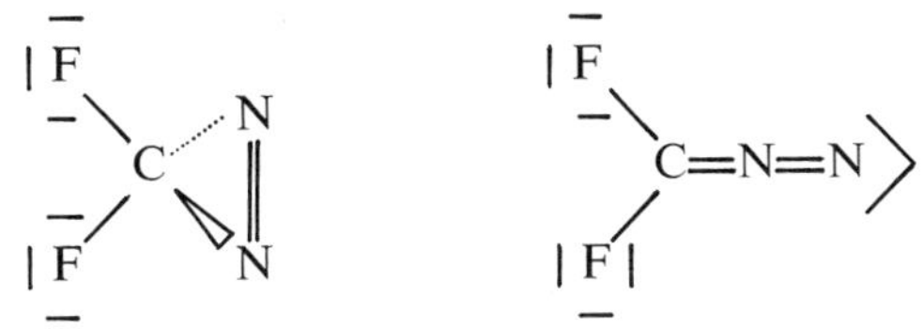

(**IX**) (**X**)

Raman spectra of pure N_2H_4, N_2D_4, and DMSO solutions of the hydrazines have been determined (*132*) and the 3189 cm^{-1} band which had been suggested to arise from a "polymer" was examined carefully. It was found to be composed of components for a vibration of the monomer and a hydrogen-bonded ν(N—H). Measurements of the relative Raman intensity, I, of the hydrogen-bonded and nonhydrogen-bonded ν(N—H) gave the enthalpy of hydrogen bond formation as -1430 cal/mole from plots of log I_{3189}/I_{3260} versus $1/T$.

The nitronium ion, isoelectronic with carbon dioxide, has been studied recently as the perchlorate (*133*) and tetrafluoro borate (*134*) salts, $[NO_2]^+[ClO_4]^-$ and $[NO_2]^+[BF_4]^-$. The NO_2^+ ion has approximately the same linear $D_{\infty h}$ structure as CO_2, but it appears to be slightly distorted in crystals. Evans et al. (*134*) use the bending frequency as a measure of the ionic nature of the compound, which is reported to be greatest with BF_4^- and least with NO_3^-.

A $\nu(N{\equiv}O)$ frequency of 2230 cm^{-1} characteristic of a nitrosyl group with much ionic character was found in the Raman spectrum of solid NOF_3CSO_3, and this compound probably has the ionic structure $[NO]^+[F_3CSO_3]$ (*135*).

The Raman spectrum of gaseous NF_3 has been redetermined (*136*), and the use of line shapes as well as polarization measurements in assigning spectra is discussed. The spectrum is in accord with the expected C_{3v} pyramidal structure and the results of the earlier investigation (*137*). Using He—Ne laser excitation, a spectrum has been obtained for the highly explosive NCl_3 (*138*). Frequencies are observed at 535 ν_1, 347 ν_2, 637 ν_3, and 254 ν_4 cm^{-1}. Spectra for the related compounds PCl_3, $AsCl_3$, and $SbCl_3$ have long been known.

The cation NF_4^+ has been obtained in the compound $[NF_4]^+[AsF_6]^-$ prepared by reacting $NF_3+F_2+AsF_5$ in a glow discharge (*139*). For NF_4^+, a four line Raman spectrum indicating a tetrahedral structure was obtained. The related compounds $[PCl_4]^+[AsF_6]^-$, $[PCl_4]^+[SbCl_6]^-$, $[PCl_4]^+[TaCl_6]^-$, $[AsCl_4]^+[SbCl_6]^-\cdot AsCl_3$ (*141*) and $[AsCl_4]^+[AsF_6]^-$ (*142*) also have been studied. The cation frequencies are tabulated in Table 3, and the anion fundamentals are listed in Table 4. There are indications of rather strong interactions in these crystals tending to reduce the symmetry from that of the free ions (*141*).

In somewhat similar studies, Raman spectroscopy has been used extensively for the investigation of pentacovalent phosphorus compounds.

TABLE 3

Tetrahedral Group V—Halogeno Cations (T_d)

Cation	State	ν_1	ν_2	ν_3	ν_4	References
NF_4^+	xtal	813	488	1159	625	(*139*)
PCl_4^+	xtal	458	171	658	251	(*144*)
$AsCl_4^+$	xtal	412	154	492	184	(*141*)
$SbCl_4^+$	xtal	353	143	399	153	(*143*)

TABLE 4

Octahedral Group V—Halogeno Anions (O_h)[a]

Anion	State	ν_1	ν_2	ν_3	ν_4	ν_5	References
PF_6^-	xtal	750	566	825	552	466	(*141*)
PCl_6^-	xtal	360	281	449	62	150	(*144*)
AsF_6^-	xtal	679	565	700	410–389	372	(*139,140*)
$SbCl_6^-$	xtal	334	281–290	336	185	168	(*141*)
$TaCl_6^-$	xtal	384	156	318–305	154	188	(*141*)

[a] Splitting of some of the degenerate vibrations and the observed breakdown of some of the O_h selection rules indicate that the correct symmetry is somewhat lower than cubic in the crystals. Fundamentals ν_1, ν_2, and ν_5 are Raman active; infrared values are reported for ν_3 and ν_4.

The structures of these compounds are of particular interest for two reasons. Many of them exist as ionic solids with 4 or 6 coordination about the phosphorus atom. When they have the basically trigonal bipyramidal five-coordinate structure **(XI)**, it is of interest to determine which ligands occupy the three equatorial and which the two axial positions.

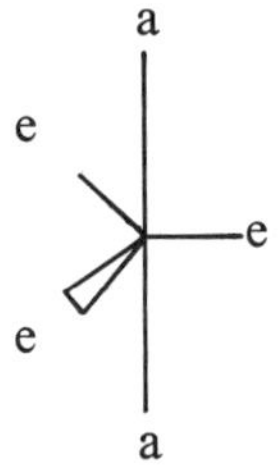

(XI)

The first compound of this type to be studied was phosphorus pentachloride, PCl_5. It was shown to exist in the solid state as the ionic compound $[PCl_4]^+[PCl_6]^-$ (*145*), while in solution PCl_5 has a covalent trigonal bipyramidal structure (*146*). The early solution spectra were shown by Taylor and Woodward (*147*) to contain lines from $POCl_3$ produced by hydrolysis of the PCl_5. Carlson (*144*) reinvestigated the spectra of PCl_5 both as the solid and solution. For $[PCl_4]^+$, vibrations were observed at 458 ν_1, 171 ν_2, 658 ν_3, and 251 cm^{-1} ν_4. In this case, the vibrations of PCl_4^+ were identified by comparison with the adduct $PCl_5 \cdot AlCl_3$ which has the ionic structure $[PCl_4]^+[AlCl_4]^+$. The tetrahedral cation $[AsCl_4]^+$ is also well known, and it forms addition compounds with phenanthroline, tetrahydrofuran, and tetrahydrothiophene much like the isoelectronic molecule $GeCl_4$. The stereochemistry of these adducts has been investigated with Raman spectroscopy by Beattie et al. (*148*). Beattie and his coworkers also have reinvestigated and reassigned the spectra of PCl_5 (*149*). They examined the adducts $AsCl_5 \cdot SbCl_5$ and $PCl_5 \cdot AsCl_5$ and suggested that these were $[AsCl_4][SbCl_6]$ and $[PCl_4][AsCl_6]$, respectively.

The anion $AsCl_4^-$ should have a structure based on the trigonal bipyramid (**XI**) with a lone pair of electrons in an equatorial position. The structure is therefore approximately square pyramidal with C_{2v} symmetry, and spectra of this anion obtained by extracting an aqueous solution of As(III) in HCl with di-*n*-butyl ether are consistent with this (*150*).

The molecule $SbCl_5$ which is known by X-ray and electron diffraction studies to have the trigonal pyramidal structure in both crystals and vapor gave spectra which were consistent throughout with the D_{3h} point group (*144*). The related transition metal compounds $NbCl_5$ and $TaCl_5$ also were investigated. These compounds are known to exist in both the crystalline state and in solution as dimers with octahedral coordination about the metals (**XII**) i.e., they are Nb_2Cl_{10} and Ta_2Cl_{10}. In spite of this,

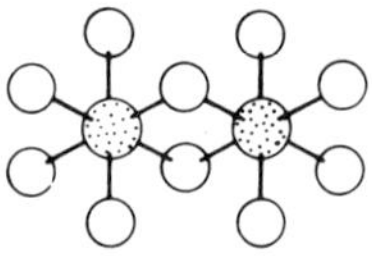

(**XII**)

their Raman and infrared spectra are in close agreement with those predicted on the basis of a D_{3h} monomeric structure which points out the kind of difficulties encountered in attempting to determine the structures of more complex molecules from comparisons of predicted and observed spectra. This use of spectra to ascertain symmetry is especially hazardous when, as is the case in these examples, the central atom is heavy so that relatively little coupling among the different internal coordinates occurs.

Fluorination of molecular $SbCl_5$ with ClF produces $SbFCl_4$ and chlorine. In the solid state $SbFCl_4$ has an ionic structure $[SbCl_4]^+F^-$ (*143*).

The skeletal frequencies found below 800 cm^{-1} for the alkyl substituted phosphorus pentachlorides $P(CH_3)_nCl_{5-n}$ indicated clearly that these compounds have the ionic structures $[P(CH_3)_nCl_{4-n}]^+Cl^-$ (*151,152*). The cation spectra resemble those of the isoelectronic methylchlorosilanes $(CH_3)_nSiCl_{4-n}$ closely. Fluorination of $P(CH_3)_3Cl_2$ with benzoyl fluoride yields $P(CH_3)_3FCl$ which Raman spectra show also to be ionic $[P(CH_3)_3F]Cl^-$ (*152*). The value of ν(P—F) is unusually low, 668 cm^{-1}, in this compound.

Several inorganic planar ring compounds have been studied by Raman spectroscopy. With the symmetrically substituted borazoles $B_3N_3H_3X_3$ (**XIII**), X = H, F, Cl, Br, and I, which have D_{3h}, symmetry, it was found that the totally symmetric vibrations were easily distinguished because of their high intensity as well as their polarization (*153*).

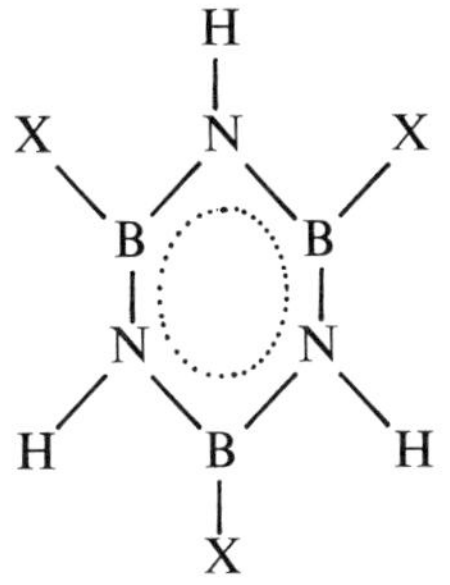

(**XIII**)

Variation of the X group hardly affects the frequency at ~ 850 cm^{-1} which must consequently be principally a breathing mode of the N atoms, while the 938 cm^{-1} fundamental of $B_3N_3H_6$ involving primarily motion of the boron atoms is decreased to 522 with X = F, 360 X = Cl, and 223 cm^{-1} X = Br. The value of ν(N—H) is approximately constant at 3440 cm^{-1} in CS_2 solution, indicating that the X groups exert little inductive effect.

The phosphonitrilic halides $(PNX_2)_n$ n = 3, 4, 5, and 6; X = F, Cl, Br, and NCS have been investigated in detail by Steger and co-workers (*154–157*). The spectra support planar $(PN)_3$ and $(PN)_4$ frameworks for the molecules in solution or in melts. The vibrational spectra can be used to characterize the different polymers which are very difficult to separate except by gas phase chromatography. For the trimer $P_3N_3Cl_nBr_{6-n}$, three strong, polarized lines are observed. The parent molecule $P_3N_3Cl_6$ (**XIV**) has D_{3h} symmetry. The two higher frequencies are ring modes and vary smoothly with the replacement of Cl by Br from 786 to 754 and 669 to 640 cm^{-1}. For the isothiocyanate, $P_3N_3(NCS)_6$, the values are 783 and 688 cm^{-1}. The third, low frequency is primarily $\nu_s(PX_2)$. In $P_3N_3F_6$, the ring frequencies are markedly lower, 567 and 681 cm^{-1} respectively.

The spectra of P_2Cl_4 (*158*) and P_2I_4 (*159*) which contain direct P—P bonds are consistent only with a *trans* C_{2h} structure for both solid and

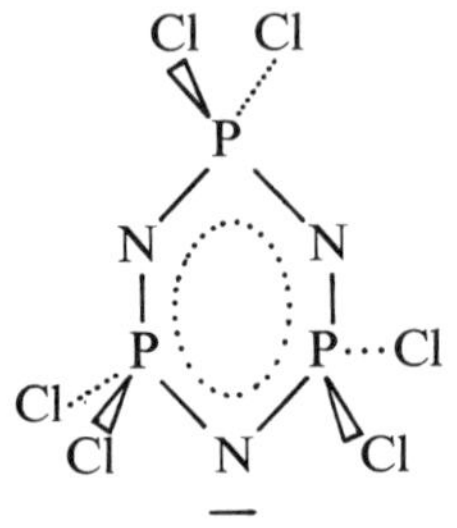

(XIV)

solutions indicating that there is an appreciable barrier to rotation about the P—P bond. The alkyl derivatives $P_2(C_2H_5)_4$ and $P_2(C_4H_{10})_4$ have similar structures, and ν(P—P) is 424 and 419 cm^{-1}, respectively (*160*). The related diphosphine disulfides $P_2S_2(CH_3)_4$ and $P_2S_2(C_2H_5)_4$ (*161–164*) were found also to have the *trans* structures (**XV**). The ranges for

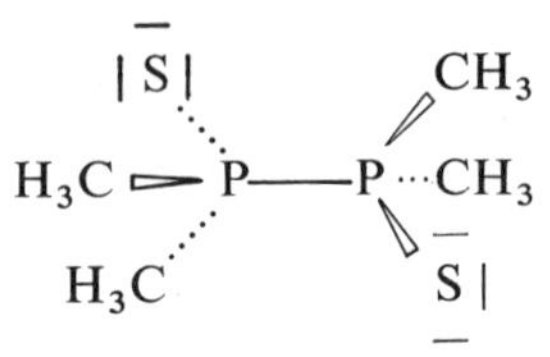

(XV)

the skeletal vibrations are ν(P—C) 700–800, ν(P=S) 500–600, and ν(P—P) 400–500 cm^{-1} (*164*). Coordination to a metal overcomes the barrier to rotation, and complexes where the diphosphine disulfide appears to act as a bidentate chelating ligand have been obtained (*165*).

The stereochemistry of many trigonal bipyramidal compounds has been investigated using Raman spectroscopy. In the sequence PCl_4F, PCl_3F_2, PCl_2F_3 (*166*), and $PClF_4$ (*167*), the usual rule that the least electronegative groups go in the equatorial positions was found to be obeyed, i.e., the compounds have the structures (**XVI–XVIII**).

In general, the axial bonds are weaker than the equatorial bonds to a given ligand. Phosphorus pentafluoride PF_5 has the covalent trigonal bipyramidal structure (*166*) even in the solid state unlike PCl_5 which is ionic.

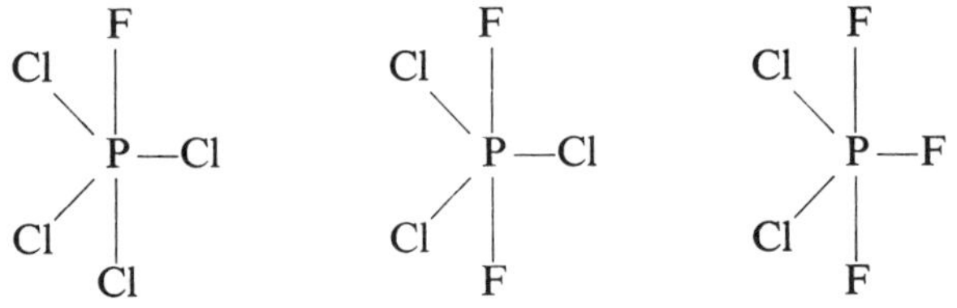

C_{3v} (XVI) D_{3h} (XVII) C_{2v} (XVIII)

In $(CF_3)PCl_4$ (*168*) and $(CF_3)_2PCl_3$ (*169*), the trifluoromethyl groups also occupy the axial positions consistent with the observations that the effective electronegativity of CF_3 is approximately 3.5 compared to 4.0 for fluorine and 3.0 for chlorine. With the simple methyl derivatives $(CH_3)PF_4$ (*170*), $(CH_3)_2PF_3$, and $(CH_3)_3PF_2$ (*171*), the methyl groups occupy the equatorial positions consistent with their lower electronegativity. The most intense Raman line below 1000 cm^{-1} in the spectra of PF_5, $(CH_3)PF_4$, and $(CH_3)_2PF_3$ is the totally symmetric ν(P—F) for the equatorial bonds, and this decreases steadily from 817 (PF_5) to 646.5 ($(CH_3)_2PF_3$) (*170*). In their stereochemical behavior, the methyl groups resemble lone electron pairs. While $(CH_3)PCl_4$ is monomeric in nonionizing solvents, the Raman spectrum indicates that in crystals it is $[(CH_3)PCl_3]Cl$ (*172*).

Fewer studies have been made with trivalent phosphorus, since it forms compounds which have simple pyramidal structures. Nielsen and Walker (*173*) have investigated liquid $(CH_3)PH_2$ which has a very intense $\nu_s(PH_2)$ line at 2297 cm^{-1}. The $\delta(PH_2)$ fundamental is observed at 1086 cm^{-1}. Spectra have been obtained for $(CH_3)_3P$ and $(CH_3)_3As$ (*174*) to assist in assignment of the vibrations of complexes like $[Ni(CO)_3P(CH_3)_3]$ and $[Ni(CO)_3As(CH_3)_3]$. Triphenylphosphine, triphenylphosphine oxide, and their complexes have been studied, and the "X" sensitive modes of the metal complexes $MX_n(P(C_6H_5)_3)_m$ have been tabulated (*175*). Similar studies have been made for the arsenic donors $(CH_3)_2(C_6H_5)As$, $(CH_3)(C_6H_5)_2As$, $(C_6H_5)_3As$, and "diarsine" or o-phenylenebis(dimethylarsine) (*176*). Spectra also have been reported for $(CH_3)PCl_2$ and

$(CF_3)PCl_2$ (*177*). The vibrations of the tricyanides $P(CN)_3$ (*178,179*), and $As(CN)_3$ (*178*) proved to be difficult to assign; the totally symmetric $\nu(C{\equiv}N)$ occurs at 2206 cm^{-1} in the phosphorus compound.

Spectra of the compounds $(R_3Ge)_3P$ and $(R_3Sn)_3P$, R = C_6H_5 and CH_3 (*180,181*) are consistent with a pyramidal structure about phosphorus. Four Raman active skeletal vibrations are observed (*181*):

$[(CH_3)_3Ge]_3P$—ν_s 320, ν_{as} 366, δ_s 84, δ_{as} 156

$[(CH_3)_3Sn]_3P$—ν_s 284, ν_{as} 349, δ_s 62, δ_{as} 123

$[(C_6H_5)_3Ge]_3P$—ν_s 311, ν_{as} 366, δ_s 85, δ_{as} 171

$[(C_6H_5)_3Sn]_3P$—ν_s 294, ν_{as} 350, δ_s 88, δ_{as} not observed

5. Silicon, Germanium, and Tin

The methyldisilylamines $H_3CN(SiH_3)_2$ and $H_3CN(SiD_3)_2$ show ν(C—N) 1095, ν_s(N—Si) 562, and ν_{as}(N—Si) 940 cm^{-1} (*182*). Donor-acceptor complexes formed by reaction of Lewis acids like $SiCl_4$ and $SnCl_4$ with bases are well known and have been studied extensively by infrared spectroscopy. Beattie (*183*) recently has reviewed such studies on the stereochemistry of $SnCl_4$ adducts.

Brune and Zeil (*184*) in an early investigation determined the Raman spectra of $SnCl_4$ plus various bases such as water, alcohols, ethers, nitriles, and $POCl_3$. Because of the simplicity of the spectra, they suggested that all of the 2:1 adducts, $SnCl_4 \cdot 2L$, had the *trans* structure **(XIX)**,

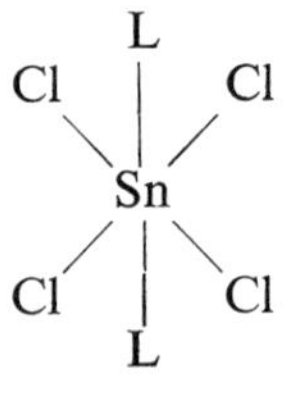

(XIX)

and that the skeletal vibrations obeyed D_{4h} selection rules. The frequencies assigned to ν_s(Sn—Cl) were used as a measure of the ligand donor strengths, a reasonable procedure so long as all complexes have the same structure and the normal modes involve essentially only Sn—Cl bond stretching. The 1:1 adducts $SnCl_4 \cdot L$ gave more complicated spectra than the 2:1 adducts, and C_{2v} symmetry **(XX)** was assigned to all of these on the basis of the skeletal modes. The possibility of ligand bridging was not considered.

Beattie and Rule (*185*) investigated the spectra of such adducts in more detail. They noted that ν_s(Sn—Cl) of the *cis* $SnCl_4 \cdot 2L$ complexes which is found at ca. 300 cm^{-1} was more than 20 times as intense as the non-totally symmetric stretching modes. Consequently, unless care is taken to

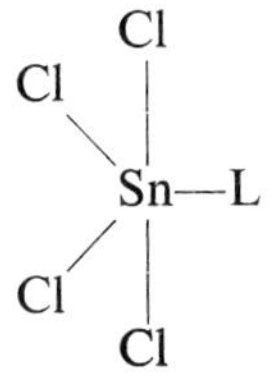

(XX)

record the weaker fundamentals, only one Raman line may be observed. This usually coincides with the middle of the three infrared active bands in this region. As a result, on the basis of a Raman spectrum alone, it is easy to assign the *trans* structure to complexes which are really *cis*. In contrast the *trans* adducts were observed to give two intense Raman lines at ca. 300(*p*) and 250 (*dp*) cm^{-1}.

The reaction between $SnCl_4$ and tetrahydrothiophene has also been studied by Raman spectroscopy (*186*) and the data indicate that here the $SnCl_4 \cdot 2THT$ adduct does have the *trans* structure (**XXI**).

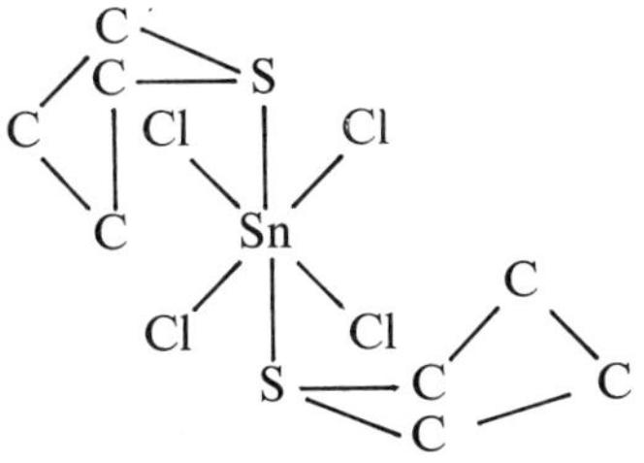

(XXI)

In addition to these investigations, Raman spectra have been used extensively in the study of alkyl and aryl derivatives of the Group IVB elements, and these will be discussed in the section on organometallic compounds.

6. Boron, Aluminum, and Gallium Compounds

The Raman and infrared spectra of $C_6H_5BCl_2$ have been obtained recently (*187*). Thc lowest frequency observed in the Raman spectrum, 139 cm^{-1}, is intense and depolarized, and it is assigned to the torsional mode for the phenyl group rotating with respect to the BCl_2 moiety. This leads to a calculated value for the barrier to rotation of 45 kcal/mole indicating significant π bonding in the C—B bond.

The substituted diboranes, monomethyldiborane, 1,1-dimethyldiborane, trimethyldiborane, and tetramethyldiborane have all been examined at −70°C. It was possible to use very small samples by sealing them in 1.5 mm bore capillary tubing and exciting the spectra with 4880 Å radiation from an Ar^+ laser (*188*).

Wartenburg and Goubeau (*189*) have reported Raman as well as infrared spectra for solid adducts of the type $Cl_3B{\cdot}OPCl_3$, $Cl_3B{\cdot}OPBr_3$, $Br_3B{\cdot}OPCl_3$, $Br_3B{\cdot}OPBr_3$, and $Cl_3Al{\cdot}2OPCl_3$. In all cases bonding occurs via the oxygen atom (**XXII**) as shown by the decrease in ν(P=O) upon coordination. With the group IIIB trihalides, the decreases are as

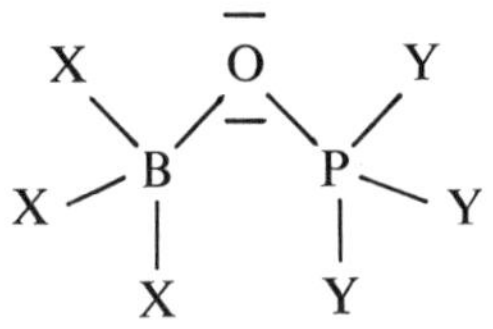

(**XXII**)

follows: BX_3, 133–173; AlX_3, 65–85; GaX_3, 52–85; InX_3 50–90; TlX_3, 15 cm^{-1}.

Ammine adducts of boron and aluminum Lewis acids have been studied by several groups. In the compounds $X_3Z{\cdot}NR_3$ (X = H, CH_3, F, Cl, Br; Z = B, Al; and R = H, CH_3), ν(B—N) was observed in the range 650–780 cm^{-1} while ν(Al—N) was ca. 550 cm^{-1} (*190*). Taylor has made detailed studies of the trimethylamine adducts of the boron trihalides (*191*). The $(CH_3)_3N$ vibrations remain relatively unchanged, while the BX_3 modes undergo marked alterations because of the boron rehybridization from sp^2 to sp^3. For this reason, shifts in the trimethylamine frequencies are more reliable indicators of electronic effects than shifts in the BX_3 frequencies. The values of ν(C—N) drop as the nitrogen is coordinated indicating a drift of the bonding electrons toward the boron atom.

The spectrum of gallium trichloride, Ga_2Cl_6 indicates that the dimeric structure persists from the solid to the melt and solutions to the vapor (*192,193*). In the solid gallane adduct $H_3Ga \cdot N(CH_3)_3$, the ν(Ga—H) is at ca. 1850 cm^{-1} and appreciably higher than the corresponding frequency for $H_3Al \cdot N(CH_3)_3$ (*194*). Beattie and co-workers (*195*) have obtained spectra for the dimers Al_2Br_6, Al_2I_6, Ga_2Br_6, Ga_2I_6, and In_2I_6. Frequencies were calculated using a very simple model force field to assist in the assignments. Adducts of the type $MX_3 \cdot 2N(CH_3)_3$, (MX_3 = $AlCl_3$, $GaCl_3$, $InCl_3$, and $InBr_3$), were examined, and they appear to be isostructural with the isoelectronic cations of the group IV elements $[M'Cl_3 \cdot 2N(CH_3)_3]^+$; ($M'$ = Si, Ge), and have D_{3h} effective symmetry (*196*). Adams and Churchill also have used a simple model for vibrational analyses of the bridged trihalides Al_2Br_6, Al_2I_6, and In_2I_6 (*197*).

B. Oxyanions

One of the earliest applications of Raman spectroscopy was to the study of the structure of the simple trigonal planar and tetrahedral oxy-anions, particularly in aqueous solutions. Many of these early reports contain errors arising because of the presence of impurities or because of hydrolysis of the ions. In addition, many of the tetrahedral transition metal oxyanions exhibit near degeneracy of the bending modes ν_2 and ν_4, and many of the reports published before 1960 (*198*) appear to list impurity lines for ν_4.

Recent investigations of these ions have dealt with the more unusual transition metal ions, the structures of polycondensed anions, and with the nature of interactions between simple oxyanions and metal cations in solutions and melts. The latter topic will be discussed in later sections dealing with these interactions.

Nitrate ion has been used frequently as a probe to study cation-anion interactions. Nitrate has a simple three line spectrum, and the degenerate vibrations split significantly upon coordination of the anion to a metal cation. Addison et al. (*199*) have studied spectra of nitrato complexes of known structures. Their results confirm the expectation based on a very simple model that the highest frequency nitrate vibration of a complex should be polarized (N=O stretching, A_1) when nitrate functions as a bidentate ligand and depolarized (NO_2 asymmetric stretching, B_2) when it acts as a unidentate ligand. Hester and co-workers (*200,201*) using a simple valence force field to represent this model have calculated frequencies for both cases for a range of force constant values. Weidlein,

Muller, and Dehnicke (*202*) have suggested that the nitrates are bidentate in $Zr(NO_3)_4$ and the compound is isostructural with $Sn(NO_3)_4$ and $Ti(NO_3)_4$ (*202*).

Data for recent investigations of tetrahedral transition metal oxyanions are given in Table 5. Because of the near degeneracy of ν_2 and ν_4,

TABLE 5

Tetrahedral Transition Metal Oxyanions and Oxides, T_d

Anion	State	ν_1	ν_2	ν_3	ν_4	References
VO_4^{-3}	aq	827	340	780	340	(*205*)
CrO_4^{-2}	aq	847	368	884	368	(*206*)
MoO_4^{-2}	aq	897	318	841	318	(*207*)
WO_4^{-2}	aq	931	(324)[a]	833	(324)[a]	(*207*)
MnO_4^{-3}	aq	863	348	770	348	(*209*)
MnO_4^{-2}	aq, xtal	810	328	862	328	(*209*)
MnO_4^-	aq, xtal	838	355	921	429	(*210*)
TcO_4^-	aq	912	325	—	325	(*207*)
ReO_4^-	aq, xtal	972	332	916	332	(*204,212*)
FeO_4^{-2}	aq	778	320	800	320	(*209*)
RuO_4^{-2}	aq	856	330	807	330	(*209*)
RuO_4	1, aq, xtal	882	323	914	334	(*208, 211*)
OsO_4	1, aq, xtal	964	338	953	334	(*211*)

[a] Data in parentheses are from infrared spectra.

most of these anions give three line spectra. Some earlier workers suggested that expansion of the coordination number of the transition metal from four to six occurred as the anion passed from the crystal into aqueous solution. Thus the perrhenate ion ReO_4^- was described as octahedral because of hydration (*203*). This was not very reasonable, since an anion like $ReO_4(OH_2)_2^-$ would certainly not obey O_h selection rules nor is it likely that $ReO_2(OH)_4^-$ would, and no ion such as ReO_6^{-5} could exist in neutral solution. The discovery of coincidences between the Raman and infrared spectra ruled out the octahedral structure (*204*). Claassen and Zielen (*204*) used the three observed Raman frequencies to calculate bond stretching, angle bending, and O ... O nonbonded force constants for ReO_4^- and found that the near degeneracy of ν_2 and ν_4 was to be expected. Woodward and Roberts (*208*) and Busey and Keller (*207*) used the same force field and noted that while ν_4/ν_2 was greater than 1 for many of the oxyanions which had been studied the ratio approached unity as the ratio of masses M_x/M_y of the XY_4 tetrahedron increased. A simple valence force field always makes $\nu_3 > \nu_1$, and the ratio ν_3/ν_1 also approaches unity as M_x/M_y increases (*208*).

Griffith (*209*) has noted that the ratio ν_3/ν_1 depends upon the metal oxidation state and mass. Within a given family, e.g. CrO_4^{-2}, MoO_4^{-2}, and WO_4^{-2}, the ratio decreases with the metal mass and with the same metal it decreases as the oxidation state decreases, e.g., RuO_4, RuO_4^{-2} or MnO_4^-, MnO_4^{-2}, MnO_4^{-3}.

Recently, Hendra (*210*) has succeeded in recording the permanganate spectrum using He—Ne laser excitation, a difficult task because of the intense charge transfer absorption. Additional lines attributed to MnO_2 were observed with both solutions and crystals.

Raman spectra have been used to study the protonation and polycondensation reactions of oxyanions, and quantitative measurements of acid dissociation constants will be discussed later. If several ionic species exist in a solution in equilibrium, it often is difficult to assign the spectra without information from other kinds of experiments. Thus spectra incorrectly attributed to VO_4^{-3} were obtained with solutions saturated with K_3VO_4. Chemists have long recognized that ions which exist in a crystal do not necessarily exist in a solution prepared from it, and in this case (*198*) the orthovanadate ion, VO_4^{-3}, hydrolyzed giving a mixture of species. This is also obvious from measurements of the degree of protonation of VO_4^{-3} as a function of solution pH (*213*). Griffith (*205*) has obtained the true spectrum of VO_4^{-3} by dissolving K_3VO_4 in 10 *M* KOH. Below pH 11.6, there is evidence for the formation of HVO_4^{-2} and for the condensation reaction

$$2HVO_4^{-2} \leftrightharpoons V_2O_7^{-2} + H_2O \tag{10}$$

Raman lines assigned to $V_2O_7^{-4}$ are observed at 810 ν_{as}(V—O—V), 503 ν_s(V—O—V), and 228 cm^{-1} δ(V—O—V). At pH 8, the spectrum indicates principally one species $(VO_3)_n^{-n}$ defined by the solution equilibrium measurements as $(VO_3)_3^{-3}$ (*213*) or $(VO_3)_4^{-4}$ (*214,215*); $\nu_s(VO_2)$ 945, $\nu_{as}(VO_2)$ 905, $\delta(VO_2)$ 360, ν_{as}(V—O—V) 634, and ν_s(V—O—V) 490 cm^{-1}. The value of ν_s(V—O) for bonds to nonbridging oxygens increases reflecting an increase in multiple bond character as the number of nonbridging oxygens decreases, i.e., VO_4^{-3} 827 and $(VO_3)_n^{-n}$ 945 cm^{-1}. The analogous dichromate ion, $Cr_2O_7^{-2}$ (**XXIII**) has ν_{as}(Cr—O—Cr) 772, ν_s(Cr—O—Cr) 558, and δ(Cr—O—Cr) 220 cm^{-1} (*216,217*).

Solutions containing more than 80% by weight of $HReO_4$ also show a new Raman line in addition to the spectrum of the tetrahedral ReO_4^-

ion, and this line at 845 cm^{-1} is assigned to the symmetric stretching of the (Re—O—Re) bridge of a dimer (*218*).

Raman spectra have been used to show that certain large polycondensed anions exist both in crystals and aqueous solutions and in some cases to make deductions about the ionic symmetry. This technique must be used with care, since usually only a few lines are observed and the frequencies for stretching of metal to nonbridging oxygen bonds are often almost independent of the degree of condensation. In the case of the polymolybdates, erroneous conclusions were drawn concerning the ionic

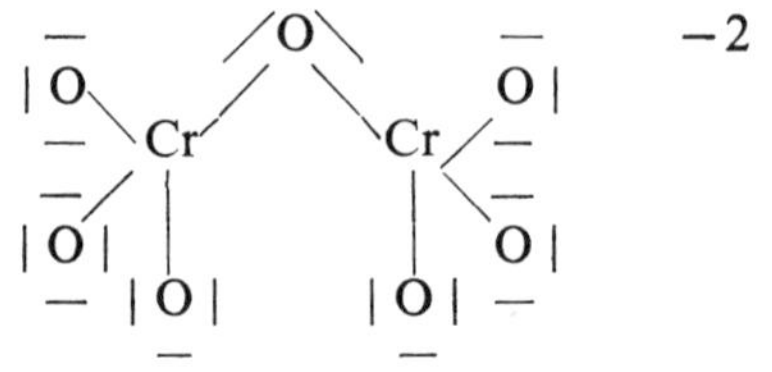

(XXIII)

structures from early Raman data (*219*). The use of Raman spectra of aqueous solutions in the assignment of conformations to polycondensed ring systems also is limited. Because of accidental degeneracy and low intensity of some of the vibrations, often relatively few lines are observed, and an erroneous structure of high symmetry is assigned.

Aveston, Anacker, and Johnson (*220*) found that molybdate solutions to which 8/7 mole H^+ had been added per mole MoO_4^{-2} had a Raman spectrum which was very similar to that of crystalline $(NH_4)_6Mo_7O_{24} \cdot 4H_2O$. This suggests that the solutions contain the same $Mo_7O_{24}^{-6}$ anion known from X-ray studies to exist in the crystals. The crystal spectrum shows 16 lines and the solution 10, each of which agrees with one of the crystal lines to within ± 8 cm^{-1}. Similarly the Raman spectrum of tungstate solutions acidified to a $[H^+]/[WO_4^{-2}]$ ratio of 7/6 is very similar to that of crystalline $Na_{10}W_{12}O_{41} \cdot 28H_2O$ which contains $W_{12}O_{41}^{-10}$ ions, and all 14 solution spectrum lines have crystal spectrum counterparts within ± 5 cm^{-1} (*221*). The spectra of crystals of $K_8Ta_6O_{19} \cdot 16H_2O$ and alkaline solutions of the salt were found to be very similar (*222*). The absence of coincidences between Raman and infrared spectra was consistent with the known cubic symmetry of the $Ta_6O_{19}^{-8}$ ion which is present in the crystals. The results of several other kinds of physical measurements already had indicated that the formula of the ion in solution was the same as that in the crystal. Spectra of crystals and aqueous solutions of $K_{14}Nb_{12}O_{37}\cdot 27H_2O$ and of $K_8Ta_6O_{19}\cdot 16H_2O$ were all very similar indicating that isostructural $Ta_6O_{19}^{-8}$ and $Nb_6O_{19}^{-8}$ ions were present (*223*). For the stretching of the bonds to nonbridging oxygens, ν_s(Nb—O) was 878 and ν_s(Ta—O) was 852 cm^{-1}, and these values are very similar to that for the monomeric VO_4^{-3} ion ν_s 827 cm^{-1}.

The germanate anion $GeO_2(OH)_2^{-2}$ has been studied by Walrafen (*224*) in solution and crystals, and fundamentals were recorded at 667 ν_s and ν_{as}(Ge—OH), 765 ν_s and ν_{as}(Ge—O). At germanium concentrations of greater than 2 *M* there was evidence for the presence of the condensation product $Ge_2O_5^{-2}$ which is probably **(XXIV)**:

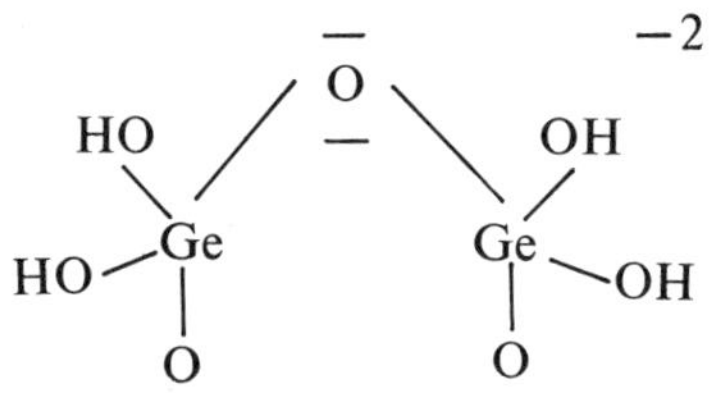

(XXIV)

For the binuclear ion, ν_s(Ge—O—Ge) was observed at 529 cm^{-1}.

Steger and co-workers have studied solutions of PO_4^{-3}, HPO_4^{-2} and $H_2PO_4^-$ as a function of concentration and temperature (*225*) and also the polyphosphates $P_2O_7^{-4}$ (*226*), $H_2P_2O_7^{-2}$ (*226*), $P_3O_9^{-3}$ (*227,228*), and $P_4O_{12}^{-4}$ (*229,230*). Although phosphate solutions have been investigated by Raman spectroscopy since 1929, the tabulation of fundamentals and assignments is complicated greatly by the low Raman intensity of many of the phosphate vibrations (*225*). The appreciable breadth of the ν_s(P—O—P) fundamental of $H_2P_2O_7^{-2}$ at 715 cm^{-1} was attributed to the presence of rotational isomers (*226*) of **(XXV)**, although it is more likely a consequence of hydrogen bonding and interionic interactions. For the

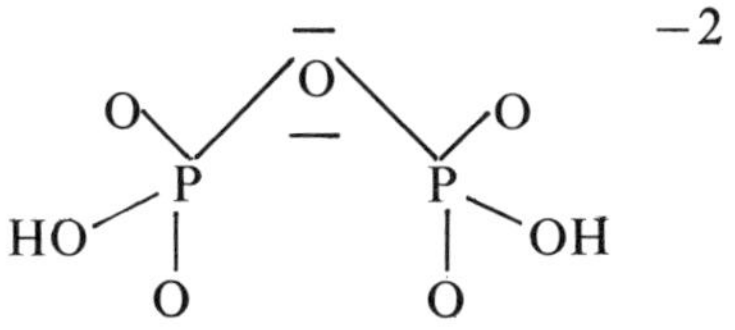

(XXV)

trimetaphosphate ion, $P_3O_9^{-3}$, reasonable structures are the chair form C_{3v}, the planar ring D_{3h}, and the boat form C_s. Steger (*228*) has suggested that $P_3O_9^{-3}$ has the flat ring structure in solution, but Griffith (*231*) finds that the spectra are consistent only with the chair configuration (**XXVI**) on the basis of the presence of at least 5 and perhaps 6 polarized

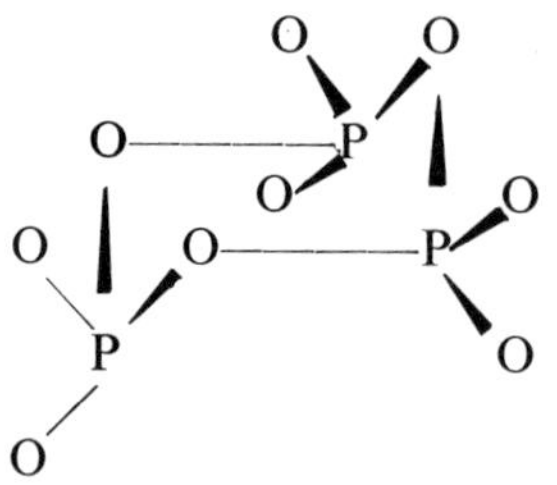

(**XXVI**)

lines and coincidences between the Raman and infrared spectra. The similarity of the solution spectra to that of $Na_3P_3O_9 \cdot 6H_2O$ crystals where the ion is known to have the chair conformation also supports this structure (*231*). Spectra of tetrametaphosphate ion in aqueous solution are consistent with C_{2v} symmetry (**XXVII**) (*230,231*), and the same structure is assigned to the $As_4O_{12}^{-4}$ ion (*231*).

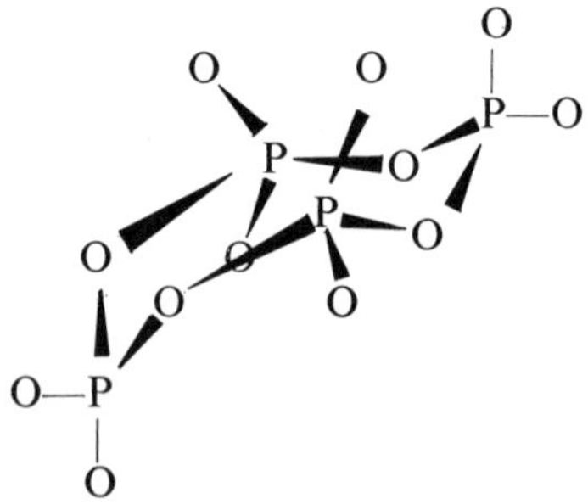

(**XXVII**)

The hyponitrite ion, $N_2O_2^{-2}$, has been studied in 0.7 *M* NaOH solution (*232*), because it decomposes producing N_2O in acidic solution. The structure is that of the *trans* conformer with C_{2h} symmetry (**XXVIII**), since only three Raman lines at 1383, 1115, and 692 cm^{-1} are observed.

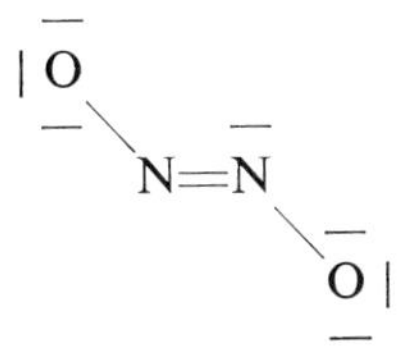

(**XXVIII**)

Reports of the nitrite, NO_2^-, spectrum in the past have been confused because of nitrate impurities, and the fundamentals occur at 1330 ν_1, 810 ν_2, and 1240 ν_3 cm^{-1} (*233,234*).

Raman spectroscopy has been used to study the SO_3—H_2O system for 40 years. Recent investigations by Gillespie and Robinson (*235*) show that SO_3 exists in solution as both the monomer and as the cyclic trimer which was assigned the "chair" conformation on the basis of the spectrum. Spectra have been reported for H_2SO_4, D_2SO_4, FSO_3H, $ClSO_3H$, and CH_3SO_3H (*236*), and the frequencies have been correlated with the electronegativity of the substituents in the sulfonic acids (*237*). The chain-like poly acids $H_2S_2O_7$, $H_2S_3O_{10}$, and $H_2S_4O_{13}$ have been identified in the SO_3—H_2O system (*238*), and similar polymers are formed with FSO_3H and $ClSO_3H$ (*239*). Careful measurements have been made of the spectrum of the methanesulfonate ion $CH_3SO_3^-$ (*240*) and of the trifluoromethanesulfonate and trichloromethanesulfonate ions $CF_3SO_3^-$ and $CCl_3SO_3^-$ (*241*). Analogous studies have been carried out for the H_2SeO_4—H_2O system (*242,243*).

Spectra have been obtained by several groups for crystalline compounds such as $H_3O^+ClO_4^-$ (*244,245,246*), and the hydronium ion vibrations have been assigned (*245,246*). Raman spectra were obtained for crystalline $HClO_4$ (*247*), since a phase study of the system Cl_2O_7—H_2O suggested that solid $HClO_4$ did not exist because of the reaction (11a):

$$3HClO_4 \rightarrow Cl_2O_7 + H_3O^+ClO_4^- \quad (11a)$$

The spectrum of the crystalline compounds was very similar to that of liquid $HClO_4$ and showed neither the intense totally symmetric stretch of ClO_4^- nor any lines of Cl_2O_7. Consequently, the solid must contain perchloric acid molecules.

C. Metal Halide and Pseudohalide Complexes

Raman spectra have been reported for a very large number of four and six coordinate metal-halide complexes, particularly by Woodward and co-workers. These ions are usually highly symmetric, point groups T_d, D_{4h}, or O_h, so Raman as well as infrared spectra are essential to any study of the vibrations. Fundamentals have been tabulated for these complexes by several authors (*1,3,248,249*), and a particularly thorough review of metal-halide vibrations has been published recently (*250*). These data are very useful for the purpose of comparing the nature and strength of metal–ligand bonds. With the tetrahedral, square planar, and octahedral complexes, only the ligands move in the highest frequency totally symmetric vibration. In the simple valence force field approximation, the metal–ligand bond stretching force constant can be calculated from this single frequency and used to establish trends in the bonding in different ions (*251*).

Spectra have been obtained both from measurements on crystals and on aqueous solutions. Many of the complexes are "weak," i.e., the equilibrium constants for their dissociation in aqueous solutions are appreciable, and the spectra must be obtained on solutions containing the metal ion plus a large excess of ligand. Under these conditions, the complex is formed in which the metal has its maximum coordination number for the ligand. In many of these systems, other complexes with fewer halide ligands are present in solutions with moderate halide ion concentrations, and the assignment of the spectra and stoichiometries of these complexes is a considerably more difficult task. This will be discussed below when solution equilibria are considered.

1. Tetrahedral Complexes

Data for tetrahedral halogeno complexes are given in Table 6. These frequencies may also be compared with those for isoelectronic cations listed in Table 3. With T_d symmetry all four normal modes of an MX_4 complex are Raman active. The totally symmetric fundamental is recognized easily because of its high Raman intensity and narrow line width as well as its polarization. The deformation modes usually appear with medium intensity, while the antisymmetric stretching mode is weak and sometimes difficult to observe with spectra of dilute solutions.

Since most of these complexes have the maximum number of halide ions which can be coordinated to the metal, since the ions are also known in crystals, and since the spectra are typical of the tetrahedral structure, there is little uncertainty that the ions have the suggested structure in solution. In the case of the tetrachlorozincate(II) ion, $[ZnCl_4]^{-2}$, it was suggested that this complex actually was *trans* $[ZnCl_4(OH_2)_2]^{-2}$ (*280*) in

TABLE 6

Tetrahedral Metal-Halide Complexes (T_d)[a]

Ion	State	ν_1(A)	ν_2(E)	ν_3(F_2)	ν_4(F_2)	References
BeF_4^{-2}	aq	543	800	500 (?)	500 (?)	(*253*)
$MnCl_4^{-2}$	soln	249	—	301, 278[b]	120[b]	(*254*)
$FeCl_4^{-2}$	ether soln	330	106	385	133	(*252*)
$ZnCl_4^{-2}$	aq, xtal, melt, soln	278	116	298	130	(*255,263,280*)
$HgCl_4^{-2}$	aq, xtal, mt, sl	267	180 (?)	276	192 (?)	(*264–267*)
$MnBr_4^{-2}$	soln	195	65	226	81	(*254*)
$FeBr_4^{-2}$	soln	202	—	—	—	(*254*)
$ZnBr_4^{-2}$	aq, xtal	178	80	212	89	(*255,256,258*)
$CdBr_4^{-2}$	aq	167	53 (?)	185	62	(*264,268*)
$HgBr_4^{-2}$	aq, soln	166	—	—	—	(*264,265*)
MnI_4^{-2}	soln	116	46	193, 188[b]	58	(*254*)
ZnI_4^{-2}	xtal	130	60	172	70	(*255,257,258,268*)
CdI_4^{-2}	aq	117	37	147	45	(*257,258,264*)
HgI_4^{-2}	aq, xtal, soln	122	—	—	50	(*264,266*)
$AlCl_4^-$	xtal, melt, soln	349	145	580	183	(*270,271*)
$GaCl_4^-$	aq, melt, soln	346	114	386	149	(*252,270,271*)
$InCl_4^-$	soln	321	89	337	112	(*252*)
$TlCl_4^-$	aq, xtal	312	60	296	78	(*273,274,275*)
$GaBr_4^-$	aq, melt	210	71	280	102	(*276,277*)
$InBr_4^-$	soln	197	55	239	79	(*278*)
$TlBr_4^-$	xtal	184	58	201	69	(*273,274,275*)
GaI_4^-	aq	145	52	222	73	(*279*)
InI_4^-	aq	139	42	185	58	(*279*)
TlI_4^-	xtal	133	—	156	—	(*273,274,275*)

[a] Where data are available, frequencies are taken from measurements on aqueous solutions. Surprisingly large discrepancies often exist between values of different workers. In some cases these result from the different phases used, in others from incorrect assignments caused by lines from other complexes besides the one under study, and apparently sometimes from poor spectrometer calibration. ν_1 = symmetric stretching, ν_2 = deformation, ν_3 = antisymmetric stretching, ν_4 = deformation.

[b] Infrared data.

solution, since the cation is certainly $[Zn(OH_2)_6]^{+2}$. Careful comparisons of the Raman spectra of crystals known to contain tetrahedral $ZnCl_4^{-2}$ ions with the solution spectrum indicate that the anion is tetrahedral in aqueous solution (*255*), i.e., the coordination number of zinc decreases from 6 to 4 as water molecules are replaced by chloride ions.

Although Siebert reported a line for ν_s(Cd—Cl) at 243 cm^{-1} (*281*) from measurements on aqueous solutions and assigned this to $CdCl_4^{-2}$, Rolfe et al. found that solutions of $CdCl_2$ plus excess chloride ion showed no Raman lines at all attributable to chloro complexes of cadmium (*264*). Melts of $CdCl_2 + KCl$ show a line at 259 cm^{-1} variously attributed to $CdCl_3^-$ (*282*) or $CdCl_4^{-2}$ (*283*). In aqueous solution, significant complexing of cadmium(II) by chloride ion has been established by solution equilibrium measurements (*284*). A somewhat analogous situation was observed in studies of the chloro complexing of $(CH_3)_2Sn^{+2}$ (*443*) in aqueous solutions. Although a line assigned to ν(Sn—Cl) was observed, measurements of the Raman intensity as a function of chloride ion concentration gave a much smaller value for the association constant than potentiometric measurements. It is apparent that the activity measurements reflect a different cation–anion interaction than the spectroscopic experiments. Perhaps the initial association occurs in a complex where cation and anion are still separated by a solvent molecule.

In some cases with very unstable complexes the tetrahedral anion is not significant in aqueous solutions even with a high concentration of halide ion. Since uni-negative anions are often extracted preferentially into an organic phase, it has been possible to obtain good spectra in this way. For example, $InCl_4^-$ is not a major species in aqueous solutions, but this ion can be extracted into diethyl ether (*252*).

Only a few pseudohalide complexes aside from cyanide complexes which will be discussed later have been studied by Raman spectroscopy. Forster and Horrocks (*285*) have obtained spectra for $Zn(NCO)_4^{-2}$, $Zn(NCS)_4^{-2}$, and $Zn(NCSe)_4^{-2}$ using nitromethane or acetone solutions. They are consistent with T_d symmetry, and a normal coordinate analysis was made. The skeletal stretching modes ν_s(Zn—N) were found at 330 cm^{-1} for $Zn(NCO)_4^{-2}$ and 225 cm^{-1} for $Zn(NCS)_4^{-2}$; none was observed with the selenocyanate complex. The azido complex $Zn(N_3)_4^{-2}$ was also studied (*286*), and the spectrum shows that the complex has lower than full tetrahedral symmetry because of the nature of coordination by N_3^-. The vibrations were assigned assuming D_{2d} symmetry for the complex. Dehnicke and co-workers have obtained Raman spectra of organometallic azides where N_3^- can be either bridging (*287*) or terminal (*288*).

2. Square Planar MX_4^{-Z} Complexes

The known square planar halogenometal complexes are those of the transition metal ions with d^8 electronic configurations. In spite of the fact that these ions are well known in crystals and are inert to substitution so that they persist in solutions, spectra have been obtained only recently for most of them. The ions have broad charge transfer bands extending into the blue region of the spectrum. Consequently, mercury arcs have not proved very useful in exciting the spectra, and other lamps and recently He—Ne lasers have been necessary. Data for these ions are collected in Table 7.

TABLE 7

Square Planar Metal Halide Complexes (D_{4h})[a]

Ion	State	$\nu_1(A_{1g})$	$\nu_2(B_{1g})$	$\nu_4(B_{2g})$	References
$PdCl_4^{-2}$	xtal	310	275	198	*(290,292)*
$PdBr_4^{-2}$	xtal	192	165	125	*(290,292)*
$PtCl_4^{-2}$	aq, xtal	332	314	170	*(289,290,291,292)*
$PtBr_4^{-2}$	aq, xtal	208	194	(125)[b]	*(290,291,292)*
PtI_4^{-2}	xtal	148	126	—	*(290,291,292)*
$AuCl_4^-$	aq, xtal	350	326	173	*(289,290,291)*
$AuBr_4^-$	aq, xtal	215	197	104	*(289,290,291,292)*
AuI_4^-	xtal	148	110	75	*(290,291,292)*

[a] Values reported are from aqueous solution data, where available; ν_1 = symmetric stretching, ν_2 = antisymmetric stretching, ν_4 = symmetric in-plane bending.

[b] Crystal spectrum value.

These ions give simple three line spectra with only one polarized line. In the examples reported so far, the intensities do not seem to form a pattern, although the intensity of the totally symmetric stretching mode is usually high. Calculations have been made *(292)* using the Urey Bradley and a 5 parameter general valence force field. Both indicate that the force constants fall in the order Au–X > Pt–X > Pd–X, and with a given metal they fall as the mass of X increases as would be expected from the chemical properties.

Hiraishi and Shimanouchi (*293*) have suggested that coupling of the vibrations of square planar anions with lattice modes should cause shifts of up to $\pm 50\ cm^{-1}$ on going from solid to solution. Effects of this magnitude would cause large errors in normal coordinate calculations if solid state data were employed. Fortunately, the observed differences between the Raman active frequencies for crystalline samples and aqueous solutions are generally small and, at most, $\pm 25\ cm^{-1}$ (*292*).

3. Octahedral Complexes

Data for MX_6^{-z} complexes are collected in Table 8. In general, octahedral complexes are recognized readily, because they give a three line spectrum with one intense, polarized line, ν_1. All that have been investigated appear to have full cubic symmetry. Most of the metals in these complexes have d^0, t_{2g}^6, or d^{10} electronic configurations for which a regular octahedral complex is expected. Significant static Jahn Teller distortions have not been observed in other experiments for ions such as $OsCl_6^{-2}$ (t_{2g}^4) or $IrCl_6^{-2}$ (t_{2g}^5). The ions with $d^{10}s^2$ configurations, e.g., $SbCl_6^{-3}$ and $BiCl_6^{-3}$, appear to be regular octahedral indicating that *sp* mixing is not important.

The intensity pattern is relatively consistent for the ions where the metal has the d^{10} configuration. The totally symmetric stretch ν_1 is intense, the antisymmetric stretch ν_2 is weak, and the deformation ν_5 is of medium intensity. Studies on the uncharged, third transition series hexafluorides where the metal is in the +6 oxidation state indicated that ν_2 was unusually low in intensity compared to ν_1 for the electronic configurations t_{2g}^1 and t_{2g}^2. This is what might be expected from a dynamic Jahn Teller effect occurring because the relaxation energy associated with the distortion was comparable to the vibrational energy. Further investigations with hexachloro complexes show that this does not hold there, and $ReCl_6^{-2}$ (t_{2g}^3) and $OsCl_6^{-2}$ (t_{2g}^4) also show unusually low intensities for ν_2.

Another kind of intensity anomaly is observed with $PtCl_6^{-2}$ and $PtBr_6^{-2}$ but not with PtF_6^{-2} (*298,307*). In this case, ν_2 is much more intense than ν_1, and this was attributed to delocalization of charge from the filled t_{2g} orbitals into π type orbitals of Cl^- and Br^-. Since F^- does not have low energy vacant π type orbitals, it would not be expected to exhibit the anomalous intensity pattern. As additional evidence for π bonding with chloride ligands, the bond stretching force constants increase with the number of d electrons in the sequence $ReCl_6^{-2} < OsCl_6^{-2} < PtCl_6^{-2}$ while the opposite is true with the hexafluorides $WF_6 > ReF_6 > OsF_6 > IrF_6 > PtF_6$.

TABLE 8

Octahedral Metal Halide Complexes[a] (O_h)

Ion	State	ν_1	ν_2	ν_5	References
TiF_6^{-2}	aq, xtal	619	—	277	*(294,295)*
ZrF_6^{-2}	aq, xtal	588	—	228	*(294,295)*
HfF_6^{-2}	aq	593	—	234	*(294,295)*
NbF_6^{-}	aq, xtal	685	562[b]	280	*(296)*
TaF_6^{-}	aq	691	—	277	*(294,297)*
PtF_6^{-2}	aq	600	576	210	*(298)*
SiF_6^{-2}	aq, xtal	655	474	395	*(295,299)*
GeF_6^{-2}	aq, xtal	627	454	318	*(295,300)*
SnF_6^{-2}	aq, xtal	585	470	241	*(295,301,302)*
$CeCl_6^{-2}$	xtal	295	265	120	*(275)*
UCl_6^{-2}	soln	299	237	121	*(303)*
$ThCl_6^{-2}$	soln	294	255	114	*(303)*
$TiCl_6^{-2}$	xtal	331	284	194	*(304)*
$ZrCl_6^{-2}$	xtal, aq	327	237	153	*(304,294)*
$HfCl_6^{-2}$	xtal	333	237	157	*(304)*
$TaCl_6^{-}$	aq	312	—	—	*(294,141)*
$ReCl_6^{-2}$	aq, xtal	346	275	159	*(305,306)*
$FeCl_6^{-3}$	xtal	313, 283	—	—	*(275)*
$OsCl_6^{-2}$	aq, xtal	346	274	165	*(305,306)*
$IrCl_6^{-2}$	xtal	352	—	190	*(306)*
$PdCl_6^{-2}$	aq, xtal	324	294	172	*(291,306,307)*
$PtCl_6^{-2}$	aq, xtal	343	322	159	*(291,306,307)*
$InCl_6^{-3}$	xtal	277	193	149	*(308)*
$TlCl_6^{-3}$	xtal	264	192	135	*(273,308)*
$SnCl_6^{-2}$	aq	311	229	158	*(309)*
$PbCl_6^{-2}$	aq, xtal	285	215	137	*(308,310)*
$SbCl_6^{-3}$	xtal	267	214	111	*(308)*
$SbCl_6^{-}$	xtal	329	285	184	*(141)*
$BiCl_6^{-3}$	xtal	259	222	108	*(308,311)*
$ReBr_6^{-2}$	aq, xtal	213	174	104	*(305,306)*
$PdBr_6^{-2}$	xtal	198	176	100	*(306)*
$PtBr_6^{-2}$	aq, xtal	215	191	110	*(291,306,307)*
$TlBr_6^{-3}$	xtal	161	153	—	*(274,298,306)*
$SnBr_6^{-2}$	aq	185	137	95	*(309)*

[a] Values reported are from aqueous solution data, where available; ν_1 = symmetric stretching, ν_2 = antisymmetric stretching, ν_5 = deformation.

[b] Value from crystal spectrum.

4. Miscellaneous Halide Complexes and Metal Halides

Clarke and Woodward (*312*) have obtained spectra for the simple monohalogeno complexes HgX^+ (X = Cl, Br, and I); ν(Hg—Cl) 338, ν(Hg—Br) 234, and ν(Hg—I) 191 cm^{-1}. These frequencies are similar to those of the H_3C—Hg—X molecules. The complexes probably have a coordinated water molecule with a linear O—Hg—X skeleton, but no Hg—O stretching line was observed. With high $[Hg^{+2}]:[I^-]$ ratios, a three line spectrum was obtained and attributed to an angular Hg—I—Hg (**XXIX**), ν_s(Hg—I) 168, ν_{as}(Hg—I) 205, δ(Hg—I—Hg) 52 cm^{-1}.

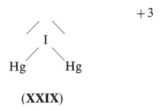

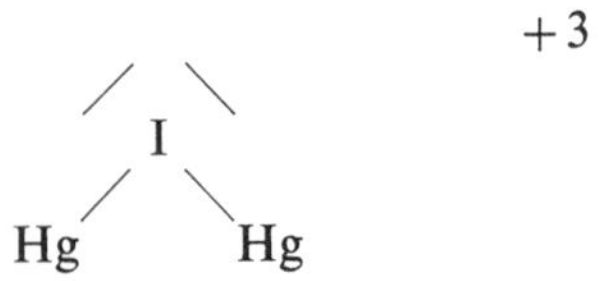

(XXIX)

Spectra of the linear complexes Cl—Cu—Cl^-, ν_s 296; and Br—Cu—Br^-, ν_s 190 cm^{-1}, have been obtained with ether solutions of the complexes (*313*). Aqueous solutions of CuCl+HCl and CuBr+HBr gave very broad bands suggesting overlap of lines for several complexes, e.g., CuX_3^{-2} and CuX_4^{-3}. Only the anions $CuCl_2^-$ and $CuBr_2^-$ were extracted into an ether phase, and the ether solutions gave good spectra of the uninegative complex. These linear complexes are analogous to the mercury(II) halides $HgX_2(D_{\infty h})$ (*258*) which have been observed in studies of higher mercury halide complexes (see Table 6). Cooney, Hall, and Hooper have also studied the yellow crystalline form of HgI_2 which contains linear HgI_2 molecules and observed Raman active vibrations at 133 ν_s(Hg—I) and 33 cm^{-1} δ(I—Hg—I) (*314*). Lippincott and co-workers have studied the red to yellow HgI_2 phase transition and obtained spectra for both forms (*314a*).

Ether extractions of aqueous solutions of $SnCl_2$+HCl and $SnBr_2$ +HBr (*315*) gave good spectra consistent only with a pyramidal (C_{3v}) structure for the uninegative anions $SnCl_3^-$ ν_1 297, ν_2 128, ν_3 256, ν_4 103, and $SnBr_3^-$ 211, 83, 181, and 65 cm^{-1}, respectively. Since a free tin(II) ion has an s^2 electronic configuration, the pyramidal structure indicates that appreciable *sp* mixing of the valence orbitals occurs, and that the lone electron pair occupies the fourth coordination site of a tetrahedron.

Szymanski et al. (*316*) have assigned the spectra of the square pyramidal anion $SbCl_5^{-2}$ (C_{4v}), where the lone electron pair can be considered to occupy the sixth site of an octahedral coordination sphere. The five coordinate complexes $InCl_5^{-2}$ and $TlCl_5^{-2}$ have been studied with both crystalline samples and nitromethane solutions (*317*).

Spectra attributed to TaF_7^{-2} as well as TaF_6^- have been observed for tantalum solutions with very high concentrations of HF (*297*). Spectra of the square antiprismatic TaF_8^{-3} were obtained from crystals (*318*).

D. Metal Ammines

Raman spectroscopy is quite useful for the study of the skeletal vibrations of ammine complexes. With the heavier metals, particularly, the infrared active metal–nitrogen stretching vibrations are so low in intensity that often they cannot be detected in infrared spectra (*31*). In spite of the advantages of using Raman spectroscopy, few investigations of ammine complexes have been made, primarily because many of them absorb at the blue line of the mercury arc. In some very early work, Damaschun (*319*) reported Raman frequencies assigned to metal–nitrogen bond stretching in ammoniacal solutions of Cu(II), Zn(II), and Cd(II). Spectra have been reported for aqueous solutions of $Rh(NH_3)_6^{+3}$ and $Ni(NH_3)_6^{+2}$ (*28*) and for $[Pt(NH_3)_4]Cl_2$ and $[Pt(NH_3)_4Cl_2]Cl_2$ (*320*). Haas and Hall (*29*) used Ne—He laser excitation to determine the skeletal stretching vibrations for $Co(NH_3)_6^{+3}$, ν_s 495, ν_{as} 440 cm^{-1}. For $Co(ND_3)_6^{+3}$, the values are approximately 30 cm^{-1} lower. Griffith (*321*) determined Raman spectra for aqueous solutions of $M(NH_3)_6^{+3}$ complexes with M = Ru, Ir, and Rh. The polarized lines near 500 cm^{-1} are assigned to the totally symmetric metal–nitrogen breathing modes, the weaker depolarized lines near 475 cm^{-1} to the antisymmetric skeletal stretch, and the weak broad, depolarized bands at ca. 250 cm^{-1} are assigned to the skeletal deformations. The intensity ratios for these modes were approximately 10:4:1. Griffith (*322*) also has studied complexes of the type $Co(NH_3)_5Cl^{+2}$ and $Co(NH_3)_5XO_4^+$ (X = Cr, Mo, and S). Plane (*323*) has reported briefly on some data for the tetraammines of Zn(II), Cd(II), and Hg(II). Raman spectra have been obtained for the complexes $Ag(NH_3)_2^+$ and $Hg(NH_3)_2^{+2}$ as part of a vibrational analysis of linear diammine and dimethido complexes (31). Clegg and Hall (*324*) compared the vibrations of $[Pt(CH_3)_3(NH_3)_3]^+$, ν(Pt—N) = 390, with those of $[Pt(NH_3)_6]^{+4}$, ν_s(Pt—N) = 569, ν_{as} = 545 cm^{-1}, and concluded that the methyl groups lead to weakening of the *trans* Pt—N bonds. Hendra (*325*) examined $[Pd(NH_3)_4]Cl_2$ and the *trans* complexes $[Pd(NH_3)_2Cl_2]$, $[Pt(NH_3)_2Cl_2]$, $[Pt(NH_3)_2Br_2]$, and $[Pt(NH_3)_2I_2]$, and found that the force constants for Pt—N stretching were greater than those for Pd—N stretching.

In general, infrared spectra are satisfactory for studying the vibrations which involve primarily internal motion of the ammine groups, and relatively little additional information is gained from a Raman spectrum. These vibrations also are rather low in intensity in the Raman effect, and Clegg and Hall (*324*) and Haas and Hall (*29*) report that they observed only the metal–nitrogen stretching modes in spectra taken with aqueous solutions. Data for ammine complexes are collected in Table 9.

TABLE 9

Vibrational Frequencies of Ammonia and Ammine Complexes from Raman Spectra

Ion	State	$\nu_{as}(NH_3)$	$\nu_s(NH_3)$	$\delta_d(NH_3)$	$\delta_s(NH_3)$	$\rho(NH_3)$	ν_s(M-N)	Ref.
NH_3	aq	3400	3313	1642	1109			(*31*)
$Ag(NH_3)_2^+$	aq	3373	3287	1624	1224	—	372	(*31*)
$Hg(NH_3)_2^{+2}$	xtal, mull	3280	3212	1678 1605	1289	—	413	(*31*)
$Ru(NH_3)_6^{+3}$	aq	—	3077	1618	1368 1342	788	500	(*321*)
$Ir(NH_3)_6^{+3}$	aq	—	3155	1587	1350 1323	857	527	(*321*)
$Rh(NH_3)_6^{+3}$	aq	—	3200	1618	1352 1318	845	514	(*321,28*)

E. Acetylacetonates

Since acetylacetonato chelates appear to have an essentially planar ring with C_{2v} effective symmetry, (**XXX**), the in-plane vibrations are of species A_1 and B_2. Consequently, they are all Raman and infrared active. Although many infrared studies have been made on metal acetylacetonates, there have been few Raman investigations. In the following discussion, acac will be used for the 2,4-pentanedionato group, $C_5H_7O_2^-$. Hester and Plane (*326*) studied $Al(acac)_3$, $Ga(acac)_3$, and $Tl(acac)_3$, while Tobias and co-workers have obtained Raman spectra for the organometallic acetylacetonates $(CH_3)_2Sn(acac)_2$(*327*), $(CH_3)_2Au(acac)$ (*77*), and $(CH_3)_2Ga(acac)$ (*78*).

Recently Na(acac) has been studied both in the solid state and in aqueous solution (*328*), and there is evidence that the acetylacetonat

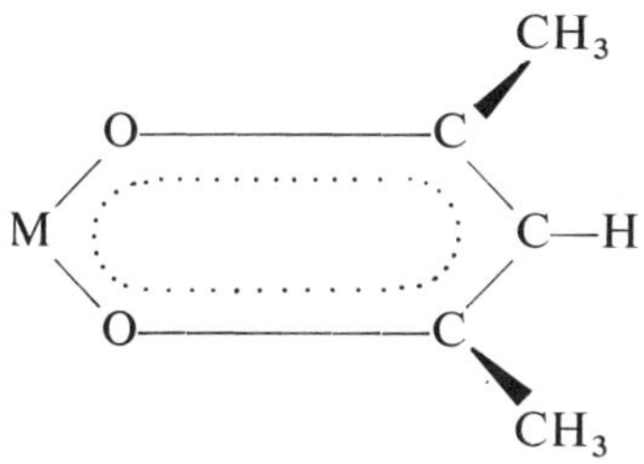

(XXX)

symmetry is lower than C_{2v} in the solutions. With dimethylsulfoxide solutions, the spectrum is very similar to that of the crystalline sample.

Data for some typical acetylacetonates are collected in Table 10. The

TABLE 10

Acetylacetonate Fundamentals Taken from Raman Spectra

$(CH_3)_2Ga(acac)$ [melt (*78*)]	$(CH_3)_2Au(acac)$ [xtal (*77*)]	$(CH_3)_2Sn(acac)_2$ [xtal, soln (*327*)]	$Al(acac)_3$ [soln (*326*)]	Assignment
1591 *w*	—	1590 *vw*	1600 *w*	ν(C⋯O) A_1
1526 *vw*,	—	—	—	ν(C⋯C) B_2
1433 *w*	—	—	1450 *w*	$\delta_{as}(CH_3)$
1371 *s*	1359 *m*	1368 *s*	1373 *s*	$\delta_s(CH_3)$
1281 *vs*	1270 *vs*	1262 *m*	1298 *vvs*	ν(C⋯C) A_1
1200 *m*	—	1198 *m*	1190 *ms*	δ(C—H)
1026 *w*	—	1033 *w*	1033 *mw*	$\rho_r(CH_3)$
940 *m*	931 *w*	928 *ms*	956 *mw* 938 *mw*	ν(C—CH_3) A_1
681 *m*	692 *w*	668 *ms*	690 *m*	ν(*M*—O)+ ring def A_1
561 *w*	559 *w*	567 *w*	570 *mw*	π(acac)
454 *s*	445 *vs*	414 *s*	465 *s*	ν_s(*M*—O) A_1

assignments are based on the most recent normal coordinate analysis of Behnke and Nakamoto (*329*). The Raman polarizations are in accord with these assignments but not with those of the earlier normal coordinate calculations (*330–331*).

The spectra of acetylacetonates provide an excellent example of the difference in the intensities of vibrations in the Raman and infrared spectra. In particular, the (C—O) and (C—C) stretching modes above 1500 cm^{-1} which are very intense in the infrared spectra are almost undetectable in the Raman spectra. Only in the spectrum of $(CH_3)_2Ga(acac)$ which was studied as a melt (*78*) are these observed clearly. Because of the low carbonyl intensities, Raman are much less useful than infrared spectra in assigning chelated as opposed to non-chelated structures to complexes on the basis of the carbonyl stretching frequencies. The strongest lines in the spectra are those from the totally symmetric C—C ring mode. This is also the case for the benzene molecule and for π bonded cyclopentadienyl rings. Metal–oxygen stretches too give intense Raman scattering. Matwiyoff and Morris (*332*) have obtained a spectrum of $Be(acac)_2$ in benzene solution and have studied the reaction [Eq. (11b)]

$$Be(DMF)_4^{+2} + Be(acac)_2 \rightarrow 2Be(DMF)_2(acac)^+ \qquad (11b)$$

in dimethylformamide (DMF) solution by Raman spectroscopy. Fay and Pinnavaia (*333*) obtained Raman spectra in a study of the stereochemistry of the complexes *cis* $X_2M(acac)_2$ and $XM(acac)_3$ (M = Zr, Hf and X = Cl, Br).

F. Metal Carbonyls

Of all of the classes of coordination compounds, metal complexes of carbon monoxide and the related complexes of the isoelectronic cyanide ligand have probably been the object of more spectroscopic studies than any other. Numerous normal coordinate analyses of varying degrees of rigor and completeness have been made for these molecules and ions. It would appear that Raman spectra should be essential for these studies. With the tetrahedral $M(CO)_4$ complexes there are nine fundamentals, $(2A_1+2E+F_1+4F_2)$, of which the four F_2 vibrations are infrared active and the eight A_1, E, and F_2 vibrations are Raman active. With the octahedral $M(CO)_6$ carbonyls, $(2A_{1g}+2E_g+F_{1g}+4F_{1u}+2F_{2g}+2F_{2u})$, the four F_{1u} fundamentals are infrared active and the six A_{1g}, E_g, and F_{2g} fundamentals are Raman active. In addition, all of the fundamentals except the CO stretching vibrations usually occur below 750 cm^{-1}, and this greatly complicates the vibrational assignments. In the light of experience, it can be concluded that it is not possible to make reliable assignments of the vibrations of these complexes without complete Raman and infrared data including polarization measurements.

In spite of the desirability of having Raman spectra, most of the studies of the vibrations of carbonyl complexes have been made with infrared spectroscopy alone. There have been several reasons for this. First, the chemist has been mostly concerned with the assignment of structures and the detection of trends in the bonding. For these purposes, a knowledge of the infrared active C—O stretching fundamentals from 1800 to 2100 cm^{-1} is often sufficient, and these are easily measured because of their exceedingly high infrared intensity. Indeed, the totally symmetric C—O stretch is often very low in intensity in the Raman spectrum. Second, a more serious problem results from the broad charge transfer bands of many of the metal carbonyls, which lead to absorption throughout virtually the entire visible spectrum. Additionally, many of the compounds are decomposed photochemically. As a consequence, the earlier assignments and normal coordinate analyses often were based on inadequate infrared data. Many of these earlier studies of metal carbonyls have been reviewed by Huggins and Kaesz (*334*), by Cable and Sheline (*335*), and by Dobson et al. (*33*).

The orange iron pentacarbonyl, $Fe(CO)_5$, may be cited as an example of the problems which have plagued spectroscopists. O'Dwyer (*336*) reported in 1958 a normal coordinate analysis on the basis of infrared data alone in which he assumed a square pyramidal structure (C_{4v}). This was subsequently shown to be incorrect on the basis of the Raman spectrum, and the molecule has the same trigonal bi-pyramidal (D_{3h}) structure as shown for the vapor by electron diffraction. In 1956, a very incomplete Raman spectrum was obtained by King and Lippincott (*337*) with difficulty because of the photodecomposition of the compound to $Fe_2(CO)_9$. Fateley and Lippincott in 1957 (*338*) and Murata and Kawai in 1958 (*339*) reported normal coordinate analyses based on the trigonal bipyramidal structure and the infrared and limited Raman data. Stammreich et al. in 1959 (*340*) using excitation in the far red and infrared obtained a complete Raman spectrum with the pure liquid compound and benzene solutions. Another normal coordinate analysis was reported by Pistorius and Haarhoff in 1959 (*341*) using the complete Raman but inadequate infrared data. The spectra were then reassigned by Edgell et al. (*342*) in 1963 on the basis of an improved infrared spectrum, and finally some modifications of Edgell's assignments were suggested by Jones and McDowell in 1964 (*343*). These included corrections in the C—O stretching fundamentals. Earlier Raman and infrared data were taken with different phases, and the frequency changes from one phase to another are comparable to the separation of these fundamentals.

The colorless molecule nickel tetracarbonyl (T_d) has a rather similar history. Spectra were first obtained in 1931 by Dadieu and Schneider (*344*) and in 1932 by Anderson (*345*), and these showed C—O stretching fundamentals. Duncan and Murray in 1934 (*346*) and Crawford and Horowitz in 1948 (*347*) obtained more complete spectra. In 1960 Bigorgne (*348*) reported spectra of the liquid and solutions at low temperature, and Stammreich et al. (*349*) published similar complete spectra in 1961. The latter publication reviews five normal coordinate calculations which had

TABLE 11

Stretching Fundamentals of Metal Carbonyls from Raman Spectra

Compound	Symmetry	State	ν(C—O)[a]	ν(M—C)[a]	References
CO	—	gas	2143	—	(*34*)
$Cr(CO)_6$	O_h	xtal, soln	2113 p, 2019	381 p, 394	(*353,354,355*)
$Mo(CO)_6$	O_h	xtal, soln	2117 p, 2019	390 p, 400	(*353,354,355*)
$W(CO)_6$	O_h	xtal, soln	2121 p, 2013	430 p, 417	(*353,354,355*)
$Re(CO)_6^+$	O_h	xtal	2224 p, 2139	444 p, 430	(*356*)
$Fe(CO)_5$	D_{3h}	liq	2031, 2014, 1984	414 p[b], 377 p[c]	(*337, 340*)
$Fe(CO)_4^{-2}$	T_d	aq	1788, —	464 p, 550	(*357*)
$Co(CO)_4^-$	T_d	aq	1918, 1883	439 p, 532	(*357*)
$Ni(CO)_4$	T_d	gas, liq, soln	2125.0 p, 2044.5	379.8 p, —	(*344*–352)

[a] p = polarized line.
[b] axial and equatorial CO in phase.
[c] axial and equatorial CO out of phase.

been made up to that time. Bigorgne and Chelkowski (*350*) determined the spectrum of the vapor in 1960, Bouquet and Bigorgne (*351*) measured the spectrum of the isotopically substituted molecule $Ni(C^{18}O)_4$ in the liquid state in 1965, and Jones et al. (*352*) have observed the spectra of both $Ni(^{13}CO)_4$ and $Ni(C^{18}O)_4$ and calculated force constants from a general quadratic force field.

Data for the simple metal carbonyls are collected in Table 11. With these complexes, it is usual for the carbon–oxygen stretching force constant to decrease as the metal–carbon force constant increases. This is consistent with the picture that the metal–carbon bond has appreciable π character involving overlap of the filled metal *d* orbitals with the antibonding CO molecular orbitals. A critical evaluation of the force constants which have been calculated is beyond the scope of this work. Let it only be noted that too much significance should not be placed on small differences in these parameters, especially interaction constants, in view of the difficulties in assigning all of the fundamentals, the effect of anharmonicity, etc. The very large decrease in the C—O stretching frequencies in the isoelectronic sequence $Ni(CO)_4$, $Co(CO)_4^-$, and $Fe(CO)_4^{-2}$ reflects the increase in metal–CO π back donation as the nuclear charge of the metal decreases. A higher degree of rigor has been attained in the normal coordinate analyses of these simple metal carbonyls than is generally the case for coordination compounds. This has been achieved by taking Raman and infrared spectra with the same phase and applying anharmonicity corrections (*355,358,359*) to the observed CO stretching frequencies. Jones developed a force field for the metal tetracarbonyls (*360*) and hexacarbonyls (*361*) considering the π interactions, and in the case of $Ni(CO)_4$, where spectra of isotopically substituted molecules were available, he was able to use a general quadratic force field (*352*).

Other metal carbonyls which have been studied include $Ir_4(CO)_4$ (*362*) which has tetrahedral symmetry in crystals. The intense lines at 208, 164, and 105 cm^{-1} were assigned to vibrations involving primarily the metal–metal bonds of the tetrahedral cluster of metal atoms. A line at 120 cm^{-1} assigned to Re–Re stretching was observed in the spectrum of $Re_2(CO)_{10}$ (**XXXI**) (*363*). In this case there are interactions across the metal–metal

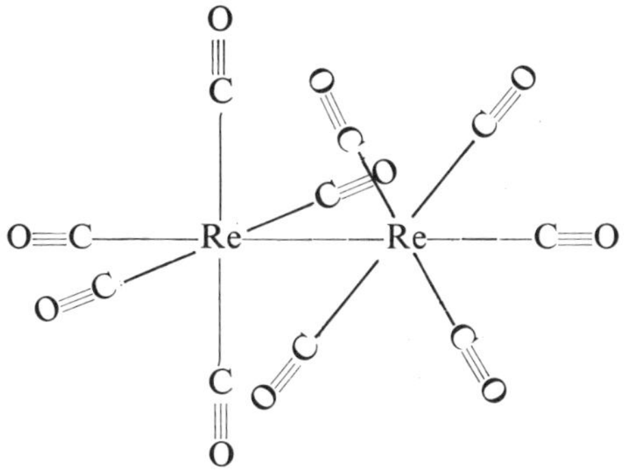

(**XXXI**)

bond probably *via* the metal d_π orbitals, so the $Re(CO)_5$ groups cannot be considered to have C_{4v} local symmetry. The polynuclear carbonyls $Os_3(CO)_{12}$ and $Ru_3(CO)_{12}$ which effectively have D_{3h} symmetry have been studied and low frequency vibrations assigned to metal–metal bond stretching (*364*). A simple valence force field was used to calculate the normal modes of the metal cluster.

Much interest has centered on the effect which replacement of some of the CO ligands by other donors has on the strength of the M—C and C—O bonds. In general, as ligands which are better σ donors replace carbon monoxide, the metal–(CO) π interaction increases with a concomitant increase in the M–(CO) stretching force constant and a decrease in the C—O stretching force constant. Cotton and Kraihanzel (*365*) developed a set of rules for estimation of C—O stretching and the CO—CO stretch–stretch interaction force constants which applies to complexes with octahedral coordination about the metal, i.e. $ML_x(CO)_{6-x}$. The treatment neglects all other force constants and all fundamentals except the C—O stretches. While semi-empirical, it is based on considerations of the nature of the π interactions between the filled metal t_{2g} and carbon monoxide antibonding orbitals. This approach was used with complexes where $x = 1$ and 2 and where M was Cr, Mo, and W (*366,367*), and also particularly with the mono-substituted manganese carbonyls XMn(Co)$_5$ (*368*). Recently Jones has discussed the significance of the numerical values of the CO—CO stretch–stretch interactions obtained with such a simplified force field (*369*) and also the importance of applying anharmonicity corrections to the C—O stretching frequencies (*358,359*). Poilblanc and Bigorgne (*371*) have obtained Raman spectra for octahedral complexes of the type $M(CO)_3[P(OC_2H_5)_3]_3$.

Hendra and Qurashi (*372*) have suggested that the ratio of the intensities of the totally symmetric C—O and M—C stretching vibrations, ν_1/ν_2, of metal hexacarbonyls should become smaller as the extent of metal–carbon π bonding increases. The intensity ratios determined with methylene chloride solutions decrease in the order M = Re > Mo > W > Cr.

The substituted nickel carbonyls have been studied particularly thoroughly. Again coordination of basic ligands leads to a progressive decrease in the C—O stretching because of the increase in CO antibonding character and causes an increase in all of the lower skeletal frequencies. Among the compounds for which Raman spectra have been obtained are those with phosphines, R_3P (*379,375*); phosphites, $P(OR)_3$ (*371,375*); PCl_3 (*375*); PF_3 (*374,375*); arsines AsR_3 (*373*); arsenites, $As(OR)_3$ (*373*); alkyl sulfides, SR_2 (*373*); and isonitriles, CNR (*376*).

Some spectra have been obtained for carbonyl hydrides, and the low hydrogen stretching frequencies observed with $[Re(CO)_4H]_3$, 1100 cm^{-1} and $[Re(CO)_4D]_3$, 787 cm^{-1} are consistent with a structure in which the hydrogens are bridging (*377*). In the hydrides $HMn(CO)_5$ (**XXXII**), $\nu(Mn—H) = 1780\ cm^{-1}$; and $HRe(CO)_5$, $\nu(Re—H) = 1840\ cm^{-1}$, the metal hydrogen stretching fundamentals are very intense and the spectra are consistent with C_{4v} molecular symmetry (*378,379*). Spectra of aqueous solutions of the hydride $HFe(CO)_4^-$ clearly show the decrease in symmetry from T_d to C_{3v} brought about by protonation of the tetrahedral anion $Fe(CO)_4^{-2}$ (*357*).

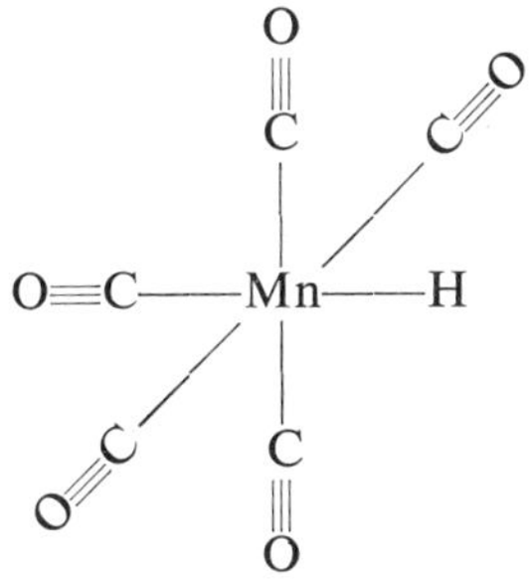

(**XXXII**)

Stammreich, Kawai, Sala, and Krumholz (*380*) have obtained a complete Raman spectrum for $Cd[Co(CO)_4]_2$ and a partial spectrum of the orange-red, photosensitive compound $Hg[Co(CO)_4]_2$. The spectra are quite simple, suggesting a D_{3d} centrosymmetric structure (**XXXIII**).

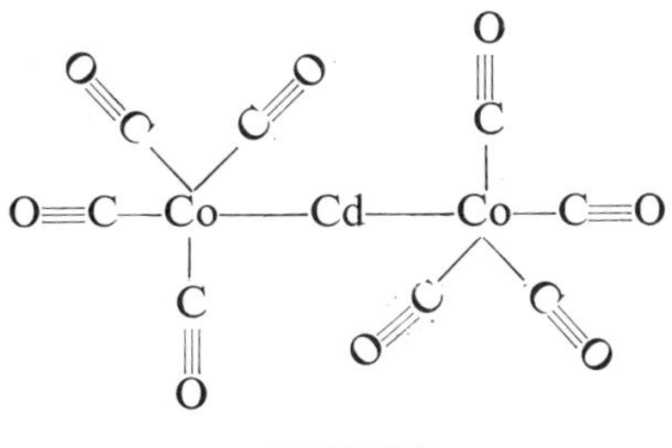

(**XXXIII**)

G. Cyanide Complexes

The literature dealing with cyanide complexes is very extensive, and various aspects of this chemistry have been reviewed in recent years (*381,382,383*). The (C—N) stretching fundamentals appear in the region from 2000 to 2250 cm^{-1}, the C—*M*—C bending frequencies occur around 100 cm^{-1}, and the *M*—C stretching and the *M*—C—N bending frequencies appear from ca. 300 to 600 cm^{-1}. As in the case of metal carbonyls, the assignment of fundamentals below 600 cm^{-1} is a difficult problem without complete infrared and Raman data. Since these complexes are usually ions, infrared spectra are, as a rule, taken with crystalline samples and Raman spectra with aqueous solutions, so the additional complication of frequency shifts with phase change is introduced.

The bonding in cyanide complexes is similar to that in metal carbonyls, and their vibrational spectra have many features in common. The (*M*—C)—(C—N) stretch–stretch interactions are significant, although the (C—N)—(C′—N) interactions of the different ligands seem to be smaller than the corresponding parameters for carbonyl complexes. Suitable force fields for these complexes have been discussed by Jones (*384,385*).

As with the metal carbonyls, Raman spectroscopy has been used relatively little compared to infrared spectroscopy. The (C—N) bond stretching vibrations, as the (C—O) stretches, lead to very intense absorption in the infrared. Often these provide adequate information to the chemist for the assignment of a structure to a new compound. In addition, ions like the hexacyano complexes of the transition metals absorb in the blue region of the spectrum, making excitation of a Raman spectrum with the blue mercury 4358 Å line impossible. Unfortunately, the metal–carbon stretching frequencies which are often very difficult to detect in infrared spectra also give very weak Raman scattering. As a consequence of the low intensity coupled with the relatively low solubility of many cyanide complexes in water, there is a paucity of data for the low frequency vibrations. Jones (*386*) has noted a relatively strong interaction between Li^+ and $Au(CN)_2^-$ which causes new Raman lines in concentrated aqueous solutions in addition to those of the dicyanoaurate(I) complex. Similar effects may account for some of the spurious frequencies reported. It was suggested that solutions prepared from $K[Hg(CN)_3]$ contained a dimeric ion $[Hg_2(CN)_6]^{-2}$, because three C—N stretching vibrations were observed at 2147, 2166, and 2195 cm^{-1} (*387*). A structure with a mercury–mercury bond and D_{3h} symmetry was assigned, but it now seems certain that only $Hg(CN)_3^-$ ions exist, and the additional lines were probably caused by other monomeric cyano complexes of mercury in equilibrium with $Hg(CN)_3^-$.

There have been three main contributions of Raman spectroscopy to cyanide complex chemistry. First, complexes present in aqueous solutions have been identified when several exist in equilibrium, e.g., $Cu(CN)_2^-$,

$Cu(CN)_3^{-2}$, and $Cu(CN)_4^{-3}$ (*388*). It should be noted that infrared spectra have proved almost equally satisfactory for this purpose (*389*), since the C—N stretching frequencies fall in a "window" in the water absorption spectrum. Second, Raman spectra of the symmetric complexes are needed to provide sufficient data for normal coordinate analyses. In some cases isotopic substitution of the carbon and nitrogen atoms has been effected (*391,392*). Third, Raman intensities of the C—N stretching vibrations and the components of the derived polarizability tensor calculated from them provide information about differences in the carbon–nitrogen bonds in related complexes. Raman data for cyano complexes are collected in Table 12.

TABLE 12

Stretching Fundamentals of Cyano-Complexes from Raman Spectra

Compound	Symmetry	State	ν(C—N)[a]	ν(M—C)[a]	References
$Cr(CN)_6^{-3}$	O_h	aq	2130 p, —		(*392*)
$Fe(CN)_6^{-4}$	O_h	aq	2090 p, 2056	505	(*392,393,394,395,396*)
$Fe(CN_6^{-3}$	O_h	xtal, aq	2136 p, —		(*392,396,398*)
$Ru(CN)_6^{-4}$	O_h	aq	2100 p, 2067		(*392*)
$Os(CN)_6^{-4}$	O_h	aq	2109 p, 2062	465	(*392,399*)
$Co(CN)_6^{-3}$	O_h	aq, xtal	2153 p, 2135	413 p	(*392,393,396,407*)
$Rh(CN)_6^{-3}$	O_h	aq	2166 p, 2147	445 p, 435	(*392,396*)
$Ir(CN)_6^{-3}$	O_h	aq	2167 p, 2143	463 p, 450	(*392,396,400*)
$Ni(CN)_4^{-2}$	D_{4h}	aq, xtal	2144 p, 2138	410 p, 433 421, 390	(*392,396,397*)
$Pd(CN)_4^{-2}$	D_{4h}	aq	2159 p, 2147	439 p	(*392,396*)
$Pt(CN)_4^{-2}$	D_{4h}	aq	2168 p, 2149	465 p, 455	(*392,396*)
$Au(CN)_4^-$	D_{4h}	aq, xtal	2209 p, 2201	461 p, 452	(*392,401*)
$Cu(CN)_2^-$	$D_{\infty h}$	aq	2113		(*402,388*)
$Cu(CN)_3^{-2}$		aq	2110		(*402*)
$Cu(CN)_4^{-3}$	T_d	aq	2094	288	(*392,393,402–405*)
$Ag(CN)_2^-$	$D_{\infty h}$	aq	2139		(*402*)
$Ag(CN)_3^{-2}$		aq	2108		(*386,402*)
$Ag(CN)_4^{-3}$	T_d	aq	2097		(*392,402*)
$Au(CN)_2^-$	$D_{\infty h}$	aq	2164	450	(*386,391*)
$Zn(CN)_4^{-2}$	T_d	aq	2143		(*392,393,396*)
$Cd(CN)_3^-$		aq	2140	339	(*406*)
$Cd(CN)_4^{-2}$	T_d	aq	2145	321	(*392,393,406*)
$Hg(CN)_2$	$D_{\infty h}$	aq, soln	2189	412	(*386,387,406,408,409*)
$Hg(CN)_3^-$		aq	2160	358	(*406*)
$Hg(CN)_4^{-2}$	T_d	aq, soln	2148	342	(*387,392,393,406,408*)

[a] Where both polarized and depolarized fundamentals of a given type are observed, the polarized lines are identified by "p."

All three complexes $Cu(CN)_2^-$, $Cu(CN)_3^{-2}$, and $Cu(CN)_4^{-3}$ have been identified in solutions containing different CN^-:Cu ratios (*388,393*), and similar results have been obtained for the system $Ag(CN)_2^-$, $Ag(CN)_3^{-2}$, and $Ag(CN)_4^{-3}$ (*393*). Cooney and Hall (*410*) examined spectra of aqueous solutions of the linear complex $Hg(CN)_2$ plus halide ion, since earlier infrared studies had indicated that mixed halogeno-cyano complexes probably were formed. With Br^- and I^-, Hg—*X* stretching vibrations were observed, ν(Hg—Br) 160, ν(Hg—I) 120 cm^{-1}. Coordination of the halide ion to give $[Hg(CN)_2X]^-$ caused a decrease in ν(C—N) by as much as 26 cm^{-1}. No new lines were observed with F^- or Cl^-, either because the interaction was weaker, or because the bonds were very polar and the vibrations gave low Raman intensities. Cooper and Plane (*411*) made similar studies of aqueous solutions containing CuCN + NaCN + Na*X*. No new lines were found for solutions containing the tetrahedral complex $Cu(CN)_4^{-3}$ with up to 6 *M* Na*X*, there was no change in ν(C—N), and the intensity of the totally symmetric C—N stretching fundamental remained constant. Thus it can be concluded that no mixed complexes are formed.

In the square planar complexes, $Au(CN)_4^-$ and *trans* $[Au(CN)_2X_2]^-$, X = Cl, Br, I, the C—N and Au—C force constants are all large indicating strong Au—C bonding and very little π bonding (*412,413*). For the halogen substituted complexes, there is a parallel decrease in both force constants in the sequence $Cl^- > Br^- > I^-$ indicating a progressive weakening of the Au—C bond. Similar trends are observed with the platinum(IV) complexes $K_2[Pt(CN)_4X_2]$, (X = Cl, Br, I) (*414*). Raman spectra show that with these gold(III) complexes cyanide will replace coordinated halide, but halide did not replace coordinated cyanide in aqueous solution, i.e. the equilibrium constants favor the cyanocomplex (*415*).

Jones (*386*) noted that ν(C—N), the line intensity, and the depolarization ρ were all greater for $Au(CN)_2^-$ than for $Ag(CN)_2^-$ or $Hg(CN)_2$. Taking the *x* axis along the C_∞ principal symmetry axis, ρ will increase as α'_{xx} becomes greater than α'_{yy}. The higher intensity and the larger ρ for the C—N stretching vibration both indicate that the electrons are concentrated more along the bond with the gold(I) complex than with the Ag(I) or Hg(II) complexes, probably as a consequence of enhanced π bonding. Chantry and Plane (*393*) found that the derived bond polarizabilities α'_{CN} fell into two groups for a series of cyanide complexes. In the first group containing $Zn(CN)_4^{-2}$, $Cd(CN)_4^{-2}$, $Hg(CN)_4^{-2}$, and $Co(CN)_6^{-3}$, both the values for α'_{CN} and the C—N stretching intensities were much lower than for the second group which contained $Cu(CN)_4^{-3}$, $Ag(CN)_4^{-3}$, and $Fe(CN)_6^{-4}$. There appears to be much more electron delocalization in the latter complexes because of π bonding, and it is likely that the idea of localized bond polarizabilities is inadequate to treat them.

Stammreich and Sala (*416,417*) investigated the spectrum of aqueous solutions of the octacyanomolybdate(IV) anion, $Mo(CN)_8^{-4}$ which has a bisdisphenoidal (dodecahedral) D_{2d} structure in crystals. They suggested that the ion has a more symmetric D_{4d} (square antiprism) structure in solution. This view now has been confirmed by two other groups of workers for $Mo(CN)_8^{-4}$ (*318,418*), and the same is true for $W(CN)_8^{-4}$ (*418*). The anions $Mo(CN)_8^{-3}$ and $W(CN)_8^{-3}$ appear to have the square antiprism structure in crystals of the $[Co(NH_3)_6]^{+3}$ salts (*418*).

H. Organometallic Compounds

Raman spectroscopy has been used relatively little in the study of organometallic compounds. A general review of the applications of Raman, and, mainly, infrared spectroscopy to the study of these compounds has been given by Huggins and Kaesz (*334*). Fritz (*419*) has reviewed the vibrations of π-bonded ring systems.

1. Sandwich Complexes

Investigations here have been concerned mainly with the π-bonded cyclopentadienyl group. Because of the complexity of the spectra of these compounds, there has been some controversy over the assignment of the fundamentals, a problem which can only be settled with complete Raman and infrared data. Because most of the compounds are brightly colored, Raman investigations are few. Lippincott and Nelson (*420,421*) obtained the first spectrum for a compound of this type, the red–orange ferrocene $(\pi\text{–}C_5H_5)Fe$, excited with a sodium source, and also reported spectra of ruthenocene $(\pi\text{–}C_5H_5)_2Ru$. There is very little interaction between the rings which effectively have C_{5v} symmetry. The ring–metal–ring symmetric stretching fundamentals appear at 303 cm^{-1} with ferrocene and 330 cm^{-1} with ruthenocene. The most intense line in the Raman spectrum is from the ring breathing mode, 1108 cm^{-1} in ferrocene. Fritz (*419*) questioned this assignment on the basis of an unpublished Raman spectrum of ferrocene obtained by Stammreich, but the assignment now seems certain in the light of investigations on dimethylferrocene (*422*), cyclopentadienylnickel nitrosyl (*423*), and cyclopentadienyl-manganesetricarbonyl (**XXXIV**) (*424*). Spectra of the latter yellow compound were excited with the mercury 5461 Å line using both solutions and a melt. There is little coupling through the metal; and the ring vibrations can be treated in terms of C_{5v} local symmetry, while the vibrations of the $Mn(CO)_3$

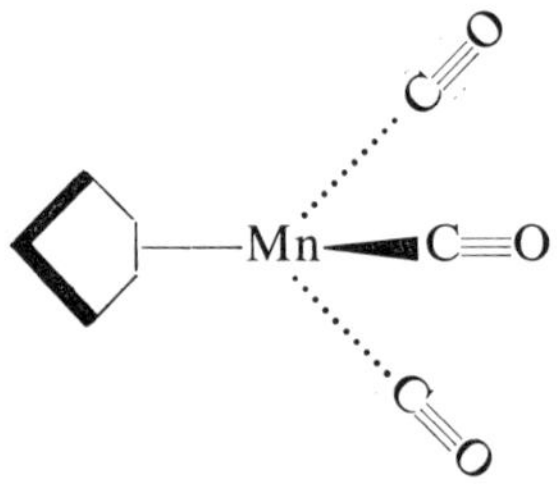

(XXXIV)

moiety conform to C_{3v} selection rules. The intense, totally symmetric ring breathing mode occurs at 1120 cm^{-1}. The ring-manganese stretching frequency is 353 cm^{-1}, and this vibration gives intense Raman scattering. Recently spectra of ferrocene have been obtained both in solution and with the solid compound using He—Ne laser excitation (*425*).

A spectrum was also obtained by Lippincott, Xavier, and Steele (*426*) for bis-(cyclopentadienyl)magnesium, and this is very similar to that of ferrocene. The ring breathing mode is at 1109 cm^{-1}, and the low ring–magnesium–ring symmetric stretching fundamental, 191 cm^{-1}, is consistent with rather weak bonding in the molecule. The sandwich complex bis(benzene)–chromium and the cation $(C_6H_6)_2Cr^+$ have been studied by Fritz et al. (*427*) who found the ring–metal–ring symmetric stretching fundamental at 270 and 279 cm^{-1}, respectively.

2. Metal Alkyls and Aryls

Spectra for most of the stable methyl derivatives were obtained many years ago, and the spectra of most of the other compounds are sufficiently complicated to defy all but qualitative assignment of the vibrations. A main area of investigation by Raman spectroscopy has been the behavior of organometallic ions in aqueous solution where changes in metal coordination number and hybridization occur frequently. Much of this work has been described in a review by Tobias (*428*). Data for the fundamentals of some simple methyl–metal cations are collected in Table 13. These may be compared with the data for the complexes of the isostructural ammine ligand, Table 9.

TABLE 13

Vibrational Frequencies of Methido Complexes from Raman Spectra

Compound	State	$\nu_{as}(CH_3)$	$\nu_s(CH_3)$	$\delta_{as}(CH_3)^a$	$\delta_s(CH_3)$	$\rho(CH_3)$	ν(M—C)	Ref.
fac $(CH_3)_3Pt^+$	aq	2978	2909	1427	1329 1290 1250	882	600	(*463*)
cis $(CH_3)_2Au^+$	aq	3012	2927	—	1260 1222	876	591	(*77*)
$(CH_3)Hg^+$	aq	3027	2942	1430	1207	707(?)	570	(*455*)
$(CH_3)_2Ga^+$	aq	2984	2919	—	1218	—	620 558 *p*	(*78*)
$(CH_3)_2Tl^+$	aq	3033	2939	1420	1195	—	498	(*451*)
$(CH_3)_2Sn^{+2}$	aq	3025	2935	—	1228	—	530	(*447*)
$(CH_3)_2Pb^{+2}$	aq	3055	2952	—	1208	—	480	(*448*)

[a] $\delta_{as}(CH_3)$ and the methyl rocking mode $\rho(CH_3)$ appear with very low intensity in the Raman spectra.

a. *Silicon, Germanium, Tin, and Lead*

Kriegsmann and co-workers have made very extensive investigations of the Raman spectra of organosilicon compounds (*429*) and particularly of the polysiloxanes (*430,431*). In the compounds $(CH_3)_2SiX_2$, (X = F, Cl, and Br), the vibrations of the $(CH_3)_2Si$ moiety are good group frequencies and little affected by the halogen. Measurements of ν_s (Si—O—Si) and the Raman intensity for this fundamental for the methyl-cyclotetrasiloxanes prepared by cohydrolysis of $(CH_3)_2SiCl_2$ and CH_3SiHCl_2 have been used to characterize the different $\{[(CH_3)_2SiO]_n[(CH_3)HSiO]_{(4-n)}\}$ compounds (*432*). Spectra have been obtained for a large number of substituted silanes of the type R_3SiH, in order to correlate substituent and solvent effects on the frequency and line shape of the Si—H fundamental at 2190–2200 cm^{-1} (*432*). The substitution of more electronegative R groups on silicon leads to the introduction of more silicon *s* character in the Si—H bond and results in an increase in ν(Si—H). The bond polarizability also increases, as indicated by increases in the Raman intensity. Studies on compounds of the type $(CH_3)_2(CH_2X)SiH$ (X = Cl, Br, and I), $(CH_3)_2(CHCl_2)SiH$, and $(CH_3)(CH_2Cl)_2SiH$ show that there is a linear relation between ν(Si—H) and the log of the rate constant for bromination of the SiH bond which in turn has been related to the Taft σ substituent constants (*433*). Janz and Mikawa have also investigated the spectra of silanes (*434*).

Griffiths (*435*) reported the spectrum of $(CH_3)_2GeCl_2$, while Durig et al. (*436,437*) have assigned many of the vibrations of $(C_6H_5)SiCl_3$, $(C_6H_5)GeCl_3$, and $(C_6H_5)SnCl_3$ by comparison with monosubstituted benzenes. The MCl_3 moieties do not behave as if they have local C_{3v} symmetry, perhaps because of a large barrier to rotation of the benzene ring with respect to the M—C bond. The molecules $M(C{\equiv}CH)_4$, M = Si, Ge, and Sn have been studied by Sacher, Lemmon, and Miller (*438*), and the spectra are consistent with full T_d symmetry. The phenyl derivatives of C, Si, Ge, and Sn have been discussed by Smith (*439*). Edgell and Ward (*440*) have assigned the spectra of $(CH_3)SnCl_3$, $(CH_3)_2SnCl_2$, and $(CH_3)_3SnCl$ and also have re-examined $(CH_3)_4Sn$. Spectra for the compounds $(CH_3)_3SnX$, X = H, F, Cl, and Br have been reported by Kriegsmann and Pischtschan (*441*). In aqueous solutions, the tin-halogen stretching fundamentals disappear because of aquation to produce $(CH_3)_3Sn^+$. Rehybridization at tin occurs, and the cation has a planar SnC_3 skeleton (*428*). The spectrum of the hydroxide $(CH_3)_3SnOH$ (*442*) in aqueous solution differs from that of the cation only by very small shifts in the fundamentals indicating a predominantly ionic interaction. For the condensation product $(CH_3)_3$Sn—O—Sn$(CH_3)_3$, ν_s(Sn—O—Sn) is observed at 411 cm^{-1}. Geissler and Kriegsmann (*443*) have examined the n-butyl derivatives $(n\text{-}C_4H_9)_4Sn$, $(n\text{-}C_4H_9)_3SnCl$, $(n\text{-}C_4H_9)_2SnCl_2$, and $(n\text{-}C_4H_9)SnCl_3$ for which the values of ν_s(Sn—C) are in the range 500–600 cm^{-1}. Jackson and Nielsen (*444*) obtained spectra for the photochemically unstable compounds $(CH_3)_4Pb$, $(CH_3)_3(C_2H_5)Pb$, $(CH_3)_2(C_2H_5)_2Pb$, $(CH_3)(C_2H_5)_3Pb$, $(C_2H_5)_4Pb$, $(C_2D_5)_4Pb$, and $(C_2H_5)_3Bi$ by holding the samples at temperatures as low as $-125°$. The most intense fundamentals in the spectrum of $(CH_3)_4Pb$ are ν_s(Pb—C) 462 and ν_{as}(Pb—C), 475 cm^{-1}. Clark et al. (*445*) have tabulated spectra for a large number of organolead compounds.

Several studies have been made of the nature of organo-germanium, tin, and lead compounds in aqueous solution. Raman spectra of $(CH_3)_2Ge(OH)_2$ obtained by hydrolysis of the chloride indicate that it is a hydroxide and not an oxide (*446*). The vibrations of the $(CH_3)_2Ge$ portion are very much like those of $(CH_3)_2GeCl_2$ (*435*), while the vibrations of the $Ge(OH)_2$ portion are very similar to those of $[O_2Ge(OH)_2]^{-2}$ (*224*). Dissolution of tetrahedral $(CH_3)_2SnCl_2$ in water gives $(CH_3)_2Sn^{+2}$ and chloride ions. The Raman spectrum of the dilute aqueous solution studied by McGrady and Tobias (*447*) shows no ν(Sn—Cl), is identical to that of the perchlorate and nitrate salts, and is consistent only with a linear H_3C—Sn—CH_3^{+2} ion with effective D_{3d} symmetry. The ion is isostructural with the isoelectronic $Cd(CH_3)_2$, and the cation–water molecule interactions are nondirectional in character. The $(CH_3)_2Pb^{+2}$ ion also has a similar spectrum and structure (*448*). With ligands such as acetylacetone, the coordination number of tin expands to 6, for example, in $(CH_3)_2Sn(acac)_2$ (**XXXV**) which the Raman spectrum shows to have the *trans* structure (*327,449*). Only ν_s(Sn—C) is active, with the value 519 cm^{-1}.

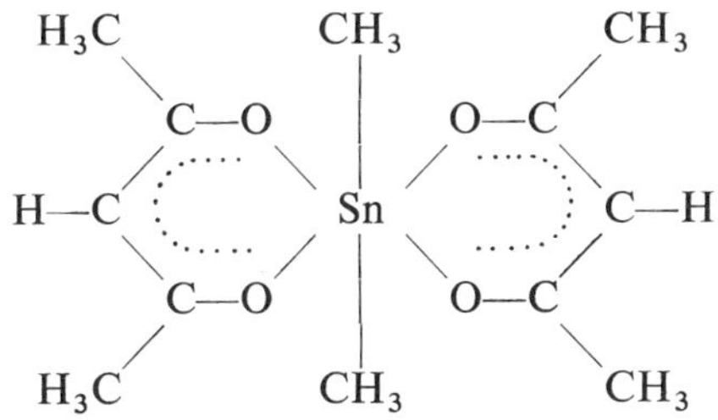

(**XXXV**)

b. *Gallium, Indium, and Thallium*

A spectrum of the unstable compound $(CH_3)_3In$ has been reported by Hall et al. (*450*). The aquo ion $(CH_3)_2Ga^+$ produced by hydrolysis of $(CH_3)_3Ga$ or $(CH_3)_2GaX$ compounds was found by Tobias et al. (*78*) to have a spectrum consistent only with a basically tetrahedral $(CH_3)_2Ga(OH_2)_2{}^+$ structure. Spectra were also obtained for the hydroxide $[(CH_3)_2GaOH]_4$. In contrast, Goggin and Woodward (*451*) found that the $(CH_3)_2Tl^+$ ion has a linear structure like that of $(CH_3)_2Sn^{+2}$ and $(CH_3)_2Pb^{+2}$. Spectra of the cyclic compounds $[(CH_3)_2GaF]_3$ and $[(C_2H_5)_2GaF]_3$ suggest that the compounds have planar rings with skeletal symmetry D_{3h} rather than the chair (C_{3v}) or boat (C_s) forms (*452*).

c. *Mercury*

The spectra of organo-mercury compounds have been investigated extensively. This results, in part, from their simplicity, since mercury has mostly a coordination number of two in these compounds. Downs (*453*) found that spectra of $(CF_3)_2Hg$ were consistent with the linear (D_{3d}) structure in aqueous and methanol solution. There was neither evidence for reactions of the type Eq. (12)

$$(CF_3)_2Hg + X^- \rightarrow (CF_3)_2HgX^- \tag{12}$$

since no changes in the spectrum occured upon the addition of halide ions, X^-, nor for Eq. (13),

$$(CF_3)_2Hg + HgX_2 \rightarrow 2(CF_3)HgX \tag{13}$$

since the mixture showed only the spectra of the two unreacted compounds. The latter type of redistribution reaction was detected by Raman spectroscopy for $Hg(SCF_3)_2$ and the mercuric halides HgX_2 (*454*).

There has been considerable interest in the $(CH_3)Hg^+$ cation and its reactions in aqueous solution. The cation spectrum (*455*) shows a ν(Hg—O) fundamental at 464 cm^{-1} and there probably is one bound water, i.e., the cation is H_3C—Hg—$OH_2{}^+$. Hydrolysis produces $[(H_3CHg)_2OH]^+$ for which ν_s(Hg—O—Hg] is assigned at 415 cm^{-1} (*456*). Splitting of the degenerate nitrate fundamentals observed with aqueous solutions of $H_3CHg(NO_3)$ indicates that the nitrate is incompletely dissociated in solution, although no line due to Hg—ONO_2 stretching was observed. Since mercury in the methylmercury(II) cation tends to form only one additional bond, it is somewhat like a proton, e.g., $H_3CHgONO_2$ may be compared to $HONO_2$, nitric acid. An oxonium type of ion is formed $(H_3CHg)_3O^+$, and also $(H_3CHg)_3S^+$ (*458*). The former appears to have an almost planar skeleton while the latter is pyramidal. Spectra for H_3CHgX, $X = Cl^-$, Br^-, I^-, and CN^- have been reported by Goggin and Woodward (*459*), and the cyanide also has been studied by Hall and Mills (*460*) as a melt and in solution. For the latter compound, $\nu(C{\equiv}N) = 2180$, $\nu(Hg{-}CH_3) = 565$, and $\nu(Hg{-}CN) = 386$ cm^{-1}. Additional measurements of the spectra and normal coordinate analyses for compounds of the type H_3CHgL have been made by Green (*461*). Spectra of several dialkylmercury compounds have been reported (*462*).

d. *Transition Metals*

Careful measurements by Miles, Glass, and Tobias (*77*) of Raman spectra of aqueous solutions of $(CH_3)_2AuNO_3$ and $(CH_3)_2AuClO_4$ including depolarization ratios showed that the cation which probably has two bound water molecules, i.e. $(CH_3)_2Au(OH_2)_2{}^+$, has the *cis* structure **(XXXVI)** and C_{2v} effective symmetry for the skeletal vibrations. In

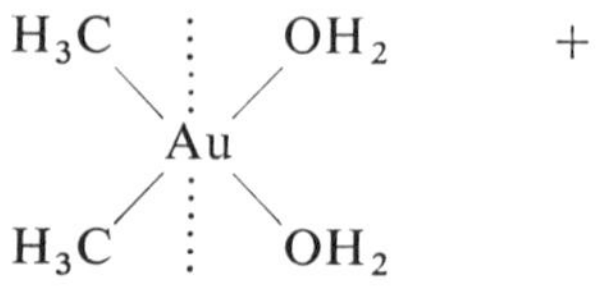

(XXXVI)

moderately concentrated solutions, there is no complexing of either perchlorate or nitrate ion. The spectrum of the *fac*$(CH_3)_3Pt(OH_2)_3{}^+$ cation has been assigned (*463*), and again interaction with anions is very weak.

Ware and Woodward [quoted in (*464*)] have examined aqueous solutions of Zeise's salt and assigned lines at 401 with $Cl_3PtC_2H_4{}^-$ and at 393 cm^{-1} with $Br_3PtC_2H_4{}^-$ to symmetric stretching (**XXXVII**) of the platinum ethylene linkage. The antisymmetric mode (**XXXVIII**) in which the two

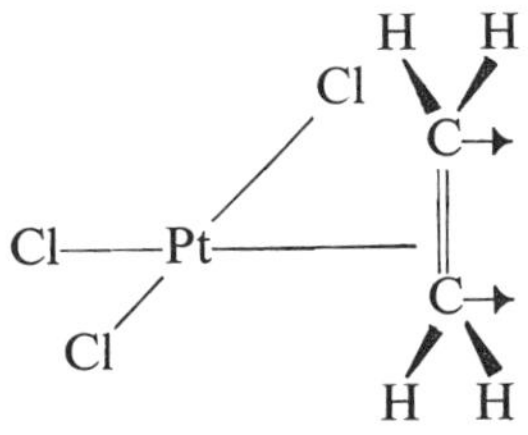

(**XXXVII**)

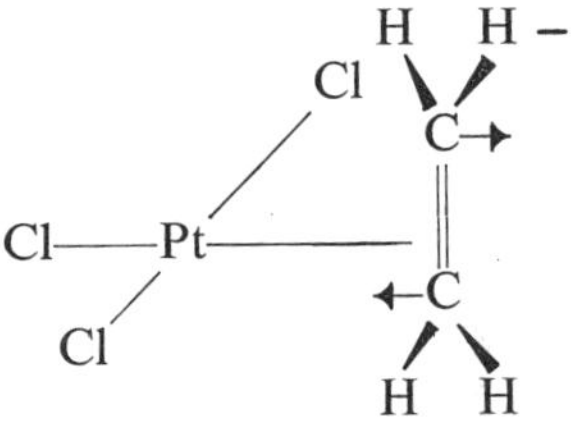

(**XXXVIII**)

carbon atoms move out of phase and in which the ethylene molecule consequently rocks back and forth has the frequencies 490 and 485 cm^{-1} for the chloride and bromide complexes, respectively. The high values suggest significant π bonding from platinum to ethylene.

It has been concluded from the Raman spectra of the compounds $(C_2H_5)ZnX$, X = halide, that these are monomeric in ether solution (*465*). The arithmetic mean of the symmetric and antisymmetric C—Zn—C stretching vibrations was used as a measure of the strength of coordination of solvents to $(C_2H_5)_2Zn$. Decreasing frequency indicates stronger coordination, and the values decrease in the order diethyl ether > tetrahydrofuran > dimethoxyethane > pyridine > 2,2′-dipyridyl > N,N,N′,N′-tetramethylethylenediamine.

IV. SOLUTION EQUILIBRIA AND STRUCTURE

A. Aqueous Solutions

Detailed studies of the Raman spectra of water and of aqueous solutions have been made by many workers for two principal reasons. First the Raman spectrum of pure water provides information on the hydrogen bond induced structure in the liquid. Changes in the water spectrum as electrolytes are dissolved reflect the manner in which the ions affect the water structure. Second, as noted previously, water is almost an ideal Raman solvent for the study of the structure and reactions of ions.

1. Water

Although water is chosen as a Raman solvent because of the simplicity of its spectrum and the low intensity of scattering, there are weak, broad bands at ca. 60 (hydrogen bond deformation), 152–175 (hydrogen bond stretching) and 450 and 780 cm^{-1} (libration) (*466–468*) in addition to the weak, broad bending fundamental at 1645 cm^{-1} and the very broad, intense band from 3100 to 3700 cm^{-1} due to the symmetric and anti-symmetric stretching fundamentals centered at 3450 and 3690 (*470–472*). Simply running a spectrum of pure water is not a completely satisfactory method to subtract out the background scattering from that of a solution, since the addition of electrolytes to water markedly affects the intensity of most of the bands (*466–472*). The broad bands centered at 175, 450, and 780 caused by intermolecular interactions are all depolarized which helps in their identification. The addition of an electrolyte or an increase in temperature reduces the intensity of these intermolecular bands, and the decrease usually varies linearly with solute concentration. Anions like Br^- and Cl^- seem to have a particularly large effect on the water structure, while cations are less important (*466,468*).

Wall and Hornig (*473*) examined the spectrum of HDO in H_2O and D_2O where 80% of the band intensity was due to uncoupled HDO molecules. The stretching bands are narrower than in pure H_2O or D_2O, but still only broad bands were observed; and there was no evidence for distinctly different kinds of water structure. The full band widths at half maximum intensity, 278 cm^{-1} for ν(O—H) and 160 cm^{-1} for ν(O—D), were attributed to the range of vibrational frequencies available to the oscillator because of the different kinds of hydrogen bonds. The values of ν(O—H) were related to the O···O distances, and distribution functions for these distances were calculated. Walrafen (*468*) has taken a different view and has discussed the spectrum of liquid water in terms of the two structure or "iceberg" model. In a recent investigation (*469*) he has measured the D—O stretching contour which occurs in the range 2500–2600 cm^{-1} from 16° to 97°C. This band was resolved with an analogue computer into two overlapping Gaussian components at 2510–2540 and 2630–2660 cm^{-1}. The temperature dependence of the two components is opposite, and these results support the two structure model for water.

2. METAL CATION-WATER INTERACTIONS: HYDROLYSIS

The bonds between metal ions and water molecules in the first coordination sphere are highly polar, and the intensity of the symmetric metal–oxygen stretching fundamental is usually very low. In crystal spectra of hydrated nitrates (*474*) and sulfates (*475*), lines have been observed which were assigned to metal–water oxygen bond stretching, although these modes are best studied with infrared spectra. With solutions, the scattering is of such low intensity that there has been rather poor agreement among the results of different investigators. Da Silveira, Marques, and Marques (*476,477,478*) observed one polarized and two depolarized lines each in spectra of aqueous solutions of magnesium(II), zinc (II), and aluminum(III) salts at 365 p, 315, 240; 390 p, 335, 240; and 524 p, 447, and 342 cm^{-1}, respectively. The ratios of the frequency of the polarized lines with H_2O to the corresponding values with a D_2O solution were 1.04 to 1.05, that which would be expected for the change from H_2O to D_2O for a stretching vibration. Beryllium(II) solutions gave complex spectra, but a polarized line at 533 and a depolarized line at 345 cm^{-1} were approximately independent of the anion present. Hester and Plane (*479*) report the same values for the polarized lines with Mg^{+2}, Zn^{+2}, and Al^{+3} and found with a large number of other multivalent metal ions weak polarized lines in the range from 350 to 550 cm^{-1} which they also assigned to the breathing mode of the first hydration sphere. In the case of Hg^{+2}, this assignment seems doubtful, since the polarized line has been reported to decrease in intensity as the concentration of mercury increases (*312*). A Raman spectrum has been obtained for $Be(OH_2)_4^{+2}$ from the crystal spectrum of $BeSO_4 \cdot 4H_2O$ (*480*).

One assignment of such a water oxygen–metal stretching mode which seems beyond question is that for $(CH_3)Hg^+$, where a polarized line is observed at 464 cm^{-1} (*455*), and where a strong bond to only one water molecule is expected. For the cation *fac*$[(CH_3)_3Pt(OH_2)_3]^+$ for which the hydration number in solution has been established by oxygen-17 NMR measurements (*481*), a broad band centered at 357 cm^{-1} is assigned to ν_s(Pt—O) (*463*). With the related transition metal ion *cis* $[(CH_3)_2Au(OH_2)_n]^+$, ν_s(Au—O) (ρ corrected = 0.11) was assigned at 418 cm^{-1} (*77*). Hester and Grossman (*482*) report a very intense polarized band from 320 to 450 cm^{-1} for $In(ClO_4)_3$ solutions assigned to a totally symmetric vibration of a large hydrogen bonded aggregate of water molecules about the cation. In conclusion, it seems likely that most of these polarized bands do result from a breathing mode of the first hydration sphere. Since these water molecules will, in turn, be strongly hydrogen bonded to the bulk solvent, the frequency and molar intensity of the vibration may be strongly influenced by the concentration of the solution and nature of the anion present.

Raman spectroscopy provides a simple method for establishing whether ions contain one strongly bonded oxo group or two hydroxo groups, a point which cannot be established by thermodynamic measurements on dilute solutions since these differ only by a molecule of solvent. Vanadyl ion (*483*) is clearly $[VO(OH_2)_n]^{+2}$ and not $[V(OH)_2(OH_2)_n]^{+2}$ with $\nu(V{=}O)$ = ca. 1000 cm^{-1}. Similarly with niobium, the ion $[NbOF_5]^{-2}$, $\nu(Nb{=}O) = 935$ cm^{-1}, and not $[Nb(OH)_2F_5]^{-2}$ has been shown to exist in HF solutions (*484*).

Maroni and Spiro have obtained spectra for the hydrolyzed cations $[Bi_6(OH)_{12}]^{+6}$ (*485*) and $[Pb_4(OH)_4]^{+4}$ (*486*) and shown that they are consistent with cubic and tetrahedral symmetry, respectively, for the ions. Lippincott, Psellos, and Tobin (*487*) assigned lines at 470, 420, and 300 cm^{-1} with alkaline zinc(II) and at 615 and 310 cm^{-1} with alkaline aluminum(III) solutions to the ions $Zn(OH)_4^{-2}$ and $Al(OH)_6^{-3}$ respectively. In agreement with the results of Lippincott et al., Fordyce and Baum (*488*) found lines at 484 (ν_1), 285 (ν_2), 430 (ν_3), and 322 (ν_4) for ZnO dissolved in KOH, and these were assigned to the four skeletal modes of $Zn(OH)_4^{-2}$. Plumb and co-workers (*489*) made a detailed study of hydrolyzed aluminum(III) solutions and concluded that a polymeric anion existed up to pH 12 and that at higher pH AlO_2^- ions with $D_{\infty h}$ symmetry were present.

3. Weak Cation-Anion Interactions

While much work has been done on weak complexes where well defined cation–anion stretching fundamentals are observed, there also has been considerable interest in interactions where no such stretching vibrations can be found. This situation can result from ion pairs where cation and anion are separated by at least one solvent molecule, or the bond may be so ionic that the polarizability is little affected by bond stretching and consequently the scattering may be too weak to detect. Some of the earlier work has been reviewed by Young (*490,491*) and other aspects have been discussed by Hester (*1*) and by Irish (*249*).

Jones et al. (*492*) obtained spectra for aqueous solutions of 17 perchlorate salts, but only with Tl^+, La^{+3}, and Mg^{+2} was there any possible indication of cation–anion complex formation. It is almost certain that no such interaction exists with the large unipositive Tl^+ ion. Hester and Plane (*493*) investigated a large number of near-saturated solutions of nitrates, sulfates, and perchlorates. With Ag^+, Cu^{+2}, Zn^{+2}, Hg^{+2}, Ca^{+2}, Al^{+3}, In^{+3}, Ce^{+3}, and Th^{+4}, new lines assigned to bound nitrate were observed. Although sulfates of multivalent metal ions are known to be associated, only with In^{+3} (*494*) were new lines observed suggesting that in all of the other cases the cation and sulfate ion are separated by at least one solvent molecule. With 14 perchlorate salts (*493*) no new lines at all were observed even with concentrated solutions. On this basis the suitability of perchlorate ion as an internal intensity standard is established.

In contrast to perchlorate and sulfate ions, it has been known for many years that nitrate shows marked splitting of the degenerate modes in many concentrated solutions (*495*). It is possible that this may be primarily associated with the planar structure, since the tetrahedral anions do not show this splitting; and they may fit into the water structure better. Any interaction which removes the threefold axis of the free nitrate ion will lift the degeneracy of ν_3 and of ν_4. If this effect were strictly caused by cation association, the splitting might be expected to approach zero as the concentration became vanishingly small, and yet measurements by Irish and Walrafen (*496*) on $Ca(NO_3)_2$ solutions and by Irish and Davis on alkali metal nitrates (*497*) show that it does not. Even in 1 *M* $NaNO_3$ solution, ν_3 gives a very broad, markedly asymmetric band. Vollmar (*498*) found that both the frequency and line width for the totally symmetric breathing mode of the nitrate ion increased with concentration for several cations suggesting that the complexes are not well defined structurally.

In their studies of $Ca(NO_3)_2$ solutions, Hester and Plane (*499*) in contrast to the conclusions of Irish and Walrafen assumed a well-defined complex was formed, that the 717 cm^{-1} line was from free nitrate, that the 740 cm^{-1} was from bound nitrate, and calculated values of 0.12 to 0.17 for the association constant in concentrated solutions obtained by dilution of a 3 $Zn(NO_3)_2$—2 NH_4NO_3—15 H_2O eutectic. Because of the weak cation–anion interaction in this system, the model is questionable, and concentration equilibrium constants (quotients) are probably of little physical meaning in such concentrated electrolyte solutions. Nevertheless, in some cases well defined nitrato complexes undoubtedly exist in solution. Aqueous solutions of $(CH_3)HgNO_3$ show in addition to the free nitrate spectrum another set of lines which are very similar to the spectrum of undissociated $(CH_3)HgONO_2$ determined in benzene solution (*456*). Miller and Irish (*500*) using Job's method (see next section) found well defined

3:1 $NO_3^-:Ce^{+4}$ complexes with the highly charged ceric ion. Other recent investigations of nitrato complexing include $HgNO_3^+$ and $Hg(NO_3)_2$ where nitrate functions as a unidentate ligand (*501*), studies of the effect of cations on the 740 cm^{-1} band (*502*), spectra of alkali and alkaline earth metal nitrate glasses (*503*), and studies of alkali metal nitrate solutions (*504*). Whatever the precise nature of these interactions, it is apparent that the nitrate ion has no higher than C_{2v} effective symmetry in concentrated solutions.

4. Determination of Equilibrium Constants

Raman spectroscopy enjoys many advantages as a method for the determination of equilibrium constants where the values are not too greatly different from unity. At first glance, it would appear to be almost ideal, and indeed with a single equilibrium such as that represented by Eq. (14).

$$A + nB \leftrightharpoons AB_n \tag{14}$$

it can be. Raman lines can be assigned in many cases to a single solute species. Integrated Raman intensities vary linearly with scatterer concentration to a very good approximation, in general much better than integrated infrared absorbances. Contemporary Raman spectrophotometers permit accurate evaluation of integrated intensities. For the determination of dissociation constants of strong monoprotic acids, the Raman method is unsurpassed.

For systems where several equilibria with constants K_i occur simultaneously

$$A + B \leftrightharpoons AB \qquad K_1 \tag{15}$$

$$AB + B \leftrightharpoons AB_2 \qquad K_2 \tag{16}$$

$$\begin{matrix} \cdot & \cdot & \cdot & \cdot \\ \cdot & \cdot & \cdot & \cdot \\ \cdot & \cdot & \cdot & \cdot \end{matrix}$$

$$AB_{n-1} + B \leftrightharpoons AB_n \qquad K_n \tag{17}$$

the situation is not so favorable. From spectra of solutions with varying total A and B concentrations, C_A and C_B, the pertinent values of n must be determined, i.e., the composition of the complexes. If we assume solution ideality, $2n$ constant parameters must be evaluated, i.e., the n equilibrium constants and the n molar intensities J_n [see Eq. (6), Section II, D, 4] which relate intensity to concentration. Mathematically, $2n$ intensity measurements on solution of different composition should suffice, but in practice the relations between intensity and C_A and C_B are rather "ill conditioned," i.e., large variations in stoichiometry often cause relatively small changes in intensity.

To establish the composition of the complexes, Job's method [(*505*) see Ref. (*70*) for a discussion] is often used. For a single equilibrium and assuming solution ideality, the concentration of AB_n and consequently its Raman intensity will be a maximum when the ratio $C_B/(C_A+C_B)$, $(C_A+C_B$ = constant), has the value $n/(n+1)$. A similar plot of Raman intensity versus C_B/C_A will have a maximum at the ratio $C_B/C_A = n$. With many systems, Job's method is only partially successful or it fails completely. First, Raman scattering by most inorganic systems is rather low in intensity so quite concentrated, highly non-ideal solutions are required. The Raman intensities are proportional to concentration, and the assumption that activities can be replaced by concentrations in the equilibrium constant expressions with such non-ideal systems is not often justified. Second, if the equilibrium constant K_n is not large, it is often difficult to locate the maximum in the plot of intensity versus $C_B/(C_A+C_B)$ with the necessary accuracy. Third, if several equilibria exist simultaneously, Job's method does not yield precise values of the ligand numbers, n. The failings of the method in this situation have been discussed by Woldbye (*506*) and by Katzin and Gebert (*507*).

Once a trial set of species has been established, the best procedure is to use a least squares computer program to refine trial values of the equilibrium constants, K_n, and if necessary the molar intensities, J_n. Assuming the data are sufficiently precise to warrant it, the sum of the squares of the residuals in the Raman intensities is minimized by adjusting the equilibrium constants. Such procedures have been used with conventional spectrophotometric data (*508*).

As discussed in Section II, D, the calculation of concentrations by the use of Eq. (6) involves certain problems. Over a wide range of concentrations, deviations from linearity are observed. Conveniently but not rigorously, these deviations can be separated into two types: (a) the purely optical effects which result from changes in solution refractive index and (b) the internal field effect. The use of an internal standard eliminates the correction for changes in refractive index, or an external reference can be adjusted to have the same refractive index as the sample. Corrections for the internal field effect, i.e., the effect of intermolecular forces on the intrinsic scattering power of the molecule, are much more difficult to estimate and are usually neglected entirely. The effect appears to be small, and usually it reduces the intensity of concentrated solutions a few percent below that expected. When deviations are appreciable, there is usually significant broadening of the Raman band to serve as a warning.

a. *Acid Dissociation Constants*

Although there were some admirable efforts to measure the dissociation constants of nitric acid (*509*) and perchloric acid by Redlich and co-workers (*510,511*) using photographically recorded Raman spectra, these were imprecise because of the difficulty in measuring integrated intensities from the blackening of a photographic plate. This early work was reviewed by Young and Blatz (*512*). Young and co-workers later made very precise studies of some of these equilibria using a photoelectric instrument (*490,491*).

In 15 *M* sulfuric acid, the reaction [Eq. (18)] is not quite complete as determined from measurements of the intensity of the band at 1040 cm^{-1}

$$H_2O + H_2SO_4 \rightarrow H_3O^+ + HSO_4^- \tag{18}$$

(*513*). The species H_2SO_4, HSO_4^-, H_3O^+, and $H_5SO_5^+$ all appear to be significant in more concentrated solutions (*514*). Raman data for relatively dilute sulfuric acid solutions support the value $K_2 = 0.0101_5$ for the second acid dissociation constant of H_2SO_4 at 25° (*491*).

From the data of Krawitz (*515*) for the intensity of the breathing mode of NO_3^- ion in solutions of nitric acid together with a value for the molar intensity J_{NO_3-}, the degree of dissociation $\alpha = [NO_3^-]/[HNO_3]_{Total}$ may be obtained as a function of concentration of the nitric acid solution. From these data, the quantity $K \cdot \beta$ can be calculated from Eq. (19).

$$K \cdot \beta = \frac{\gamma_{\pm}^2 \alpha^2 [HNO_3]_{Total}}{(1-\alpha)} \tag{19}$$

Here K is the conventional acid dissociation constant, $\gamma_{\pm}$ is the mean activity coefficient for $H^+NO_3^-$, and β is the activity coefficient for undissociated HNO_3 molecules. In the case of nitric acid, adequate data for $\gamma_{\pm}$ are available, so that the product $K \cdot \beta$ can be calculated. To obtain K, an extrapolation to infinite dilution where $\beta = 1$ is required. From information on the behavior of nonelectrolytes, McKay (*516*) has concluded that a linear extrapolation of K versus $[HNO_3]_{Total}$ is justified. In this way, the dissociation constant for nitric acid was determined to be 23.5 ± 0.5 at 25° (*516,517*).

Similar studies on perchloric acid indicate that the acid is completely dissociated up to 10 *M* above which concentration there is too little water to form $H_9O_4^+$. Covington et al. (*518,519*) made measurements of the intensity of the perchlorate breathing mode relative to an external $NaClO_4$ standard. The relative molar intensity of the perchlorate ion was obtained from the most dilute solution, 0.3 *M*, where the acid is completely dissociated. Corrections for the effect of refractive index on $J_{ClO_4^-}$ were obtained by measuring the intensity of $NaClO_4$ solutions to which varying amounts of NaCl had been added to adjust the refractive index. Heinzinger and Weston (*520*) compared solutions of $HClO_4$ and $NaClO_4$ for which the refractive index values are almost the same. Above 8 *M*, the limit of solubility of $NaClO_4$, two $HClO_4$ solutions differing by 1 *M* in concentration were compared, and the refractive index correction was made using an extrapolation of the relation found for $NaClO_4$ solutions.

Bonner and Torres (*521*) obtained dissociation constants for toluene sulfonic acid, $CH_3 \cdot C_6H_4SO_3H$, and 2,5-dimethylbenzene sulfonic acid, $(CH_3)_2C_6H_3SO_3H$, from intensity measurements of ν_s(S—O) for the sulfonate ions. For these measurements, the intensity of ν_s(C—H) from the methyl groups was used as an internal standard, since this vibration is uncoupled from the other normal modes and the same for acid and anion. The molar intensities $J_{RSO_3^-}$ were evaluated from measurements on solutions of the sodium salts. Data for the mean activity coefficients $\gamma_\pm$ were used to calculate $K \cdot \beta$, and a linear extrapolation was made to infinite dilution. Clarke and Woodward (*522*) found the dissociation constant for methane-sulfonic acid $CH_3 \cdot SO_3H$ was larger than had been estimated from acidity function data. A 2 *M* NH_4NO_3 external reference was used, since the breathing mode of NO_3^- almost coincides with the 1051 cm^{-1} ν_s(S—O) line of $CH_3 \cdot SO_3^-$ of which the intensity was measured. The molar intensity, $J_{CH_3 . SO_3^-}$, of the methanesulfonate ion was corrected for refractive index effects by assuming the intensity deviations of standard $NH_4^+CH_3 \cdot SO_3^-$, solutions arose only from this source. Similar measurements were used to determine the dissociation constant of iodic acid HIO_3 (*523*). The intensity of the breathing mode of IO_3^- was measured versus an external $NaIO_3$ standard. Corrections for changes in refractive index do not seem to have been made, but this may have been unnecessary if the values for the solutions and references were similar.

b. *Complex Stability Constants*

In principle, it should be possible to measure the equilibrium constant for the interaction of a metal ion and a ligand just as for the reaction of a proton with a ligand. In practice the necessary activity coefficient data are almost always lacking, so it is not possible to obtain an accurate value of *K*. Clarke and Woodward (*456*) have studied the dissociation of methylmercury(II) nitrate $H_3CHg—O—NO_2$ in experiments very similar to those used to determine K_d for nitric acid. The intensity of the NO_3^- breathing mode was measured versus a 4 *M* $NaNO_3$ external standard. Refractive index corrections were estimated using $NH_4^+NO_3^-$ solutions. It was assumed that the observed deviations of a plot of NO_3^- Raman intensity versus $NH_4^+NO_3^-$ concentration from linearity were caused by refractive index effects only. The value of $J_{NO_3^-}$ was determined with the NH_4NO_3 solutions. Only degrees of dissociation could be calculated, since the activity coefficients $\gamma_\pm$ for the concentrated solutions used in the Raman measurements were lacking. Similar measurements were made for methylmercuric methanesulfonate and methylmercuric sulfate (*457*).

Yellin and Plane (*268*) measured intensities of the 172, 186, and 205 cm^{-1} lines of solutions of $ZnBr_2 + Br^-$ which were assigned to $ZnBr_4^{-2}$, $ZnBr_2$, and $ZnBr^+$. An internal ClO_4^- standard was used. The relative intensities of these three lines are very dependent upon the bromide ion concentration, and the intensity increases in the order 205 < 186 < 172 as $[Br^-]:[Zn^{+2}]$ is increased. Thus the number of bromide ions in the complexes must also increase in this order, and the line at 172 cm^{-1} certainly results from $ZnBr_4^{-2}$. Job's method was used to find the compositions of the other complexes, but this was difficult since all three lines overlap and the baseline is not horizontal because of the Rayleigh scattering of the solution. There is some question as to whether the other two lines come from $ZnBr_2$ and $ZnBr_3^-$ or $ZnBr^+$ and $ZnBr_2$. Yellin and Plane (*268*) calculated equilibrium constants for the formation of $ZnBr^+$, $ZnBr_2$, and $ZnBr_4^{-2}$. Since the ionic strength of the solutions varied from 3.5 to 8.5, these must be regarded as only order of magnitude values. Nixon and Plane (*277*) made similar measurements for $Ga^{+3}—Br^-$ solutions. Ortel and Plane (*311*) used the Job method to establish that the limiting complex in Bi^{+3} solutions with high chloride ion concentrations is $BiCl_6^{-3}$, and spectral characteristics of the complexes $BiCl_n^{3-n}$, $n = 1$ to 6, were discussed. Kon and Plane recently have examined the formation of mixed complexes in the systems $Zn^{+2}—CN^-—NH_3$ and $Hg^{+2}—CN^-—NCS^-$ (*524*).

Gilbert (*263*) has made an extensive study of $Zn^{+2}—Cl^-$ solutions which have been studied earlier by several other groups (*255–263,280*). Intensities of the lines at 297 cm^{-1} assigned to $ZnCl_2$ and $ZnCl^+$ and at 278 cm^{-1} assigned to $ZnCl_4^{-2}$ were measured relative to a 2 *M* $ZnCl_2$ + 8 *M* LiCl ($ZnCl_4^{-2}$) reference. The badly overlapping lines were resolved, and $J_{ZnCl_4^{-2}}$ was determined from measurements on a solution with a large excess of chloride ion. The assumption of all 4 complexes $ZnCl^+$, $ZnCl_2$, $ZnCl_3^-$, and $ZnCl_4^{-2}$ would require the determination of 4 equilibrium constants and 3 molar intensities besides that of $ZnCl_4^{-2}$, and this is not possible with the data. It was assumed that only $ZnCl_2$ and $ZnCl_4^{-2}$ were

TABLE 14

Equilibrium Constants Determined by Raman Spectroscopy[a]

System	Temp.	Medium	Constants	References
$H^+—NO_3^-$	25°	∞	$K_d = 23.5 \pm 0.5\ M$	(*516,517*)
$H^+—CH_3 \cdot C_6H_4SO_3^-$	?	∞	$K_d = 11.6 \pm 0.5\ M$	(*521*)
$H^+—$ 2,5-$(CH_3)_2C_6H_3SO_3^-$	?	∞	$K_d = 2.7 \pm 0.5\ M$	(*521*)
$H^+—CH_3SO_3^-$	25°	∞	$K_d = 73\ M$	(*522*)
$H^+—IO_3^-$	ca. 32°	∞	$K_d = 0.18 \pm 0.01$	(*523*)
$Zn^{+2}—Cl^-$	?	var	$\beta_2 = 0.0315\ M^{-2}$, $K_3 \cdot K_4 = 0.040\ M^{-2}$; $\beta_4 = 0.0013\ M^{-4}$	(*263*)
$(CH_3)_2Sn^{+2}—Cl^-$	25°	var	$K_1 < 0.05\ M^{-1}$, evidence for outer sphere complexing	(*525*)
$Zn^{+2}—Br^-$	25°	var	$K_1 = 0.3\ M^{-1}$, $K_2 = 1\ M^{-1}$; $K_3 \cdot K_4 = 0.2\ M^{-2}$	(*268*)
$Ga^{+3}—Br^-$	25°	var $\mu = 10$	$\log \beta_4 = -4.3$; for $Ga^{+3} + 4\ Br^- = GaBr_4^-$ $\Delta H°f = 9.5$ kcal/mole, $\Delta S°f = 12.5$ cal/mole degree	(*277*)
$Zn^{+2}—C_2O_4^{-2}$	43°	$\mu = 8.9 - 10.2$	$K_3 \simeq 3.6 \pm 0.6\ M^{-1}$	(*526*)
Hg^{+2}—en en = $H_2NCH_2CH_2NH_2$	?	var	$K_3 \simeq 0.3$	(*527*)

[a] The nomenclature for the equilibrium constants is that of the Chemical Society "Tables of Stability Constants," Ref. 284.

present, and equilibrium constants were calculated for the formation of these complexes. It is questionable whether these constants are physically meaningful.

Farrer, McGrady, and Tobias (*525*) measured the intensity of the 325 cm^{-1} line assigned to ν(Sn—Cl) for solutions of $(CH_3)_2Sn^{+2} + Cl^-$ versus an internal ClO_4^- standard. From electrochemical measurements, the equilibrium constant for $(CH_3)_2Sn^{+2}+Cl^- \rightleftharpoons (CH_3)_2SnCl^+$ had been determined to be 0.380 M^{-1}. The Raman intensities indicated that the value for the equilibrium constant was an order of magnitude smaller. Although no corrections for the internal field effect could be made, it is unlikely to account for the discrepancy. It appears that the complex which causes the Raman scattering is structurally different from that which is formed in more dilute solutions. Gruen and Plane (*526*) have estimated the equilibrium constant for the reaction

$$Zn(C_2O_4)_2^{-2}+C_2O_4^{-2} \rightleftharpoons Zn(C_2O_4)_3^{-4},$$

and the spectra are consistent with D_3 symmetry for the trisoxalatozincate(II) anion.

Values for equilibrium constants obtained from Raman intensity measurements are collected in Table 14. Most of the investigations reviewed were conducted with spectrophotometers using mercury arc sources. Consequently, it has been necessary to have high solute concentrations to obtain measurable intensities, and the solutions are highly non-ideal. Equilibrium constants calculated from these data are of little value as thermodynamic data. On the other hand, the spectra do demonstrate the existence of inner sphere interactions between cation and anion. The use of sources such as the argon ion laser which attain very high power levels will make it possible to investigate much more dilute solutions. A good deal more is known about the deviations of dilute electrolyte solutions from ideality, and it should be possible to obtain meaningful thermodynamic data providing, of course, that the complexes are sufficiently stable.

B. Nonaqueous Solutions

So far, few studies have been made on the structure and equilibria of solutes in nonaqueous solutions. With most of these solvents, infrared spectroscopy is satisfactory and in the case of most colored solutions preferable. Most of the work has been concerned with weak donor–acceptor interactions, and a review of these complexes and the techniques for their study has been published (*528*).

Stammreich and co-workers (*529*) made some studies of the effect of different solvents on the vibrations of halogen molecules. Klaboe (*530*) has studied the effect of 16 bases on the vibrations of I_2, Br_2, and ICl using He—Ne laser excitation. The force constants for halogen molecules were decreased to as little as one half the free halogen values. In only one system, I_2+pyridine, could a fundamental be assigned tentatively to the charge transfer bond. Here a line at 163 cm^{-1} was assigned to the iodine–pyridine bond. Bahnick (*531,532*) has measured changes in the intensity of the ICN vibration as complexing occurs in several solvents and determined a formation constant of $3.1 \pm 0.5\ M^{-1}$ for complexing of ICN by tetrahydrofuran in the mixed solvent CH_2Cl_2–$CHCl_3$. The comparable constant with benzene in place of tetrahydrofuran was too small to measure ($<0.5\ M^{-1}$).

Begun and co-workers have studied interactions of $^{10}BF_3$ and $^{11}BF_3$ with the donors, D, diethyl ether (*533*), tetrahydrofuran (*533*), dimethylsulfoxide (*534*), dimethyl ether (*535,536*), and used the vibrational frequencies to calculate equilibrium constants for the isotopic exchange equilibria, e.g., Eq. (20).

$$^{10}BF_3 + {}^{11}BF_3 \cdot D \rightleftharpoons {}^{11}BF_3 + {}^{10}BF_3 \cdot D \tag{20}$$

Michel and Duyckaerts (*537*) studied the interactions of the acceptors, $AsCl_3$ and $SbCl_3$ with ethyl acetate, methyl benzoate, and acetophenone. In diethyl ether solution both methyl benzoate and acetophenone form 1:1 complexes with $SbCl_3$ as determined by Job's method, and the dissociation constants for the adducts were found to be 0.37 ± 0.06 and $1.26 \pm 0.18\ M$, respectively. Lindqvist and co-workers (*538*) used Raman spectra to establish the relative strengths of different donors. Mixtures of $POCl_3$ and $PO(CH_3)_3$ with an excess of the acceptor $SbCl_5$ show the spectrum of unreacted $POCl_3$ plus that of the complexed $PO(CH_3)_3$.

A number of crystalline donor–acceptor complexes have been examined including those with aromatic hydrocarbons $2SbBr_3 \cdot C_6H_6$ (*539*), $2SbCl_3 \cdot C_6H_6$ (*540*), $2SbCl_3 \cdot C_6H_5OH$ (*540*), $2SbCl_3 \cdot C_6H_5CH_3$ (*540*), $AgClO_4 \cdot C_6H_6$ (*542*), $2SbCl_3 \cdot C_{10}H_8$ (*543*), and $2SbCl_3 \cdot (C_6H_5)_2O$ (*543*). New lines appear as the symmetry of the $SbCl_3$ or $SbBr_3$ is lowered, and the frequencies of the ring breathing modes of the aromatic molecules decrease.

Dembitskii and co-workers (*544–546*) have studied the donor–acceptor complexes formed by $SnCl_4$ with several esters. Shifts in $\nu(C{=}O)$ of the free and complexed ester were observed, and the intensities were used to calculate equilibrium constants.

The interaction between $InCl_3$ and diethyl ether has been studied by Taylor (*547*). Hayward and Hendra (*548*) have obtained spectra of crystalline donor acceptor complexes of S_8 with CHI_3; 1,4-dithian, $C_4H_8S_2$; and 1,4-diselan, $C_4H_8Se_2$. Maywiyoff and Movius (*332*) studied Be^{+2} in dimethyl formamide solution but did not observe any fundamental assignable to Be—O bond stretching. Hester and Plane (*549*) obtained spectra for methanol solutions of LiCl, $ZnCl_2$, $Zn(ClO_4)_2 \cdot 6H_2O$, $MgCl_2 \cdot 6H_2O$, $Mg(ClO_4)_2 \cdot 6H_2O$, $Mg(NO_3)_2 \cdot 6H_2O$, $MgSO_4 \cdot 7H_2O$, $LiClO_4 \cdot 2H_2O$, $NaClO_4$, NaF, and $Ca(NO_3)_2 \cdot 4H_2O$. The degenerate NO_3^- vibrations were split significantly with Ca^{+2} and Mg^{+2} but no lines assignable to *M*–ONO_2 stretching were observed, so the lowering of the nitrate symmetry was attributed to ion pair formation. The $ZnCl_2$ solutions showed ν(Zn—Cl) at 300 cm^{-1} because of undissociated $ZnCl_2$ and $ZnCl_4^{-2}$ complexes.

V. FUSED SALTS

Raman studies of molten salt systems tend to fall into two categories. The first is comprised of studies of single component melts like molten metal nitrates or mercury(II) halides. These investigations are designed to provide information on the structure of the melts and in the case of the ionic nitrates on the interaction between cations and anions. Since molten salts are structurally similar in many ways to concentrated electrolyte solutions, these investigations resemble those described for aqueous solutions in Section IV, A, 3. The second type of study involves examination *in situ* of species which are produced most readily by reactions in the molten state.

Several reviews have been published on Raman investigations of molten salts (*550–553*).

A. Cation–Anion Interactions

Nitrate melts have been studied extensively, since they have rather low melting points. Just as with aqueous solutions, the nitrate ion makes a good probe to measure the strength of the cation–anion interaction. Bues (*554*) and Janz and James (*555*) have studied melts of Li^+, Na^+, K^+, Rb^+, Cs^+, and Ag^+ nitrates. The frequencies of all three Raman active fundamentals decrease in the alkali metal ion sequence Li (ν_1 = 1067 cm^{-1}) to Cs (ν_1 = 1043 cm^{-1}). Silver ion appears to be somewhat irregular, and there may be well-defined $Ag^+NO_3^-$ ion pairs in the melt. It is clear that the threefold axis of the free nitrate ion has been lost in the melt but whether structurally well-defined complexes exist is still in doubt (*556*); Li^+ as well as Ag^+ splits the doubly degenerate N—O stretching fundamental, ν_3. Wait, Ward, and Janz (*557*) have made normal coordinate calculations using a Urey Bradley field for ion pairs assigned a structure of the type (**XXXIX**) and obtained values of the metal–oxygen

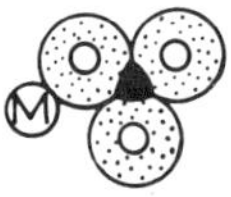

(**XXXIX**)

stretching force constant of from 0.15 mdyne/Å with Cs^+ to 0.84 mdyne/Å with Ag^+. Since the force field involved 9 constants and only 5 fundamentals were observed experimentally, the absolute values of the constants are of questionable significance. Thallium(I) nitrate melts show an even greater shift of ν_1 than found for silver(I) nitrate, and ν_3 is greatly split suggesting a somewhat covalent interaction (*558*).

Sulfate melts which must be studied at ca. 1100° show a similar cation effect on ν_1 with $Li^+ > Na^+ > K^+$ (*48*). The decrease in frequency is almost linear with ionic potential, Z/r. The general features of the spectra are similar to those of aqueous sulfate solutions except that all four lines are much broader for the melt. No splitting of the degenerate modes was observed.

B. Reactions in Molten Salts

Several metal halide complexes have been studied in melts where many of the same species present in aqueous solutions (compare Section III, C) are found. Melts of the mercury(II) halides, HgX_2, show very broad lines at 313 cm^{-1}, ν_s(Hg—Cl) and at 195 cm^{-1}, ν_s(Hg—Br) (*559*). The antisymmetric stretching fundamentals are weakly Raman active, $\nu_{as} = 376$ and 271 cm^{-1}, respectively, indicating that the $D_{\infty h}$ symmetry of the free linear molecules is lost in the melt. Molten HgBrCl shows the spectra of both $HgCl_2$ and $HgBr_2$ because of the disproportionation reaction in addition to three Raman lines at 335 (ν_{as}), 236 (ν_s), and 111 cm^{-1} (δ) from linear Br—Hg—Cl molecules. Addition of KCl to a melt of $HgCl_2$ gives new lines assigned to $HgCl_3^-$ at 282, 287, 210 cm^{-1} and $HgCl_4^{-2}$ at 267 (ν_1), 180 (ν_2), 276 (ν_3), and 192 (ν_4) (*560*). Using He—Ne laser excitation, HgI_2 has been studied as a solute in melts of $HgCl_2$ and $HgBr_2$ (*561*). The symmetric I—Hg—I stretch is observed at 146 cm^{-1}, and the mixed species HgICl and HgIBr also are present in the melts. Zinc chloride (*44,261,282*) and bromide (*261*) melts have been examined by many workers because of their similarity to concentrated aqueous solutions of ZnX_2. With a melt of pure $ZnCl_2$, a broad line at ca. 230 cm^{-1} similar in frequency to that assigned to the "polymers" $[ZnCl_2]_n$ in concentrated aqueous solutions is observed. Addition of KCl to the melt produces new polarized lines at 305 cm^{-1} assigned to $ZnCl_2$ molecules, 290 cm^{-1} assigned to $ZnCl_3^-$, and 275 from $ZnCl_4^{-2}$. The identification of $ZnCl_2$ and $ZnCl_3^-$ complexes is based on the somewhat uncertain assignments for aqueous solutions (*261*). Also, considering that all of the species except $ZnCl_4^{-2}$ probably have water in the first coordination sphere about zinc in aqueous solutions, rather large frequency shifts comparable to the differences between the complexes would be expected with the change in phase, so comparisons with aqueous spectra may not be reliable. Thiocyanate melts show very little evidence for perturbation of the free $N{\equiv}C{-}S^-$ ($C_{\infty v}$) ion (*562*). Similar investigations have been made on $MgCl_2+KCl$ (*478*) and $SnCl_2+KCl$ melts (*564*).

Walrafen, Irish, and Young (*565*) examined the reactions of the bisulfate ion in melts and found evidence for (21) and (22):

$$2HSO_4^- \rightleftharpoons S_2O_7^{-2}+H_2O \tag{21}$$

$$S_2O_7^{-2} \rightleftharpoons SO_4^{-2}+SO_3 \tag{22}$$

The existence of $S_2O_7^{-2}$ is indicated clearly by the appearance of the fundamental ν_s(S—O—S) at 730 cm^{-1}. Analogous studies of selenious acid melts (*566*) demonstrate the occurrence of the condensation reaction (23)

$$2H_2SeO_3 \leftrightharpoons H_2Se_2O_5+H_2O \tag{23}$$

and ν_s(Se—O—Se) is found at 525 cm^{-1}.

Corbett (*567*) has used Raman spectroscopy to demonstrate the existence of the unstable Cd_2^{+2} ion as the $AlCl_4^-$ salt in melts of $CdCl_2+AlCl_3$ in which cadmium metal had been dissolved. Similar melts of $GaCl_3$ plus gallium metal (*272*) and $GaBr_3+Ga$ (*568*) with the composition GaX_2 show no evidence for Ga_2^{+4} ions and instead contain gallium in two oxidation states, i.e., they are ionic $Ga^+[GaX_4^-]$.

VI. SUMMARY AND OUTLOOK

In the next few years, laser Raman spectrophotometers should become as commonplace as infrared spectrometers in the inorganic chemist's laboratory. Their primary use is likely to continue to be in the determination of molecular symmetry or, as it is more generally but less accurately described, molecular structure. It will be most useful in the study of new ions and molecules with either high symmetry or relatively few atoms or both. Inorganic chemists still are able to synthesize many new and interesting compounds which fit this description. With larger molecules, useful information will be forthcoming mainly in the cases where there are good group vibrations, and the principle of local symmetry can be employed to simplify the problem.

It is likely that the majority of the samples studied by the inorganic chemist will be solids because of the ease of the excitation of the spectra of these samples with lasers. This stands in marked contrast to the older work where most spectra were obtained with solutions. While studies of the absorption of polarized infrared radiation by oriented single crystals have been made by only a few spectroscopists, the inorganic chemist is certain to find single crystal Raman studies useful. When a single crystal large enough to be handled conveniently is available, it is the simplest kind of sample to study. The goniometer holding a crystal for an X-ray structure determination can be transferred directly to a laser Raman spectrophotometer for the determination of the sample spectrum.

One of the most interesting and challenging problems of inorganic chemistry is the description of the nature of the wide variety of chemical bonds found in these compounds. Often trends in frequencies in a series of closely related molecules reflect trends in the strengths of the chemical bonds. More and more chemists are subjecting their frequency data to normal coordinate analyses in order to obtain force constants which can be used to establish trends in the strengths of chemical bonds. The availability of Raman as well as infrared data will make this a more meaningful process. Still, it is necessary to examine these calculations critically before placing much faith in the precise values of the constants. When the molecule is large or the symmetry low, it usually is impossible to calculate anywhere near the number of force constants found in, e.g., a general valence force field. Although there is relatively little information available to the inorganic chemist to help him set up a simplified force field, there is enough to show that most of these give only a crude description of the molecular force field. Consequently, the absolute values of the force constants may have relatively little meaning, and the descriptions of the normal coordinates may be very imprecise even in some cases where very good frequency fits are obtained. Little is known about the transferability of force constants except with the simplest molecules, and this is particularly troublesome where redundancies exist.

Raman intensities are certain to be investigated more and more, not just for the determination of concentrations in solution, but also for the measurement of the molecular polarizability changes as the scatterer vibrates. With laser excitation and single crystals, it is possible to determine all of the elements of the derived polarizability tensor for an ion or molecule or, at least, for the unit cell. For these data to be of much use to the chemist he must be able to translate these changes in polarizability with the normal vibrational coordinates to changes in polarizability with variations of bond lengths and angles in the molecule. This requires a precise knowledge of the normal coordinates. A beginning has been made with certain simple structures, e.g., tetrahedral and octahedral complexes, where symmetry restrictions determine the nature of at least one normal mode (*569,323*). Vibrations involving a light atom, e.g., hydrogen, bound to a much heavier one, *M*, are also relatively easy to study because there will be a normal mode which involves essentially only *M–H* bond stretching (*570*). Even when the change in polarizability with bond stretching or angle bending is known, it is still difficult to relate this to the nature of the bonding (*571*).

Studies of solution equilibria should benefit much from the development of high energy sources like the CW Ar^+ and Kr^+ lasers. Much less concentrated solutions can be studied than was possible before. It should be possible to obtain Raman spectra for relatively dilute solutions, i.e., less than 0.1 molal, for which conventional thermodynamic data are available or can be determined. From these studies chemists should gain a much better understanding of the structure of solutions.

Finally, Raman spectroscopy is certain to be applied more and more to the study of reactions under unusual conditions. Fairly extensive studies already have been made of molten salts at moderate temperatures. The very small samples which can be used with laser excitation will make it much easier to study systems under extreme conditions of temperature, pressure, etc. Raman spectroscopy provides an ideal method for the study of the structure and reactions of species in solvents like liquid ammonia.

Laser Raman spectroscopy for the inorganic chemist is probably the most exciting new tool developed in the last decade. Future instrumental developments are certain to extend its usefulness greatly. It is to be hoped that this will be accompanied by comparable advances in our knowledge of the force fields for more complicated molecules and of the factors relating Raman intensities, the derived polarizability tensor components, and the electronic structure and chemical bonding in molecules.

Acknowledgments

The author would like to express his appreciation to Professor G. Wilkinson, F.R.S., of Imperial College for making the facilities of his laboratory available during the preparation of this review. This was written during the tenure of a National Science Foundation Senior Post Doctoral Fellowship, and thanks are due NSF for financial support. Thanks are also due Dr. Charles W. Hobbs for the spectra in Figs. 7 and 9. The author's research in the Raman spectra of inorganic compounds has been supported by the National Science Foundation, Grants GP-5022 and GP-7899 and by the Petroleum Research Fund administered by the American Chemical Society.

REFERENCES

1. R. E. Hester, *Coordin. Chem. Revs.*, **2,** 319 (1967).

2. I. R. Beattie, *Chem. Brit.*, **3,** 347 (1967).

3. R. S. Tobias, *J. Chem. Educ.*, **44,** 70 (1967).

4. R. E. Hester, *Anal. Chem.*, **40,** 320 (1968); *Ibid.*, **42R,** 231R (1970).

4a. P. J. Hendra and P. M. Stratton, *Chem. Rev.*, **69,** 325 (1969).

5. H. A. Szymanski, ed., *Raman Spectroscopy*, Plenum, New York, 1967.

6. H. Kriegsmann, in *Einführung in die Ramanspektroskopie*, J. Brandmüller and H. Moser, D. Steinkopff, Darmstadt, C–VI, 1962.

7. D. B. Powell, *Annual Reports* (London), **63,** 112 (1966).

8. D. A. Long, *Annual Reports* (London), **60,** 120 (1963).

9. L. A. Woodward, *Annual Reports* (London), **56,** 67 (1959).

10. L. A. Woodward, *Quart. Revs.* (London), **10,** 185 (1956).

10a. D. W. James and M. J. Nolan, *Prog. Inorg. Chem.*, **9,** 195 (1968).

11. T. F. Anderson, E. N. Lassettre, and D. M. Yost, *J. Chem. Phys.*, **4,** 703 (1936); D. M. Yost, D. DeVault, T. F. Anderson, and E. N. Lassettre, *J. Chem. Phys.*, **6,** 424 (1938).

12. H. Lévy and L. O. Brockway, *J. Am. Chem. Soc.*, **59,** 2085 (1937).

13. G. Kujumzelis, *Z. Phys.*, **109,** 586 (1938).

14. W. L. Bragg, *Proc. Royal Soc. (London) Ser. A*, **89,** 468 (1914).

15. L. A. Woodward, *Phil. Mag.*, **18,** 823 (1934).

16. A. Ogg, *Z. phys. Chem.*, **27,** 285 (1898).

17. R. J. Havighurst, *J. Am. Chem. Soc.*, **48,** 2113 (1926).

18. H. M. Gager, J. Lewis, and M. J. Ware, *Chem. Comm.*, 616 (1966).

19. E. B. Wilson, J. C. Decius, and P. C. Cross, *Molecular Vibrations*, McGraw Hill, New York, 1955.

20. J. H. Schachtschneider and R. G. Snyder, *Spectrochim. Acta*, **19,** 117 (1963) and E. Wu, Ph.D. thesis, Univ. of Minnesota, 1962.

21. D. M. Adams, *Metal-Ligand and Related Vibrations*, Arnold, London, 1967.

22. H. Siebert, *Anwendungen der Schwingungsspektroskopie in der Anorganischen Chemie*, Springer, Berlin-Heidelberg-New York, 1966.

23. K. Nakamoto, *Infrared Spectra of Inorganic and Coordination Compounds*, 2nd ed., Wiley, New York, 1970.
24. F. A. Cotton, *Modern Coordination Chemistry*, J. Lewis and R. G. Wilkins, eds., Wiley-Interscience, 1960, Chapter 5.
25. F. A. Cotton, *Chemical Applications of Group Theory*, Wiley-Interscience, New York, 1963.
26. I. Nakagawa and T. Shimanouchi, *Spectrochim. Acta*, **22,** 759 (1966).
27. J. Overend and J. R. Scherer, *J. Opt. Soc. Am.*, **50,** 1203 (1960).
28. J. M. Terrasse, H. Poulet, and J. P. Mathieu, *Spectrochim. Acta*, **20,** 305 (1965).
29. T. E. Haas and J. R. Hall, *Spectrochim. Acta*, **22,** 988 (1966).
30. R. J. H. Clark and C. S. Williams, *J. Chem. Soc. Sect. A*, 1425 (1966).
31. M. G. Miles, J. H. Patterson, C. W. Hobbs, M. J. Hopper, J. Overend, and R. S. Tobias, *Inorg. Chem.*, **7,** 1721 (1968).
32. C. W. Hobbs and R. S. Tobias, *Inorg. Chem.* **9,** 245 (1970).
33. G. R. Dobson, I. W. Stolz, and R. K. Sheline, *Adv. Inorg. Chem. Radiochem.*, **8,** 1 (1966).
34. D. H. Rank, G. Skorinko, D. P. Eastman, and T. A. Wiggins, *J. Mol. Spectrosc.*, **4,** 518 (1960).
34a. *Raman Newsletter*. P. R. Wakeling, ed., 1613 Nineteenth Street, N.W., Washington D.C. 20009.
35. D. D. Tunnicliff and A. C. Jones, *Spectrochim. Acta*, **18,** 569 (1962).
36. A. Lau and J. H. Hertz, *Spectrochim. Acta*, **22,** 1935 (1966).
37. G. F. Bailey, S. Kent, and J. R. Scherer, *Anal. Chem.*, **39,** 1040 (1967).
38. G. E. Walrafen, *J. Chem. Phys.*, **44,** 1546 (1966).
39. N. C. Craig and J. Overend, *Spectrochim. Acta*, **20,** 1561 (1964).
40. J. E. Griffiths, R. P. Carter, Jr., and R. R. Holmes, *J. Chem. Phys.*, **41,** 863 (1964).
41. J. R. Ferraro, J. S. Ziomek, and K. Puckett, *Rev. Sci. Instrum.*, **35,** 754 (1964).
42. J. A. Rolfe and L. A. Woodward, *Trans. Faraday Soc.*, **50,** 1030 (1954).
43. W. F. Edgell and C. E. May, *J. Chem. Phys.*, **22,** 1808 (1954).
43a. D. F. Shriver, B. Swanson, and N. Nelson, *Appl. Spectrosc.*, **23,** 274 (1969).
43b. F. A. Miller and B. M. Harney, *ibid.*, **24,** 291 (1970).
43c. B. Swanson and D. F. Shriver, *Inorg. Chem.*, **9,** 1406 (1970).
44. D. E. Irish and T. F. Young, *J. Chem. Phys.*, **43,** 1765 (1965).
45. G. J. Janz and D. W. James, *J. Chem. Phys.*, **35,** 739 (1961).
46. G. J. Janz, Y. Mikawa, and D. W. James, *Appl. Spectrosc.*, **15,** 47 (1961).
47. L. A. Woodward, G. Garton, and H. L. Roberts, *J. Chem. Soc.*, 3723 (1956).
48. G. E. Walrafen, *J. Chem. Phys.*, **43,** 479 (1965).
49. H. H. Selig, L. A. Quarterman, and H. H. Hyman, *J. Inorg. Nuclear Chem.*, **28,** 2063 (1966).
50. J. Shamir and H. H. Hyman, *J. Phys. Chem.*, **70,** 3132 (1966).
51. L. S. Areghi and M. V. Evans, *Appl. Spectrosc.*, **21,** 43 (1967).
52. M. Harrand, *J. chim. Phys.*, **64,** 989 (1967).
53. B. Schrader and G. Bergmann, *Z. analyt. Chem.*, **225,** 230 (1967).
54. A. Simon, H. Kriegsmann, and E. Steger, *Z. phys. Chem.* (Leipzig), **205,** 181 (1956).
55. A. Simon, H. Kriegsmann, and E. Steger, *Z. phys. Chem.* (Leipzig), **205,** 190 (1956).
56. A. Simon and H. Kriegsmann, *Z. phys. Chem.* (Leipzig), **204,** 369 (1955).
57. R. H. Busey and O. L. Keller, Jr., *J. Chem. Phys.*, **41,** 215 (1964).

58. M. V. Stein, A. Maschka, F. Wollrab, and W. Gnilsen, *Z. phys. Chem.*, **201,** 261 (1952).
59. J. R. Ferraro, J. S. Ziomek, and G. Mack, *Spectrochim. Acta*, **17,** 802 (1961).
60. B. Schrader, F. Nerdel, and G. Kresze, *Z. anal. Chem.*, **170,** 43 (1959).
61. R. C. Hawes, K. P. George, D. C. Nelson, and R. Beckwith, *Anal. Chem.*, **38,** 1842 (1966).
62. R. N. Jones, J. B. DiGiorgio, J. J. Elliott, and G. A. A. Nonnemacher, *J. Org. Chem.*, **30,** 1822 (1965).
63. R. D. Fisher and E. R. Lippincott, *Anal. Chem.*, **26,** 435 (1954).
64. J. R. Ferraro, *Spectrochim. Acta*, **20,** 901 (1964).
65. H. J. Bernstein and G. Allen, *J. Opt. Soc. Amer.*, **45,** 237 (1955).
66. D. A. Long, R. B. Gravenor, and D. C. Milner, *Trans. Faraday Soc.*, **59,** 46 (1963).
67. D. G. Rea, *J. Opt. Soc. Amer.*, **49,** 90 (1959).
68. D. G. Rea, *J. Mol. Spectrosc.*, **4,** 507 (1960).
69. G. Michel and R. Gueibe, *Bull. soc. chim. Belges*, **70,** 323 (1961).
70. P. R. Ryason, *J. Mol. Spectrosc.*, **8,** 164 (1962).
71. H. Schrotter and H. J. Bernstein, *J. Mol. Spectrosc.*, **12,** 1 (1964).
72. D. D. Tunnicliff and A. C. Jones, *Spectrochim. Acta*, **18,** 579 (1962).
73. G. W. Chantry and R. A. Plane, *J. Chem. Phys.*, **32,** 319 (1960).
74. F. J. C. Rossotti and H. Rossotti, *The Determination of Stability Constants*, McGraw Hill, New York, 1961.
75. J. T. Edsall and E. B. Wilson, Jr., *J. Chem. Phys.*, **6,** 124 (1938).
76. J. A. Koningstein and H. J. Bernstein, *Spectrochim. Acta*, **18,** 1249 (1962).
77. M. G. Miles, G. E. Glass, and R. S. Tobias, *J. Am. Chem. Soc.*, **88,** 5738 (1966).
78. R. S. Tobias, M. J. Sprague, and G. E. Glass, *Inorg. Chem.*, **7,** 1714 (1968).
79. H. Hyman, ed., *Noble Gas Compounds*, Univ. of Chicago Press, Chicago, Illinois, 1963.
80. D. F. Smith, *Noble Gas Compounds* (H. Hyman, ed.), Univ. of Chicago Press, Chicago, Illinois, 1963, p. 297.
81. D. F. Smith, *J. Chem. Phys.*, **38,** 270 (1963).
82. H. H. Claassen, G. L. Goodman, J. G. Malm, and F. Schreiner, *J. Chem. Phys.*, **42,** 1229 (1965).
83. H. H. Claassen, C. L. Chernick, and J. G. Malm, *J. Am. Chem. Soc.*, **85,** 1927 (1963).
84. E. L. Gasner and H. H. Claassen, *Inorg. Chem.*, **6,** 1937 (1967).
85. W. K. Glass, *Chem. Commun.*, 455 (1968).
86. L. S. Bartell, R. M. Gavin, Jr., H. B. Thompson, and C. L. Chernick, *J. Chem. Phys.*, **43,** 2547 (1965).
87. H. H. Hyman and L. A. Quarterman, in *Noble Gas Compounds*, H. Hyman, ed., Univ. of Chicago Press, Chicago, Illinois, 1963, p. 300.
88. D. F. Smith, in *Noble Gas Compounds*, H. Hyman, ed., Univ. of Chicago Press, Chicago, Illinois, 1963, p. 300.
89. C. L. Chernick, H. H. Claassen, J. G. Malm, and P. L. Plurien, in *Noble Gas Compounds* (H. Hyman, ed.), Univ. of Chicago Press, Chicago, Illinois, 1963, p. 106, H. H. Claassen, C. L. Chernick, and J. G. Malm, p. 287.
90. D. F. Smith, *Science*, **140,** 899 (1963).
91. H. H. Hyman, *Science*, **145,** 778 (1964).
92. G. M. Begun, W. H. Fletcher, and D. F. Smith, *J. Chem. Phys.*, **42,** 2236 (1965).

93. K. O. Christe, W. Sawodny, and J. P. Guertin, *Inorg. Chem.*, **6,** 1159 (1967).
94. J. C. Evans and G. Y.-S. Lo, *J. Chem. Phys.*, **44,** 3638 (1966).
95. J. C. Evans and G. Y.-S. Lo, *Inorg. Chem.*, **6,** 1483 (1967).
96. W. B. Person, G. R. Anderson, J. N. Fordemwalt, H. Stammreich, and R. Forneris, *J. Chem. Phys.*, **35,** 908 (1961).
97. A. G. Maki and R. Forneris, *Spectrochim. Acta*, **23A,** 867 (1967).
98. G. C. Hayward and P. J. Hendra, *Spectrochim. Acta*, **23A,** 2309 (1967).
99. K. O. Christe and W. Sawodny, *Inorg. Chem.*, **6,** 313 (1967).
100. D. F. Smith and G. M. Begun, *J. Chem. Phys.*, **43,** 2001 (1965).
101. H. Stammreich and Y. Karvano, *Spectrochim. Acta*, **24A,** 899 (1968).
102. K. O. Christe and W. Sawodny, *Inorg. Chem.*, **6,** 1783 (1967).
103. K. O. Christe, J. P. Guertin, and W. Sawodny, *Inorg. Chem.*, **7,** 626 (1968).
104. J. Shamir, J. Binenboym, and H. H. Claassen, *J. Am. Chem. Soc.*, **90,** 6223 (1968).
105. W. H. Smith and G. E. Leroi, *J. Chem. Phys.*, **45,** 1767 (1966).
106. W. H. Smith and G. E. Leroi, *J. Chem. Phys.*, **45,** 1778 (1966).
107. E. L. Pace and H. V. Samuelson, *J. Chem. Phys.*, **44,** 3682 (1966).
108. D. A. Long and R. T. Bailey, *Trans. Faraday Soc.*, **59,** 594 (1963).
109. T. Birchall and R. J. Gillespie, *Spectrochim. Acta*, **22,** 681 (1966).
110. R. Paetzold and K. W. Ziegenbalg, *Z. Chem.*, **4,** 461 (1964).
111. F. A. Miller, G. L. Carlson, and W. B. White, *Spectrochim. Acta*, **15,** 709 (1959).
112. R. J. Gillespie and E. A. Robinson, *Spectrochim. Acta*, **18,** 1473 (1962).
113. J. E. Griffiths, *Spectrochim Acta*, **23A,** 2145 (1967).
114. S. Abramowitz and I. W. Lewin, *J. Chem. Phys.*, **44,** 3353 (1966).
115. L. A. Nimon, V. D. Neff, R. E. Cantley, and R. O. Buttlar, *J. Mol. Spectrosc.*, **22,** 105 (1967).
116. J. Berkowitz, W. A. Chupka, E. Bromels, and R. L. Belford, *J. Chem. Phys.*, **47,** 4320 (1967).
117. P. J. Hendra and P. J. D. Park, *J. Chem. Soc., Sect. A*, 908 (1968).
118. P. J. Hendra and Z. Jovic, *J. Chem. Soc., Sect. A*, 735 (1967).
119. I. W. Lewin and C. V. Berney, *J. Chem. Phys.*, **44,** 2557 (1966).
120. G. C. Hayward and P. J. Hendra, *J. Chem. Soc., Sect. A*, 643 (1967).
121. P. J. Hendra and Z. Jovic, *J. Chem. Soc., Sect. A*, 600 (1968).
122. J. A. Creighton and J. H. S. Green, *J. Chem. Soc., Sect. A*, 808 (1968).
123. H. Gerding and H. Houtgraaf, *Rec. Trav. Chim. Pays-Bas*, **73,** 737 (1954).
124. R. E. Dodd, L. A. Woodward, and H. L. Roberts, *Trans. Faraday Soc.*, **52,** 1052, (1956).
125. J. R. Allkins and P. J. Hendra, *Spectrochim. Acta*, **22,** 2075 (1966); **23A,** 1671, (1967).
126. K. G. Alleim, J. A. Creighton, J. H. S. Green, G. J. Menhoff, and L. J. S. Prince, *Spectrochim. Acta*, **24A,** 927 (1968).
127. S.-T. King and J. Overend, *Spectrochim. Acta*, **22,** 689 (1966).
128. J. Shamir and H. H. Hyman, *Spectrochim. Acta*, **23A,** 1191 (1967).
129. S.-T. King and J. Overend, *Spectrochim. Acta*, **23A,** 61 (1967).
130. J. R. Durig and J. W. Clark, *J. Chem. Phys.*, **48,** 3216 (1968).
131. C. W. Bjork, N. C. Craig, R. A. Mitsch, and J. Overend, *J. Am. Chem. Soc.*, **87,** 1186 (1965).
132. J. R. Durig, S. F. Bush, and E. E. Mercer, *J. Chem. Phys.*, **44,** 4238 (1966).
133. J. W. Nebgen, A. D. McElroy, and H. F. Klodowski, *Inorg. Chem.*, **4,** 1796 (1965).

134. J. C. Evans, H. W. Rinn, S. J. Kuhn, and G. A. Olah, *Inorg. Chem.*, **3,** 857 (1964).
135. R. E. Noftle and G. H. Cady, *Inorg. Chem.*, **5,** 2182 (1966).
136. J. Shamir and H. H. Hyman, *Spectrochim. Acta*, **23A,** 1899 (1967).
137. E. L. Pace and L. Pierce, *J. Chem. Phys.*, **23,** 1248 (1955).
138. P. J. Hendra and J. R. MacKenzie, *Chem. Commun.*, 760 (1968).
139. K. O. Christe, J. P. Guertin, A. E. Pavlath, and W. Sawodny, *Inorg. Chem.*, **6,** 533 (1967).
140. W. Sawodny and K. Dehnicke, *Z. anorg. Chem.*, **349,** 169 (1967).
141. P. Reich and H. Preiss, *Z. Chem.*, **7,** 115 (1967).
142. J. Weidlein and K. Dehnicke, *Z. anorg. allgem. Chem.*, **337,** 113 (1965).
143. K. Dehnicke and J. Weidlein, *Ber.*, **98,** 1087 (1965).
144. G. L. Carlson, *Spectrochim. Acta*, **19,** 1291 (1963).
145. H. Gerding and H. Houtgraff, *Rec. Trav. Chim. Pays-Bas*, **74,** 5 (1955).
146. J. K. Wilmshurst and H. J. Bernstein, *J. Chem. Phys.*, **27,** 661 (1957).
147. M. J. Taylor and L. A. Woodward, *J. Chem. Soc.*, 4670 (1963).
148. I. R. Beattie, K. Livingstone, and M. Webster, *J. Chem. Soc.*, 7421 (1965).
149. I. R. Beattie, T. Gibson, K. Livingstone, V. Fawcett, and G. A. Ozin, *J. Chem. Soc., Sect. A*, 712 (1967).
150. J. E. D. Davies and D. A. Long, *J. Chem. Soc., Sect. A*, 1761 (1968).
151. J. Goubeau and R. Baumgärtner, *Z. Elektrochem.*, **64,** 598 (1960).
152. R. Baumgärtner, W. Sawodny, and J. Goubeau, *Z. anorg. allgem. Chem.*, **333,** 171 (1964).
153. R. E. Hester and C. W. J. Scaife, *Spectrochim. Acta*, **22,** 455 (1966).
154. E. Steger and G. Mildner, *Z. Naturforsch.*, **16,** 836 (1961).
155. R. Stahlberg and E. Steger, *Spectrochim.Acta*, **23A,** 2005, 2057, 2185 (1967).
156. E. Steger and R. Stahlberg, *Z. Naturforsch.*, **17b,** 780 (1962).
157. E. Steger and R. Stahlberg, *Z. anorg. allgem. Chem.*, **326,** 243 (1964).
158. S. G. Frankiss and F. A. Miller, *Spectrochim. Acta*, **21,** 1235 (1965).
159. S. G. Frankiss, F. A. Miller, H. Stammreich, and T. Teixeira Sans, *Spectrochim. Acta*, **23A,** 543 (1967).
160. E. Steger and K. Stopperka, *Ber.*, **94,** 3029 (1961).
161. G. Goubeau, H. Reinhardt, and D. Bianchi, *Z. phys. Chem.* (Frankfurt am Main), **12,** 387 (1957).
162. P. J. Christen, L. M. van der Linde, and F. N. Hóoge, *Rec. Trav. Chim. Pays-Bas*, **78.** 161 (1959).
163. P. J. D. Park, G. Chambers, E. Wyn-Jones, and P. J. Hendra, *J. Chem. Soc., Sect. A*, 646 (1967).
164. A. H. Cowley and W. D. White, *Spectrochim. Acta*, **22,** 1431 (1966).
165. D. W. Meek and P. Nicpon, *J. Am. Chem. Soc.*, **87,** 4951 (1965).
166. J. E. Griffiths, R. P. Carter, Jr., and R. R. Holmes, *J. Chem. Phys.*, **41,** 863 (1964).
167. R. R. Holmes, *J. Chem. Phys.*, **46,** 3718 (1967).
168. J. E. Griffiths, *J. Chem. Phys.*, **41,** 3510 (1964).
169. J. E. Griffiths and A. L. Beach, *J. Chem. Phys.*, **44,** 2686 (1966).
170. A. F. Downs and R. Schmutzler, *Spectrochim. Acta*, **21,** 1927 (1965).
171. A. F. Downs and R. Schmutzler, *Spectrochim. Acta*, **23A,** 681 (1967).
172. I. R. Beattie, K. Livingstone, and T. Gilson, *J. Chem. Soc., Sect. A*, 1 (1968).
173. J. R. Nielsen and J. D. Walker, *Spectrochim. Acta*, **21,** 1163 (1965).
174. G. Bouquet and M. Bigorgne, *Spectrochim. Acta*, **23A,** 1231 (1967).

175. G. B. Deacon and J. H. S. Green, *Spectrochim. Acta*, **24A,** 845 (1968).
176. J. H. S. Green, W. Kynaston, and G. A. Rodley, *Spectrochim. Acta*, **24A,** 853 (1968).
177. J. E. Griffiths, *Spectrochim. Acta*, **21,** 1135 (1965).
178. F. A. Miller, S. G. Frankiss, and O. Sala, *Spectrochim. Acta*, **21,** 775 (1965).
179. J. Goubeau, H. Haeberle, and H. Ulmer, *Z. anorg. allgem. Chem.*, **311,** 110 (1961).
180. R. E. Hester and K. Jones, *Chem. Commun.*, 317 (1966).
181. G. Engelhardt, P. Reich, and H. Schumann, *Z. Naturforsch.*, **22b,** 352 (1967).
182. M. J. Buttler, D. C. McKean, R. Taylor, and L. A. Woodward, *Spectrochim. Acta*, **21,** 1379 (1965).
183. I. R. Beattie, *Quart. Rev.* (London), **17,** 382 (1963).
184. H. A. Brune and W. Zeil, *Z. physik. Chem.* (Frankfurt am Main), **32,** 384 (1962) and references therein.
185. I. R. Beattie and L. Rule, *J. Chem. Soc.*, 2995 (1965).
186. I. R. Beattie, R. Hulme, and L. Rule, *J. Chem. Soc.*, 1581 (1965).
187. J. C. Lockhart, *J. Chem. Soc., Sect. A*, 1552 (1966).
188. J. H. Carpenter, W. J. Jones, R. W. Jothan, and L. H. Long, *Chem. Commun.*, 881 (1968).
189. E. W. Wartenberg and J. Goubeau, *Z. anorg. allgem. Chem.*, **329,** 269 (1964).
190. W. Sawodny and J. Goubeau, *Z. physik. Chem.* (Frankfurt am Main), **44,** 227 (1965).
191. R. L. Amster and R. C. Taylor, *Spectrochim. Acta*, **20,** 1487 (1964).
192. I. R. Beattie, T. Gilson, and P. Cocking, *J. Chem. Soc., Sect. A*, 702 (1967).
193. A. Balls, A. J. Downs, N. N. Greenwood, and B. P. Straughan, *Trans. Faraday Soc.*, **62,** 521 (1966).
194. D. F. Shriver, R. L. Amster, and R. C. Taylor, *J. Am. Chem. Soc.*, **84,** 1321 (1962).
195. I. R. Beattie, T. Gilson, and G. A. Ozin, *J. Chem. Soc., Sect. A*, 813 (1968).
196. I. R. Beattie, T. Gilson, and G. A. Ozin, *J. Chem. Soc., Sect. A*, 1092 (1968).
197. D. M. Adams and R. G. Churchill, *J. Chem. Soc., Sect. A*, 2141 (1968).
198. H. Siebert, *Z. anorg. allgem. Chem.*, **275,** 225 (1954).
199. C. C. Addison, D. W. Amos, D. Sutton, and W. H. H. Hoyle, *J. Chem. Soc., Sect. A*, 808 (1967).
200. H. Brintzinger and R. E. Hester, *Inorg. Chem.*, **5,** 980 (1966).
201. R. E. Hester and W. E. L. Grossman, *Inorg. Chem.*, **5,** 1308 (1966).
202. J. Weidlein, U. Muller, and K. Dehnicke, *Spectrochim. Acta*, **24A,** 253 (1968).
203. R. Fonteyne, *Natuurw. Tijdschr. (Belg.)*, **20,** 20 (1938).
204. H. H. Claassen and A. J. Zielen, *J. Chem. Phys.*, **22,** 707 (1954).
205. W. P. Griffith and T. D. Wickins, *J. Chem. Soc., Sect. A*, 1087 (1967).
206. H. Stammreich, D. Bassi, and O. Sala, *Spectrochim. Acta*, **12,** 403 (1958).
207. R. H. Busey and O. L. Keller, *J. Chem. Phys.*, **41,** 215 (1964).
208. L. A. Woodward and H. L. Roberts, *Trans. Faraday Soc.*, **52,** 615 (1956).
209. W. P. Griffith, *J. Chem. Soc., Sect. A*, 1467 (1966).
210. P. J. Hendra, *Spectrochim. Acta*, **24A,** 125 (1968).
211. W. P. Griffith, *J. Chem. Soc., Sect. A*, 1663 (1968).
212. K. Ulbricht and H. Kriegsmann, *Z. Chem.*, **6,** 232 (1966).
213. N. Ingri and F. Brito, *Acta Chem. Scand.*, **13,** 1971 (1959).
214. F. Brito, N. Ingri, and L. G. Sillén, *Acta Chem. Scand.*, **18,** 1557 (1964).
215. H. P. Stock, *Z. Naturforschung*, **20b,** 933 (1965).

216. H. Stammreich, D. Bassi, O. Sala, and H. Siebert, *Spectrochim. Acta*, **13,** 192 (1968).
217. Luu Dang Vinh, J. Reynaud, and R. Lafont, *C. R. Acad. Sci. Paris*, *Ser. A, B*, **263B,** 192 (1966).
218. K. Ulbricht, R. Radeglia, and H. Kriegsmann, *Z. anorg. allgem. Chem.*, **356,** 22 (1967).
219. I. Lindqvist, Symposium on the Structure and Properties of Heteropoly Anions, 130th National Meeting, A.C.S., Atlantic City, N.J., Sept. 1956, p. 20.
220. J. Aveston, E. W. Anacker, and J. S. Johnson, *Inorg. Chem.*, **3,** 735 (1964).
221. J. Aveston, *Inorg. Chem.*, **3,** 981 (1964).
222. J. Aveston and J. S. Johnson, *Inorg. Chem.*, **3,** 1051 (1964).
223. R. S. Tobias, *Can. J. Chem.*, **43,** 1222 (1965).
224. G. E. Walrafen, *J. Chem. Phys.*, **42,** 485 (1965).
225. E. Steger and K. Herzog, *Z. anorg. allgem. Chem.*, **331,** 169 (1964).
226. E. Steger and C. Fischer-Bartelk, *Z. anorg. allgem. Chem.*, **338,** 15 (1965).
227. A. Simon and E. Steger, *Z. anorg. allgem. Chem.*, **277,** 209 (1954).
228. E. Steger, *Z. anorg. allgem. Chem.*, **296,** 305 (1958).
229. E. Steger and A. Simon, *Z. anorg. allgem. Chem.*, **291,** 76 (1957).
230. E. Steger and A. Simon, *Z. anorg. allgem. Chem.*, **294,** 1 (1958).
231. W. P. Griffith, *J. Chem. Soc.*, *Sect. A*, 905 (1967).
232. J. E. Rauch and J. C. Decius, *Spectrochim. Acta*, **22,** 1963 (1966).
233. M. H. Brooker and D. E. Irish, *Can. J. Chem.*, **46,** 229 (1968).
234. M. H. Brooker and D. E. Irish, *Inorg. Chem.*, **8,** 219 (1969).
235. R. J. Gillespie and E. A. Robinson, *Can. J. Chem.*, **39,** 2189 (1961).
236. R. J. Gillespie and E. A. Robinson, *Can. J. Chem.*, **40,** 644 (1962).
237. E. A. Robinson, *Can. J. Chem.*, **39,** 247 (1961).
238. R. J. Gillespie and E. A. Robinson, *Can. J. Chem.*, **40,** 658 (1962).
239. R. J. Gillespie and E. A. Robinson, *Can. J. Chem.*, **40,** 675 (1962).
240. R. J. Capwell, K. H. Ree, and K. S. Seshadri, *Spectrochim. Acta*, **24A,** 955 (1968).
241. M. G. Miles, G. Doyle, R. P. Cooney, and R. S. Tobias, *Spectrochim. Acta*, **25A,** 1515 (1969).
242. G. E. Walrafen, *J. Chem. Phys.*, **39,** 1479 (1963).
243. R. Paetzold, *Spectrochim. Acta*, **24A,** 717 (1968).
244. D. J. Millin and E. G. Vaal, *J. Chem. Soc.*, 2913 (1956).
245. J. T. Mullhaupt and D. F. Hornig, *J. Chem. Phys.*, **24,** 169 (1956).
246. R. C. Taylor and G. L. Vidale, *J. Am. Chem. Soc.*, **78,** 5999 (1956).
247. A. J. Dahl, J. C. Trowbridge, and R. C. Taylor, *Inorg. Chem.*, **2,** 654 (1963).
248. J. P. Mathieu, *J. Inorg. Nuclear Chem.*, **8,** 33 (1958).
249. D. E. Irish, in *Raman Spectroscopy* (H. A. Szymanski, ed.), Plenum, New York, 1967, chapter 7.
250. R. J. H. Clark, *Halogen Chem.*, **3,** 85 (1967).
251. L. A. Woodward, *Trans. Faraday Soc.*, **54,** 1271 (1958).
252. L. A. Woodward and M. J. Taylor, *J. Chem. Soc.*, 4473 (1960).
253. R. E. Mesmer and C. F. Baes, Jr., *Inorg. Chem.*, **8,** 618 (1969).
254. H. G. M. Edwards, M. J. Ware, and L. A. Woodward, *Chem. Commun.*, 540 (1968).
255. C. O. Quicksall and T. G. Spiro, *Inorg. Chem.*, **5,** 2232 (1966).
256. D. F. C. Morris, E. L. Short and D. N. Watters, *J. Inorg. Nuclear Chem.*, **25,** 975 (1963).
257. M. L. Delwaulle, *C. R. Acad. Sci. Paris*, **240,** 2132 (1955).

258. M. L. Delwaulle, *Bull. Soc. Chim. France.* 1294 (1955).
259. Z. Kecki and J. Mankowski, *Roczniki Chem.*, **36,** 345 (1962).
260. Z. Kecki, *Spectrochim. Acta*, **18,** 1165 (1962).
261. R. B. Ellis, *J. Electrochem. Soc.*, **113,** 485 (1966).
262. J. R. Moyer, J. C. Evans, and G. Y.-S. Lo, *J. Electrochem. Soc.*, **113,** 158 (1966).
263. B. Gilbert, *Bull. Soc. Chim. Belges*, **76,** 493 (1967).
264. J. A. Rolfe, D. E. Sheppard, and L. A. Woodward, *Trans. Faraday Soc.*, **50,** 1275 (1954).
265. E. L. Short, D. N. Watters, and D. F. C. Morris, *J. Inorg. Nucl. Chem.*, **25,** 902 (1964).
266. G. B. Deacon, J. H. S. Green, and W. Kynaston, *Aust. J. Chem.*, **19,** 1603 (1966).
267. G. J. Janz and D. W. James, *J. Chem. Phys.*, **38,** 905 (1963).
268. W. Yellin and R. A. Plane, *J. Am. Chem. Soc.*, **83,** 2448 (1961).
269. H. Gerding and H. Houtgraaf, *Rec. Trav. Chim. Pays-Bas*, **72,** 21 (1953).
270. K. Balasubrahmanyam and L. Nanis, *J. Chem. Phys.*, **42,** 676 (1965).
271. L. A. Woodward and A. A. Nord, *J. Chem. Soc.*, 3721 (1956).
272. L. A. Woodward, G. Garton, and H. L. Roberts, *J. Chem. Soc.*, 3723 (1956).
273. T. G. Spiro, *Inorg. Chem.*, **4,** 731, 1290 (1965).
274. T. G. Spiro, *Inorg. Chem.*, **6,** 569 (1967).
275. D. M. Adams and D. M. Morris, *J. Chem. Soc., Sect. A*, 694 (1968).
276. L. A. Woodward and A. A. Nord, *J. Chem. Soc.*, 2655 (1955).
277. J. Nixon and R. A. Plane, *J. Am. Chem. Soc.*, **84,** 4445 (1962).
278. L. A. Woodward and P. T. Bill, *J. Chem. Soc.*, 1699 (1955).
279. L. A. Woodward and G. H. Singer, *J. Chem. Soc.*, 716 (1958).
280. D. E. Irish, B. McCarroll, and T. F. Young, *J. Chem. Phys.*, **39,** 3436 (1963).
281. H. Siebert, *Z. anorg. allgem. Chem.*, **274,** 34 (1953).
282. W. Bues, *Z. anorg. allgem. Chem.*, **279,** 104 (1955).
283. M. A. Bredig and E. R. Van Artsdalen, *J. Chem. Phys.*, **24,** 478 (1956).
284. L. G. Sillén and A. E. Martell, *Stability Constants of Metal Ion Complexes*, Special Publication No. 17, The Chemical Society, London, 1964.
285. D. Forster and W. DeW. Horrocks, Jr., *Inorg. Chem.*, **6,** 339 (1967).
286. D. Forster and W. DeW. Horrocks, Jr., *Inorg. Chem.*, **5,** 1510 (1966).
287. J. Muller and K. Dehnicke, *J. Organometallic Chem.*, **12,** 36 (1968).
288. K. Dehnicke and D. Seybold, *J. Organometallic Chem.*, **11,** 226 (1968).
289. H. Stammreich and R. Forneris, *Spectrochim. Acta*, **16,** 363 (1960).
290. P. J. Hendra, *Nature*, **212,** 179 (1966).
291. P. J. Hendra, *Spectrochim. Acta*, **23A,** 2871 (1967).
292. P. J. Hendra, *J. Chem. Soc. Sect. A*, 1298 (1967).
293. J. Hiraishi and T. Shimanouchi, *Spectrochim. Acta*, **22,** 1483 (1966).
294. W. P. Griffith and T. D. Wickins, *J. Chem. Soc., Sect. A*, 675 (1967).
295. P. A. W. Dean and D. F. Evans, *J. Chem. Soc., Sect. A*, 698 (1967).
296. O. L. Keller, Jr., *Inorg. Chem.*, **2,** 783 (1963).
297. O. L. Keller, Jr. and A. Cheltham-Strode, Jr., *Inorg. Chem.*, **5,** 367 (1966).
298. L. A. Woodward and M. J. Ware, *Spectrochim. Acta*, **19,** 775 (1963).
299. R. B. Badachhape, G. Hunter, L. D. McCory, and J. L. Margrave, *Inorg. Chem.* **5,** 929 (1966).
300. J. E. Griffiths and D. E. Irish, *Inorg. Chem.*, **3,** 1134 (1964).
301. H. Kriegsmann and G. Kessler, *Z. anorg. allgem. Chem.*, **318,** 277 (1962).

302. H. Kriegsmann and G. Kessler, *Naturwissenschaften*, **47**, 393 (1960).
303. L. A. Woodward and M. J. Ware, *Spectrochim. Acta*, **24A**, 921 (1968).
304. D. M. Adams and D. C. Newton, *J. Chem. Soc., Sect. A*, 2262 (1968).
305. L. A. Woodward and M. J. Ware, *Spectrochim. Acta*, **20**, 711 (1964).
306. P. J. Hendra and P. J. D. Park, *Spectrochim. Acta*, **23A**, 1635 (1967).
307. L. A. Woodward and J. A. Creighton, *Spectrochim. Acta*, **17**, 594 (1961).
308. T. Barrowcliffe, I. R. Beattie, P. Day, and K. Livingstone, *J. Chem. Soc., Sect. A*, 1810 (1967).
309. L. A. Woodward and L. E. Anderson, *J. Chem. Soc.*, 1284 (1957).
310. J. A. Creighton and L. A. Woodward, *Trans. Faraday Soc.*, **58**, 1077 (1962).
311. R. P. Oertel and R. A. Plane, *Inorg. Chem.*, **6**, 1960 (1967).
312. J. H. R. Clarke and L. A. Woodward, *Trans. Faraday Soc.*, **61**, 207 (1965).
313. J. A. Creighton and E. R. Lippincott, *J. Chem. Soc.*, 5134 (1963).
314. R. P. J. Cooney, J. R. Hall, and M. A. Hooper, *Aust. J. Chem.*, **21**, 2145 (1968).
314a. A. J. Melveger, R. K. Khanna, B. R. Guscott, and E. R. Lippincott, *Inorg. Chem.*, **7**, 1630 (1968).
315. L. A. Woodward and M. J. Taylor, *J. Chem. Soc.*, 407 (1962).
316. H. A. Szymanski, R. Yelin and L. Marabella, *J. Chem. Phys.*, **47**, 1877 (1967).
317. I. Wharf and D. F. Shriver, *Chem. Commun.*, 526 (1968).
317a. S. R. Leone, B. Swanson, and D. F. Shriver, *Inorg. Chem.* **9**, 2189 (1970).
318. K. O. Hartman and F. A. Miller, *Spectrochim. Acta*, **24A**, 669 (1968).
319. G. Joos and I. Damaschun, *Physik. Z.*, **32**, 553 (1931); I. Damaschun, *Z. physik. Chem.*, **B16**, 81 (1932); I. Damaschun-Hansen. *Z. physik. Chem.*, **B22**, 97 (1933).
320. H. Poulet, P. Delorme, and J. P. Mathieu, *Spectrochim. Acta*, **20**, 1855 (1964).
321. W. P. Griffith, *J. Chem. Soc.*, 899 (1966).
322. R. Coomber and W. P. Griffith, *J. Chem. Soc., Sect. A*, 1128 (1968).
323. R. A. Plane, Proc. 8th International Conference on Coordination Chemistry, Springer, Vienna, 1964, p. 17.
324. D. E. Clegg and J. R. Hall, *Spectrochim. Acta*, **23A**, 263 (1967).
325. P. J. Hendra, *Spectrochim. Acta*, **23A**, 1275 (1967).
326. R. E. Hester and R. A. Plane, *Inorg. Chem.*, **3**, 513 (1964).
327. M. M. McGrady and R. S. Tobias, *J. Am. Chem. Soc.*, **87**, 1909 (1965).
328. W. O. George and F. V. Robinson, *J. Chem. Soc., Sect A*, 1950 (1968).
329. G. T. Behnke and K. Nakamoto, *Inorg. Chem.*, **6**, 433 (1967).
330. K. Nakamoto and A. E. Martell, *J. Chem. Phys.*, **32**, 588 (1960).
331. K. Nakamoto, P. J. McCarthy, A. Ruby, and A. E. Martell, *J. Am. Chem. Soc.*, **83**, 1066, 1272 (1961).
332. N. A. Matwiyoff and W. G. Movius, *J. Am. Chem. Soc.*, **89**, 6077 (1967).
333. R. C. Fay and T. J. Pinnavaia, *Inorg. Chem.*, **7**, 508 (1968).
334. D. K. Huggins and H. D. Kaesz, *Prog. Solid State Chem.*, **1**, 417 (1964).
335. J. W. Cable and R. K. Sheline, *Chem. Rev.*, **56**, 1 (1956).
336. M. F. O'Dwyer, *J. Mol. Spectrosc.*, **2**, 144 (1958).
337. F. T. King and E. R. Lippincott, *J. Am. Chem. Soc.*, **78**, 4192 (1956).
338. W. G. Fateley and E. R. Lippincott, *Spectrochim. Acta*, **10**, 8 (1957).
339. H. Murata and K. Kawai, *J. Chem. Phys.*, **28**, 516 (1958).
340. H. Stammreich, O. Sala, and Y. Tavares, *J. Chem. Phys.*, **30**, 856 (1959).
341. C. W. F. T. Pistorius and P. C. Haarhoff, *J. Chem. Phys.*, **31**, 1439 (1959).
342. W. F. Edgell, W. E. Wilson, and R. Summitt, *Spectrochim. Acta*, **19**, 863 (1963).

343. L. H. Jones and R. S. McDowell, *Spectrochim. Acta*, **20**, 248 (1964).
344. A. Dadieu and F. A. Schneider, *Anzeiger der Acad. der Wiss. in Wien, Math. Naturwiss. Klasse*, **68**, 191 (1931).
345. J. S. Anderson, *Nature*, **130**, 1002 (1932).
346. A. B. F. Duncan and J. W. Murray, *J. Chem. Phys.*, **2**, 636 (1934).
347. B. L. Crawford and W. Horowitz, *J. Chem. Phys.*, **16**, 147 (1948).
348. M. Bigorgne, *C. R. Acad. Sci., Paris*, **251**, 355 (1960).
349. H. Stammreich, K. Kawai, O. Sala, and P. Krumholz, *J. Chem. Phys.*, **35**, 2168 (1961).
350. M. Bigorgne and A. Chelkowski, *C. R. Acad. Sci., Paris*, **251**, 538 (1960).
351. G. Bouquet and M. Bigorgne, *C. R. Acad. Sci., Paris*, **261**, 2865 (1965).
352. L. H. Jones, R. S. McDowell, and M. Goldblatt, *J. Chem. Phys.*, **48**, 2663 (1968).
353. A. Danti and F. A. Cotton, *J. Chem. Phys.*, **28**, 736 (1958).
354. R. L. Amster, R. B. Hannan, and M. C. Tobin, *Spectrochim. Acta*, **19**, 1489 (1963).
355. J. M. Smith and L. H. Jones, *J. Mol. Spectrosc.*, **20**, 248 (1966).
356. E. W. Abel, R. A. N. McLean, M. G. Norton, and S. P. Tyfield, *Chem. Commun.*, 900 (1968).
357. H. Stammreich, K. Kawai, Y. Tavares, P. Krumholz, J. Behmoiras, and S. Bril, *J. Chem. Phys.*, **32**, 1482 (1960).
358. L. H. Jones, *Inorg. Chem.*, **6**, 1269 (1967).
359. L. H. Jones, *J. Chem. Phys.*, **47**, 1196 (1967).
360. L. H. Jones, *J. Mol. Spectrosc.*, **5**, 133 (1960).
361. L. H. Jones, *J. Mol. Spectrosc.*, **8**, 105 (1962).
362. C. O. Quicksall and T. G. Spiro, *Chem. Commun.*, 839 (1967).
363. F. A. Cotton and R. M. Wing, *Inorg. Chem.*, **4**, 1328 (1965).
364. C. O. Quicksall and T. G. Spiro, *Inorg. Chem.*, **7**, 2365 (1968).
365. F. A. Cotton and C. S. Kraihanzel, *J. Am. Chem. Soc.*, **84**, 4432 (1962).
366. F. A. Cotton and C. S. Kraihanzel, *Inorg. Chem.*, **2**, 533 (1963).
367. F. A. Cotton, *Inorg. Chem.*, **3**, 702 (1964).
368. F. A. Cotton, A. Musco, and G. Yagupsky, *Inorg. Chem.*, **6**, 1357 (1967).
369. L. H. Jones, *Inorg. Chem.*, **6**, 1269 (1967).
370. W. F. Edgell and M. P. Dunkle, *Inorg. Chem.*, **4**, 1629 (1965).
371. R. Poilblanc and M. Bigorgne, *J. Organometal. Chem.*, **5**, 93 (1966).
372. P. J. Hendra and M. M. Qurashi, *J. Chem. Soc., Sect. A*, 2963 (1968).
373. G. Bouquet and M. Bigorgne, *Bull. Soc. Chim. Fr.*, 433 (1962).
374. A. Loutellier and M. Bigorgne, *Bull. Soc. Chim. Fr.*, 3186 (1965).
375. M. Bigorgne and A. Zelwer, *Bull. Soc. Chim. Fr.*, 1986 (1960).
376. M. Bigorgne and A. Bouquet, *J. Organometal Chem.*, **1**, 101 (1963).
377. J. M. Smith, W. Fellmann, and L. H. Jones, *Inorg. Chem.*, **4**, 1361 (1965).
378. A. Davison and J. W. Faller, *Inorg. Chem.*, **6**, 845 (1967).
379. H. D. Kaesz, R. Bau, D. Hendrickson, and J. M. Smith, *J. Am. Chem. Soc.*, **89**, 2844 (1967).
380. H. Stammreich, K. Kawai, O. Sala, and P. Krumholz, *J. Chem. Phys.*, **35**, 2175 (1961).
381. W. P. Griffith, *Quart. Rev.* (London), **16**, 196 (1962).
382. B. M. Chadwick and A. G. Sharp, *Adv. Inorg. Chem. Radiochem.*, **8**, 841 (1966).
383. M. F. Lappert and H. Pyszora, *Adv. Inorg. Chem. Radiochem.*, **9**, 133 (1966).
384. L. H. Jones, *Inorg. Chem.*, **2**, 777 (1963).

385. L. H. Jones, *Coord. Chem. Rev.*, **1,** 351 (1966).
386. L. H. Jones, *Spectrochim. Acta*, **19,** 1675 (1963).
387. H. Poulet and J. P. Mathieu, *C. R. Acad. Sci. Paris*, **248,** 2079 (1959).
388. M. J. Reisfeld and L. H. Jones, *J. Mol. Spectrosc.*, **18,** 222 (1965).
389. R. A. Penneman and L. H. Jones, *J. Chem. Phys.*, **24,** 293 (1956).
390. L. H. Jones, *J. Chem. Phys.*, **43,** 594 (1965).
391. J. M. Smith and L. H. Jones, *J. Chem. Phys.*, **44,** 3643 (1966).
392. J. P. Mathieu and H. Poulet, *C. R. Acad. Sci., Paris*, **248,** 2315 (1959).
393. G. W. Chantry and R. A. Plane, *J. Chem. Phys.*, **35,** 1027 (1961).
394. C. B. Bonino and O. Salvetti, *Atti. Accad. Nazl. Lincei, Rend., Cl. Sci. Fis. Mat. Nat.*, **20,** 150 (1956); *Chem. Abstr.*, **50,** 14364i (1956).
395. P. Chiorboli and F. Cappellina, *Ann. Chim.* (Rome), **46,** 875 (1956).
396. J. P. Mathieu and S. Cornevin, *J. Chim. Phys.*, **36,** 271 (1939); J. P. Mathieu, *J. Chim. Phys.*, **36,** 308 (1939).
397. D. Jones, I. J. Hyams, and E. R. Lippincott, *Spectrochim. Acta*, **24A,** 973 (1968).
398. J. Deveze and M. Krauzman, *C. R. Acad. Sci., Paris, Ser. A, B*, **263B,** 864 (1966).
399. J. P. Mathieu and H. Poulet, *Spectrochim. Acta*, **19,** 1966 (1963).
400. L. H. Jones, *J. Chem. Phys.*, **41,** 856 (1964).
401. L. H. Jones and J. M. Smith, *J. Chem. Phys.*, **41,** 2507 (1964).
402. G. W. Chantry and R. A. Plane, *J. Chem. Phys.*, **33,** 736 (1960).
403. P. Chiorboli, *J. Inorg. Nucl. Chem.*, **8,** 133 (1958).
404. P. Chiorboli and C. Testa, *Ann. Chim. (Rome)*, **47,** 639 (1957).
405. H. Poulet and J. P. Mathieu, *Spectrochim. Acta*, **15,** 932 (1959).
406. W. P. Griffith, *J. Chem. Soc.*, 4070 (1964).
407. P. Chiorboli and E. Tedeschi, *Atti. Accad. Nazl. Lincei, Rend., Cl. Sci. Fis. Mat. Nat.*, **22,** 44 (1957); *Chem. Abstr.*, **52,** 16869h (1958).
408. L. A. Woodward and H. F. Owen, *J. Chem. Soc.*, 1055 (1959).
409. J. M. Smith and L. H. Jones, *J. Chem. Phys.*, **44,** 3643 (1966).
410. R. P. J. Cooney and J. R. Hall, *J. Inorg. Nuclear Chem.*, **28,** 1679 (1966).
411. D. Cooper and R. A. Plane, *Inorg. Chem.*, **5,** 16 (1966).
412. L. H. Jones, *Inorg. Chem.*, **3,** 1581 (1964).
413. L. H. Jones, *Inorg. Chem.*, **4,** 1472 (1965).
414. L. H. Jones and J. M. Smith, *Inorg. Chem.*, **4,** 1677 (1965).
415. J. M. Smith, L. H. Jones, I. K. Kressin, and R. A. Penneman, *Inorg. Chem.*, **4,** 369 (1965).
416. H. Stammreich and O. Sala, *Z. Elektrochem.*, **64,** 741 (1960).
417. H. Stammreich and O. Sala, *Z. Elektrochem.*, **65,** 149 (1961).
418. R. V. Parish, P. G. Simms, M. A. Wells, and L. A. Woodward, *J. Chem. Soc., Sect. A*, 2882 (1968).
419. H. P. Fritz, *Adv. Organometal. Chem.*, **1,** 239 (1964).
420. E. R. Lippincott and R. D. Nelson, *J. Chem. Phys.*, **21,** 1307 (1953).
421. E. R. Lippincott and R. D. Nelson, *Spectrochim. Acta*, **10,** 307 (1958).
422. R. T. Bailey and E. R. Lippincott, *Spectrochim. Acta*, **21,** 389 (1965).
423. I. J. Hyams and E. R. Lippincott, *Nature*, **214,** 267 (1967).
424. I. J. Hyams, R. T. Bailey, and E. R. Lippincott, *Spectrochim. Acta*, **23A,** 273 (1967).
425. T. V. Long, Jr. and F. R. Huege, *Chem. Commun.*, 1239 (1968).
426. E. R. Lippincott, J. Xavier, and D. Steele, *J. Am. Chem. Soc.*, **83,** 2262 (1961).

427. H. P. Fritz, W. Lüttke, H. Stammreich, and R. Forneris, *Spectrochim. Acta*, **17,** 1068 (1961).
428. R. S. Tobias, *Organometal. Chem. Revs.*, **1,** 93 (1966).
429. H. Kriegsmann, *Z. Elektrochem.*, **62,** 1033 (1958).
430. H. Kriegsmann, *Z. anorg. allgem. Chem.*, **298,** 223 (1959).
431. H. Kriegsmann, *Z. anorg. allgem. Chem.*, **299,** 78 (1959).
432. H. Kreigsmann, *Pure Appl. Chem.*, **13,** 203 (1966).
433. H. Kriegsmann, P. Reich, G. Schott, and H. Werner, *Z. anorg. allgem. Chem.*, **343,** 101 (1966).
434. G. J. Janz and Y. Mikawa, *Bull. Chem. Soc. Japan*, **34,** 1495 (1961).
435. J. E. Griffiths, *Spectrochim. Acta*, **20,** 1335 (1964).
436. J. R. Durig, C. W. Sink, and S. F. Bush, *J. Chem. Phys.*, **45,** 66 (1966).
437. J. R. Durig and C. W. Sink, *Spectrochim. Acta*, **24A,** 575 (1968).
438. R. E. Sacher, D. H. Lemmon, and F. A. Miller, *Spectrochim. Acta*, **23A,** 1169 (1967).
439. A. L. Smith, *Spectrochim. Acta*, **24A,** 695 (1968).
440. W. F. Edgell and C. H. Ward, *J. Mol. Spectrosc.*, **8,** 343 (1962).
441. H. Kriegsmann and S. Pischtschan, *Z. anorg. allgem. Chem.*, **308,** 212 (1961).
442. H. Kriegsmann, H. Hoffmann, and S. Pischtschan, *Z. anorg. allgem. Chem.*, **315,** 283 (1962).
443. H. Geissler and H. Kriegsmann, *J. Organometal. Chem.*, **11,** 85 (1968).
444. J. A. Jackson and J. R. Nielsen, *J. Mol. Spectrosc.*, **14,** 320 (1964).
445. R. J. H. Clark, A. G. Davies, and R. J. Puddephatt, *J. Am. Chem. Soc.*, **90,** 6923 (1968).
446. R. S. Tobias and S. Hutcheson, *J. Organometal. Chem.*, **6,** 535 (1966).
447. M. M. McGrady and R. S. Tobias, *Inorg. Chem.*, **3,** 1157 (1964).
448. C. E. Freidline and R. S. Tobias, *Inorg. Chem.*, **5,** 354 (1966).
449. Y. Kawasaki, T. Tanaka, and R. Okawara, *Bull. Chem. Soc. Japan*, **37,** 903 (1964).
450. J. R. Hall, L. A. Woodward, and E. A. V. Ebsworth, *Spectrochim. Acta*, **20,** 1249 (1964).
451. P. L. Goggin and L. A. Woodward, *Trans. Faraday Soc.*, **56,** 1591 (1960).
452. H. Schmidbaur, J. Weidlein, H. F. Klein, and K. Eiglemeir, *Ber.*, **101,** 2268 (1968).
453. A. J. Downs, *J. Chem. Soc.*, 5273 (1963).
454. A. J. Downs, E. A. V. Ebsworth, and H. J. Emeleus, *J. Chem. Soc.*, 3187 (1961).
455. P. L. Goggin and L. A. Woodward, *Trans. Faraday Soc.*, **58,** 1495 (1962).
456. J. H. R. Clarke and L. A. Woodward, *Trans. Faraday Soc.*, **62,** 3022 (1966).
457. J. H. R. Clarke and L. A. Woodward, *Trans. Faraday Soc.*, **64,** 1041 (1968).
458. J. H. R. Clarke and L. A. Woodward, *Spectrochim. Acta*, **23A,** 2077 (1967).
459. P. L. Goggin and L. A. Woodward, *Trans. Faraday Soc.*, **62,** 1423 (1966).
460. J. R. Hall and J. C. Mills, *J. Organometal. Chem.*, **6,** 445 (1966).
461. J. H. S. Green, *Spectrochim. Acta*, **24A,** 863 (1968).
462. D. Seybold and K. Dehnicke, *J. Organometal. Chem.*, **11,** 1 (1968).
463. D. E. Clegg and J. R. Hall, *Spectrochim. Acta*, **21,** 357 (1965).
464. L. A. Woodward, *Pure Appl. Chem.*, **11,** 261 (1965).
465. D. F. Evans and I. Wharf, *J. Chem. Soc., Sect. A*, 783 (1968).
466. G. E. Walrafen, *J. Chem. Phys.*, **36,** 1035 (1962).
467. G. E. Walrafen, *J. Chem. Phys.*, **40,** 3249 (1964).
468. G. E. Walrafen, *J. Chem. Phys.*, **44** 1546 (1966).

469. G. E. Walrafen, *J. Chem. Phys.*, **48** 244 (1968).
470. R. E. Weston, Jr., *Spectrochim. Acta*, **18,** 1257 (1962).
471. Z. A. Gabrichidze, *Opt. Spektrosk.*, **19,** 575 (1965); Engl. trans., 329.
472. Z. Kecki, J. Watanowski, K. Akst-Lipszyc, and S. Minc, *Roczniki Chem.*, **40,** 919 (1968).
473. T. T. Wall and D. F. Hornig, *J. Chem. Phys.*, **43,** 2079 (1965).
474. J. P. Mathieu, *C. R. Acad. Sci., Paris*, **231,** 896 (1950); *C. R. Acad. Sci., Paris*, **229,** 1068 (1949).
475. R. Lafont, *C. R. Acad. Sci., Paris*, **244,** 1481 (1957).
476. A. da Silveria, M. A. Marques, and N. M. Marques, *C. R. Acad. Sci., Paris*, **252,** 3983 (1961).
477. M. Marques, *Rev. Fac. Cien. Univ. Lisboa, 2a Ser.*, **B8,** 5 (1960–61); *Chem. Abstr.*, **57,** 10609i (1962).
478. A. da Silveria, M. A. Marques, and N. M. Marques, *Mol. Phys.*, **9,** 271 (1965).
479. R. E. Hester and R. A. Plane, *Inorg. Chem.*, **3,** 768 (1964).
480. A. I. Grigor'ev, V. A. Sirachev, and A. V. Novoselova, *Dokl. Akad. Nauk. SSSR*, **160,** 383 (1965); *Chem. Abstr.*, **62,** 14053e (1965).
481. G. E. Glass and R. S. Tobias, *J. Am. Chem. Soc.*, **89,** 6371 (1967).
482. R. E. Hester and W. E. L. Grossman, *Spectrochim. Acta*, **23A,** 1945 (1967).
483. J. C. Evans, *Inorg. Chem.*, **2,** 372 (1963).
484. O. L. Keller, Jr., *Inorg. Chem.*, **2,** 783 (1963).
485. V. A. Maroni and T. G. Spiro, *J. Am. Chem. Soc.*, **88,** 1410 (1966).
486. V. A. Maroni and T. G. Spiro, *J. Am. Chem. Soc.*, **89,** 45 (1967).
487. E. R. Lippincott, J. A. Psellos, and M. C. Tobin, *J. Chem. Phys.*, **20,** 536 (1952).
488. J. S. Fordyce and R. L. Baum, *J. Chem. Phys.*, **43,** 843 (1965).
489. L. A. Carreira, V. A. Maroni, J. W. Swaine, Jr., and R. C. Plumb, *J. Chem. Phys.*, **45,** 2216 (1966).
490. T. F. Young, *Proc. Kresge Hooker Sci. Library*, **12,** 18 (1951).
491. T. F. Young, L. F. Maranville, and H. M. Smith in *Structure of Electrolyte Solutions* (W. J. Hamer, ed.), Wiley, New York, 1959, p. 35.
492. M. M. Jones, E. A. Jones, D. F. Harmon, and R. T. Semmes, *J. Am. Chem. Soc.*, **83,** 2038 (1961).
493. R. E. Hester and R. A. Plane, *Inorg. Chem.*, **3,** 769 (1964).
494. R. E. Hester, R. A. Piane, and G. E. Walrafen, *J. Chem. Phys.*, **38,** 249 (1963).
495. J. P. Mathieu and M. Lounsbury, *Disc. Faraday Soc.*, **9,** 196 (1950).
496. D. E. Irish and G. E. Walrafen, *J. Chem. Phys.*, **46,** 378 (1967).
497. D. E. Irish and A. R. Davis, *Can. J. Chem.*, **46,** 943 (1968).
498. P. M. Vollmar, *J. Chem. Phys.*, **39,** 2236 (1963).
499. R. E. Hester and R. A. Plane, *J. Chem. Phys.*, **45,** 4588 (1966).
500. J. T. Miller and D. E. Irish, *Can. J. Chem.*, **45,** 147 (1967).
501. A. R. Davis and D. E. Irish, *Inorg. Chem.*, **7,** 1699 (1968).
502. R. E. Hester and K. Krishnan, *J. Chem. Phys.*, **46,** 3405 (1967).
503. R. E. Hester and K. Krishnan, *J. Chem. Soc., Sect. A*, 1955 (1968).
504. H. Lee and J. K. Wilmshurst, *Aust. J. Chem.*, **17,** 943 (1964).
505. P. Job, *Ann. Chim. (Paris)*, **9,** 113 (1928).
506. F. Woldbye, *Acta Chem. Scand.*, **9,** 299 (1955).
507. L. I. Katzin and E. Gebert, *J. Am. Chem. Soc.*, **72,** 5455 (1950).
508. R. C. Splinter, S. J. Harris, and R. S. Tobias, *Inorg. Chem.*, **7,** 897 (1968).

509. O. Redlich and J. Bigeleisen, *J. Am. Chem. Soc.*, **65,** 1883 (1943).
510. O. Redlich, E. K. Holt, and J. Bigeleisen, *J. Am. Chem. Soc.*, **66,** 13 (1944)
511. G. C. Hood, O. Redlich, and C. A. Reilly, *J. Chem. Phys.*, **22,** 2067 (1954).
512. T. F. Young and L. A. Blatz, *Chem. Rev.*, **44,** 93 (1949).
513. T. F. Young and G. E. Walrafen, *Trans. Faraday Soc.*, **57,** 34 (1961).
514. G. E. Walrafen and D. M. Dodd, *Trans. Faraday Soc.*, **57,** 1286 (1961).
515. A. A. Krawetz, Ph.D. thesis, Univ. of Chicago, 1955.
516. H. A. C. McKay, *Trans. Faraday Soc.*, **52,** 1568 (1956).
517. O. Redlich and G. C. Hood, *Disc. Faraday Soc.*, **24,** 87 (1957).
518. J. W. Akitt, A. K. Covington, J. G. Freeman, and T. H. Lilley, *Chem. Comm.*, 349 (1965).
519. A. K. Covington, M. J. Tate, W. F. K. Wynne-Jones, *Proc. Royal Soc.*, **A 286,** 235 (1965).
520. K. Heinzinger and R. E. Weston, Jr., *J. Chem. Phys.*, **42,** 272 (1965).
521. O. D. Bonner and A. L. Torres, *J. Phys. Chem.*, **69,** 4109 (1965).
522. J. H. R. Clarke and L. A. Woodward, *Trans. Faraday Soc.*, **62,** 2226 (1966).
523. J. R. Durig, O. D. Bonner, and W. H. Breazeale, *J. Phys. Chem.*, **69,** 3886 (1965).
524. S. Kon, Ph.D. thesis, Cornell Univ., 1967; *Diss. Abs.*, **28B,** 137 (1967).
525. H. N. Farrer, M. M. McGrady, and R. S. Tobias, *J. Am. Chem. Soc.*, **87,** 5019 (1965).
526. E. C. Gruen and R. A. Plane, *Inorg. Chem.*, **6,** 1123 (1967).
527. K. Krishnan and R. A. Plane, *Inorg. Chem.*, **5,** 852 (1966).
528. G. Briegleb, *Elektronen-Donator Acceptor Komplexe*, Springer, Berlin, 1961.
529. H. Stammreich, R. Forneris, and V. Tavares, *Spectrochim. Acta*, **17,** 1173 (1961).
530. P. Klaboe, *J. Am. Chem. Soc.*, **89,** 3667 (1967).
531. D. A. Bahnick, Ph.D. thesis, Univ. of Iowa, 1966; *Diss. Abs.*, **27B,** 3035 (1967).
532. D. A. Bahnick and W. B. Person, *J. Chem. Phys.*, **48,** 5637 (1968).
533. G. M. Begun and A. A. Palko, *J. Chem. Phys.*, **38,** 2112 (1963).
534. G. M. Begun and A. A. Palko, *J. Chem. Phys.*, **47,** 967 (1967).
535. G. M. Begun, W. H. Fletcher, and A. A. Palko, *Spectrochim. Acta*, **18,** 655 (1962).
536. A. A. Palko, G. M. Begun, and L. Landau, *J. Chem. Phys.*, **37,** 552 (1962).
537. G. Michel and G. Duyckaerts, *Spectrochim. Acta*, **21,** 279 (1965).
538. P.-O. Kinell, I. Lindqvist, and M. Zackrisson, *Acta Chem. Scand.*, **13,** 190 (1959).
539. A. T. Kozulin, *Opt. Spektrosk.*, **18,** 337 (1965); *Engl. trans.*, 189.
540. Sh. Sh. Raskin, *Fiz. Sbornik L'vov. Univ.*, **203** (1957); *Chem. Abstr.*, **55,** 16143f (1961).
541. Sh. Sh. Raskin, *Opt. Spektrosk.*, **1,** 516 (1956).
542. Sh. Sh. Raskin, *Dokl. Akad. Nauk SSSR*, **141,** 900 (1961); *Chem. Abstr.*, **56,** 15062c (1962).
543. Sh. Sh. Raskin, *Dokl. Akad. Nauk SSSR*, **123,** 645 (1958); *Chem. Abstr.* **55,** 1183d (1961).
544. A. D. Dembitskii, T. N. Sumarokova, and M. I. Usanovich, *Dokl. Akad. Nauk SSSR*, **137,** 1357 (1961); *Chem. Abstr.*, **55,** 17342i (1961).
545. A. D. Dembitskii and T. N. Sumarokova, *Opt. Spektrosk.*, **12,** 369, 484 (1962); *Chem. Abstr.*, **57,** 4200g, 5480c (1962).
546. A. D. Dembitskii, T. N. Sumarokova, and M. I. Usanovich, *ibid.*, **15,** 48 (1963); *Chem. Abstr.*, **59,** 9482d (1963).
547. M. J. Taylor, *J. Chem. Soc., Sect. A*, 1462 (1967).

548. G. C. Hayward and P. J. Hendra, *Spectrochim. Acta*, **23A**, 1937 (1967).
549. R. E. Hester and R. A. Plane, *Spectrochim. Acta*, **23A**, 2289 (1967).
550. W. Bues, in *Physico-Chemical Measurements at High Temperatures*, Academic, New York, 1959.
551. S. C. Wait, Jr. and G. J. Janz, *Quart. Rev. (London)*, **17**, 225 (1963).
552. D. W. James, in *Molten Salt Chemistry* (M. Blander, ed.), Wiley-Interscience, New York, 1964.
553. G. J. Janz and S. C. Wait, Jr., in *Raman Spectroscopy* (H. Szymanski, ed.), Plenum, New York, 1967.
554. W. Bues, *Z. Phys. Chem. (Frankfurt am Main)*, **10**, 1 (1957).
555. G. J. Janz and D. W. James, *J. Chem. Phys.*, **35**, 739 (1961).
556. G. E. Walrafen and D. E. Irish, *J. Chem. Phys.*, **40**, 911 (1964).
557. S. C. Wait, Jr., A. T. Ward, and G. J. Janz, *J. Chem. Phys.*, **45**, 133 (1966).
558. G. J. Janz, T. R. Kozlowski, and S. C. Wait, *J. Chem. Phys.*, **39**, 1809 (1963).
559. G. J. Janz and D. W. James, *J. Chem. Phys.*, **38**, 902 (1963).
560. G. J. Janz and D. W. James, *J. Chem. Phys.*, **38**, 905 (1963).
561. J. H. R. Clarke and C. Solomons, *J. Chem. Phys.*, **48**, 528 (1968).
562. C. B. Baddiel and G. J. Janz, *Trans. Faraday Soc.*, **60**, 2009 (1964).
563. K. Balasubrahmanyam, *J. Chem. Phys.*, **44**, 3270 (1966).
564. J. H. R. Clarke and C. Solomons, *J. Chem. Phys.*, **47**, 1823 (1967).
565. G. E. Walrafen, D. E. Irish, and T. F. Young, *J. Chem. Phys.*, **37**, 662 (1962).
566. G. E. Walrafen, *J. Chem. Phys.*, **37**, 1468 (1962).
567. J. D. Corbett, *Inorg. Chem.*, **1**, 700 (1962).
568. L. A. Woodward, N. N. Greenwood, J. R. Hall, and I. J. Worrall, *J. Chem. Soc.*, 1505 (1958).
569. D. A. Long and E. L. Thomas, *Trans. Faraday Soc.*, **59**, 1029 (1963).
570. H. Kriegsmann, R. Heess, P. Reich, and O. Nillius, *Z. Chem.*, **7**, 449 (1967).
571. T. V. Long, Jr. and R. A. Plane, *J. Chem. Phys.*, **43**, 457 (1965).

Compound Index

The compounds are listed alphabetically under the symbol of the first element appearing in the chemical formula as conventionally written, with the following exceptions:

(1) For certain compounds, e.g., organometallics, the central atom is placed first in the formula;

(2) Compounds containing complex anions are listed under the central element of the anion (with cation omitted).

The following abbreviations are used: acac = acetylacetonate, R = alkyl or aryl group, X = halide or pseudohalide.

G

H

I

P

R

S

T

U

V

CHAPTER 8

Electronic Raman Transitions

J. A. KONINGSTEIN

CARLETON UNIVERSITY
OTTAWA, CANADA

O. S. MORTENSEN

UNIVERSITY OF COPENHAGEN
COPENHAGEN, DENMARK

I. INTRODUCTION

After the discovery of the Raman effect, many researchers have relied on the works of Placzek (*1*) to explain features of the spectra of solids, liquids, and gases. Although the initial developments in Raman spectroscopy were due to physicists, in the period from 1935 to the advent of the laser, considerable use was made of this type of spectroscopy by chemists as a tool to unravel structure of molecules. The low pressure mercury light source was nearly always used to excite the vibrational and rotational Raman spectra, making it not directly possible to relate specific experimental data to the theory. For instance, information on the individual elements of the scattering tensor was hard to obtain, because the direction of propagation of the incident exciting radiation was not exactly parallel or perpendicular to the direction of observation of the scattered radiation. Measurement of the depolarization ratio of Raman lines of liquids and gases nearly always deviated from the theoretical value, and the calculation of depolarization ratios of certain types of vibrations or a priori computations of the absolute intensities is still an extremely cumbersome process. The greater part of the experimental work in the above period was devoted to the excitation of Raman transitions between vibrational or rotational levels of molecules. All these levels are associated with the electronic ground state of the molecule.

Raman transitions between two electronic levels were observed only for the case of the NO molecule. In 1932 Rasetti (*2*) assigned a Raman band of this molecule to the $^2\Pi_{1/2} - ^2\Pi_{3/2}$ transition which occurred with a shift of 121 cm^{-1}. Some experiments on rare earth ions were attempted by Gerding (*3*) and Gorter during the Second World War, but only in 1964 did Hougen and Singh (*4*) succeed in exciting electronic Raman transitions of the Pr^{3+} ion in $PrCl_3$. Just prior to their paper, Elliott and Loudon (*5*) predicted the possibility of observation of electronic Raman transitions of the lanthanide ions. Another electronic Raman effect, that of Ce^{3+} in $CaWO_4$, was found by Chau (*6*). The excitation source for all these experiments was still the mercury arc and photographic plates were employed to record the transitions. Very little information became available on the relative intensity of this effect, compared to the intensities of strong Raman lines of some well known liquids. Placzek (*7*) pointed out that the scattering tensor for the electronic transitions is different from the tensor for the vibrational or rotational transitions. This tensor in the latter case is symmetric while for electronic transitions the tensor can become asymmetric.

Many crystals are now available of compounds which contain rare earth ions and if the Raman phonon spectrum of these crystals is to be separated from the electronic effects, then a detailed study of the elements of the scattering tensor is required. In 1966, we initiated a program devoted to exciting the electronic Raman transitions of rare earth ions in certain crystals with the 6328 Å radiation of the He–Ne gas laser. By that time, it became clear that individual elements of the Raman tensor for the vibrational effect in crystals could be measured, and it was hoped that the same type of measurements could be performed for the electronic transitions. The He–Ne laser was chosen because the energy level diagram of the lanthanide ions suggests that only a few ions have excited states with energies equal to the energy of the laser radiation. Employing a rather sensitive electronic detection system, we succeeded in 1966 in exciting Raman spectra of a number of trivalent rare earth ions in the yttrium-gallium-garnet host lattice (*7*,*8*), and this was followed by a whole series of experiments on these ions in other crystals (*9–13*).

In Placzek's polarizability theory for the vibrational Raman effect, emphasis is placed on the polarizability of the ground state of the molecule, and the role of the intermediate states is very much restricted. In the expression for an element of the scattering tensor matrix, elements of the electric dipole operator between ground state and the intermediate states appear, and in general our knowledge of the wave functions of these states is insufficient to compute these matrix elements and thus an element for the scattering tensor for vibrational transitions.

This situation is nearly completely reversed for the trivalent rare earth ions. Wave functions of the states of the lanthanide ion—free or in a surrounding of known symmetry—have been computed, and Axe (*14*) employed these wave functions to compute the absolute intensities of electronic Raman transitions of some of the lanthanide ions. In these calculations, the effect of asymmetry of the scattering tensor was neglected. Mortensen and Koningstein (*15*), however, showed that for many ions large contributions to the overall intensities can be expected from the antisymmetric part of these tensors. In fact, in some cases the contribution of the antisymmetric tensors is larger than that of the symmetric tensors, and in at least one situation, it was found that the Raman transitions are related to a completely antisymmetric tensor (*10*). Apart from absolute intensities, the Rayleigh to Raman ratio for electronic Raman effects of all the lanthanides were also computed (*16*), and in later publications the relation between the strength and symmetry of the crystal field and the polarization features of complete electronic Raman spectra were established (*17*,*18*).

The occurrence of an antisymmetric scattering tensor has a profound effect on the selection rules for the electronic Raman effect, if these rules are compared to those for the vibrational Raman effect in the non-resonance case. In addition, the lowest lying electronic state of the rare earth ions does not necessarily have to belong to the totally symmetric irreducible representation of the point group, which describes the site symmetry of the ions in the crystals. For the vibrational Raman effect, the ground state is nearly always of such high symmetry that the state belongs to the totally symmetric species. Here again differences exist between the two types of Raman scattering.

II. SYMMETRY OF THE SCATTERING TENSOR

We are concerned here with the situation where a rare earth ion has replaced certain ions of the host lattice, or with rare earth compounds. The electronic configuration of the lanthanide ions can be written as: $Xe(4f)^n(5s)^2(5p)^6$, where $n = 1$–14. Such electronic configurations give rise to a large number of states. The states are labeled with the quantum numbers L, S, and J, and are situated anywhere from 0–70,000 cm^{-1}.

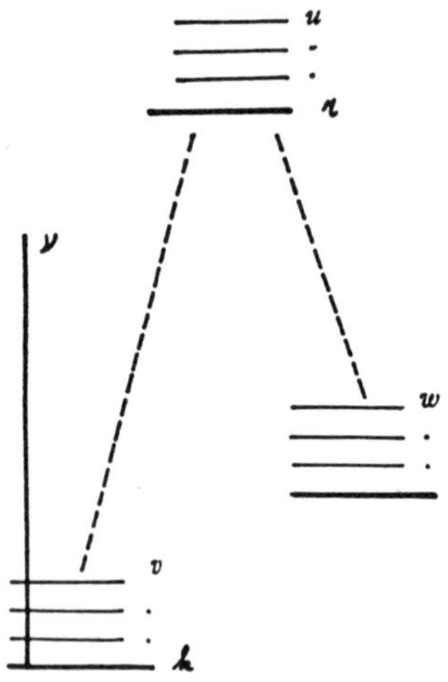

Fig. 1. Vibronic coupling and the electronic Raman transitions. The k, n, and r are electronic levels and v, w, and u are the quantum numbers of one particular normal coordinate Q_a; ν is the frequency of the primary radiation.

These Russell–Saunders J manifolds are in principle $(2J+1)$-fold degenerate. If the rare earth ions are located in crystals, then the symmetry which the ions experience is in all cases lower than the symmetry of the full rotational group, and the free ion degeneracy will be removed to a certain degree. The removal can be complete if the symmetry of the crystal field in the lattice is very low. Even if the symmetry of the surrounding is high, then the J manifolds are split and electronic Raman transitions can take place between the crystal field components of the ground J manifold.

Associated with electronic levels are series of vibrational levels and in Fig. 1 the situation is depicted for one particular type of vibration, which involves the central ion. In particular the energy of the vibrational states is given, relative to the energy of the electronic states. Also indicated is the energy of the exciting radiation with frequency ν.

The intensity of a Raman transition is related to an element of the scattering tensor. In the case where the transition takes place between any of the states k, v and n, w the following expression can be written for an element of the scattering tensor $(\alpha_{\rho\sigma})_{k,v;n,w}$

$$(\alpha_{\rho\sigma})_{k,v;n,w} = \frac{1}{h}\sum_{r,u}\frac{(M_\rho)_{n,w;r,u}(M_\sigma)_{r,u;k,v}}{\nu_{r,u}-\nu_{k,v}-\nu_0}+\frac{[\rho\leftrightarrow\sigma]}{\nu_{r,u}+\nu_{n,w}+\nu_0}. \tag{1}$$

σ and ρ stand for the cartesian coordinates x, y, or z. The summation has to be carried out over all states r of the system. $(M_\rho)_{n,w\,;\,r,u}$ is the matrix element of the electric dipole operator $e\hat{\rho}$ between the states n, w and r, u. The reader is referred to the works of Placzek (*1*) and Dirac (*19*) for the derivation of Eq. (1).

Of special interest here is the role of the wave functions which appear in the matrix elements of the dipole operator. These elements are equal to the following integral: $\int \psi^*_{n,w} e\rho\psi_{r,u} d\tau$. $\psi_{n,w}$ and $\psi_{r,u}$ are total wave functions. Such wave functions can be written as a product of an electronic wave function $\psi_n(\mathbf{r}, Q)$ and a vibrational wave function $\varphi_w(Q_a)$. The Q_a is the normal coordinate; the energy levels of this vibration relative to the electronic energy levels can be seen in Fig. 1. The motions of the electrons of the central ion may, to a certain degree, depend on movements of the nuclei (described by the normal coordinate Q_a). The vibronic coupling effects are assumed to be small, and the following expression can be written for $\psi_n(\mathbf{r}, Q)$.

$$\psi_n(\mathbf{r}, Q) = \psi_n{}^0(\mathbf{r}) + \sum_{l\neq n}\frac{\int\psi_l^{*0}(\mathbf{r})(\partial\mathscr{H}/\partial Q_a)_{Q_a=0}\psi_n{}^0(\mathbf{r})\cdot Q_a d\tau}{E_l{}^0 - E_n{}^0}\cdot\psi_l{}^0(\mathbf{r}) \tag{2}$$

The derivative $\partial\mathscr{H}/\partial Q_a$ enters the equation because the Hamiltonian of the system has been expanded to first order in the nuclear coordinate Q_a. A rather complicated expression is obtained if the expanded electronic wave function is incorporated in the expressions for the matrix element of the dipole operators, followed by introduction of these matrix elements in the expression for the scattering tensor. A simplification can however be made. The variation of the denominator of Eq. (1) with the vibrational quantum number can be neglected if the energy of the excited states r, u is far removed from the energy of the exciting radiation. The closure rule can then be applied in the space of the vibrational wave functions and the following expressions are obtained (*20*):

$$(\alpha_{\rho\sigma})^{\text{static}}_{k,v;n,w} = \frac{1}{h} \langle \varphi_v \mid \varphi_w \rangle \sum_r \frac{(M_\rho)_{nr}(M_\sigma)_{rk}}{\nu_r - \nu_k - \nu_0} + \frac{[\rho \leftrightarrow \sigma]}{\nu_r - \nu_n + \nu_0} \tag{3a}$$

$$(\alpha_{\rho\sigma})^{\text{dynamic}}_{k,v;n,w} = \frac{1}{h} \langle \varphi_v \mid Q \mid \varphi_w \rangle \sum_r \frac{(M_\rho)_{nr}\{(M_\sigma)_{rl} h^Q_{lk} + (M_\sigma)_{lk} h^{*Q}_{lr}\}}{\nu_r - \nu_k - \nu_0} + c \cdot t \tag{3b}$$

The constant h^Q_{lk} stands for the integral $\int \psi_l^*(\mathbf{r}) \mid Q_a \mid \psi_k^0(\mathbf{r})\, d\tau$. Such integrals are small and the conclusion is reached that the main contribution to the elements of the scattering tensor arises from $(\alpha_{\rho\sigma})^{\text{static}}_{k,u;n,w}$. In other words, vibronic coupling is not important as an intensity giving process for the electronic Raman transitions.

It is interesting to replace the quantum number n by k in Eqs. (3a) and (3b). The former is only nonvanishing if the quantum number $v = w$ and the new expression thus describes the intensity of the Rayleigh scattered light. The result of the replacement of n by k in Eq. (3b) leads to the following expression:

$$(\alpha_{\rho\sigma})_{k,v;\,k,w} = \frac{1}{h} \langle \varphi_w \mid Q \mid \varphi_v \rangle \sum_r \frac{(M_\rho)_{kr}\{(M_\sigma)_{rl} h^Q_{lk} + (M_\rho)_{lk} h^{*Q}_{lr}\}}{\nu_r - \nu_k - \nu_0} + c \cdot t \tag{4}$$

The Raman transition now takes place between two vibrational levels, both associated with the electronic groundstate k. This is a vibrational Raman effect, but now explained in terms of a model where vibronic interactions are employed. This model was proposed by Albrecht (*21*).

The symmetry of the scattering tensor for the various Raman processes can be investigated by replacing the coordinate ρ by σ. It follows that for the electronic Raman effect $\alpha_{\rho\sigma} \neq \alpha_{\sigma\rho}$, and that electronic transitions are thus related to a tensor which can be asymmetric. On the other hand we have for the vibrational Raman effect $\alpha_{\rho\sigma} = \alpha_{\sigma\rho}$ and the tensor is symmetric. It is perhaps worthwhile to point out that the expansion of the electronic wave function in terms of nuclear displacements (Eq. 2) is only valid if the wave function is nondegenerate. For degenerate states the vibronic model breaks down, and it can be shown that in such a situation the scattering tensor for the vibrational Raman effect can also become asymmetric. This is also true if the electronic wave functions happen to be complex. A Raman transition between the states k and n is allowed if the integral $\int \psi_k \hat{\alpha}_{\rho\sigma} \psi_n dt \neq 0$. The operator $\hat{\alpha}_{\rho\sigma}$ can be written as:

$$\hat{\alpha}_{\rho\sigma} = \frac{\langle \mid \sum_i e_i \rho_i \mid \psi_r \rangle \langle \psi_r \mid \sum_i e_i \sigma_i \mid \rangle}{\nu_r - \nu_k - \nu_0} + \frac{[\rho \leftrightarrow \sigma]}{\nu_r - \nu_n + \nu_0} \tag{5}$$

The transformation properties of the electronic states n and k and the symmetry properties of the operator $\hat{\alpha}_{\rho\sigma}$ are thus required in order to establish if the totally symmetric representation occurs in the product of the representations $\Gamma_{\psi_n} \times \Gamma_{\rho\sigma} \times \Gamma_{\psi_k}$. For the electronic Raman effect we thus need the transformation properties of the antisymmetric combinations $\alpha_{\rho\sigma} - \alpha_{\sigma\rho}$, and a glance at the character tables of the more familiar point groups reveals that these properties are not directly given. It is thus not immediately clear from these character tables what the appropriate selection rules are for the electronic Raman transitions, even if the symmetry of the wave functions of the states k and n are known.

III. TRANSFORMATION PROPERTIES OF THE SCATTERING TENSOR; IN PARTICULAR THE ANTISYMMETRIC COMPONENTS

When discussing the symmetry of tensor components, it is customary to describe a second order cartesian tensor by products of the type xy, etc. It is easily shown that a tensor component α_{xy} transforms as the product xy, if the latter product indeed transforms as an irreducible representation. This is, however, rarely the case; more often, products of the type xy will transform into products of the type yx. Most physical cartesian tensors and in particular the ordinary rotational and vibrational Raman tensor are symmetrical so that $\alpha_{yx} = \alpha_{xy}$. The correlation with cartesian products of the type xy and yx is immediately clear. Such a correlation is much less clear when the tensor is nonsymmetric; i.e., expressions of the type $\alpha_{yx} - \alpha_{xy}$ describe nonvanishing quantities. The similar expression $xy - yx$ will in general be vanishing quantities, and in order to stretch the analogy between these products and the tensor components one must introduce the fiction that quantities like xy and yx are noncommutative so that $xy - yx$ will not be equal to zero. In such a situation, which is in fact the appropriate one in discussing the electronic Raman effect, it seems profitable to skip this somewhat artificial analogy with coordinate products, and instead introduce some quantities that are more closely related to the whole concept of symmetry groups and symmetry operations.

Under general rotations of the molecular framework, the nine cartesian tensor components will in general transform into each other in a very complicated way and the symmetry transformation must be described by a 9×9 matrix. This, however, is not the only way to find the species of the components of the scattering tensor. It is possible to choose certain linear combinations of the cartesian tensor components that under an arbitrary rotation around a particular axis transform into themselves, and to collect these components in three sets so that members of each set under an arbitrary rotation transform only into members of the same set. These linear combinations, often given the name irreducible tensor components, are connected to the usual cartesian components in the way shown in Table 1.

To get a picture of what these irreducible tensor components stand for, we may remark that there exists a close analogy between the three sets of irreducible tensor components and the well known type *s*, *p*, and *d* orbitals. Thus $\alpha_0{}^0$ is completely invariant under all rotations, while the three members of the $\alpha_Q{}^1$ set generally transform into combinations of themselves under arbitrary rotations. The same is true for the five components of the $\alpha_Q{}^2$ set in complete analogy with the five *d* orbitals. There is however a slight difference between the three $\alpha_Q{}^1$ components and the three *p* orbitals: p_x, p_y, and p_z. The latter change sign under inversion of the coordinate system, while all the tensor components are invariant under this operation.

In the preceding Section II, it was pointed out that electronic Raman transitions are allowed if the product of the representations $\Gamma_{\psi_K} \times \Gamma_{\alpha_{\rho\sigma}} \times \Gamma_{\psi_n}$ contains the totally symmetric species. The operator $\boldsymbol{\alpha}_Q{}^K$ can be expressed as a linear combination of $\alpha_{\rho\sigma}$'s by the relations given in Table 1, and the whole problem of the selection rules of the electronic Raman transitions is now reduced to finding the transformation properties of *s*, *p*, and *d* orbitals. Of special interest here, of course, is the transformation properties of the antisymmetric components of the scattering tensor, and it is

TABLE 1

Relation of Cartesian and Irreducible Tensor Components

$$
\begin{aligned}
\alpha_0{}^0 &= (-1/\sqrt{3})(\alpha_{xx}+\alpha_{yy}+\alpha_{zz}) \\
\alpha_1{}^1 &= \tfrac{1}{2}(-\alpha_{xz}+\alpha_{zx}-i\alpha_{yz}+i\alpha_{zy}) \\
\alpha_0{}^1 &= (\tfrac{1}{2})^{1/2}(i\alpha_{xy}-i\alpha_{yx}) \\
\alpha_{-1}{}^1 &= -\tfrac{1}{2}(\alpha_{xz}-\alpha_{zx}-i\alpha_{yz}+i\alpha_{zy}) \\
\alpha_2{}^2 &= \tfrac{1}{2}(\alpha_{xx}-\alpha_{yy}+i\alpha_{xy}+i\alpha_{yx}) \\
\alpha_1{}^2 &= \tfrac{1}{2}(\alpha_{xz}+\alpha_{zx}+i\alpha_{yz}+i\alpha_{zy}) \\
\alpha_0{}^2 &= (6)^{-1/2}(2\alpha_{zz}-\alpha_{xx}-\alpha_{yy}) \\
\alpha_{-1}{}^2 &= \tfrac{1}{2}(\alpha_{xz}+\alpha_{zx}-i\alpha_{yz}-i\alpha_{zy}(\\
\alpha_{-2}{}^2 &= \tfrac{1}{2}(\alpha_{xx}-\alpha_{yy}-ia_{xy}-i\alpha_{yx})
\end{aligned}
$$

thus found that we can find the properties by investigating the symmetry of p_x, p_y, and p_z orbitals. They behave identically to the coordinates x, y, and z respectively, and the species of these coordinates are given in most of the character tables of the more familiar point groups. It shall be pointed out later, that in some cases double groups have to be used to derive the proper selection rules, but even in such instances, the transformation properties of the complete tensor are directly obtained.

IV. ABSOLUTE INTENSITIES AND DEPOLARIZATION RATIOS

It is well known in Raman spectroscopy that, if an attempt is to be made to compute absolute intensities of the transitions, a prerequisite is a knowledge of the wave functions of the states which are involved in the transitions and of the intermediate states. In the expression for the elements of the scattering tensor, see Eq. (1), matrix elements of the electric dipole operator occur between the ground state and these intermediate states; and the intermediate states and the state on which the Raman transition terminates.

During the last 20 years, it has become possible to derive the energy level diagram of the trivalent rare earth ions from a detailed study of the optical properties of compounds which contained these ions (*22*). As a direct result of these experimental studies, attempts were made to calculate the energy level diagram, and these calculations yielded the wave functions of the states of the trivalent rare earth ions (*23*). Actually, much experimental work was obtained from crystals containing small amounts of the Lanthanide ions, and the complications produced by the effect of the crystal field had to be taken into account. In the calculations of the energy level diagram of the ions, tensor algebra played a rather important role, and the introduction of irreducible tensor components for the electronic Raman effect is not only extremely convenient to find the transformation properties of the complete tensor, but is of even greater importance if the electric dipole matrix elements, and thus the scattering tensor, is to be computed from first principles. The details of the calculations fall somewhat outside the scope of this chapter, and so we will give only the more important points of the theoretical treatment.

A mean value of the energy of the states of ground and excited electronic configurations of the lanthanide ions is established. The summation over the excited states is now carried out in such a way that first the ground configuration is considered, next the electronic first excited configuration and so on. Even if the states are crystal field levels rather than the levels of the free trivalent ions, such a procedure can be carried out if use is made of tensor algebra. In the final expression the most important contribution arises from a 3j-symbol:

$$\begin{pmatrix} J' & K & J \\ -J_z' & Q & J_z \end{pmatrix}$$

J' is the total angular momentum quantum number of the Russell-Saunders manifold on which the electronic Raman transition terminates, J is the quantum number of the manifold in which the transition originates. The substates of the manifolds are J_z' and J_z and may in some instances be the correct quantum number of states, if the rare earth ion experiences the effect of the crystal field; K and Q have the same meaning as the super and subscripts of the irreducible tensor components $(\alpha)_Q{}^K$. Part of the selection rules of the electronic Raman transitions are given by the intrinsic properties of this 3j-symbol. The symbol automatically equals zero unless $-J_z' + Q + J_z = 0$ and $J' + K + J$ satisfy usual triangular conditions (with $J = 0$, this amounts to $J' = K$). The contents in the above can perhaps best be demonstrated by consideration of the electronic Raman transitions of the trivalent europium ion. The ground state of this ion is $^7F_0$ ($S = 3$, $L = 3$, and $J = 0$). This state cannot be split if the ion is placed in a crystal. Levels of the $^7F_1$ manifold are found some 350 cm^{-1} above the ground state. This J manifold can be split into a maximum number of three crystal field components. For the Raman transition $^7F_0$–$^7F_1$, it follows from the triangular condition of the 3j symbol that $K = 1$, while the other relation gives the result that the values for Q are 1, 0, and -1. The Raman transition is apparently related to a tensor which is antisymmetric. The contribution of the ordinary symmetric scattering tensor is zero in this case. Similarly for the Raman transition $^7F_0$–$^7F_2$, it is shown that the tensor is now symmetric and that the contribution of the antisymmetric tensor is zero (*9*).

From the theory, the following set of selection rules are found for the electronic Raman transitions of the lanthanide ions: (a) the symmetric part of the scattering tensor contributes if $\Delta J \leqslant 2$, $\Delta L \leqslant 2$, and $\Delta S = 0$ and (b) the antisymmetric part of the tensor contributes if $\Delta J \leqslant 1$, $\Delta L = \Delta S = 0$. From the position of excited states of the lanthanide ions, one concludes that the electronic Raman effects can appear with shifts between 0 and 5000 cm^{-1}, and such effects, if measured from rare earth ions in single crystals, can thus take place in the spectral interval where phonon modes are also apt to appear.

For some of the trivalent lanthanide ions it has been observed that strong electric dipole transitions occur between the ground state, which belongs to the $(4f)^n$ configuration and some of the states arising from the $(4f)^{n-1}(5d)$ configuration. To a first approximation, it thus seems appropriate to calculate the scattering tensor by employing matrix elements of the electric dipole operator between the ground state and these intermediate states of the $(4f)^{n-1}(5d)$ configuration and the matrix elements between these states and the state of the $(4f)^n$ configuration on which the Raman transition terminates. Approximate values of the absolute intensities of the Raman effect are obtained and are given for the ions Pr^{3+} and Tm^{3+} in Table 2. Also indicated is the value of the cross section of the

TABLE 2

Absolute Intensities and Raman to Rayleigh Ratios of Some Electronic Raman Transitions

Ion	Transition	Raman cross-section[a]	Raman/Rayleigh
Pr^{3+}	$^3H_4 \rightarrow {}^3H_5$	0.6×10^{-31}	0.67×10^{-2}
Tm^{3+}	$^3H_6 \rightarrow {}^3H_4$	0.2×10^{-34}	0.15×10^{-5}

[a] The cross-sections are calculated for 6328 Å primary radiation; the experimental value for the cross section of the 992 cm^{-1} line of the benzene molecule is approximately $\sim 10^{-29}$ cm^{-1}.

Raman band of the benzene molecule with a shift of 992 cm^{-1}. The electronic Raman effect is smaller by more than two orders of magnitude if compared to the vibrational Raman effect, and even if lasers are employed as exciting sources, refined detection schemes are necessary to photoelectrically record the electronic transitions. Not all of the presently available lasers can be used in electronic Raman spectroscopy. Some of the excited states have energies which are very close to the energy of the laser radiation, and are thus directly absorbed by the molecules. This results in the excitation of fluorescence processes, and the intensity of the fluorescence lines is much stronger than the intensities of the electronic transitions. Consequently the fluorescence spectrum may be the only spectrum which appears on the chart paper of the recorder.

The radiation of the principal line of the He–Ne laser is not absorbed by the rare earth ions and is thus very suitable; however, the power in this laser line is not more than 100 mW, and also the quantum efficiency of the detectors is very low in the spectral region of 6328 Å to 7500 Å.

The most important feature of a Raman spectrum is the polarization properties of the Raman lines. It is well known that the depolarization ratio of Raman lines of a system of random oriented molecules or atoms is $0 < \rho < \frac{3}{4}$. It is true here that the scattering tensor should be symmetric. If the depolarization ratio of a Raman line is measured, for which the scattering tensor is antisymmetric, then the value for $\rho = \infty$. If both the symmetric and the antisymmetric tensors contribute to the Raman intensity then $0 < \rho < \infty$. It is interesting to note that for single crystals no differences should be observed if Raman lines are studied which are associated with the different tensors, if the direction of propagation of the incident light and the direction of the scattered radiation are along crystallographic axes. But differences of the polarization properties of Raman lines are obtained, if the crystals are rotated around some of these crystallographic axes (*18*).

V. EXPERIMENTAL SECTION

In the introductory section it was indicated that the first observation of an electronic Raman effect was made by Rasetti (*2*) in 1932. In 1964 Hougen and Singh (*4*) found many transitions of the Pr^{3+} ion in $PrCl_3$. The Raman spectra were excited with the 2536 Å radiation of the mercury light source. Photographic techniques were employed to record the spectra.

The mercury light source can only be used in a few isolated cases, since many trivalent rare earth ions will absorb the radiation of the Toronto lamp and fluorescence might be excited. In fact this kind of radiation can be excited for nearly every rare earth ion if the ultraviolet radiation of a mercury lamp is impinging on a rare earth doped crystal.

The laser found its way into Raman spectroscopy as an excitation source during this decade, and by now it has become abundantly clear that these devices have come to stay. Much attention has lately also been given to electronic detection techniques, and the only weak spot in a Laser Raman apparatus is now perhaps the photomultiplier tube. In the spectral range of 6400 Å to 7000 Å the quantum efficiency of these detectors is not more than 10%, and if one adds that with the presently employed optical systems not more than one-fiftieth of the total amount of scattered radiation can be collected, only one out of a minimum of 500 Raman photons will give rise to the ejection of a photoelectron from the cathode of the photomultiplier tube. Nevertheless, with the photon counting systems now available one might even try to detect this electron in the presence of the noise of the phototube.

Electronic Raman effects have been excited with the 6328 Å radiation of an 80 mW He–Ne laser, and in this section a discussion is given of the experimental apparatus used in the investigations by the authors.

Small single crystals (5 mm long and approximately 2 mm in diameter) were mounted on top of the cold finger of a He research Dewar. This Dewar was provided with the necessary windows, and the laser beam entered the Dewar via a window in the bottom. The laser radiation was focussed in the small crystals by means of a long ($f = 20$ cm) focal length lens. The diameter of the laser beam inside the crystal was estimated at 200 μ. The direction of propagation of the laser radiation and the direction of observation of the scattered radiation were orthogonal. The scattered radiation was collected with an $F1.5$ lens, and another lens was employed to fill the collimator of the 1 m Czerny–Turner monochromator. This instrument was equipped with an 1100 grooves/mm grating blazed for 7000 Å. The light which emerged from the exit slit of the monochromator was guided by means of a silver coated lucite lightpipe to an area of 4×4 mm of the photocathode of a noncooled EMI 9558B photomultiplier tube. Directly surrounding the cathode part of the tube was placed a solenoid. The magnetic field generated by the solenoid prevented the arrival of photoelectrons from the nonilluminated part of the cathode on the first dynode. The photoelectrons from the illuminated part of the photocathode were not affected by the B lines of the magnet, and the overall result was that the dark current of the photo tube could be reduced by two orders of magnitude without changing the current produced by a small light signal. The current—of the order of 10^{-10} amp—was amplified in a picoammeter, and the output of this meter was fed into an integrating digital voltmeter. The scanning speed of the monochromator was reduced to 1.25 Å/min while the sampling time of the voltmeter was in nearly all experiments 20 sec. For every wave number one signal averaged value was produced, and the summed results were displayed on a strip chart recorder. In order to get rid of the discontinuity in the signals, a capacitor was placed over the input of the recorder. The advantage of using the integrating digital voltmeter over any other device which can give long time constants is that no evidence was found of "long time constant drifts" in the recorded spectra

In order to reduce the scattered radiation of the single monochromator extensive use was made of interference filters. These filters rejected the

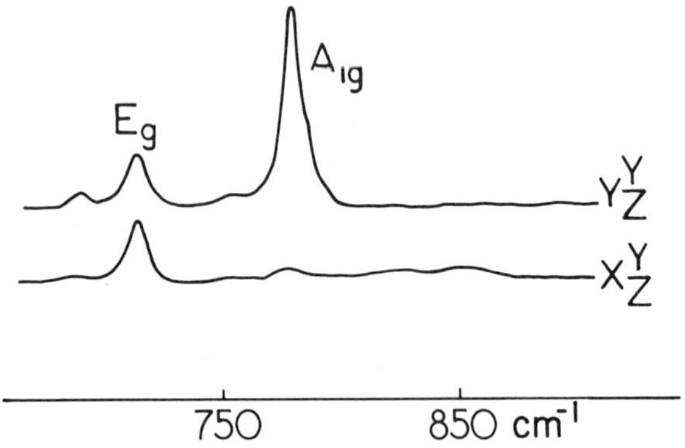

Fig. 2. Part of the Raman spectrum of the compound dysprosium aluminum garnet. The line of symmetry A_{1g} is related to the totally symmetric vibration of the AlO_4^{5-} group. The Raman line of symmetry E_g is also related to this kind of movement, and the distance of the two lines indicate that strong factor group splitting effects exist in the aluminum garnet crystal.

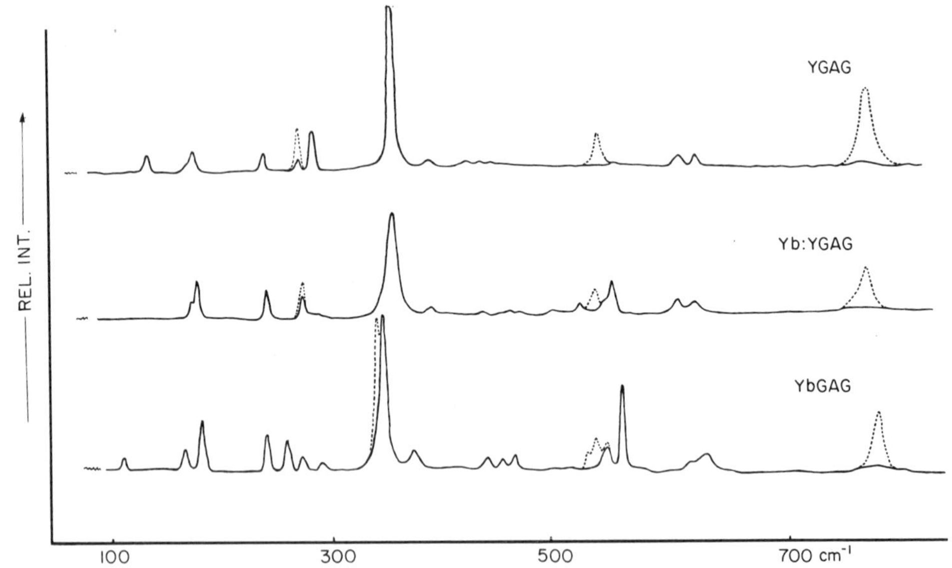

Fig. 3. The 80°K Raman spectra of some gallium garnet crystals. The peaks with dotted lines have strong intensity in the experimental situation where the direction of polarization of the laser beam is perpendicular to the optical axis of the spectrometer. These lines can be of symmetry A_{1g} or E_g.

He–Ne laser line and allowed Raman lines with shifts $>80\ \mathrm{cm}^{-1}$ to appear in the spectra. Also an interference filter was used to reject the fluorescence lines of the plasma of the laser tube. A typical run of part of the Raman spectrum of the compound dysprosium-aluminum-garnet; $Dy_3Al_5O_{12}$ (DyAlG) is shown in Fig. 2 and the averaged spectra of the compounds $Y_3Ga_5O_{12}$ (YGaG), ytterbium in YGaG and $Yb_3Ga_5O_{12}$ are shown in Fig. 3. The averaged spectrum is a result of three runs, each of them obtained under the experimental conditions described above. From Fig. 2 it can be seen that rather clean Raman spectra can be recorded from the rare earth garnet crystals employing the He–Ne laser as an exciting source.

Energy levels of trivalent lanthanides in the garnet host lattices have been the subject of many investigations (*24*), and in the next section a discussion is offered of the observation of an electronic Raman effect of one of the ions, while at the same time the theoretical ideas are applied in order to find the selection rules for the effect.

VI. SELECTION RULES AND EXPERIMENTAL RESULTS OF THE ELECTRONIC RAMAN EFFECT OF YTTERBIUM ION IN YTTRIUM-GALLIUM GARNET

The electronic configuration of the trivalent ytterbium ion is $Xe(4f)^{13}(5s)^2(5p)^6$. Only one electron more would be sufficient to fill the $4f$-shell, and the system can thus be described as having a "hole" in the $4f$-shell. Application of the Russell–Saunders coupling scheme reveals that two J manifolds arise from this electronic configuration. The $^2F_{7/2}$

TABLE 3

Activity Table for the Double Group D_2

D_2	E	E	C_2 C_2	C_2' C_2'	C_2'' C_2''	Cartesian	Irr. tensor comp.
Γ_1	1	1	1	1	1	xx, yy, zz	$\alpha_0^0; \alpha_2^2+\alpha_2^{-2}$
Γ_2	1	1	−1	1	−1	$xz \pm zx$	$\alpha_0^1; \alpha_2^2-\alpha_{-2}^2$
Γ_3	1	1	1	−1	−1	$yz \pm zy$	$\alpha_1^2-\alpha_{-1}^2; \alpha_1^1+\alpha_{-1}^1$
Γ_4	1	1	−1	−1	1	$xy \pm yx$	$\alpha_1^2+\alpha_{-1}^2; \alpha_1^1-\alpha_{-1}^1$
Γ_5	2	−2	0	0	0		

All four Kramers pairs of $^2F_{7/2}$ belong to the species Γ_5.

and $^2F_{5/2}$ manifolds are separated by some 10,000 cm^{-1}. If the ytterbium ion is placed in the gallium garnet host lattice, it will occupy a position in the unit cell (*25*) with an overall symmetry described by the point group D_2. The symmetry of the crystal field which the ion now experiences is thus very low (orthorhombic), and the J manifolds will be split. The $J = 7/2$ state splits into four Kramers pairs, and the $J = 5/2$ manifold splits into three Kramers pairs. Only the presence of an external magnetic field can remove the twofold degeneracy of the Kramers pairs. Several investigations have dealt with the relative positions of the crystal field levels of the J manifolds, and attempts have been made to perform crystal field calculations (*26*).

TABLE 4

Scattering Tensors for Electronic Raman Transitions of the Ytterbium Ion in the Garnet Host Lattice

Double group D_2		Double group O_h	
Species	Tensor	Species	Tensor
Γ_1	xx, yy, zz	Γ_1	$xx+yy+zz$
Γ_2	$xz+zx$	Γ_4	$xz+zx$
	$xz-zx$	Γ_5	$zx-xz$
Γ_3	$yz+zy$	Γ_4	$yz+zy$
	$yz-zy$	Γ_5	$yz-zy$
Γ_4	$yx+xy$	Γ_4	$yx+xy$
	$yx-xy$	Γ_5	$yx-xy$

Scattering Matrices for the Species of the Group O_h

	Normal case	Tensors rotated around z-axis through an angle of 45°
Γ_1	$\begin{bmatrix} a^2 & & \\ & a^2 & \\ & & a^2 \end{bmatrix}$	$\begin{bmatrix} a^2 & & \\ & a^2 & \\ & & a^2 \end{bmatrix}$
Γ_4	$\begin{bmatrix} 0 & b^2 & b^2 \\ b^2 & 0 & b^2 \\ b^2 & b^2 & 0 \end{bmatrix}$	$\begin{bmatrix} b^2 & 0 & b^2 \\ 0 & b^2 & b^2 \\ b^2 & b^2 & 0 \end{bmatrix}$
Γ_5	$\begin{bmatrix} 0 & c^2 & c^2 \\ c^2 & 0 & c^2 \\ c^2 & c^2 & 0 \end{bmatrix}$	$\begin{bmatrix} 0 & c^2 & c^2 \\ c^2 & 0 & c^2 \\ c^2 & c^2 & 0 \end{bmatrix}$

The symmetry at the place of the rare earth ion is thus given by the point group D_2, and consequently the labeling of the crystal field components of the split ground manifold ($^2F_{7/2}$) should be made in terms of the irreducible representation of this group. A complication now occurs in this particular case. The number of optically active electrons of the ytterbium ion is 13, and in order to label the energy levels, use has to be made of the double groups. The energy levels of YbYGaG should thus be labeled according to the irreducible representations of the double group D_2. Also the components of the scattering tensor belong to some of these representations, and the exact labeling of the crystal field levels and the tensor elements is shown in Table 3. All levels apparently belong to the representation and the product of the representations $\Gamma_5 \times \Gamma_5 = \Gamma_1 + \Gamma_2 + \Gamma_3 + \Gamma_4$. The scattering tensor of the electronic Raman transitions thus belong to the representations $\Gamma_1 + \Gamma_2 + \Gamma_3 + \Gamma_4$, and the result is that a rather complicated scattering matrix is obtained, the elements of which can be related to the observed transitions (*17*). The actual Raman spectra are, however, measured from a single crystal which happens to have cubic symmetry, and the relation between the Cartesian components of the scattering tensor for the site group and the space group of the crystal is given in Table 4. The space group of the garnet crystals is $O_h^{10}(Ia3d)$, and the phonon modes of the host lattice have also to be labeled according to the species of the factor group O_h^{10}. The factor group analysis for this compound has been made (*27*), and the main results are now given. In total, there are 80 atoms in the primitive cell of the garnet crystals. They give rise to some 237 phonon modes, and the distribution of these phonon modes over the representations of the factor group is given in Table 5. In the unit cell, there are, to a first and perhaps somewhat crude approximation, 12 GaO_4^{5-} groups.

The site symmetry at the place of the Ga (or Al) ions in the unit cell is S_4. The vibration of the groups can be expected to occur with frequencies between 700 and 800 cm^{-1} and the transition is Raman active. The garnet crystals are extremely hard, and it is not unreasonable to assume that interactions between the atoms in the unit cell take place. Interaction of the GaO_4 or AlO_4 groups results in factor group splitting effects of some of the phonon modes (*27*); an example can be seen in Fig. 2. The twelve vibrations of the AlO_4^{5-} ions can give rise to Raman active modes of symmetry A_{1g} and E_{1g} (see Table 5). The Raman spectrum of the aluminum garnet compounds, shown in Fig. 2, shows the presence of two lines which are of symmetry A_{1g} and E_g. On the other hand, only one Raman line of symmetry A_{1g} at a shift of 780 cm^{-1} is observed for the gallium

TABLE 5

Phonon Symmetries and Scattering Tensor in Garnet Crystals

Unit and site group[a]	Type of motion	Representations: Site group	Representations: Factor group
		B_1	$A_{2g}+A_{2u}+E_g+E_u+T_{1g}+T_{1u}$
$X(D_2)$	trans	B_2	$T_{1g}+T_{1u}+T_{2g}+T_{2u}$
		B_3	$T_{1g}+T_{1u}+T_{2g}+T_{2u}$
$M(C_{3i})$	trans	A_u	$A_{1u}+A_{2u}+T_{1u}+T_{2u}$
		E_u	$2E_u+2T_{1u}+2T_{2u}$
	trans	B	$A_{2g}+A_{2u}+E_g+E_u+T_{2g}+T_{2u}$
		E	$2T_{1g}+2T_{1u}+2T_{2g}+2T_{2u}$
	rot	A	$A_{1g}+A_{2u}+E_g+E_u+T_{1g}+T_{1u}$
		E	$2T_{1g}+2T_{1u}+2T_{2g}+2T2_u$
$MO_4(S_4)$			
	ν_1	A	$A_{1g}+A_{2u}+E_g+E_u+T_{1g}+T_{1u}$
	ν_2	B	$A_{2g}+A_{2u}+E_g+E_u+T_{2g}+T_{2u}$
		A	$A_{1g}+A_{2u}+E_g+E_u+T_{1g}+T_{1u}$
	ν_3, ν_4	B	$A_{2g}+A_{2u}+E_g+E_u+T_{2g}+T_{2u}$
		E	$2T_{1g}+2T_{1u}+2T_{2g}+2T_{2u}$

Scattering Tensor—Ordinary case[b]

Species A_{1g} $\begin{bmatrix} a & & \\ & a & \\ & & a \end{bmatrix}$

Species E_g $\begin{bmatrix} b & & \\ & b & \\ & & -2b \end{bmatrix} \begin{bmatrix} b\sqrt{3} & & \\ & -b\sqrt{3} & \\ & & \end{bmatrix}$

Species T_{2g} $\begin{bmatrix} & c & \\ c & & \\ & & \end{bmatrix} \begin{bmatrix} & & c \\ & & \\ c & & \end{bmatrix} \begin{bmatrix} & & \\ & & c \\ & c & \end{bmatrix}$

Species T_{1g} $\begin{bmatrix} & d & \\ -d & & \\ & & \end{bmatrix} \begin{bmatrix} & & d \\ & & \\ -d & & \end{bmatrix} \begin{bmatrix} & & \\ & & d \\ & -d & \end{bmatrix}$

Table 5 (*cont.*)

Scattering Tensor—Special case[c]

Species A_{1g}	$\begin{bmatrix} a & & \\ & a & \\ & & a \end{bmatrix}$		
Species E_g	$\begin{bmatrix} b & & \\ & b & \\ & & -2b \end{bmatrix}$	$\begin{bmatrix} & -b\sqrt{3} & \\ b\sqrt{3} & & \\ & & \end{bmatrix}$	
Species T_{2g}	$\begin{bmatrix} c & & \\ & -c & \\ & & \end{bmatrix}$	$\begin{bmatrix} & & c/\sqrt{2} \\ & & -c/\sqrt{2} \\ c/\sqrt{2} & -c/\sqrt{2} & \end{bmatrix}$	$\begin{bmatrix} & & c/\sqrt{2} \\ & & c/\sqrt{2} \\ c/\sqrt{2} & c/\sqrt{2} & \end{bmatrix}$
Species T_{1g}	$\begin{bmatrix} & d & \\ -d & & \\ & & \end{bmatrix}$	$\begin{bmatrix} & & d/\sqrt{2} \\ & & -d/\sqrt{2} \\ d/\sqrt{2} & -d/\sqrt{2} & \end{bmatrix}$	$\begin{bmatrix} & & d/\sqrt{2} \\ & & d/\sqrt{2} \\ d/\sqrt{2} & d/\sqrt{2} & \end{bmatrix}$

[a] *X* stands for Y, Yb; *M* stands for Ga, Al.
[b] *x*, *y* and *z* are the crystallographic axes.
[c] tensor rotated through 45° around the *z*-axis.

garnet crystal. Also, in other parts of the spectra, differences are found in the factor group splitting effects, so that the appearance of new lines in the rare earth garnet crystal as compared to the spectrum of the yttrium garnet compound does not necessarily suggest that electronic Raman effects take place.

All cartesian scattering tensors of Tables 4 and 5 refer specifically to the case where the direction of propagation of the incident radiation, and the direction of observation of the scattered light are orthogonal and coincide with the crystallographic axes of the cubic crystal. The polarization properties of Raman lines related to a symmetric or an antisymmetric tensor are thus identical. If the tensors are rotated through an angle of say 45° around the *z*-axis, then the said properties are different. The rotated tensors are also indicated in Tables 4 and 5.

Low temperature laser excited spectra of small crystals of the compounds yttrium gallium garnet, ytterbium gallium garnet, and ytterbium in yttrium gallium garnet (YbYGaG) are shown in Fig. 3. The orientation of the crystals was not in all cases known. However, all crystals have cubic symmetry, and Raman lines of symmetry A_{1g} should have vanishing intensity in all experimental situations where the polarization of the laser beam is parallel to the direction of observation of the scattered radiation. Figure 3 shows, indeed, the presence of lines which are highly polarized.

VII. ASSIGNMENT OF ELECTRONIC RAMAN TRANSITIONS

If the spectra of YbYGaG and YGaG of Fig. 3 are compared, at first glance it appears that extra lines do occur in the former compound. Detailed polarization studies of the Raman lines of YGaG suggest that the line at 358 cm^{-1} is of symmetry T_{2g} and either E_g or A_{1g}. The two Raman lines of YbGaG at 346 cm^{-1} and 339 cm^{-1} are of symmetry T_{2g} and E_g or A_{1g} respectively, and the line of the compound YbYGaG at 354 cm^{-1} is in fact slightly asymmetric if the shape of the band is investigated. The data suggest that factor group splitting effects of the various crystal are different giving rise to the features in the Raman spectra in the 350 cm^{-1} spectral region.

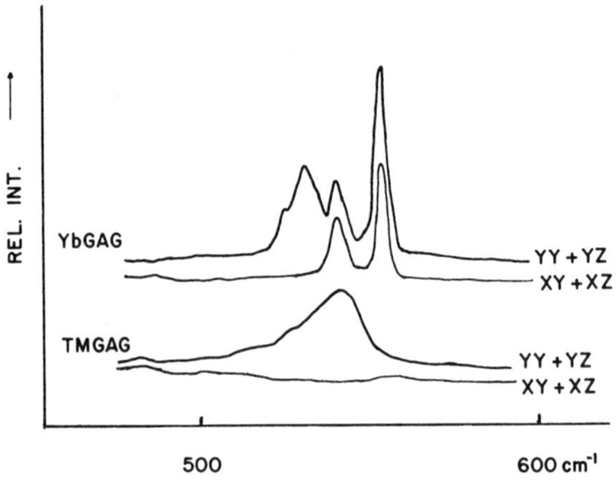

Fig. 4. A comparison of the low temperature laser excited Raman spectra of the compounds ytterbium gallium garnet and thulium gallium garnet. *XY*, *YZ*, etc., refer to the components of a scattering matrix. The symmetry of the phonon mode is seen to be A_{1g} and the electronic transitions of the ytterbium ion are of a different symmetry.

Of special interest to this chapter is the Raman spectra of the crystals with shifts of >400 cm^{-1}. A polarized Raman line of symmetry A_{1g} is recorded for the crystal YGaG, with a shift of 531 cm^{-1}. The same phonon mode is present in the spectrum of YbGaG, but extra lines appear at 539 cm^{-1} and 554 cm^{-1}. The intensity of these Raman lines is dependent on the concentration of the trivalent ytterbium ion because the lines are of intermediate intensity in the YbYGaG crystal. In Fig. 4 the Raman spectrum of the compound thulium gallium garnet is shown in the spectral interval of 500–600 cm^{-1} and only one phonon mode of symmetry A_{1g} is observed, similar to the spectrum of the YGaG crystal. The exact scattering tensors of the two Raman lines of YbGaG at 539 cm^{-1} and 554 cm^{-1} have not yet been determined, but experimental data indicate that the tensor is not quite identical to the tensors of the phonon modes of this crystal. Furthermore from a comparison of the spectrum of TmGAG and YbGaG, it follows that factor group splitting effects are different for some of the phonon modes, and that the appearance of the two lines for YbGaG is indeed unique. Based on the above, the Raman lines are assigned to electronic transitions of the ytterbium ion.

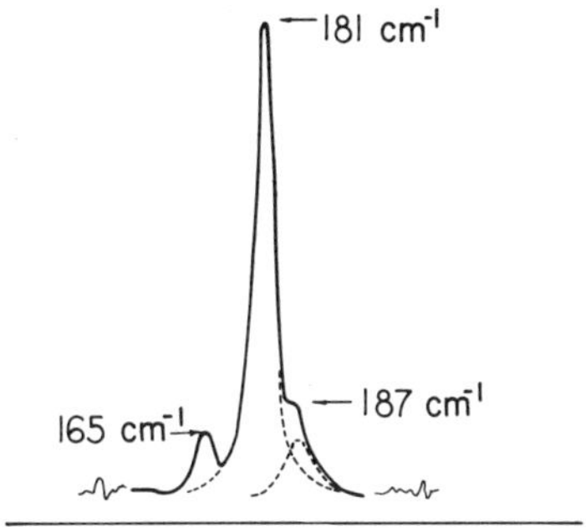

Fig. 5. Part of the Raman spectrum of thulium gallium garnet. The line with a shift of 187 cm^{-1} is an electronic Raman transition of the thulium ion. The other lines are phonon modes.

Employing the same techniques, evidence has also been found for an electronic Raman effect in the thulium ion. In Fig. 5 part of the spectrum of the compound TmGaG is shown (*28*). A comparison of the spectrum of YGaG in the same spectral region (see Fig. 3) shows one phonon mode located at 179 cm^{-1} which has symmetry $E_g + T_{2g}$. This phonon mode of YbGaG is split into two components, of symmetry E_g at 171 cm^{-1} and T_{2g} at 182 cm^{-1}, respectively. For TmGaG these phonon modes occur at 171 cm^{-1} (E_g) and 181 cm^{-1} (T_{2g}). A new line is found with a shift of 187 cm^{-1} and is of symmetry T_{2g}. We assign this line to an electronic Raman transition of the thulium ion for the following reasons: (a) theoretical calculation of the scattering tensor reveals that the amount of asymmetry in the tensor for all transitions within the ground manifold is small, (b) the rare earth has an even number of 4*f* electrons, and the group D_2 can now be used to label the electronic levels and the elements of the scattering tensor (*29*), and (c) other experimental data suggest that the crystal field components of the ground manifold of TmGaG are situated some hundreds of wavenumbers above the groundstate.

The experimental data on the electronic Raman transitions suggest that the intensity of this effect is smaller than the intensity of the vibrational Raman effect of the host lattice, and the electronic configuration has a profound effect on the position and intensity of intermanifold electronic Raman transitions.

VIII. CONCLUSION

The main conclusion which can be drawn from the experimental data is that electronic Raman transitions of trivalent rare earth ions are very weak. Because of this, care should be taken to make first an assignment of all possible phonon modes of the host lattice, so that information is available on factor group splitting effects of the Raman lines. It should also be kept in mind that the energy levels of many of the lanthanides can be close to the energy of the exciting radiation and that the appearance of extra lines in the spectra of the rare earth compounds can be fluorescence lines. Polarization measurements, or better, the measurement of the scattering tensor elements of all Raman lines, are a prerequisite in order to make a correct assignment. In Table 6 available information on the

TABLE 6

Experimental Data on the Laser Excited Electronic Transitions of Travalent Lanthanides

Ions	Ce	Nd	Eu	Tb	Dy	Tm	Yb
Host lattice	$CeCl_3$	YGaG	YGaG YAlG YVO_4	YAlG	YAlG	YGaG	YGaG
States involved in the transition	$^2F_{5/2}$	$^4I_{9/2}$	$^7F_{0,1}$	$^7F_6$	$^3H_{15/2}$	$^3H_6$	$^2F_{7/2}$
Intensity[a]	10^{-30}	10^{-31}	10^{-31}	10^{-31}	10^{-31}	10^{-33}	10^{-31}
Tensor	symm asymm	?	asymm	?	?	symm	?
Laser	Argon	HeNe	HeNe	HeNe	HeNe	HeNe	HeNe
References	5, 30	7	7, 8, 9	11	33	29	7, 31, 32

[a] The intensities are in cm^2 and are only approximate.

electronic Raman transitions of the lanthanides is given. Asymmetry of the scattering tensor has been observed in a number of cases. This is particularly true for the rare earth ions with less than 7 electrons in the 4*f* shell. These findings are in agreement with the theory, which predicts that for these ions the amount of asymmetry should be large, and that for rare earth ions with more than 7 electrons in the 4*f* shell the symmetric part of the tensor dominates.

Electronic Raman effects are not restricted to the case of the lanthanides. For some transition metal hexafluoride molecules, low lying electronic levels are observed some three thousand wave numbers above the ground-state. Electronic Raman transitions between the ground and the first excited electronic states are allowed, because both states arise in this particular case from the same electronic configuration and thus have equal parity. Electronic Raman transitions of a system of randomly oriented particles are characterized by specific rules with respect to the depolarization ratio of these bands. Electric dipole transitions between the same levels of these randomly oriented systems do not have polarization properties, and consequently the electronic Raman effect can become an important tool in unraveling the electronic structure of some transition metal compounds. It was recently demonstrated (*18*) that rather strict relations exist between the polarization properties of the electronic Raman transitions and the strength and symmetry of the crystal field, and one might be able to use this area of spectroscopy as a testing ground for crystal field theory. Polarization measurements and Zeeman–Raman studies of the electronic lines are in this respect probably the most profitable areas of research.

Acknowledgments

The research described in this chapter has been supported by grants from the National Research Council of Canada, the Defence Research Board of Canada, and the Department of University Affairs of the province of Ontario.

The authors also wish to thank Dr. L. G. Van Uitert of Bell Telephone Laboratories, Murray Hill, N.J., and Dr. R. A. Buchanan of Lockheed Research Laboratories, Palo Alto, California, for supplying the garnet crystals.

REFERENCES

1. G. Placzek, Marx Handbuch der Radiologie, 2nd ed., Vol. 6, 205 (1934).
2. F. Rasetti, *Z. Phys.*, **66,** 646 (1930).
3. H. Gerding, private communication.
4. J. Hougen and S. Singh, *Phys. Rev. Letters*, **10,** 406 (1963).
5. R. J. Elliott and R. Loudon, *Phys. Letters*, **3,** 189 (1963).
6. J. Y. H. Chau, *J. Chem. Phys.*, **44,** 1708 (1966).
7. J. A. Koningstein, *J. Opt. Soc. Am.*, **56,** 1405 (1966).
8. J. A. Koningstein, *J. Chem. Phys.*, **46,** 2811 (1967).
9. J. A. Koningstein and O. Sonnich Mortensen, *Phys. Rev. Letters*, **18,** 831 (1967).
10. J. A. Koningstein and O. Sonnich Mortensen, *Nature*, **217,** 445 (1968).
11. J. A. Koningstein and Toa-ning Ng, *Cam. J. Chem.*, **47,** 1395 (1969).
12. J. A. Koningstein, *Chem. Phys. Letters*, **2,** 38 (1968).
13. J. A. Koningstein and Toa-ning Ng, to be published.
14. J. D. Axe, *Phys. Rev.*, **136,** A42 (1964).
15. O. Sonnich Mortensen and J. A. Koningstein, *J. Chem. Phys.*, **48,** 3971 (1968).
16. J. A. Koningstein and O. Sonnich Mortensen, *Phys. Rev.*, **168,** 75 (1968).
17. J. A. Koningstein and O. Sonnich Mortensen, *Chem. Phys. Letters*, **2,** 693 (1968).
18. J. A. Koningstein and O. Sonnich Mortensen, *J. Opt. Soc. Am.*, **58,** 1208 (1968).
19. P. Dirac, *Proc. Roy. Soc. (London)*, **114,** 710 (1927).
20. O. Sonnich Mortensen and J. A. Koningstein, *Chem. Phys. Letters*, **1,** 409 (1967).
21. A. C. Albrecht, *J. Chem. Phys.*, **34,** 1476 (1961).
22. G. H. Dieke and H. M. Crosswhite, *Appl. Opt.*, **7,** 675 (1963).
23. B. G. Wybourne, *J. Chem. Phys.*, **32,** 639 (1960).
24. J. A. Koningstein, *Phys. Rev.*, **136,** A711–729 (1964).
25. Optical Properties of Ions in Crystals, eds. H. M. Crosswhite and H. M. Moos, Wiley-Interscience, New York, 1967, pp. 105–115.
26. R. A. Buchanan, K.A. Wickersheim, J. J. Pearson, and G. F. Herrmann, *Phys. Rev.*, **159,** 245 (1967).
27. J. A. Koningstein and O. Sonnich Mortensen, *J. Mol. Spectr.*, **27,** 343 (1968).
28. J. A. Koningstein and Toa-ning Ng, *J. Opt. Soc. Am.*, **58,** 1402 (1968).
29. J. A. Koningstein, *Phys. Rev.*, **174,** 477 (1968).
30. A. Kiel, in Light Scattering Spectra of Solids, ed. G. B. Wright, Springer-Verlag, New York, 1969, p. 245.
31. J. A. Koningstein, *Phys. Rev.*, **174,** 477 (1968).
32. J. A. Koningstein, *Appl. Spec.*, **22,** 438 (1968).
33. J. A. Koningstein, Solid State Comm., **7,** 351 (1969).

CHAPTER 9

High Resolution Raman Studies of Gases

ALFONS WEBER

PHYSICS DEPARTMENT
FORDHAM UNIVERSITY
BRONX, NEW YORK

I. INTRODUCTION

In this chapter the rotational Raman effect will be described. This effect has received scant attention on account of the rather difficult procedures that must be followed for a successful execution of the experiments. The experimental difficulties that afflict the study of the Raman effect in liquids and solids are enhanced in the study of gases. With the exception of hydrogen (*1*,*2*), the rotational motions of molecules are greatly hindered for substances in the liquid and solid states of aggregation; a resolved rotational fine structure in the rotation and rotation-vibration spectra of liquids and solids has not been observed.

The field of high resolution Raman spectroscopy has come to denote the study of the resolved pure rotational and rotation-vibrational Raman bands of low pressure gases and vapors. In this sense it is fully complementary to the fields of infrared and microwave spectroscopy in being capable of providing accurate values of the moments of inertia, rotational distortion constants, Coriolis coupling coefficients, and anharmonicity constants for the various vibrational states of a polyatomic molecule.

One can distinguish three main periods of the development of the subject. After the discovery of the Raman effect the spectra of gaseous hydrogen chloride (*3*), hydrogen (*1*,*4*,*5*,*6*), oxygen (*4*,*7*,*8*), nitrogen (*4*,*7*), carbon monoxide (*9*,*10*), nitric oxide (*4*,*10*,*11*), carbon dioxide (*12*,*13*), nitrous oxide (*13*), ammonia (*14*,*15*,*16*), methane (*14*,*18*,*18*), ethane (*16*,*18*), ethylene (*16*,*18*), and acetylene (*16*,*18*) were studied under moderate resolution and high pressures. This early work culminated in 1933 in the comprehensive theory of the rotational Raman effect by Placzek and Teller (*19*,*20*). Except for the work on hydrogen and its isotopes by Bhagavantam (*21*) and Teal and MacWood (*22*), and the work of Cabannes and Rousset (*23*) and Nielsen and Ward (*24*), the field of Raman spectroscopy of gases lay neglected until the early 1950's.

The second period was marked by the significant advances in experimental techniques which were achieved by Prof. H. L. Welsh and his co-workers at the University of Toronto. Their invention of the water cooled, high current, low pressure mercury-arc lamp provided a light source of very high intensity which emits radiation consisting of very sharp lines whose hyperfine structure is largely resolved (*25,26*). Their additional invention of a Raman tube equipped with a multiple reflection mirror system (*27,28*) provided the experimenter with a much improved apparatus with which the rotational and rotation-vibrational Raman bands of polyatomic molecules can be studied with a resolution unthought of before. The study of the pure rotational Raman spectra of a series of symmetric top and quasi-symmetric top rotor molecules by Stoicheff and his co-workers provided structural information for molecules which elude the powerful technique of microwave absorption spectroscopy.

These results are described in detail in two review articles by Stoicheff (*29,30*) which also give detailed expositions of the experimental techniques in use prior to the invention of the laser. An all-encompassing review of the status of Raman spectroscopy is available in the book by Brandmüller and Moser (*31*), the appearance of which in 1960 marked the end of the era when Raman spectra were excited by incoherent mercury-arc radiation.

The invention of the laser in 1960 marks the beginning of the third and current period. The availability of this light source has caused a tremendous revival of interest in the field of Raman spectroscopy, and many of the accomplishments made possible with the laser are described in other chapters of this book. The use of laser sources allows the performance of experiments that were previously either impossible or too difficult to carry out. Thus, the use of the polarization of laser light allows the study of the isotropic and anisotropic contributions to a given $\Delta J = 0$ transition. The directionality and collimation allows a direct study of the angular dependence of the scattering, and the intensity allows a more favorable observation of very weak and, heretofore, unobserved transitions. For these reasons it may not be out of order to present an abbreviated form of the important features of the theory of the rotational Raman scattering by free molecules as developed by Placzek and Teller (*19,20*). A redevelopment of the theory has recently been initiated by Rasmussen and Brodersen (*20a*), but it is not available in its completed form at this time. After a survey of the older work, the laser technique of exciting Raman spectra of low pressure gases will be described together with the results that have been obtained thus far.

II. THEORY OF ROTATIONAL RAMAN SCATTERING

A. General Theory

As shown in many texts on quantum mechanics (*32*) the interaction of a molecule with radiation gives rise to spontaneously scattered radiation. A second-order time-dependent perturbation calculation shows that the total power emitted in a Raman transition between two stationary states k and n of a molecule is given by

$$I_{kn} = \frac{64\pi^4}{3c^3}(\nu_0+\nu_{kn})^4 \mid \mathbf{C}_{kn} \mid^2 \tag{1}$$

where I_{kn} is the power in ergs/sec, ν_0 is the frequency of the incident light in cycles/sec, and $\nu_{kn} = (E_k - E_n)/h$ is the transition frequency between the states k and n whose energies are E_k and E_n, respectively. The amplitude of the matrix element of the induced dipole moment is

$$\mathbf{C}_{kn} = \frac{1}{h}\sum_r \left\{ \frac{(\mathbf{A}\cdot\mathbf{M}_{kr})\mathbf{M}_{rn}}{\nu_{rk}-\nu_0} + \frac{\mathbf{M}_{kr}(\mathbf{A}\cdot\mathbf{M}_{rn})}{\nu_{rn}+\nu_0} \right\} \tag{2}$$

In Eq. (2) $\mathbf{M}_{kr}$ is the matrix element of the electric moment

$$\mathbf{M}_{kr} = \int \Psi_k{}^*\mathbf{M}\Psi_r \, d\tau \tag{3}$$

where Ψ_k and Ψ_r are the unperturbed wave functions of the molecule in the states k and r, and $\mathbf{A}$ is the complex amplitude of the electric field of the incident light wave:

$$\mathscr{E} = \mathbf{A}\, e^{-i\omega_0 t} + \mathbf{A}^*\, e^{i\omega_0 t} \tag{4}$$

where $\omega_0 = 2\pi\nu_0$ and $\mathbf{A} = \mid \mathbf{A} \mid \mathbf{a}, \quad \mid \mathbf{a} \mid = 1.$

Instead of the total scattered radiation given by Eq. (1) it is often of interest to know the intensity of radiation of specified polarization $\mathbf{s}$ ($\mid \mathbf{s} \mid = 1$) scattered into a given direction. This is given by

$$I_{kn}(\mathbf{s}) = \frac{8\pi^3}{r^2c^3}(\nu_0+\nu_{kn})^4 \mid \mathbf{C}_{kn}\cdot\mathbf{s} \mid^2 \tag{5}$$

where $I_{kn}(\mathbf{s})$ is given in ergs/sec/ster, and r is the distance from the molecule to the observer.

Equation (2) may be written out for each Cartesian component (ρ, $\sigma = x,y,z$ in a space fixed coordinate system)

$$(C_\rho)_{kn} = \sum_\sigma (c_{\rho\sigma})_{kn}\, A_\sigma \tag{6}$$

where the scattering tensor $(c_{\rho\sigma})_{kn}$ is

$$(c_{\rho\sigma})_{kn} = \frac{1}{h}\sum_r \left\{\frac{(M_\sigma)_{kr}(M_\rho)_{rn}}{\nu_{rk}-\nu_0} + \frac{(M_\rho)_{kr}(M_\sigma)_{rn}}{\nu_{rn}+\nu_0}\right\} \tag{7}$$

In general the tensor $(c_{\rho\sigma})_{kn}$ is complex and unsymmetric for $k \neq n$. For $k = n$, which gives the Rayleigh scattering,

$$(c_{\rho\sigma})_{kk} = \frac{1}{h}\sum_r \left\{\frac{(M_\sigma)_{kr}(M_\rho)_{rk}}{\nu_{rk}-\nu_0} + \frac{(M_\rho)_{kr}(M_\sigma)_{rk}}{\nu_{rk}+\nu_0}\right\} \tag{8}$$

and $(c_{\rho\sigma})_{kk} = (c_{\sigma\rho})_{kk}$. For the static case ($\nu_0 = 0$) this tensor is real and symmetric $(c_{\rho\sigma})_{kk} = (c_{\sigma\rho})_{kk}$. For this case we have

$$\begin{aligned}(C_\rho)_{kk} &= \sum_\sigma (c_{\rho\sigma})_{kk} A_\sigma \\ &= \sum_\sigma \alpha_{\rho\sigma}^{(k)} A_\sigma\end{aligned} \tag{9}$$

where

$$\alpha_{\rho\sigma}^{(k)} \equiv (c_{\rho\sigma})_{kk} \tag{10}$$

is the "polarizability of the state k."

Eqs. (1) and (5) may be rewritten in more convenient form by introducing the intensity I_0 (ergs/sec/cm^2) of the incident light

$$I_0 = \frac{c}{2\pi} | \mathbf{A} |^2 \tag{11}$$

And, therefore, Eqs. (12) and (13) follow:

$$I_{kn} = \frac{128\pi^5}{3}\frac{(\nu_0+\nu_{kn})^4}{c^4}\sum_\rho \left| \sum_\sigma (c_{\rho\sigma})_{kn} a_\sigma \right|^2 I_0 \tag{12}$$

$$I_{kn}(\mathbf{s}) = \frac{16\pi^4}{r^2}\frac{(\nu_0+\nu_{kn})^4}{c^4}\left| \sum_{\rho\sigma} (c_{\rho\sigma})_{kn} s_\rho a_\sigma \right|^2 I_0 \tag{13}$$

Equation (12) is in the form

$$I_{kn} = Q_{kn} I_0 \tag{14}$$

where the value for Q_{kn} is

$$Q_{kn} = \frac{128\pi^5}{3}\frac{(\nu_0+\nu_{kn})^4}{c^4}\sum_\rho \left| \sum_\sigma (c_{\rho\sigma})_{kn} a_\sigma \right|^2 \tag{15}$$

Q_{kn} is the total scattering cross section associated with the transition $k \rightarrow n$, which is seen to depend on the state of polarization of the incident light.

An average cross section $\bar{Q}_{kn}$ for a given direction of propagation and polarization of the incident light is defined by averaging the Q_{kn} over all orientations of the scattering system (molecule). This computation is carried out by equivalently holding the molecule fixed and averaging over all directions of propagation and polarization of the incident light. Then

$$\bar{Q}_{kn} = \frac{128\pi^5}{3} \frac{(\nu_0 + \nu_{kn})^4}{c^4} \cdot \frac{1}{3} \sum_\rho \sum_\sigma |(c_{\rho\sigma})_{kn}|^2 \tag{16}$$

On the other hand, for isotropic illumination,

$$Q_{kn}^{\text{iso}} = \frac{128\pi^5}{3} \frac{(\nu_0 + \nu_{kn})^4}{c^4} \sum_\rho \sum_\sigma |(c_{\rho\sigma})_{kn}|^2 \tag{17}$$

so that

$$Q_{kn}^{\text{iso}} = 3\bar{Q}_{kn} \tag{18}$$

For degenerate states the scattering cross section associated with the transition $k \rightarrow n$ is given by

$$Q_{kn} = \frac{1}{g_k} \sum_{s,s'} Q_{ks,ns'} \tag{19}$$

where g_k is the statistical weight of the initial state k and the sum extends over all degenerate initial states s and final states s'.

A detailed analysis of the scattering process is facilitated by the decomposition of the tensor $(c_{\rho\sigma})_{kn}$ into an isotropic, a symmetric, and an antisymmetric part. Thus,

$$(c_{\rho\sigma})_{kn} = (c^0 \delta_\rho{}^\sigma + c_{\rho\sigma}^s + c_{\rho\sigma}^a)_{kn} \tag{20}$$

where the three parts are given by

$$(c^0)_{kn} = \tfrac{1}{3}(c_{xx} + c_{yy} + c_{zz})_{kn} = \frac{1}{3h} \sum_r \frac{\nu_{rk} + \nu_{rn}}{(\nu_{rk} - \nu_0)(\nu_{rn} + \nu_0)} \times [\sum_\sigma (M_\sigma)_{kr} (M_\rho)_{rn}] \tag{21}$$

$$(c_{\rho\sigma}^s)_{kn} = \tfrac{1}{2}(c_{\rho\sigma} + c_{\sigma\rho})_{kn} - (c^0)_{kn} \delta_\rho{}^\sigma$$

$$= \frac{1}{2h} \sum_r \frac{\nu_{rk} + \nu_{rn}}{(\nu_{rk} - \nu_0)(\nu_{rn} + \nu_0)}$$

$$\times [(M_\sigma)_{kr}(M_\rho)_{rn} + (M_\rho)_{kr}(M_\sigma)_{rn}] - (c^0)_{kn}\delta_\rho^\sigma \tag{22}$$

$$(c^a_{\rho\sigma})_{kn} = \tfrac{1}{2}(c_{\rho\sigma} - c_{\sigma\rho})_{kn}$$

$$= \frac{2\nu_0 + \nu_{kn}}{2h} \sum_r \frac{1}{(\nu_{rk} - \nu_0)(\nu_{rk} + \nu_0)}$$

$$\times [(M_\sigma)_{kr}(M_\rho)_{rn} - (M_\rho)_{kr}(M_\sigma)_{rn}] \tag{23}$$

The intensity of the scattered radiation is determined by the quantity

$$|(c_{\rho\sigma})_{kn}|^2 = |(c^0)_{kn}\delta_\rho{}^\sigma + (c^s_{\rho\sigma})_{kn} + (c^a_{\rho\sigma})_{kn}|^2 \tag{24}$$

Since the three parts do not transform into one another it is useful to study the behavior of each one of them to obtain the total scattering. Equation (21) represents a spherically symmetric tensor, and its contribution to the total scattering is referred to as isotropic scattering or trace scattering. The second part $(c^s_{\rho\sigma})_{kn}$ is a symmetric tensor with zero trace. Its contribution to the total scattering is referred to as quadrupole scattering since the selection rules for it are the same as those for quadrupole radiation. Similarly, since the selection rules for the third part $(c^a_{\rho\sigma})_{kn}$ are the same as for a magnetic dipole, its contribution is called magnetic dipole scattering.

B. The Polarizability Approximation

The general scattering formulas discussed in the previous section are too complex for direct application to a molecular system. A significant simplification, therefore, is achieved by utilizing the empirical information that is contained in the Raman effect in the development of the theory. Key factors of the ordinary Raman effect in molecules are the frequency ν_{kn} in Eq. (1) being associated with nuclear motions (vibration, rotation) and this frequency being very much less than the frequencies associated with electronic transitions, or the frequency of the exciting radiation. Based on this knowledge, several approximations are made which result in a considerably simplified conceptual picture of the Raman scattering process. This is known as the "polarizability theory" of the Raman effect and its main ideas follow (*33*).

Invoking the Born–Oppenheimer approximation, which allows the separation of the total molecular problem into an electronic problem and one that describes the nuclear motions, we split the pair of indexes k and n which designate the initial and final states into a pair of indexes which designate the electronic and nuclear configuration state of a molecule, respectively. Thus,

$$k = gi$$

$$n = gf$$

where g stands for the electronic ground state and i and f stand for the initial and final nuclear configuration states, respectively. (A further separation of the states i and f into vibrational and rotational states is not necessary at this point.) The intermediate state r is similarly separated into an electronic state e and nuclear configuration state j. Let ξ and q stand for the set of electronic and nuclear coordinates, respectively. Then the energy and wave function for the unperturbed molecule in, for example, the ground electronic state, are

$$E_k = E_g(0) + W_{gi} \tag{25}$$

$$\psi_k = \phi_g(\xi, q)U_{gi}(q) \tag{26}$$

In Eq. (25), $E_g(0)$ is the energy eigenvalue of the Schrödinger equation for nuclei clamped in the equilibrium configuration and W_{gi} is the vibration energy of the nuclei in the electronic state g. In Eq. (26), $\phi_g(\xi, q)$ is the electronic wave function in which the nuclear coordinates (q) appear as parameters and $U_{gi}(q)$ is the wave function for the nuclear motions.

Computing the wave function of the molecule in its (nondegenerate) electronic ground state when it is perturbed by the electric field of the incident light wave Eq. (27) results, to the second order of approximation and for clamped nuclei,

$$\begin{aligned}\Phi_g &= \phi_g \exp(-iE_g(q)t/\hbar)\\ &\quad + \frac{1}{h}\sum_e{}' \left\{\frac{\mathbf{A}\cdot\mathbf{M}_{eg}}{\nu_{eg}-\nu_0}\exp[-i(E_g(q)+h\nu)t/\hbar]\right.\\ &\quad \left. + \frac{\mathbf{A}^*\cdot\mathbf{M}_{eg}}{\nu_{eg}+\nu_0}\exp[-i(E_g(q)-h\nu)t/\hbar]\right\}\phi_e(\xi, q)\end{aligned} \tag{27}$$

where $\nu_{eg} = (E_e - E_g)/h$ and where $\mathbf{M}_{eg}$ is defined by Eq. (3). The summation excludes the term with $e = g$. For vibrating nuclei the wave function is

$$\Psi_{gi} = \phi_g \exp[-i(E_g(0)+W_{gi})t/\hbar] + \frac{1}{h}\sum_e \sum_j{}' \left\{ \frac{\mathbf{A}\cdot\mathbf{M}_{ej,gi}}{\nu_{ej,gi}-\nu_0} \exp[-i(E_g(0)+W_{gi}+h\nu)t/\hbar] + \frac{\mathbf{A}^*\cdot\mathbf{M}_{ej,gi}}{\nu_{ej,gi}+\nu_0} \exp[-i(E_g(0)+W_{gi}-h\nu)t/\hbar] \right\} \phi_e U_{ej} \tag{28}$$

where the denominators are

$$\nu_{ej,gi} \pm \nu_0 = (\nu_{eg} \pm \nu_0) + (W_{ej} - W_{gi})/h \tag{29}$$

Assuming that

a. the difference between the electronic frequency and the incident frequency is very much greater than the nuclear frequencies, or

$$(\nu_{eg} - \nu_0) \gg (W_{ej} - W_{gi})/h$$

b. the frequency of the incident light is very much greater than the nuclear frequencies, or

$$\nu_0 \gg \nu_{gi,gf}$$

then Eq. (28) simplifies to Eq. (30) or Eq. (31):

$$\Psi_{gi} = \left\{ \phi_g \exp[-iE_g(0)t/\hbar] + \frac{1}{h}\sum_e{}' \left[\frac{\mathbf{A}\cdot\mathbf{M}_{eg}(q)}{\nu_{eg}-\nu_0} \exp\{-i[E_g(0)+h\nu]t/\hbar\} + \frac{\mathbf{A}^*\cdot\mathbf{M}_{eg}(q)}{\nu_{eg}+\nu_0} \exp\{-i[E_g(0)-h\nu]t/\hbar\} \right] \phi_e \right\} U_{gi} \exp(-iW_{gi}t/\hbar) \tag{30}$$

$$\Psi_{gi} = \Phi_{gi}(\xi, q) U_{gi}(q) \exp(-iW_{gi}t/\hbar) \tag{31}$$

where Φ_{gi} is given by Eq. (27) with $q = 0$. Comparing Eqs. (26) and (31) we see that under the stated assumptions it is thus only the electronic part of the total eigenfunction that is modified by the perturbation.

Using Eqs. (30) and (31) we obtain for the matrix element of the electric moment that gives rise to the Raman effect

$$\mathbf{C}_{gi,gf} = \int U_{gi}^*(q) \mathbf{C}_{gg}(q) U_{gf}(q)\, dq \tag{32}$$

where

$$\mathbf{C}_{gg}(q) = \frac{1}{h}\sum_e \left\{ \frac{[\mathbf{A}\cdot\mathbf{M}_{ge}(q)]\mathbf{M}_{eg}(q)}{\nu_{eg}-\nu_0} + \frac{\mathbf{M}_{ge}(q)[\mathbf{A}\cdot\mathbf{M}_{eg}(q)]}{\nu_{eg}+\nu_0} \right\} \tag{33}$$

The other three terms that contribute to the total matrix element are ignored here since they do not describe the Raman effect. Equation (33) represents the amplitude of the electric moment of a rigid molecule in the ground electronic state g that is induced by the electric field of the incident light wave; it is a function of the nuclear configuration (q).

Equation (33) exhibits the same tensor connection between the incident field amplitude and the induced moment shown by Eqs. (6) and (8). The scattering tensor is, therefore,

$$\begin{aligned}(c_{\rho\sigma})_{gi,gf} &= \int U_{gi}^{*}[c_{\rho\sigma}(q)]_{gg} U_{gf}(q)\, dq \\ &= \int U_{gi}^{*}[\alpha_{\rho\sigma}(q)] U_{gf}(q)\, dq \\ &= (\alpha_{\rho\sigma})_{if}\end{aligned} \tag{34}$$

where the polarizability defined by Eq. (10) has been introduced. Since the polarizability is a real, symmetric tensor, its decomposition into a spherical, a symmetric, and an antisymmetric part [see Eq. (20)] gives

$$(c^{0})_{gi,gf} = a_{if}^{0} \tag{35a}$$

$$(c_{\rho\sigma}^{s})_{gi,gf} = (\alpha_{\rho\sigma}^{(1)})_{if} \tag{35b}$$

$$(c_{\rho\sigma}^{a})_{gi,gf} = 0 \tag{35c}$$

so that

$$(\alpha_{\rho\sigma})_{if} = (a^{0}\delta_{\rho}{}^{\sigma} + \alpha_{\rho\sigma}^{(1)})_{if} \tag{36}$$

The trace scattering and the quadrupole scattering are thus determined by the isotropic (spherical) and anisotropic parts of the polarizability, respectively, both of which depend on the nuclear configuration. There is no magnetic dipole scattering. The intensity formulas, Eqs. (12) and (13), become, therefore,

$$I_{if} = \frac{128\pi^{5}}{3}\frac{(\nu_{0}+\nu_{if})^{4}}{c^{4}}\sum_{\rho}\left|\sum_{\sigma}(\alpha_{\rho\sigma})_{if}a_{\sigma}\right|^{2} I_{0} \tag{37}$$

and

$$I_{if}(\mathbf{s}) = \frac{16\pi^{4}}{r^{2}}\frac{(\nu_{0}+\nu_{if})^{4}}{c^{4}}\left|\sum_{\rho\sigma}(\alpha_{\rho\sigma})_{if}s_{\rho}a_{\sigma}\right|^{2} I_{0} \tag{38}$$

The polarizability approximation breaks down when the two conditions (a) and (b) above are not fulfilled. We are then dealing with the resonance Raman effect (*34*) and the electronic Raman effect (*35*). The limitation to nondegenerate electronic ground states is not essential (*33*).

C. Molecular Rotations

We specialize the preceding results to the case where molecules can undergo free rotations in space, i.e., dilute gases (*36*). Moreover, we assume that there are no external fields that could give rise to a Stark or Zeeman effect. Splitting the indexes i and f so as to designate the vibrational and the rotational states independently, i.e., $i = v, R$ and $f = v', R'$ where v stands for the totality of vibrational quantum numbers and R stands similarly for the rotational quantum numbers, we obtain for the wave function,

$$U_{gi} = \Psi_{v,R} = \psi_v \cdot \Phi_R \tag{39}$$

where ψ_v is the vibrational wave function which depends on the normal coordinates and Φ_R is the rotational wave function whose explicit form depends on the nature of the rotator (i.e., linear molecule, spherical, symmetrical, asymmetrical top rotator). The intensity given by expressions (*37*) and (*38*) is, thus, determined by the matrix elements

$$(\alpha_{\rho\sigma})_{vR,v'R'} = \int \Phi_R{}^* \psi_v{}^* \alpha_{\rho\sigma}(q) \psi_{v'} \Phi_{R'} \, d\tau_{\text{vib}} \, d\tau_{\text{rot}} \tag{40}$$

The nuclear configuration (q) includes the specification of both the vibrational and rotational motion of the molecule. (The translational motion is exactly separable and is not included here.)

Since each angular momentum state $\mathbf{J}$ for the field free case is $(2J+1)$-fold degenerate the scattering cross section is given by Eq. (19) with $g_k = (2J+1)$. From Eqs. (16) and (19) we then have for the average cross section

$$\bar{Q}_{if} = \bar{Q}_{vR,v'R'} = \frac{128\pi^5}{9} \frac{(\nu_0+\nu')^4}{c^4} \frac{1}{(2J+1)} \sum_{\rho\sigma} \sum_{M,M'} |(\alpha_{\rho\sigma})_{vSM,v'S'M'}|^2 \tag{41}$$

where $\nu' = \nu_{vR,v'R'}$ and M and M' are the magnetic quantum numbers defined by projecting $\mathbf{J}$ onto the space fixed z-axis. The space fixed z-axis is defined by a weak magnetic field which is then ultimately removed. The remaining rotational quantum numbers are designated by S and S'.

We abbreviate Eq. (41) by writing

$$\bar{Q}_{vR,v'R'} = \frac{128\pi^5}{9} \frac{(\nu_0+\nu')^4}{c^4} G_{vR,v'R'} \tag{42}$$

where

$$G_{vR,v'R'} = \frac{1}{(2J+1)} \sum_{\rho\sigma} \sum_{M,M'} |(\alpha_{\rho\sigma})_{vSM,v'S'M'}|^2 \tag{43}$$

The quantity $G_{vR,v'R'}$ given by Eq. (43) is independent of the direction of the magnetic field. Instead of evaluating the double sum over M and M' directly, the same result is therefore also obtained by allowing the magnetic field to take on all directions in space and by computing an average over these. Since summing and averaging are commutative, we may first carry out the summation over one index, say M' and then compute the average. The result is then independent of the second summation index (M) and, therefore, from Eq. (43) we have

$$\sum_{M}\sum_{M'} |(\alpha_{\rho\sigma})_{vSM,v'S'M'}|^2 = (2J+1)\sum_{\bar{M}'} \langle|(\alpha_{\rho\sigma})_{vS\bar{M},v'S'\bar{M}'}|^2\rangle_{\text{avg}}^{(\tau)} \tag{44}$$

where the quantum numbers $\bar{M}$ and $\bar{M}'$ are those for a field different from the original, and one which is to take on all orientations τ. The averaging in Eq. (44) is performed by expressing the tensor components $(\alpha_{\rho\sigma})_{vS\bar{M},v'S'\bar{M}'}$ in terms of the tensor components in a coordinate system whose z-axis coincides with the magnetic field. This relationship is given by

$$(\alpha_{\rho\sigma})_{vSM,v'S'M'} = \sum_{\sigma\rho} (\alpha_{\bar{\rho}\bar{\sigma}})_{vSM,v'S'\bar{M}'} \cos(\rho\bar{\rho})\cos(\sigma\bar{\sigma}) \tag{45}$$

The quantities $(\alpha_{\bar{\rho}\bar{\sigma}})_{vS\bar{M},v'S'\bar{M}'}$ are then independent of the orientation of the field, and the averaging indicated in Eq. (44) is then only over the products of direction cosines. If the tensor $(\alpha_{\rho\sigma})$ is decomposed into its isotropic and anisotropic parts [Eq. (36)] then, since the average of the mixed term is zero, Eq. (44) becomes

$$\sum_{M,M'} |(\alpha_{\rho\sigma})_{vSM,v'S'M'}|^2 = (2J+1)\,\delta_{v'}^{v}\,\delta_{S'}^{S}\sum_{\bar{M}'}\langle|a_{vS\bar{M},v'S'\bar{M}'}|^2\rangle_{\text{avg}}^{(\tau)}$$
$$+(2J+1)\sum_{\bar{M}'}\langle|(\alpha_{\rho\sigma}^{(1)})_{vS\bar{M},v'S'\bar{M}'}|^2\rangle_{\text{avg}}^{(\tau)} \tag{46}$$

so that the scattering cross section and thus the intensity for free molecules is additively composed of two independent portions contributed by the isotropic and anisotropic parts of the polarizability.

The evaluation of the average of the products of direction cosines over all orientations τ may be carried out in Cartesian coordinates; and the results are available in standard references (*37*). It proves useful, however, to introduce a set of complex spherical polar coordinates [called circular coordinates in (*19* and *20*)] since these allow an easier computation of the matrix elements for rotational transitions. These coordinates are defined by the combinations.

$$r_{+1} = (x+iy)/\sqrt{2} = r\sin\theta\, e^{i\varphi} \tag{47a}$$

$$r_{-1} = (x-iy)/\sqrt{2} = r\sin\theta\, e^{-i\varphi} \tag{47b}$$

$$r_0 = z = r\cos\theta \tag{47c}$$

which are labeled by the indexes $+1$, -1, and 0, respectively. The phase convention adopted here is, of course, arbitrary. [A frequently used phase convention differs from the one used here in that $r_{+1} = -(1/\sqrt{2})(x+iy)$ with r_{-1} and r_0 given as in Eq. (47). see Refs. (*38–41*)]. The components of a vector **A** in our new coordinates are related to the Cartesian components of **A** as follows:

$$A_{+1} = (A_x + iA_y)/\sqrt{2} \tag{48a}$$

$$A_{-1} = (A_x - iA_y)/\sqrt{2} \tag{48b}$$

$$A_0 = A_z \tag{48c}$$

Similarly, the components of a second rank tensor, **T**, in the new coordinates, are related to the Cartesian components:

$$T_{11} = T^*_{-1-1} = \tfrac{1}{2}[(T_{xx} - T_{yy}) + i(T_{xy} + T_{yx})] \tag{49a}$$

$$T_{-11} = T^*_{1-1} = \tfrac{1}{2}[(T_{xx} + T_{yy}) + i(T_{xy} - T_{yx})] \tag{49b}$$

$$T_{10} = T^*_{-10} = \frac{1}{\sqrt{2}}(T_{xz} + iT_{yz}) \tag{49c}$$

$$T_{01} = T^*_{0-1} = \frac{1}{\sqrt{2}}(T_{zx} + iT_{zy}) \tag{49d}$$

$$T_{00} = T_{zz} \tag{49e}$$

Summation indexes in the new coordinates will be designated by $\lambda\mu(= +1, -1, 0)$. If $\mathbf{U}_x$, $\mathbf{U}_y$, $\mathbf{U}_z$ be the unit vectors along the Cartesian x, y, and z axes and, similarly, if $\mathbf{U}_{\pm 1} = (1/\sqrt{2})(\mathbf{U}_x \pm i\mathbf{U}_y)$ and $\mathbf{U}_0 = \mathbf{U}_z$ be the unit vectors along the new axes, then any vector **A** may be expressed in terms of its components as

$$\mathbf{A} = A_x\mathbf{U}_x + A_y\mathbf{U}_y + A_z\mathbf{U}_z = A_{-1}\mathbf{U}_{+1} + A_0\mathbf{U}_0 + A_{+1}\mathbf{U}_{-1}$$

or

$$\mathbf{A} = \sum_{\lambda=-1}^{+1} A_{-\lambda}\mathbf{U}_\lambda \tag{50}$$

as can be verified by direct substitution. The induced electric moment **M** and the incident electric field $\mathscr{E}$ are related by

$$M_\rho = \sum_\sigma \alpha_{\rho\sigma}\mathscr{E}_\sigma \tag{51a}$$

in Cartesian coordinates [see Eq. (6)], and by

$$M_\lambda = \sum_\mu \alpha_{\lambda\mu}\mathscr{E}_{-\mu} \tag{51b}$$

in the new coordinates, where α is the polarizability tensor. The matrix scheme of Eq. (51b) is

$$\begin{bmatrix} M_{+1} \\ M_0 \\ M_{-1} \end{bmatrix} = \begin{bmatrix} \alpha_{1-1} & \alpha_{10} & \alpha_{11} \\ \alpha_{0-1} & \alpha_{00} & \alpha_{01} \\ \alpha_{-1-1} & \alpha_{-10} & \alpha_{-11} \end{bmatrix} \begin{bmatrix} \mathscr{E}_{+1} \\ \mathscr{E}_0 \\ \mathscr{E}_{-1} \end{bmatrix} \tag{52}$$

Since the polarizability tensor is symmetric in the Cartesian coordinates ($\alpha_{\rho\sigma} = \alpha_{\sigma\rho}$) we see from Eqs. (49a)–(49e) that $\alpha_{10} = \alpha_{01}$, $\alpha_{-10} = \alpha_{0-1}$, and $\alpha_{1-1} = \alpha_{-11}$.

The mean value of the tensor is

$$a = \tfrac{1}{3}Tr(\alpha) = \tfrac{1}{3}(\alpha_{xx}+\alpha_{yy}+\alpha_{zz}) = \tfrac{1}{3}(\alpha_{00}+\alpha_{1-1}+\alpha_{-11})$$

or

$$a = \tfrac{1}{3} \sum_{\rho=x,y,z} \alpha_{\rho\rho} = \tfrac{1}{3} \sum_{\lambda=-1}^{+1} \alpha_{\lambda-\lambda} \tag{53}$$

Also, the anisotropy γ^2 of the tensor is given by

$$\gamma^2 = \tfrac{1}{2}(3G - |\, 3a \,|^2) \tag{54}$$

where

$$G = \sum_{\lambda} \sum_{\mu} |\, \alpha_{\lambda\mu} \,|^2$$

The transformation of the components of a vector **M** and tensor $\boldsymbol{\alpha}$ from a given coordinate frame ($\lambda\mu$) to another frame ($\lambda'\mu'$) which is rotated away from the first one is given by

$$M_{\lambda} = \sum_{\lambda'} M_{\lambda'} D_{-\lambda'\lambda} \tag{55}$$

and

$$\alpha_{\lambda\mu} = \sum_{\lambda'\mu'} \alpha_{\lambda'\mu'} D_{-\lambda'\lambda} D_{-\mu'\mu} \tag{56}$$

where the $D_{-\lambda'\lambda}$ are the direction cosines which are given in terms of the Cartesian direction cosines $D_{Xy} = \cos(Xy)$ by Eqs. (49a)–(49e).

In the complex spherical polar coordinates with the phase convention defined by Eq. (47) the tensor components $\alpha_{\lambda\mu}$ have a direct physical interpretation. Thus, linearly polarized light propagating in the y-direction and whose electric vector oscillates along the z-direction will induce an electric moment with components $M_{+1} = \alpha_{10}\mathscr{E}_0$, $M_0 = \alpha_{00}\mathscr{E}_0$, and $M_{-1} = \alpha_{-10}\mathscr{E}_0$ (see Fig. 1). M_0 is the induced moment that oscillates parallel to the incident electric vector and it gives rise to linearly polarized scattered radiation. The components M_{+1} and M_{-1} lie in the xy plane and oscillate perpendicular to the incident electric vector. An observer located on the (positive) z-axis will see left hand circularly polarized light produced by the component M_{+1} and right hand circularly polarized light produced by the component M_{-1}. Located in the xy-plane the observer

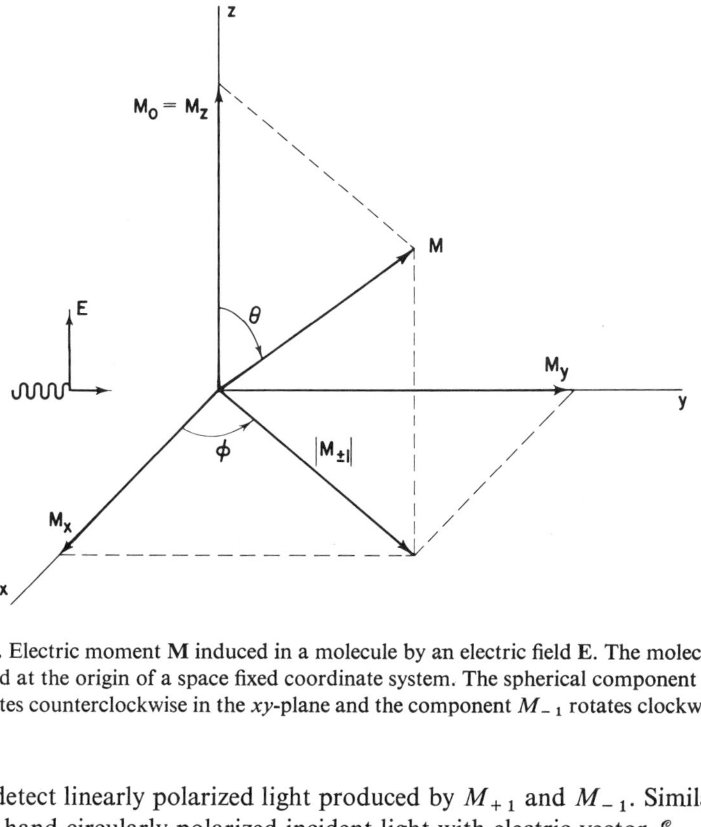

Fig. 1. Electric moment **M** induced in a molecule by an electric field **E**. The molecule is located at the origin of a space fixed coordinate system. The spherical component M_{+1} rotates counterclockwise in the xy-plane and the component M_{-1} rotates clockwise.

will detect linearly polarized light produced by M_{+1} and M_{-1}. Similarly, right hand circularly polarized incident light with electric vector $\mathscr{E}_{-1}$ will induce an electric moment with components $M_{+1} = \alpha_{11}\mathscr{E}_{-1}$, $M_{-1} = \alpha_{-11}\mathscr{E}_{-1}$, and $M_0 = \alpha_{01}\mathscr{E}_{-1}$ which have the same significance of giving rise to left hand, right hand, and linearly polarized scattered light, respectively. In general, therefore, the matrix element of $\alpha_{\lambda\mu}$ determines the λ-component of the scattering amplitude when the state of polarization of the incident light is $-\mu$.

We return now to the computation of the average of the products of direction cosines indicated by Eqs. (45) and (46). The matrix elements of the polarizability given by Eq. (40) are, in the new coordinates,

$$(\alpha_{\lambda\mu})_{vR,v'R'} = \int \Phi_R{}^* \psi_v{}^* \alpha_{\lambda\mu}(q) \psi_{v'} \Phi_{R'} \, d\tau_{\text{vib}} \, d\tau_{\text{rot}} \tag{57}$$

Since the components of a tensor transform as the products of vector components, the tensor $\alpha_{\lambda\mu}(q)$ has a dependence upon the azimuth about the space fixed z-axis which is determined by Eq. (47), namely, $\exp[i(\lambda+\mu)\varphi]$, where $\lambda, \mu = 0, \pm 1$. Since the rotational wavefunctions (Φ_R) depend upon the azimuth φ as $\exp(iM\varphi)$, then the integrand in Eq. (57) has a φ dependence of $\exp[i(M'-M+\lambda+\mu)]$. The nonvanishing of the matrix element, therefore, provides the selection rule

$$\Delta M = M - M' = \lambda + \mu \tag{58a}$$

From the definition $|\lambda+\mu| \leqq 2$ it follows that

$$\Delta M = 0, \pm 1, \pm 2 \tag{58b}$$

which, therefore, constitutes the Raman effect selection rule on the magnetic quantum number.

Combining Eqs. (44) and (45) and using the selection rule (58a), we have in the new coordinates

$$\sum_M \sum_{M'} |(\alpha_{\lambda\mu})_{vSM,v'S'M'}|^2 = (2J+1) \times$$
$$\sum_{\bar{M}'} \langle |\sum_{\bar{\lambda}\bar{\mu}} (\alpha_{\bar{\lambda}\bar{\mu}})_{vS\bar{M},v'S'\bar{M}'} D_{-\bar{\lambda}\lambda} D_{-\bar{\mu}\mu} \, \delta^{\bar{M}'}_{\bar{\lambda}+\bar{\mu}}|^2 \rangle^{(\tau)}_{\text{avg}} \tag{59}$$

where we have put $\bar{M}=0$, since summing over $\bar{M}'$ and averaging over τ yields a result that is independent of $\bar{M}$. The quantity $(\alpha_{\bar{\lambda}\bar{\mu}})_{vS\bar{M},v'S'\bar{M}'}$ is independent of the orientation τ so that the averaging involves only the direction cosine product $D_{-\bar{\lambda}\lambda} D_{-\bar{\mu}\mu}$. Separating the polarizability into its isotropic and anisotropic parts [see Eq. (46)], we have for the individual results (*19*)

$$\sum_M |(\alpha_{00})_{vSM,v'S'M}|^2 = \tfrac{1}{3} G^{(0)}_{vS,v'S'} + \tfrac{2}{15} G^{(1)}_{vS,v'S'} \tag{60a}$$

$$\sum_M |(\alpha_{1-1})_{vSM,v'S'M}|^2 = \tfrac{1}{3} G^{(0)}_{vS,v'S'} + \tfrac{1}{30} G^{(1)}_{vS,v'S'} \tag{60b}$$

$$\sum_M |(\alpha_{01})_{vSM,v'S'(M+1)}|^2 = \sum_M |(\alpha_{0-1})_{vSM,v'S'(M-1)}|^2 = \tfrac{1}{10} G^{(1)}_{vS,v'S'} \tag{60c}$$

$$\sum_M |(\alpha_{11})_{vSM,v'S'(M+2)}|^2 = \sum_M |(\alpha_{-1-1})_{vSM,v'S'(M-2)}|^2 = \tfrac{1}{5} G^{(1)}_{vS,v'S'} \tag{60d}$$

where

$$G^{(0)}_{vS,v'S'} = 3(2J+1) \mid a_{v,S,O;v'S'O} \mid^2 \tag{61a}$$

$$G^{(1)}_{vS,v'S'} = (2J+1) \sum_{\lambda\mu} \mid (\alpha^{(1)}_{\lambda\mu})_{vSO,v'S'(\lambda+\mu)} \mid^2 \tag{61b}$$

We note that the isotropic component of the polarizability contributes only to the transitions with $\Delta M = \lambda+\mu = 0$. The anisotropic component, however, contributes to all transitions. The further specification of the rotational structure requires now the discussion of special cases of interest. These are the symmetric top rotor, the linear and spherical top rotor which will be considered as limiting cases of the symmetric top, and the asymmetric top rotor.

D. The Symmetric Top

With the definition $A = h/(8\pi^2 cI_A)$ and $B = h/(8\pi^2 cI_B)$ (where $I_A \neq I_B = I_C$ are the principal moments of inertia) the term value of the rigid symmetric top is

$$F(J, K) = BJ(J+1)+(A-B)K^2 \tag{62a}$$

whereas for the centrifugally distorted rotor the term value expression is

$$F(J, K) = BJ(J+1)+(A-B)K^2 - D_J J^2(J+1)^2 - D_{JK} J(J+1)K^2 - D_K K^4 \tag{62b}$$

The rigid rotor eigenfunctions are

$$\Phi_R = \Theta_{JKM}(\theta)\, e^{iM\varphi}\, e^{iK\chi} \tag{63}$$

where χ is the azimuth about the top axis. The set of quantum numbers S, S' is now specifically $S = J, K$ and $S' = J', K'$ where J and K are the quantum numbers of the total angular momentum of the nuclear framework and its z-component along the body fixed z-axis respectively.

To evaluate Eqs. (61a) and (61b) we introduce a body fixed coordinate system $\lambda'\mu'$ and express the components $\alpha_{\lambda\mu}$ in terms of the body fixed components $\alpha_{\lambda'\mu'}$. Thus,

$$\alpha_{\lambda\mu} = \sum_{\lambda'\mu'} \alpha_{\lambda'\mu'} D_{-\lambda'\lambda} D_{-\mu'\mu} \tag{64}$$

The quantities $\alpha_{\lambda'\mu'}$ are intrinsic molecular parameters which depend only on the internal vibrational coordinates of the nuclei and not on the molecular orientation in space. Similarly, the directions cosines do not depend on the internal coordinates. The isotropic part of the cross section given by Eq. (61a) is independent of the molecular orientation so that we are here concerned only with the evaluation of Eq. (61b). Therefore,

$$\begin{aligned} G^{(1)}_{v,J,K;v',J',K'} &= (2J+1)\sum_{\lambda\mu} \left| (\alpha^{(1)}_{\lambda\mu})_{v,J,K,O;v',J',K',(\lambda+\mu)} \right|^2 \\ &= (2J+1)\sum_{\lambda\mu} \left| \sum_{\lambda'\mu'} (\alpha_{\lambda'\mu'})_{vv'} (D_{-\lambda'\lambda} D_{-\mu'\mu})_{J,K,O;J',K',(\lambda+\mu)} \right|^2 \end{aligned} \tag{65}$$

where we have omitted the superscript on $\alpha_{\lambda'\mu'}$ for brevity. The evaluation of the matrix elements of the product of the direction cosines provides the Raman effect selection rule

$$\Delta J = 0,\ \pm 1,\ \pm 2 \tag{66}$$

$$\Delta K = \lambda' + \mu' = 0,\ \pm 1,\ \pm 2 \tag{67}$$

The summation over λ' and μ' in Eq. (65) reduces, therefore, to just one term. Since the trace of the anisotropic tensor $\alpha^{(1)}_{\lambda'\mu'} = \alpha_{\lambda'\mu'}$ is zero, and since $\alpha_{-11} = \alpha_{1-1}$, we have the relation $\alpha_{00} + 2\alpha_{-11} = 0$. The expression for the cross section given by Eq. (65) becomes then, explicitly for the individual components,

$$\begin{aligned} G^{(1)}_{v,j,K;v',J',K} &= (2J+1)\sum_{\lambda\mu} \big| (\alpha_{00})_{vv'} (D_{0\lambda} D_{0\mu})_{J,K,O;J',K,(\lambda+\mu)} \\ &\qquad + (\alpha_{-11})_{vv'} (D_{1\lambda} D_{-1\mu} + D_{-1\lambda} D_{1\mu})_{J,K,O;J',K,(\lambda+\mu)} \big|^2 \\ &= \tfrac{1}{4}(2J+1) \left| (\alpha_{00})_{vv'} \right|^2 \sum_{\lambda\mu} \big| 3(D_{0\lambda} D_{0\mu})_{J,K,O;J',K,(\lambda+\mu)} \\ &\qquad - \delta^{\lambda}_{-\mu} \big|^2 \\ &= (2J+1) \left| (\alpha_{00})_{vv'} \right|^2 \cdot \tfrac{3}{2} b_{J,K;J',K} \end{aligned} \tag{68a}$$

$$\begin{aligned} G^{(1)}_{v,J,K;v',J',K\pm 1} &= (2J+1) \left| (\alpha_{0\pm 1})_{vv'} \right|^2 \times \\ &\qquad \sum_{\lambda\mu} \left| (D_{0\lambda} D_{\mp 1\mu} + D_{\mp 1\lambda} D_{0\mu})_{J,K,O;J',K\pm 1,\lambda+\mu} \right|^2 \\ &= (2J+1) \left| (\alpha_{0\pm 1})_{vv'} \right|^2 \cdot 2 b_{J,K;J',K\pm 1} \end{aligned} \tag{68b}$$

$$\begin{aligned} G^{(1)}_{v,J,K;v',J',K\pm 2} &= (2J+1) \left| (\alpha_{\pm 1,\pm 1})_{vv'} \right|^2 \times \\ &\qquad \sum_{\lambda\mu} \left| (D_{\mp 1\lambda} D_{\mp 1\mu})_{J,K,O;J',K\pm 2,\lambda+\mu} \right|^2 \\ &= (2J+1) \left| (\alpha_{\pm 1,\pm 1})_{vv'} \right|^2 b_{J,K;J',K\pm 2} \end{aligned} \tag{68c}$$

TABLE 1

Intensity Factors $b_{J,K:J',K'}$ for the Symmetric Top Rotor[a]

K' \ J'	$J-1$	$J-2$
K	$\frac{3K^2[J^2-K^2]}{J(J-1)(J+1)(2J+1)}$	$\frac{3[(J-1)^2-K^2][J^2-K^2]}{2J(J-1)(2J-1)(2J+1)}$
$K+1$	$\frac{(J+2K+1)^2(J-K-1)(J-K)}{2J(J-1)(J+1)(2J+1)}$	$\frac{[(J-1)^2-(K+1)^2][(J-K-1)(J-K)]}{J(J-1)(2J-1)(2J+1)}$
$K-1$	$\frac{(J-2K+1)^2(J+K-1)(J+K)}{2J(J-1)(J+1)(2J+1)}$	$\frac{[(J-1)^2-(K-1)^2](J+K-1)(J+K)}{J(J-1)(2J-1)(2J+1)}$
$K+2$	$\frac{[J^2-(K+1)^2](J-K-2)(J-K)}{2J(J-1)(J+1)(2J+1)}$	$\frac{(J-K-3)(J-K-2)(J-K-1)(J-K)}{4J(J-1)(2J-1)(2J+1)}$
$K-2$	$\frac{[J^2-(K-1)^2](J+K-2)(J+K)}{2J(J-1)(J+1)(2J+1)}$	$\frac{(J+K-3)(J+K-2)(J+K-1)(J+K)}{4J(J-1)(2J-1)(2J+1)}$

	J	$J+1$	$J+2$
K	$\frac{[J(J+1)-3K^2]^2}{J(J+1)(2J-1)(2J+3)}$	$\frac{3K^2[(J+1)^2-K^2]}{J(J+1)(J+2)(2J+1)}$	$\frac{3[(J+1)^2-K^2][(J+2)^2-K^2]}{2(J+1)(J+2)(2J+1)(2J+3)}$
$K+1$	$\frac{3(2K+1)^2(J-K)(J+K+1)}{2J(J+1)(2J-1)(2J+3)}$	$\frac{(J-2K)^2(J+K+1)(J+K+2)}{2J(J+1)(J+2)(2J+1)}$	$\frac{[(J+1)^2-K^2](J+K+2)(J+K+3)}{(J+1)(J+2)(2J+1)(2J+3)}$
$K-1$	$\frac{3(2K-1)^2(J+K)(J-K+1)}{2J(J+1)(2J-1)(2J+3)}$	$\frac{(J+2K)^2(J-K+1)(J-K+2)}{2J(J+1)(J+2)(2J+1)}$	$\frac{[(J+1)^2-K^2](J-K+2)(J-K+3)}{(J+1)(J+2)(2J+1)(2J+3)}$
$K+2$	$\frac{3[J^2-(K+1)^2][(J+1)^2-(K+1)^2]}{2J(J+1)(2J-1)(2J+3)}$	$\frac{[(J+1)^2-(K+1)^2](J+K+1)(J+K+3)}{2J(J+1)(J+2)(2J+1)}$	$\frac{(J+K+1)(J+K+2)(J+K+3)(J+K+4)}{4(J+1)(J+2)(2J+1)(2J+3)}$
$K-2$	$\frac{3[J^2-(K-1)^2][(J+1)^2-(K-1)^2]}{2J(J+1)(2J-1)(2J+3)}$	$\frac{[(J+1)^2-(K-1)^2](J-K+1)(J-K+3)}{2J(J+1)(J+2)(2J+1)}$	$\frac{(J-K+1)(J-K+2)(J-K+3)(J-K+4)}{4(J+1)(J+2)(2J+1)(2J+3)}$

[a] From Refs. (*19*) and (*41*).

The intensity factors $b_{J,K;J',K'}$ are given in Table 1 (*19,41*). They are not all independent but obey the relations

$$(2J+1)b_{J,K;J',K'} = (2J'+1)b_{J',K';J,K} \tag{69}$$

$$\sum_K b_{J,K;J',K'} = \tfrac{1}{5}(2J'+1) \tag{70}$$

and exhibit the symmetry $b_{J,K;J',K'} = b_{J,-K;J',-K'}$.

The intensity of the transition $J \rightarrow J'$ depends, therefore, on only one component $(\alpha^{(1)}_{\lambda'\mu'})_{vv'}$ of the nonspherical part of the molecular polarizability. If this component should vanish on account of the vibrational selection rules then the corresponding rotational branch is absent from the spectrum.

From Eqs. (68a), (68b), and (68c), as well as relations (49), we see that transitions with $\Delta K=0$ occur only for those vibrational transitions for which $(\alpha^{(1)}_{00})_{vv'} = (\alpha^{(1)}_{zz})_{vv'}$, or $(\alpha^{(1)}_{1,-1})_{vv'} = (\alpha^{(1)}_{-1,1})_{vv'} = \frac{1}{2}(\alpha^{(1)}_{xx} + \alpha^{(1)}_{yy})_{vv'}$, or both are different from zero. Rotational branches with $\Delta K = \pm 1$ can occur only for those vibrational transitions for which $(\alpha^{(1)}_{0,\pm 1})_{vv'} = (1/\sqrt{2})(\alpha^{(1)}_{zx} \pm i\alpha^{(1)}_{zy})_{vv'}$ is different from zero, i.e., for which either $(\alpha^{(1)}_{zx})_{vv'} = (\alpha^{(1)}_{xz})_{vv'}$, or $(\alpha^{(1)}_{zy})_{vv'} = (\alpha^{(1)}_{yz})_{vv'}$, or both do not vanish. Finally, transitions with $\Delta K = \pm 2$ can occur only when $(\alpha^{(1)}_{\pm 1,\pm 1})_{vv'} = \frac{1}{2}[(\alpha^{(1)}_{xx} - \alpha^{(1)}_{yy}) \pm 2i\alpha^{(1)}_{xy}]_{vv'}$ does not vanish, i.e., when either $(\alpha^{(1)}_{xx} - \alpha^{(1)}_{yy})_{vv'} \neq 0$, or $(\alpha^{(1)}_{xy})_{vv'} \neq 0$, or both. The rotational selection rules are thus seen to be related to the vibrational matrix elements of the polarizability tensor. The vibrational selection rules are most easily worked out using the methods of group theory and they are tabulated for the most important point groups (*42*). A convenient compilation of the selection rules for the various point groups has been given by Stoicheff (*29*) and is reproduced here as Table 2.

A further study of the selection rules in symmetric top molecules has been carried out by Mills (*43*) who did not use the polarizability approximation but instead worked directly with the scattering tensor given by Eq. (7). This procedure is more general, since the general scattering tensor has nine independent components in contrast to the polarizability tensor which has at most six independent components. Thus for C_{3v} molecules the Raman transitions between A_1 and A_2 vibrational states are forbidden in the polarizability approximation, whereas such transitions are allowed according to the third common level rule which is applicable to the general scattering tensor. The study of the Raman selection rules on the basis of the general scattering tensor was carried out immediately after the discovery of the Raman effect (*44*), but this method was largely ignored in view of the well-known success of the polarizability theory in providing a

TABLE 2

Selection Rules for Vibration-Rotation Raman Spectra[a]

Rotor type	Vibrational species	Nonzero component of polarizability	State of polarization	Selection rules
Linear	Totally symmetric	$\alpha_{xx}+\alpha_{yy}$; α_{zz}	Polarized	$\Delta J = 0,^{b} \pm 2$
	Degenerate	α_{yz}, α_{zx}	Depolarized	$\Delta J = 0,^{c} \pm 1, \pm 2$ always $+ \leftrightarrow +, - \leftrightarrow -, + \not\leftrightarrow -$ $(J'+J'' \geqq 0)$
Symmetric top	Totally symmetric	$\alpha_{xx}+\alpha_{yy}$; α_{zz}	Polarized	$\Delta J = 0,^{b} \pm 1, \pm 2: \Delta K = 0$
	Nontotally symmetric nondegenerate[e]	$\alpha_{xx}-\alpha_{yy}$; α_{xy}	Depolarized	$\Delta J = 0, \pm 1, \pm 2: \Delta K = \pm 2$
	Degenerate	$\alpha_{xx}-\alpha_{yy}$; α_{xy}	Depolarized	$\Delta J = 0, \pm 1, \pm 2: \Delta K = \pm 2$
		α_{yz}, α_{zx}	Depolarized	$\Delta J = 0, \pm 1, \pm 2: \Delta K = \pm 1$ $(J'+J'' \geqq 2)^{d}$
Spherical top	Totally symmetric	$\alpha_{xx}+\alpha_{yy}+\alpha_{zz}$	Completely polarized	$\Delta J = 0^{b}$
	Doubly degenerate	$\alpha_{xx}+\alpha_{yy}-2\alpha_{zz}$, $\alpha_{xx}-\alpha_{yy}$	Depolarized	$\Delta J = 0, \pm 1, \pm 2$
	Triply degenerate	α_{xy}, α_{yz}, α_{xz}	Depolarized	$\Delta J = 0, \pm 1, \pm 2$ $(J'+J'' \geqq 2)^{d}$

Asymmetric top[f]	Totally symmetric	$\alpha_{xx}, \alpha_{yy}, \alpha_{zz}$	Polarized	$\Delta J = 0, \pm 1, \pm 2\,(J'+J'' \geqq 2)$
				$++ \leftrightarrow ++,\ +- \leftrightarrow +-$
				$-+ \leftrightarrow -+,\ -- \leftrightarrow --$
	Nontotally symmetric	α_{xy}	Depolarized	$++ \leftrightarrow +-,\ -+ \leftrightarrow --$
		α_{xz}	Depolarized	$++ \leftrightarrow --,\ +- \leftrightarrow -+$
		α_{yz}	Depolarized	$++ \leftrightarrow -+,\ +- \leftrightarrow --$
Slightly asymmetric top[g]	Totally symmetric	$\alpha_{xx}+\alpha_{yy}, \alpha_{zz}, \alpha_{xy}$	Polarized	$\Delta J = 0, \pm 1, \pm 2: \Delta K = 0, \pm 1, \pm 2$
	Nontotally	$\alpha_{xx}-\alpha_{yy}, \alpha_{xy}$[h]	Depolarized	$\Delta J = 0, \pm 1, \pm 2: \Delta K = \pm 2$
	symmetric nondegenerate	α_{xz}, α_{yz}[i]	Depolarized	$\Delta J = 0, \pm 1, \pm 2: \Delta K = \pm 1$ $(J'+J'' \geqq 2)$[d]

[a] From Stoicheff, Ref. (*29*).
[b] Strong, Table 1.
[c] Weak, Table 1.
[d] For pure rotational spectra $J'+J'' \geqq 0$.
[e] Only in molecules with fourfold axes.
[f] See Herzberg [(*42*) p. 489].
[g] See Herzberg [(*42*) p. *441*].
[h] Only in molecules of point group C_{2v}, D_2, V_h.
[i] Only in molecules of point group C_s, C_2, C_{2h}, C_{2v}, D_2, V_h.

good understanding of the Raman effect, in spite of its more limited scope. Mills derived the selection rules for the degenerate vibrations of a symmetric top molecule in which the $+l$ and $-l$ components are split due to the Coriolis interaction. His results are given here in Table 3 for transitions from a totally symmetric lower state to a doubly degenerate upper state (fundamental vibrations).

TABLE 3

Selection Rules for Degenerate Raman Bands of Symmetric Top Molecules[a]

i. Point groups C_3 (C_3, C_{3v}, C_{3h}, D_3, D_{3d}, S_6)		
$\Delta K = +1$:	$E(+l) \leftarrow A$	$\Delta\nu_{sub} = 2[A(1-\zeta)-B]$
$\Delta K = -1$:	$E(-l) \leftarrow A$	
$\Delta K = +2$:	$E(-l) \leftarrow A$	$\Delta\nu_{sub} = 4[A(1+\frac{1}{2}\zeta)-B]$
$\Delta K = -2$:	$E(+l) \leftarrow A$	
ii. Point groups C_4 (C_4, C_{4v}, C_{4h}, D_4, D_{4h})		
$\Delta K = +1$:	$E(+l) \leftarrow A$	$\Delta\nu_{sub} = 2[A(1-\zeta)-B]$
$\Delta K = -1$:	$E(-l) \leftarrow A$	
$\Delta K = \pm 2$:	$B \leftarrow A$	$\Delta\nu_{sub} = 4[A-B]$
iii. Point groups C_n with $n \geqq 5$ (C_n, C_{nv}, C_{nh}, D_n, D_{nh}) D_{nd} with n odd, and S_m with $\frac{1}{2}m$ odd		
$\Delta K = +1$:	$E_1(+l) \leftarrow A$	$\Delta\nu_{sub} = 2[A(1-\zeta)-B]$
$\Delta K = -1$:	$E_1(-l) \leftarrow A$	
$\Delta K = +2$:	$E_2(+l) \leftarrow A$	$\Delta\nu_{sub} = 4[A(1-\frac{1}{2}\zeta)-B]$
$\Delta K = -2$:	$E_2(-l) \leftarrow A$	
iv. Point groups D_{nd} with n even, and S_m with $\frac{1}{2}m$ even		
a. Point groups D_{2d} and S_4:		
$\Delta K = +1$:	$E(-l) \leftarrow A$	$\Delta\nu_{sub} = 2[A(1+\zeta)-B]$
$\Delta K = -1$:	$E(+l) \leftarrow A$	
$\Delta K = \pm 2$:	$B \leftarrow A$	$\Delta\nu_{sub} = 4[A-B]$
b. Point groups D_{4d} and S_8:		
$\Delta K = +1$:	$E_3(-l) \leftarrow A$	$\Delta\nu_{sub} = 2[A(1+\zeta)-B]$
$\Delta K = -1$:	$E_3(+l) \leftarrow A$	
$\Delta K = +2$:	$E_2(+l) \leftarrow A$	$\Delta\nu_{sub} = 4[A(1-\frac{1}{2}\zeta)-B]$
$\Delta K = -2$:	$E_2(-l) \leftarrow A$	

[a] From Mills, Ref. (*43*).

E. The Band Frequencies

1. Totally Symmetric Raman Bands

Applying the selection rules $\Delta J = 0, \pm 1, \pm 2$ and $\Delta K = 0$, to Eq. (62b) we have the following equations for the Raman displacements in the customary notation where upper state and lower state constants are labeled by single and double primes, respectively, the quantum numbers (without primes) are those of the lower state, and where ν_0 is the pure vibrational Raman shift. Furthermore the transitions with $\Delta J = -2, -1, 0, +1, +2$ are labeled as the O, P, Q, R, and S branches, respectively, and the ΔK transitions are indicated by a left-hand letter superscript on the branch label. For $\Delta K = -2, -1, 0, +1, +2$ the letter designations O, P, Q, R, S are often used. For example, a transition with $\Delta J = -2$ and $\Delta K = +1$ is designated by ${}^{R}O_K(J)$ where J and K are the quantum numbers of the lower state belonging to this transition. For the Q-branch ($\Delta J = 0$, $\Delta K = 0$) the Raman displacements are

$$Q_K(J) = \nu_0 + (B' - B'')J(J+1) + [(A' - B') - (A'' - B'')]K^2 \\ - (D_J' - D_J'')J^2(J+1)^2 - (D_{JK}' - D_{JK}'')J(J+1)K^2 - (D_K' - D_K'')K^4 \tag{71}$$

The Raman displacements for the O-branch ($\Delta J = -2$, $\Delta K = 0$) and the S-branch ($\Delta J = +2$, $\Delta K = 0$) are given collectively by

$$\begin{aligned} O, S_K(J) = {} & \{\nu_0 + \tfrac{3}{4}(B' - B'') + [(A' - B') - (A'' - B'')]K^2 - \tfrac{9}{16}(D_J' - D_J'') \\ & - \tfrac{3}{4}(D'_{JK} - D''_{JK})K^2 - (D_K' - D_K'')K^4\} \\ & + \{(B' + B'') - \tfrac{3}{2}(D_J' + D_J'') - (D_{JK}' + D_{JK}'')K^2\}m \\ & + \tfrac{1}{4}\{(B' - B'') - \tfrac{11}{2}(D_J' - D_J'') - (D_{JK}' - D_{JK}'')K^2\}m^2 \\ & - \tfrac{1}{2}(D_J' + D_J'')m^3 \\ & - \tfrac{1}{16}(D_J' - D_J'')m^4 \end{aligned} \tag{72}$$

where $m = (-2J+1)$ for the O-branch and $(2J+3)$ for the S-branch. The wave numbers for the P- and R-branch lines are similarly given by

$$\begin{aligned} P, R_K(J) = {} & \{\nu_0 + [(A' - B') - (A'' - B'')]K^2 - (D_K' - D_K'')K^4\} \\ & + [(B' + B'') - (D_{JK}' + D_{JK}'')K^2]m \\ & + [(B' - B'') - (D_J' - D_J'') - (D_{JK}' - D_{JK}'')K^2]m^2 \\ & - 2(D_J' + D_J'')m^3 \\ & - (D_J' - D_J'')m^4 \end{aligned} \tag{73}$$

where $m = -J$ for the P-branch and $J+1$ for the R-branch.

We generally have that the difference between corresponding upper and lower state constants is slight, so that if we put $A' = A''$, $B' = B''$, and ignore the contributions due to the centrifugal distortion, then we note from Eq. (71) that all Q-branch transitions occur at the same frequency ν_0 which thus appears as a strong feature in the spectrum. On the other hand the P and R branch transitions do not coincide but form a series of lines with spacing $2B$ while the O and S branch transitions form a series of lines with spacing $4B$. Since every other line in the $P(R)$ branch coincides with a line in the $O(S)$ branch, there is an apparent intensity alternation in these rotational "wings" of the rotation-vibration band. If the centrifugal distortion terms are retained but with $D_J' = D_J''$ etc. then each Raman "line" splits into $J+1$ transitions, one for each value of K, which do not coincide and whose separation from one another is given by $2D_{JK}(2K+1)$ and $4D_{JK}(2K+1)$ for lines in the $P(R)$ and $O(S)$ branch, respectively.

The frequencies of the pure rotational transitions in totally symmetric states (primarily the ground vibrational state) are obtained by letting $\nu_0 = 0$, $A' = A''$, $B' = B''$, $D_J' = D_J''$, $D'_{JK} = D''_{JK}$ and $D_K' = D_K''$ in Eqs. (71), (72), and (73) and imposing the restriction that $J'+J'' \geqq 2$. The pure rotation spectrum then consists of only an R-branch and an S-branch whose frequencies (Stokes as well as anti-Stokes transitions) are given by the relations

$$S_K(J) = (4B-6D_J-4D_{JK}K^2)(J+\tfrac{3}{2})-8D_J(J+\tfrac{3}{2})^3 \tag{72'}$$

and

$$R_K(J) = 2(B-D_{JK}K^2)(J+1)-4D_J(J+1)^3 \tag{73'}$$

2. Nontotally Symmetric, Nondegenerate Raman Bands

Raman bands of this type can occur only in those symmetric top molecules which have a fourfold axis of symmetry (point groups C_4, C_{4v}, C_{4h}, D_{2d}, D_4, D_{4h}, S_4). The selection rules are $\Delta J = 0, \pm 1, \pm 2$ and $\Delta K = \pm 2$ only. The frequencies of the Raman lines for the different branches derived from Eq. (62b) are:

For the Q-branch,

$$^{O,S}Q_K(J) = \nu^{\text{sub}}(^{O,S}Q_K)+f(J, K\pm 2) \tag{74a}$$

where the sub-band origins (defined to be those frequencies with $J = 0$) are given by

$$\nu^{\text{sub}}(^{O,S}Q_K) = \nu_0+4[(A'-B')-4D_K']$$
$$\pm 4[(A'-B')-8D\ ']K$$

$$+[(A'-B')-(A''-B'')-24D_K']K^2$$
$$\mp 8D_K'K^3$$
$$-(D_K'-D_K'')K^4 \tag{74b}$$

and where

$$f(J, K\pm 2) = [(B'-B'')-D_{JK}'(K\pm 2)^2+D_{JK}''K^2]J(J+1)$$
$$-(D_J'-D_J'')J^2(J+1)^2 \tag{74c}$$

For the P- and R- branches we have

$$^{o,s}P, R_K(J) = \nu_0+[(A'-B')(K\pm 2)^2-(A''-B'')K^2]$$
$$-[D_K'(K\pm 2)^2-D_K''K^4]$$
$$+[(B'+B'')-D_{JK}'(K\pm 2)^2-D_{JK}''K^2]m$$
$$+[(B'-B'')-(D_J'-D_J'')-D_{JK}'(K\pm 2)^2+D_{JK}''K^2]m^2$$
$$-2(D_J'+D_J'')m^3$$
$$-(D_J'-D_J'')m^4 \tag{75}$$

where $m = -J$ for the P-branch and $m = (J+1)$ for the R-branch.

For the O- and S-branches we have:

$$^{o,s}O, S_K(J) = \nu_0+\tfrac{3}{4}(B'-B'')+[(A'-B')(K\pm 2)^2-(A''-B'')K^2]$$
$$-\tfrac{9}{16}(D_J'-D_J'')-\tfrac{3}{4}[D_{JK}'(K\pm 2)^2-D_{JK}''K^2]$$
$$-[D_K'(K\pm 2)^4-D_K''K^4]$$
$$+[(B'+B'')-\tfrac{3}{2}(D_J'+D_J'')-D_{JK}'(K\pm 2)^2-D_{JK}''K^2]m$$
$$+\tfrac{1}{4}[(B'-B'')-\tfrac{11}{2}(D_J'-D_J'')-D_{JK}'(K\pm 2)^2+D_{JK}''K^2]m^2$$
$$-\tfrac{1}{2}(D_J'+D_J'')m^3$$
$$-\tfrac{1}{16}(D_J'-D_J'')m^4 \tag{76}$$

where $m = (-2J+1)$ for the O-branch and $m = (2J+3)$ for the S-branch.

From Eq. (74) we see that, contrary to the case of the totally symmetric bands, the Q-branch transitions do not coincide and thus do not form a strong central feature of the band. Indeed, ignoring the centrifugal distortion terms and the difference between initial and final state constants, the spacing of the Q-branch transitions is $4(A-B)$. This is also the spacing of the sub-band origins (defined by $m = 0$, $K = 0, 1, 2, \ldots$) of the

${}^{O,S}P$, R and ${}^{O,S}O$, S branches given by Eqs. (75) and (76). These transitions of spacing $4(A—B)$ are superposed on a finer line structure in the ${}^{O,S}P$, R branches of spacing $2B$ (obtained by letting $\Delta m = \Delta J = 1$) and of spacing $4B$ in the ${}^{O,S}O$, S branches (obtained by letting $\Delta m = 2$ for $\Delta J = 1$).

The appearance of such a band is typically that of a degenerate band [see Herzberg, Ref. (*42*), p. 425 for the example of an infrared band with $\Delta J = 0, \pm 1$ and $\Delta K = \pm 1$. Except for being more complex in that it has the additional O and S branches, a Raman transition between non-degenerate states, with $\Delta J = 0, \pm 1, \pm 2$ and $\Delta K = \pm 2$ only, has a similar appearance].

3. Degenerate Raman Bands

On account of its smallness, the rotation-vibration interaction (Coriolis coupling) can be ignored in the case of transitions between non-degenerate states. For degenerate vibrational states, however, the coupling is sufficiently strong, so that the energy expressions [Eq. (62a, b)] must be modified. Thus, for degenerate vibrational states the rotational term value is

$$F(J, K) = BJ(J+1)+(A-B)K^2 \mp 2A\zeta K - D_J J^2(J+1)^2 - D_{JK}J(J+1)K^2 - D_K K^4 \quad (77)$$

where the additional quantity $\mp 2A\zeta K$ gives the Coriolis interaction. The quantity ζ (the Coriolis coupling coefficient) is, in units of $\hbar$, the vibrational angular momentum of the given vibrational state and the upper (lower) sign is used when the vibrational angular momentum points in the same (opposite) direction as the angular momentum due to molecular rotation in space.

The evaluation of the vibrational matrix elements $(\alpha_{\lambda'\mu'})_{vv'}$ and, thus, the establishment of the selection rules for doubly degenerate vibrations merits special attention. The wave function for a two dimensional harmonic oscillator in polar coordinates (r, χ) is given by (*45*)

$$\Psi_{v_t,l_t}(r_t,\chi_t) = N_{v_t,l_t}\, e^{-\rho/2}\rho^{1/2|l_t|}L_{\tau}^{|l_t|}(\rho)\exp(il_t\chi_t) \quad (78)$$

where $\rho = r_t^{\,2}$, $\tau = \frac{1}{2}(r_t + |\, l_t \,|)$, N_{v_t,l_t} is a normalization factor and $L_{\tau}^{|l_t|}(\rho)$ is an associated Laguerre polynomial. The angle χ_t is the azimuth about the top axis and v_t, l_t are the two quantum numbers of the tth mode of vibration where $|\, l_t \,| = v_t, v_t - 1, v_t - 2, \ldots, 1$ or 0 is the quantum number of the vibrational angular momentum. A study of the effect of symmetry operations on the normal coordinates of a vibration which is degenerate with respect to a p-fold axis reveals that the normal modes may be classified by an integer s_t which is defined only modulo p [see Ref. (*42*), pp. 83–99 as well as Ref. (*19* and *20*) where this integer is denoted by the letter l and l_t, respectively. We use instead s_t to avoid confusion with the quantum number of the internal vibrational angular momentum for which the standard designation is l_t]. For $s_t = 0$ and $s_t = p/2$ (for p = even only), there correspond the modes which are totally symmetric (A-species) and antisymmetric (B-species) to the p-fold axis respectively. The remaining values of s_t distinguish between the various degenerate species (E_s-species). Evaluating now the vibrational matrix element

$$(\alpha_{\lambda'\mu'})_{vv'} = \int \Psi^*_{v_t' l_t'}(\alpha_{\lambda'\mu'})\Psi_{v_t l_t}\, d\tau$$

we have, using the wave function (78), noting from Eq. (47) that $\alpha_{\lambda'\mu'}$ has a χ_t-dependence of the form $\exp[i(\lambda'+\mu')\chi_t]$ (since tensor components transform as the products of the coordinates which appear as their indexes) and letting v and v' stand for the totality of the vibrational quantum numbers that undergo a change, for the requirement that the integral not vanish

$$\lambda'+\mu'-\sum_t (l_t'-l_t)-zp = 0$$

where z is an arbitrary integer. Including now the species specification by means of the number s_t we have the general selection rule for the Raman effect in molecules belonging to axial point groups:

$$\lambda'+\mu' = zp+\sum_t s_t(l_t'-l_t) \tag{79}$$

Combining this result with relation Eq. (67) we have for a single excitation (choosing $z = 0$)

$$K'-K = \lambda'+\mu' = s_t(l_t'-l_t) \tag{80}$$

For a fundamental vibration $v_t' = 1 \leftarrow v_t = 0$ we then have two possibilities $l_t' = +1 \leftarrow l_t = 0$ and $l_t' = -1 \leftarrow l_t = 0$, so that

$$\Delta K = \lambda'+\mu' = \pm s_t = 0, \pm 1, \pm 2 \tag{81}$$

according to whether the internal vibrational angular momentum is parallel (+sign) or antiparallel (−sign) to the angular momentum due to molecular rotation in space.

The rotational energy levels with $l_t > 0$ and $l_t < 0$ are called the $+l$ levels and $-l$ levels respectively [Ref. (*42*), p. 403, see also Ref. (*46*),

Part II)] and from Eq. (77) it is seen that due to the Coriolis interaction the $+l$ levels have smaller energies than the $-l$ levels for given J and K. Which individual values of ΔK given by Eq. (81) describe the transition from the rotational level of the totally symmetric (A-species) ground state to either the $+l$ or $-l$ level of the degenerate (E-species) excited state has been deduced in a general manner by Mills (*43*), and his results are contained in the first two columns of Table 3 for the transitions with $\Delta K = \pm 1$ and ± 2. On the basis of these selection rules the following expressions are derived from Eq. (77) for the Q-branch transitions ($\Delta J = 0$). For a given situation the upper or the lower sign is used throughout.

a. *The* $\Delta K = \pm 1, \pm l$ *Transitions*

For molecules belonging to the point groups $C_3(C_3, C_{3v}, C_{3h}, D_3, D_{3d}, S_6)$, C_n with $n \geqq 4(C_n, C_{nv}, C_{nh}, D_n, D_{2h})$, and D_{nd} with n odd, and S_m with $\frac{1}{2}m$ odd:

$$^{P,R}Q_K{}^{\pm}(J) = \nu^{\text{sub}}(^{P,R}Q_K^{+,-}) + f_1(J, K) \tag{82a}$$

where the sub-band origins are

$$\begin{aligned}\nu^{\text{sub}}(^{P,R}Q_K^{+,-}) = {} & [\nu_0 + A'(1-2\zeta) - B' - D_K{}'] \\ & \pm 2[A'(1-\zeta) - B' - 2D_K{}']K \\ & + [(A'-B') - (A''-B'') - 6D_K{}']K^2 \\ & \mp 4D_K{}'K^3 \\ & - (D_K{}' - D_K{}'')K^4\end{aligned} \tag{82b}$$

and where

$$f_1(J, K) = [B' - B'' - D_{JK}{}'(K \pm 1)^2 + D_{JK}{}''K^2]J(J+1) - (D_J{}' - D_J{}'')J^2(J+)^2 \tag{82c}$$

b. *The* $\Delta K = \pm 1, \mp l$ *Transitions*

For molecules belonging to the point groups D_{nd} with n even, and S_m with $\frac{1}{2}\,m$ even:

$$^{P,R}Q_K^{-,+}(J) = \nu^{\text{sub}}(^{P,R}Q_K^{-,+}) + f_1(J, K) \tag{83a}$$

where the sub-band origins are

$$\begin{aligned}\nu^{\text{sub}}(^{P,R}Q_K^{-,+}) = {} & [\nu_0 + A'(1+2\zeta) - B' - D_K{}'] \pm 2[A'(1+\zeta) - B' - 2D_K{}']K \\ & + [(A'-B') - (A''-B'') - 6D_K{}']K^2 \mp 4D_K{}'K^3 - (D_K{}' - D_K{}'')K^4\end{aligned} \tag{83b}$$

and where $f_1(J, K)$ is given by Eq. (82c).

c. *The* $\Delta K = \pm 2, \pm l$ *Transitions*

For molecules belonging to the point groups C_n with $n \geqq 5(C_n, C_{nv}, C_{nh}, D_n, D_{nh}, D_{nd}$ with n odd, and S_m with $\frac{1}{2}m$ odd), and D_{4d} and S_8:

$$ {}^{O,S}Q_K^{+,-}(J) = \nu^{\text{sub}}({}^{O,S}Q_K^{+,-}) + f_2(J, K) \tag{84a} $$

where the sub-band origins are given by

$$ \begin{aligned} \nu^{\text{sub}}({}^{O,S}Q_K^{+,-}) = {} & \nu_0 + 4[A'(1-\zeta) - B' - 4D_K'] \pm 4[A'(1-\tfrac{1}{2}\zeta) - B' - 8D_K']K \\ & + [(A'-B') - (A''-B'') - 24D_K']K^2 \\ & \mp 8D_K'K^3 - (D_K' - D_K'')K^4 \end{aligned} \tag{84b} $$

and where

$$ f_2(J,K) = [(B'-B'') - D_{JK}'(K\pm 2)^2 + D_{JK}''K^2]J(J+1) - (D_J' - D_J'')J^2(J+1)^2 \tag{84c} $$

d. *The* $\Delta K = \pm 2, \mp l$ *Transitions*

For molecules belonging to the point groups $C_3(C_3, C_{3v}, C_{3h}, D_3, D_{3d}, S_6)$:

$$ {}^{O,S}Q_K^{-,+}(J) = \nu^{\text{sub}}({}^{O,S}Q_K^{-,+}) + f_2(J, K) \tag{85a} $$

where the sub-band origins are given by

$$ \begin{aligned} \nu^{\text{sub}}({}^{O,S}Q_K^{-,+}) = {} & \nu_0 + 4[A'(1+\zeta) - B' - 4D_K'] \\ & \pm 4[A'(1+\tfrac{1}{2}\zeta) - B' - 8D_K']K \\ & + [(A'-B') - (A''-B'') - 24D_K']K^2 \\ & \mp 8D_K'K^3 \\ & - (D_K' - D_K'')K^4 \end{aligned} \tag{85b} $$

and where $f_2(J, K)$ is given by Eq. (84c).

e. *The* $\Delta K = \pm 2$ *Transitions in Molecules Belonging to the Point Groups* $C_4(C_4, C_{4v}, C_{4h}, D_4, D_{4h})$ *and* D_{2d} *and* S_4

For these molecules $s_t = p/2 = 2 = \pm\Delta K$ is even; hence the corresponding modes of vibration are antisymmetric rather than degenerate with respect to the four-fold axis of symmetry. This case of a nontotally symmetric, nondegenerate transition has been discussed above, and the band frequencies are given by Eqs. (74a–c).

The spacings of the Q_K-branch lines are given by the coefficient of K in Eqs. (82–85). The third column of Table 3 lists these line spacings for the different cases if the contribution due to the centrifugal distortion is ignored.

The frequency expressions for the remaining transitions with $\Delta J = \pm 1$ and ± 2 are not given here. They are easily derived from Eq. (77) by use of the proper selection rules. These transitions provide a fine structure in the degenerate band, with $\Delta J = \pm 1$ transitions giving the P- and R-branches in which the line spacing is $2B$, and the $\Delta J = \pm 2$ transitions giving the O- and S-branches in which the line spacing is $4B$, when the difference between the upper and lower state B-values is ignored.

F. The Band Intensities

The intensity of the Raman transitions is obtained by collecting Eqs. (14) and (41)–(43) to give, for linearly polarized incident light of frequency ν_0 and intensity I_0 (in ergs/sec-cm^2),

$$I(v, J, K \rightarrow v', J', K') = \frac{128\pi^5}{9} \frac{(\nu_0+\nu')^4}{c^4} G_{v,J,K;v',J',K'} I_0 \tag{86}$$

where ν' is the Raman frequency shift. (The quantity I is the scattered power in ergs/sec rather than an intensity which is given in ergs/sec-cm^2.) The quantity $G_{v,J,K;v',J',K'}$ is according to Eq. (42) the frequency independent part of the scattering cross section. Limiting ourselves to the anisotropic scattering, since it alone describes the rotational Raman effect, $G_{v,J,K;v',J',K'}$ is replaced by $G^{(1)}_{v,J,K;v',J',K'}$ which is defined by Eq. (61b) and which is given in detailed form by Eqs. (68a)–(68c). Introducing a factor for an assembly of molecules in thermal equilibrium which describes the distribution of the molecules over the various energy levels, we have the following results.

For transitions with $\Delta K = 0$ $(s_t = 0)$

$$I(v, J, K; v', J', K) = \frac{64\pi^5}{3c^4} \frac{(\nu_0+\nu')^4}{Q} \cdot \tfrac{4}{9} \, |(\gamma_{vv'})|^2 \times I_0 g_{JK} b_{J,K;J',K} \exp\{-[G(v)+F(J,K)](hc/kT)\} \tag{87}$$

where the anisotropy γ has been introduced by means of the relation $\gamma = \alpha_{00} - \alpha_{-11} = \frac{3}{2}\alpha_{00}$.

For transitions with $\Delta K = \pm 1 (s_t = 1)$

$$I(v, J, K; v', J', K') = \frac{256\pi^5}{9c^4} \frac{(\nu_0 + \nu')^4}{Q} |(\alpha_{0\pm 1})_{vv'}|^2 \times I_0 g_{JK} b_{J,K;J',K\pm 1} \exp\{-[G(v)+F(J, K)](hc/kT)\} \quad (88)$$

For transitions with $\Delta K = \pm 2 (s_t = 2)$,

$$I(v, J, K; v', J', K') = \frac{128\pi^5}{9c^4} \frac{(\nu_0 + \nu')^4}{Q} |(\alpha_{\pm 1, \pm 1})_{vv'}|^2 \times b_{J,K;J',K\pm 2} g_{JK} I_0 \exp\{-[G(v)+F(J, K)](hc/kT)\} \quad (89)$$

In these expressions, the quantity Q is the partition function,

$$Q = \sum_{v,J,K} g_{JK} \exp\{-[G(v)+F(J, K)](hc/kT)\}$$

where $G(v)$ is the vibrational term value, $F(J, K)$ the rotational term value given by Eq. (77) (in which $\zeta = 0$ for the nondegenerate vibrations), and g_{JK} is the statistical weight of the initial state. This includes a factor of 2 due to the K-degeneracy for all levels with $K \neq 0$, the factor $(2J+1)$ from Eqs. (68a)–(68c), and a factor which involves the nuclear spins of the equivalent nuclei, which factor depends on the value of K (i.e., whether $K = 0$ or whether or not K is divisible by p) and on the statistics obeyed by the equivalent nuclei [see Ref. (*19*); Ref. (*42*), pp. 26–29 and Chapt. IV, Section 2a; Refs. (*47–49*); and Ref. (*50*) Chapt. 5].

To the previous intensity expressions for the anisotropic scattering there is to be added the contribution due to the isotropic scattering which is described by the spherically symmetric part of the polarizability tensor. This contribution is given by Eq. (86) with $G_{v,J,K;v',J',K'}$ replaced by $G^{(0)}_{v,J,K;v',J',K'}$ which is defined by Eq. (61a). Since the matrix element of the average polarizability is independent of the rotational state of the molecules it contributes only to the intensity of the Q-branch of a band.

G. Linear Molecules

The results presented for the symmetric top rotor can be applied to linear molecules by considering the latter to be the limiting case of the former as the moment of inertia about the top axis $I_{zz} = I_A \to 0$. [For a detailed study of this limiting case see Ref. (*51*)]. For this limiting case we replace the quantum number K by the quantum number $l(= 0, 1, 2, \ldots)$ which, in units of $\hbar$, is the vibrational angular momentum about the internuclear axis. Instead of Eq. (77) the rotational term value is given by

$$F(J) = B[J(J+1)-l^2]-D_J[J(J+1)-l^2]^2 \tag{90}$$

where, as before, B and D_J are the molecular constants for the respective vibrational states. Only those vibrations occur for which $s_t = 0$, $l = 0$ (i.e. nondegenerate vibrations, $\|$-bands) and $s_t = 1, l \neq 0$ (i.e., degenerate vibrations, $\perp$-bands). The general selection rules are that

$$\Delta J = 0, \pm 2 \quad \text{if} \quad l = 0$$

and

$$\Delta J = 0, \pm 1, \pm 2 \quad \text{if} \quad l \neq 0$$

and

$$+ \not\leftrightarrow - , \quad s \not\leftrightarrow a$$

1. The Band Frequencies

a. *Vibrations with* $s_t = 0$

This also includes the pure rotational transitions. For fundamental vibrations $K = l = 0$ and we see from Table 1 that the intensity factor $b_{J,K;J',K'}$ vanishes for $\Delta J = \pm 1$ and $\Delta K = \Delta l = 0$. Therefore only $\Delta J = 0$ (Q-branch) and $\Delta J = \pm 2$ (O- and S-branch) transitions are allowed. In the following expressions ν_0 is the vibrational frequency derived from $\nu_0 = G(1)-G(0)$. For the Q-branch we have

$$Q(J) = \nu_0+(B'-B'')J(J+1)-(D_J'-D_J'')J^2(J+1)^2 \tag{91}$$

For the O- and S-branches we have

$$\begin{aligned} O, S(J) = {} & \nu_0+\tfrac{3}{4}(B'-B'')-\tfrac{9}{16}(D_J'-D_J'') \\ & +[(B'+B'')-\tfrac{3}{2}(D_J'+D_J'')]m \\ & +\tfrac{1}{4}[(B'-B'')-\tfrac{11}{2}(D_J'-D_J'')]m^2 \\ & -\tfrac{1}{2}(D_J'+D_J'')m^3 \\ & -\tfrac{1}{16}(D_J'-D_J'')m^4 \end{aligned} \tag{92}$$

where $m = -2J+1$ for the O-branch and $2J+3$ for the S-branch. For the pure rotation spectrum we have then (setting $B' = B''$, $D_J' = D_J''$, $\nu_0 = 0$)

$$S(J) = (4B-6D_J)(J+\tfrac{3}{2})-8D_J(J+\tfrac{3}{2})^3 \tag{93}$$

As for the case of the symmetric top molecule, the spacing of the lines is $4B$ if the effect of centrifugal distortion and the difference between the upper and lower state constants is ignored.

b. *Vibrations with* $s_t = 1$

These are the degenerate vibrations. For fundamentals we have $l' = 1$ and $l = 0$ so that $|\Delta K| = |\Delta l| = 1$. From Table 1 we see that with $K = l = 0$ the intensity factors for $\Delta J = \pm 1$ do not vanish, so that all five branches (O, P, Q, R, S) will occur in the spectrum. The Q-branch intensity factor varies however as $1/J^2$ so that its intensity will be small in comparison to that of the other branches.

Due to the rotation-vibration interaction, the l-degeneracy contained in Eq. (90) for positive and negative values of l will be removed. Each rotational energy level is split into a doublet corresponding to the positive and negative values of l. The magnitude of the level splitting due to the l-type doubling is given by

$$\Delta\nu = qJ(J+1) \tag{94}$$

where q is the l-type doubling constant which is of the order of 10^{-4}–10^{-3} cm^{-1} [see for example, Refs. (*52–54*)]. Similar to the case of the symmetric top rotor the levels corresponding to the two values of l are designated as $+l$ and $-l$ levels. The molecular constants B and D for these two types of levels will be slightly different. With this in mind we have from Eq. (90) for the band frequencies of the fundamentals:
For the Q-branch,

$$Q(J) = \nu_0 - B' - D_J' + (B' - B'' + 2D_J')J(J+1) - (D_J' - D_J'')J^2(J+1)^2 \tag{95}$$

for the P- and R-branches,

$$P, R(J) = \nu_0 - B' - D_J' + (B' + B'' + 2D_J')m + (B' - B'' + D_J' + D_J'')m^2 - 2(D_J' + D_J'')m^3 - (D_J' - D_J'')m^4 \tag{96}$$

where $m = -J$ for the P-branch and $J+1$ for the R-branch; and for the O- and S-branches,

$$\begin{aligned} O, S(J) = \nu_0 &- \tfrac{1}{4}(B' + 3B'') - \tfrac{1}{16}(D_J' - 9D_J'') \\ &+ [(B' + B'') + \tfrac{1}{2}(D_J' - 3D_J'')]m \\ &+ \tfrac{1}{4}[(B' - B'') - \tfrac{1}{2}(7D_J' - 11D_J'')]m^2 \\ &- \tfrac{1}{2}(D_J' + D_J'')m^3 \\ &- \tfrac{1}{16}(D_J' - D_J'')m^4 \end{aligned} \tag{97}$$

where $m = -2J+1$ for the O-branch and $2J+3$ for the S-branch.

For pure rotational transitions [see Figures 24 and 32 for pure rotational Raman spectra of CO_2 and CS_2 (*55*, *111*)] in a doubly degenerated vibrational state ($l \neq 0$) we note from Table 1 with $K = l \neq 0$ and $\Delta K = \Delta l = 0$ that now an *R*-branch in addition to the *S*-branch will be allowed. However, the intensity of the R-branch varies as $1/J$ in comparison to that of the *S*-branch. From Eq. (90) we have for the *R*- and *S*-branch pure rotational Raman displacements

$$R(J) = 2B(J+1) - 4D_J[(J+1)^3 - l^2(J+1)] \tag{98}$$

and

$$S(J) = (4B - 6D_J)(J+\tfrac{3}{2}) - 8D_J[(J+\tfrac{3}{2})^3 - l^2(J+\tfrac{3}{2})] \tag{99}$$

where B and D_J are the molecular constants appropriate to the given vibrational state.

2. The Band Intensities

The intensities of the Raman bands of linear molecules are given by the relations derived for symmetric top transitions, namely Eq. (87) for bands with $s_t = 0$($\|$-bands) and Eq. (88) for bands with $s_t = 1$ ($\perp$-bands). The intensity factors $b_{J,K;J',K'}$ given in Table 1 are applicable by letting $K = l$. Thus, for the parallel bands of the fundamentals we get only a *Q*-branch and *O*- and *S*-branches. But for the perpendicular bands we get all five branches (*O*, *P*, *Q*, *R*, *S*) with the *Q*-branch intensity varying as $1/J$. For the pure rotational spectra of a linear molecule in a vibrational state with $s_t = 1$ the intensities are given by Eq. (87) with $\Delta K = \Delta l = 0$, but $l \neq 0$. Both *R*- and *S*-branches are allowed with the *R*-branch intensity decreasing as $1/J$.

H. Spherical Top Molecules

The results of the symmetric rotor analysis are also applicable in first approximation to the spherical top molecule considered as a limiting case ($I_A = I_B = I_C$) of the symmetric top rotor. The rotational term value for a spherical top is given by

$$F(J) = BJ(J+1) - D_J J^2(J+1)^2 \tag{100}$$

as long as Coriolis coupling is ignored. Molecules belonging to the tetrahedral and octahedral point groups have normal modes of vibration which are of the nondegenerate, totally symmetric (*A*), doubly degenerate (*E*), and triply degenerate (*F*) species. Of these, only the triply degenerate modes are split by the Coriolis interaction since only the direct product of the triply degenerate representations contain the representation of a rigid rotation (Jahn's rule) (*56*). Molecules belonging to the icosahedral groups have A (totally symmetric), F (triply degenerate), G (fourfold degenerate), and H (fivefold degenerate) species of vibrations and of these, only the F and H species are split due to Coriolis interaction (*57*).

To first order of approximation the removal of the triple degeneracy by Coriolis interaction in tetrahedral molecules results in three vibrational sublevels each of which has its own set of rotational energy levels whose term values are given by

$$F^{(+)}(J) = BJ(J+1)+2B\zeta(J+1)-D_J J^2(J+1)^2 \tag{101a}$$

$$F^{(0)}(J) = BJ(J+1)-D_J J^2(J+1)^2 \tag{101b}$$

$$F^{(-)}(J) = BJ(J+1)-2B\zeta J-D_J J^2(J+1)^2 \tag{101c}$$

While these expressions are expected to give a sufficiently accurate representation of the rotational terms for heavy molecules, they have been found to be insufficient to describe the spectrum of methane (*58–62*). According to Herranz (*61,62*) the rotational terms of the ground state of tetrahedral molecules are, instead of Eq. (100), given (in the notation of Herranz) by

$$F_0(J, \tau) = B_0 J(J+1)-D_0{}^J J^2(J+1)^2 - D^{J\tau}S_{J\tau} \tag{102}$$

which differs from the terms represented by Eq. (100) by the presence of the third term, $-D^{J\tau}S_{J\tau}$, which describes a splitting of the rotational levels due to centrifugal distortion. The coefficient $D^{J\tau}$ is an additional centrifugal distortion constant and $S_{J\tau}$ is the (J, τ) th element of the diagonal matrix representation of the fourth-order angular momentum operator S, whose values are tabulated for given quantum numbers (J, τ) up to $J = 16$ (*61*). For the F_2-triply degenerate vibrations of tetrahedral molecules (for example the ν_3 Raman band of methane), the rotational terms are, instead of Eqs. (101)–(101c), given by

$$\begin{aligned} F^{(+)}(J, \tau) = {} & (B_1-\beta_3)J(J+1)+(2B_e\zeta_3+\tfrac{3}{2}\beta_3)J \\ & - D_1{}^J J^2(J+1)^2+[\delta_3-(2J^2-5J+3)(D^{J\tau}+d^{J\tau})] \\ & \times \frac{S_{J+1,\tau}}{(J+1)(2J+1)} \end{aligned} \tag{103a}$$

$$\begin{aligned} F^{(0)}(J, \tau) = {} & (B_1+2\beta_3)J(J+1)-(2B_e\zeta_3+\tfrac{3}{2}\beta_3)-D_1{}^J J^2(J+1)^2 \\ & - [(\delta_3-30d^{J\tau})+(J^2+J-10)(D^{J\tau}-2d^{J\tau})]\frac{S_{J,\tau}}{J(J+1)} \end{aligned} \tag{103b}$$

$$F^{(-)}(J, \tau) = (B_1-\beta_3)J(J+1)-(2B_e\zeta_3+\tfrac{3}{2}\beta_3)(J+1)-D_1{}^JJ^2(J+1)^2$$
$$+[\delta_3-(2J^2+9J+10)(D^{J\tau}+d^{J\tau})]\frac{S_{J-1,\tau}}{J(2J+1)} \tag{103c}$$

where B_e and $B_1 = B_0-\alpha_3$ are the rotation constants for the ground and first excited state ($v_1 = v_2 = v_4 = 0, v_3 = 1$), respectively, ζ_3 is the Coriolis coupling coefficient and $D_1{}^J$ is the usual (second order) centrifugal distortion constant for the excited state, and δ_3, β_3 and $d^{J\tau}$ are additional higher order molecular constants.

The intensity of the transitions for the anisotropic scattering has been computed by Herranz and Stoicheff (*62*). Their result for the intensity $I_{\mathscr{L}}$ of a Raman line is

$$I_{\mathscr{L}} = (2J+1)g_T \exp[-hcF_0(J, \tau)/kT]C\beta_{\mathscr{L}}{}^2 \tag{104}$$

where g_T is the statistical weight ($g_T = 5, 2, 3$ for the A, E, F species of levels of methane where the classification is done on the basis of the point group T rather than T_d), and where

$$C = \tfrac{13}{45}AN\{\textstyle\sum (2J+1)g_T \exp[-hcF_0(J, \tau)/kT]\}^{-1} \tag{105}$$

may be considered constant for the band since N is the number of molecules per unit volume, $A = 32\pi^4\nu^4 I_0/c^4$ where I_0 is the incident intensity, and ν is the frequency of the scattered light. The quantity $\beta_{\mathscr{L}}{}^2$ is the matrix element of the anisotropy, summed over all the transitions that comprise a line. For the triply degenerate vibrations $\beta_{\mathscr{L}}{}^2$ is given in Table 4 for the 15 allowed branches. The index τ is split into three indexes n, T, ρ, where $n = 1, 2, 3\ldots$ differentiates the levels of the same J and same T, $T = A, E, F$ specifies the type of degeneracy of the sublevel and ρ distinguishes between degenerate levels having the same n and T. The notation $(n, n')T$ attached to the customary branch symbol then designates the value of n, T and n', T for the ground and upper state levels, with T being the same for both levels. The quantities $(b_J{}^{(i)})_{nT,n'T'}$ are given in Table 5 for J up to 10. The integral coefficients of the quantities in Table 4 had previously been calculated by Teller (*63*); they represent the high-J limiting values of the relative branch intensities and were the only information on the branch intensities prior to the work of Herranz and Stoicheff.

I. Asymmetric Top Molecules

The theory of the rotational energies of asymmetric top molecules has been worked out in considerable detail (*64–70*) and the infrared spectra of

TABLE 4

The Expressions $\beta_{\mathscr{L}}^2$ for Calculating the Raman Line Intensities of Spherical Top Molecules[a]

Line	$(\beta_{\mathscr{L}}^2/G)^b$
$S^+(J)(n,n')T$	$15[2J+7][2J+4]^{-1}(b_J^{(4)})_{nT,n'T}$
$S^0(J)(n,n')T$	$5[(2J+5)(2J)][(2J+4)(2J+3)]^{-1}(b_J^{(3)})_{nT,n'T}$
$S^-(J)(n,n')T$	$1[(2J-1)(2J)][(2J+4)(2J+2)]^{-1}(b_J^{(2)})_{nT,n'T}$
$R^+(J)(n,n')T$	$10[(2J+5)(2J+6)][(2J+4)(2J+3)]^{-1}(b_J^{(3)})_{nT,n'T}$
$R^0(J)(n,n')T$	$8[(2J+5)(2J+3)(2J-1)][(2J+4)(2J+2)(2J+2)]^{-1}(b_J^{(2)})_{nT,n'T}$
$R^-(J)(n,n')T$	$3[(2J-1)(2J-2)][(2J+2)(2J+1)]^{-1}(b_J^{(1)})_{nT,n'T}$
$Q^+(J)(n,n')T$	$6[(2J+5)(2J+4)][(2J+2)(2J+2)]^{-1}(b_J^{(2)})_{nT,n'T}$
$Q^0(J)(n,n')T$	$9[(2J+4)(2J-2)][(2J)(2J+2)]^{-1}(b_J^{(1)})_{nT,n'T}$
$Q^-(J)(n,n')T$	$6[(2J-2)(2J-3)][(2J)(2J)]^{-1}(b_{J-1}^{(2)})_{n'T,nT}$
$P^+(J)(n,n')T$	$3[(2J+4)(2J+3)][(2J+1)(2J)]^{-1}(b_J^{(1)})_{nT,n'T}$
$P^0(J)(n,n')T$	$8[(2J+3)(2J-1)(2J-3)][(2J)(2J)(2J-2)]^{-1}(b_{J-1}^{(2)})_{n'T,nT}$
$P^-(J)(n,n')T$	$10[(2J-3)(2J-4)][(2J-1)(2J-2)]^{-1}(b_{J-2}^{(3)})_{n'T,nT}$
$O^+(J)(n,n')T$	$1[(2J+3)(2J+2)][(2J-2)(2J)]^{-1}(b_{J-1}^{(2)})_{n'T,nT}$
$O^0(J)(n,n')T$	$5[(2J+2)(2J-3)][(2J-2)(2J-1)]^{-1}(b_{J-2}^{(3)})_{n'T,nT}$
$O^-(J)(n,n')T$	$15[2J-5][2J-2]^{-1}(b_{J-3}^{(4)})_{n'T,nT}$

[a] From Herranz and Stoicheff, Ref. *(62)*.

[b] $G = (3/70)|\alpha_v|^2$ is a constant for the band; numerical values for the $(b_J)_{nT,n'T'}$ are given in Table 5.

many asymmetric tops are well understood on its basis. On the other hand, except for the statement of the general selection rules for the Raman effect by Placzek and Teller *(71)*, a comprehensive theory of the rotational Raman effect of asymmetric top rotors is not available in the open literature. In an unpublished thesis H. H. Howe *(72)* has, however, studied this problem in great detail and presents formulae for the intensity of rotational transitions in a general asymmetric top up to $J = 4$. While the treatment resembles that of Ray *(66)*, it differs from it in the basic choice of the asymmetry parameters. A recapitulation of the gross features of Howe's treatment would be too extensive and reference is made to the original work *(72)*.

III. EXPERIMENTAL TECHNIQUES

The experimental techniques that are employed in the study of Raman scattering are dictated by the degree of resolution and wave number accuracy that is required for a given problem. The resolution of the rotational fine structure and the accurate determination of the wave

TABLE 5

Values of $(b_J^{(i)})_{nT,n'T'}$ Coefficients for the Calculation of the Raman Line Intensities of Tetrahedral Spherical Top Molecules[a]

J	nT \ $n'T'$	$[b_J^{(1)}]_{nT,n'T'}$	$[b_J^{(2)}]_{nT,n'T'}$	$[b_J^{(3)}]_{nT,n'T'}$	$[b_J^{(4)}]_{nT,n'T'}$
0	1*A*				1*A*: 4.000
1	1*F*		1*F*: 1.333	2*F*: 1.667	2*F*: 2.000
2	1*E*	1*E*: 2.500		1*E*: 1.867	1*E*: 1.529
	1*F*		1*F*: 2.000	1*F*: 1.089	1*F*: 0.010; 3*F*: 1.641
3	1*A*		1*A*: 3.394		2*A*: 1.678
	1*F*	2*F*: 1.167	2*F*: 0.121	2*F*: 1.909	1*F*: 0.024; 2*F*: 1.281
	2*F*	1*F*: 1.167	1*F*: 1.414	1*F*: 0.962; 3*F*: 0.129	3*F*: 1.469
4	1*A*			1*A*: 2.256	1*A*: 1.091
	1*E*	1*E*: 1.636	1*E*: 0.653	1*E*: 1.436	1*E*: 1.292
	2*F*	1*F*: 0.955	1*F*: 2.434; 3*F*: 0.084	3*F*: 0.180	1*F*: 0.001; 4*F*: 1.565
	1*F*	2*F*: 0.955	2*F*: 0.381	1*F*: 1.765; 2*F*: 0.012	2*F*: 0.020; 3*F*: 1.188

TABLE 5 (*cont.*)

J	$n'T'$ / nT	$[b_J^{(1)}]_{nT,n'T'}$		$[b_J^{(2)}]_{nT,n'T'}$		$[b_J^{(3)}]_{nT,n'T'}$			$[b_J^{(4)})]_{nT,n'T'}$		
		1*E*		1*E*		1*E*			1*E*	2*E*	
	1*E*	1.039		2.014		0.400			0.007	1.455	
		2*F*		1*F*	2*F*	2*F*	3*F*		2*F*	4*F*	
5	1*F*	0.078		0.128	0.135	1.897	0.216		1.031	0.002	
	3*F*	1.410		1.503	0.640	0.027	0.169		0.004	1.514	
		1*F*	3*F*	3*F*		1*F*	4*F*		1*F*	3*F*	
	2*F*	0.078	1.410	0.252		1.742	0.016		0.007	1.133	
		1*A*		1*A*					2*A*		
	2*A*	1.750		2.096					1.540		
		2*A*				1*A*			1*A*		
	1*A*	1.750				1.901			1.053		
		1*E*		1*E*		1*E*	2*E*		1*E*		
6	1*E*	0.118		0.253		2.092	0.080		0.953		
		3*F*		1*F*	4*F*	1*F*	3*F*		1*F*	3*F*	4*F*
	1*F*	0.425		0.116	0.120	1.947	0.145		0.002	0.957	0.020
	2*F*	1.121		1.608	0.090	0.064	0.490		0.002	0.033	1.351
		1*F*	2*F*	2*F*	3*F*	2*F*	4*F*		2*F*		5*F*
	3*F*	0.425	1.121	1.166	0.700	0.217	0.055		0.003	1.464	
				1*A*		1*A*			2*A*		
	1*A*			1.695		0.875			1.248		
		1*E*		1*E*	2*E*	1*E*			1*E*		2*E*
	1*E*	1.697		1.127	0.422	0.426			0.003	1.401	
		2*F*	3*F*	2*F*	4*F*	2*F*	5*F*		1*F*	2*F*	5*F*
7	1*F*	0.033	0.119	0.021	0.195	1.880	0.146		0.001	0.880	0.001
	4*F*	0.625	1.157	1.857	0.033	0.272	0.018		0.002	0.002	1.498
		1*F*	4*F*	1*F*	3*F*	1*F*	3*F*	4*F*	3*F*	4*F*	
	2*F*	0.032	0.626	0.067	0.051	2.061	0.044	0.062	0.892	0.024	
	3*F*	0.119	1.157	1.287	0.226	0.056	0.401	0.150	0.041	1.306	

TABLE 5 (*cont.*)

J	nT \ $n'T'$	$[b_J^{(1)}]_{nT,n'T'}$			$[b_J^{(2)}]_{nT,n'T'}$			$[b_J^{(3)}]_{nT,n'T'}$			$[b_J^{(4)}]_{nT,n'T'}$		
					2*A*			1*A*			1*A*		
	1*A*				0.223			2.348			0.812		
		1*E*	2*E*		1*E*			1*E*	2*E*		1*E*	2*E*	
	1*E*	0.043	0.511		0.066			2.240	0.056		0.833	0.006	
	2*E*	0.511	1.193		1.717			0.016	0.162		0.014	1.440	
8		1*F*	3*F*		1*F*	3*F*	4*F*	3*F*	4*F*		1*F*	4*F*	
	2*F*	0.099	0.061		1.368	0.115	0.124	0.631	0.256		0.000	1.219	
	4*F*	0.234	1.684		0.012	1.439	0.287	0.029	0.048		0.002	0.002	
		2*F*	4*F*		2*F*	5*F*		1*F*	2*F*	5*F*	2*F*	3*F*	5*F*
	1*F*	0.099	0.234		0.021	0.111		2.261	0.027	0.025	0.001	0.828	0.006
	3*F*	0.061	1.684		1.084	0.178		0.023	0.592	0.012	0.000	0.012	1.317
		1*A*			2*A*						1*A*	3*A*	
	2*A*	2.066			1.679						0.002	1.498	
		2*A*			1*A*			1*A*			2*A*		
	1*A*	2.066			0.997			0.734			1.292		
		1*E*			1*E*	2*E*		1*E*	2*E*		1*E*	2*E*	
	1*E*	0.196			1.245	0.245		0.869	0.109		0.001	1.172	
		2*F*	5*F*		1*F*	2*F*	5*F*	2*F*	3*F*	5*F*	2*F*	4*F*	5*F*
9	1*F*	0.004	0.161		0.008	0.012	0.126	2.387	0.017	0.004	0.760	0.002	0.003
	3*F*	0.118	0.331		1.098	0.269	0.088	0.006	0.694	0.210	0.004	1.176	0.018
	4*F*	0.323	1.472		0.061	1.401	0.071	0.008	0.097	0.162	0.006	0.026	1.387
		1*F*	3*F*	4*F*	3*F*	4*F*		1*F*	4*F*	6*F*	1*F*	3*F*	6*F*
	2*F*	0.004	0.118	0.323	0.022	0.025		2.354	0.003	0.033	0.000	0.773	0.002
	5*F*	0.161	0.331	1.472	1.284	0.322		0.006	0.085	0.028	0.001	0.006	1.457

TABLE 5 (*cont.*)

J	$n'T'$ / nT	$[b_J^{(1)}]_{nT,n'T'}$			$[b_J^{(2)}]_{nT,n'T'}$			$[b_J^{(3)}]_{nT,n'T'}$			$[b_J^{(4)}]_{nT,n'T'}$			
		1*A*			1*A*			2*A*			2*A*			
	2*A*	0.457			1.826			0.488			1.305			
		2*A*						1*A*	3*A*		1*A*			
	1*A*	0.457						2.445	0.033		0.724			
		1*E*	2*E*		1*E*	2*E*		1*E*	2*E*		1*E*	2*E*		
	1*E*	0.005	0.175		0.023	0.087		2.471	0.010		0.713	0.002		
10	2*E*	0.175	1.904		1.192	0.242		0.008	0.188		0.007	1.430		
		3*F*	4*F*		1*F*	4*F*	6*F*	1*F*	3*F*	6*F*	1*F*	3*F*	4*F*	7*F*
	1*F*	0.058	0.205		0.003	0.025	0.049	2.460	0.009	0.012	0.000	0.714	0.003	0.001
	2*F*	0.116	0.120		1.136	0.031	0.207	0.005	1.011	0.062	0.000	0.005	1.120	0.001
	5*F*	0.493	1.603		0.002	1.554	0.016	0.004	0.005	0.029	0.001	0.004	0.002	1.476
		1*F*	2*F*	5*F*	2*F*	3*F*	5*F*	2*F*	4*F*	5*F*	2*F*	5*F*	6*F*	
	3*F*	0.058	0.116	0.493	0.979	0.235	0.070	0.800	0.061	0.124	0.000	1.140	0.026	
	4*F*	0.205	0.120	1.603	0.061	1.233	0.094	0.109	0.124	0.077	0.000	0.035	1.362	

[a] From Herranz and Stoicheff, Ref. (*62*). For the nT, $n'T'$ not tabulated the values are zero.

numbers for a given Raman band which may extend over several hundred cm^{-1} presents extraordinary difficulties to the investigator due to the weakness of the Raman effect in general. Aside from fundamental limitations one desires to obtain an effective limit of resolution equivalent to that achieved in infrared absorption spectroscopy in order to be able to combine both types of data (i.e., infrared absorption and Raman scattering data) with an equal degree of confidence for the solution of molecular structure problems. If we accept the value of $\delta v = 0.02\ cm^{-1}$ as a desired limiting resolution in the visible region, say at $\lambda = 5000$Å, then an effective spectroscopic resolving power of 10^6 must be available with the equipment.

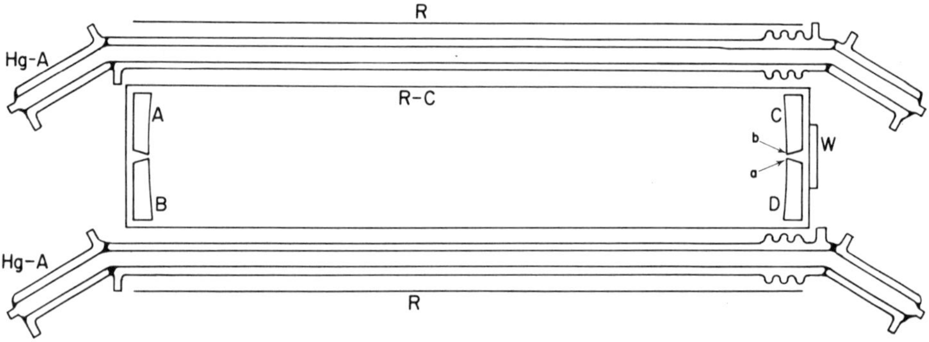

Fig. 2. Schematic diagram of prelaser Raman source for gases. $R-C$ = gas cell equipped with multiple reflection mirrors A, B, C, D: $Hg-A$ = water cooled mercury arc lamp; R = magnesium oxide coated reflector.

[As examples, the values of $\delta v = 0.03$ and $0.025\ cm^{-1}$ have been achieved with grating spectrographs in the infrared near 3μ, see Refs. (*73*) and (*74*), and $\delta v = 0.006\ cm^{-1}$ was realized with a Michelson interferometer (Fourier transform spectroscopy) near 2μ, Ref. (*75*)]. Furthermore, accurate wave number determination (at least a high relative accuracy) over a wide spectral range must simultaneously be available (a highly resolved spectrum with poorly determined wave numbers is quite useless for molecular structure studies!). These needs impose severe requirements on the spectrograph, the light source, the pressure, and the temperature under which the gas is investigated. What then is the state of the art and in what possible ways can it be improved?

The bulk of the high resolution Raman studies have been carried out with the "pre-laser" experimental technique. These techniques are well described by Stoicheff (*29,30*) and only a brief summary will be given here.

Figure 2 describes in schematic form a typical Raman light source for gases. The gas is contained in a cylindrical gas tube *R-C*, the Raman cell, at a pressure near one atmosphere. The gas is illuminated by water-cooled mercury arc lamps Hg-A which surround the tube *R-C*. These arc lamps are either in straight form, as shown, or in spiral form and are each operated at 220 V dc and 20–30 amp. Both the Raman cell and the arc lamps are enclosed by a magnesium oxide coated cylindrical reflector *R*, the whole constituting a "light furnace" which provides nearly isotropic illumination of the molecules.

To enhance the radiant flux that is received by the spectrograph (or spectrometer) the Raman cell is equipped with a set of semicircular (i.e., D-shaped) concave spherical mirrors A, B, C, D, all of which have the same radius of curvature. The mirrors are adjusted so that the centers of curvature of the front mirrors C and D are coincident and lie in the center of the gap between the two rear mirrors A and B, whereas the center of curvature of mirror A is located at point a on the edge of mirror D and that of mirror B is located at point b on the edge of mirror C. The "direct cone", defined by the slot between the two front mirrors C and D and the two rear mirrors A and B, is thereby imaged manyfold inside the gas cell. This allows Raman scattered radiation which travels within one of the "image cones" to be fed by means of multiple reflection into the "direct cone." This radiation, in addition to that which already is traveling within the "direct cone", then passes through the slot between the front mirrors C and D, and leaves the gas cell through the window W. For high reflectivity mirrors and a narrow slot between mirrors C and D a large number of image cones will be possible and the flux that emerges through the slot is then increased by a factor of nearly $1/(1-r)$, (which is the limiting value for an infinite number of images) over the flux from the direct cone alone, where r is the mirror reflectivity.

The dimensions of the gas cell, i.e., the full diameter and the radius of curvature of the mirrors are determined by the f/D number of the collimator of the spectrograph. A two lens system is customarily employed to transfer the radiant flux emerging from the Raman tube into the collimator. These transfer optics are designed in conformance with the requirement that the slot between the front mirrors C and D is imaged onto the entrance slit, and the rear mirrors A and B are imaged as one unit onto the collimator element of the spectrograph. A typical experimental apparatus has a mirror system of radius 2 m and full diameter of 5 cm. The cell volume is then slightly over 4 liters after allowing for dead space in the Raman cell. Larger and smaller variations in size have been employed and the largest gas cell that has been reported is 7.3 m long and 15 cm in diameter with an effective volume of 120 liters (*76,77,77a*).

The Raman scattered radiation is analyzed by a spectrograph (photographic detection) or a scanning spectrometer (photoelectric detection). Since the accurate recording of an extensive spectrum presents considerable difficulties when a scanning spectrometer is employed [see for instance a comment on these difficulties in the case of high resolution infrared spectroscopy by Rank, et al., Ref. (*78*)] photographic instruments have been nearly exclusively employed for molecular structure studies. On the other hand, photoelectrically recording scanning spectrometers have been employed to good advantage in the study of the intensities of Raman bands (*79*). Grating spectrographs capable of high dispersion and resolving power have thus far been employed for most of the work. These include standard instruments using a concave grating in the Wadsworth or Eagle mountings (*80,81*) and specially designed instruments that incorporate a plane grating (*82–85*). A reduction in exposure time is effected by placing in front of the photographic plate a cylindrical lens in such a manner that it images the camera element (lens or mirror) onto the emulsion (*86*). Typical recording materials are the Kodak 103a–O, 103a–F, IIa–O (baked at 61°C for 24 hr), Ia-E and IIIa-J (baked at 50°C for 20 hr) plates.

The efficacy of the above described arrangement in providing accurate data for molecular structure studies has been amply demonstrated. Figures 3–16 show a selection of pure rotation and rotation-vibration spectra obtained in three different laboratories. In spite of these successes, the restrictions on the effective limit of resolution that can be achieved and on the study of the weaker Raman bands, has prevented many interested investigators from jumping onto the bandwagon and participating in these studies. The limitation on resolution is primarily due to the width of the exciting line which is slightly over 0.2 cm^{-1} (full width at half intensity) for the central portion of the $\lambda = 4358$ Å line of mercury that was nearly exclusively employed. Figure 17 shows a microphotometer trace of this line under conditions of dispersion and resolution as would be encountered in high resolution Raman spectroscopy (*83*). The limiting resolution that has been attained with this exciting radiation and the apparatus described above is 0.245 cm^{-1} in the pure rotational Raman spectrum of 1,3,5-cycloheptatriene (*90*). The limiting resolution attained for rotation vibration spectra in which a cylindrical lens is used in front of the photographic plate has been 0.3–0.4 cm^{-1} (*62,94–96*).

The availability of laser light sources has very considerably changed the situation. Not only does one now have a much narrower exciting line

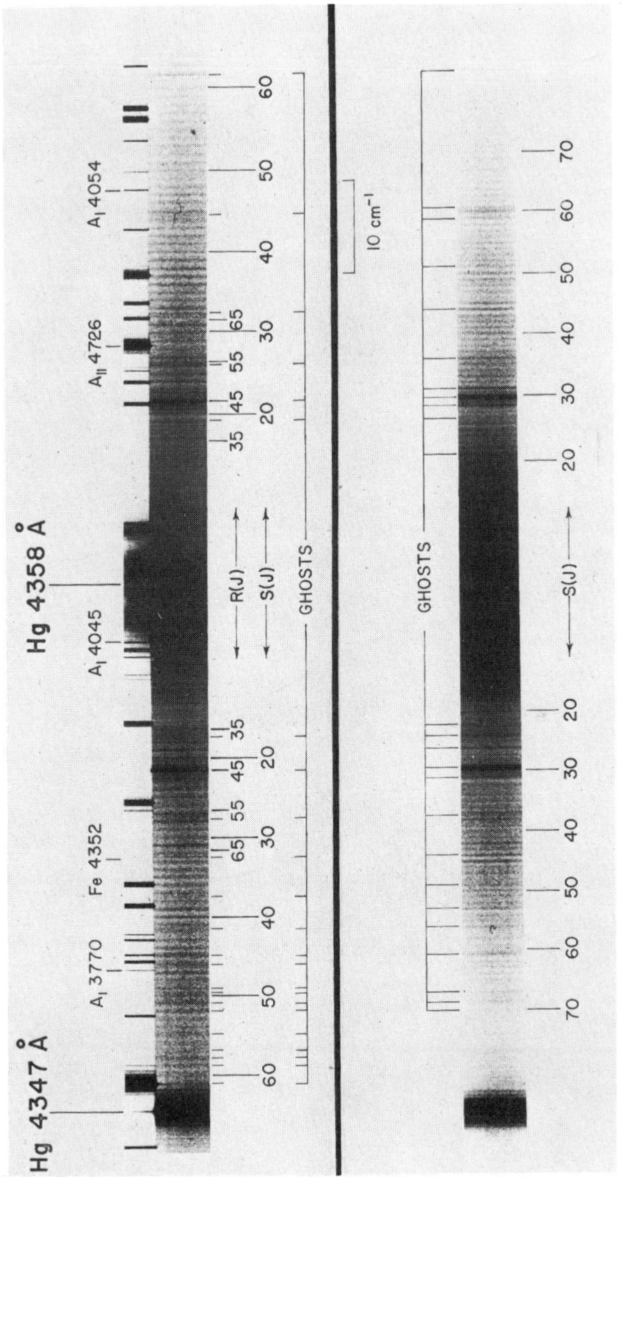

Fig. 3. Pure rotational Raman spectrum of cyclopentane (d_0, top; d_{10}, bottom) [Ref. (*87*)].

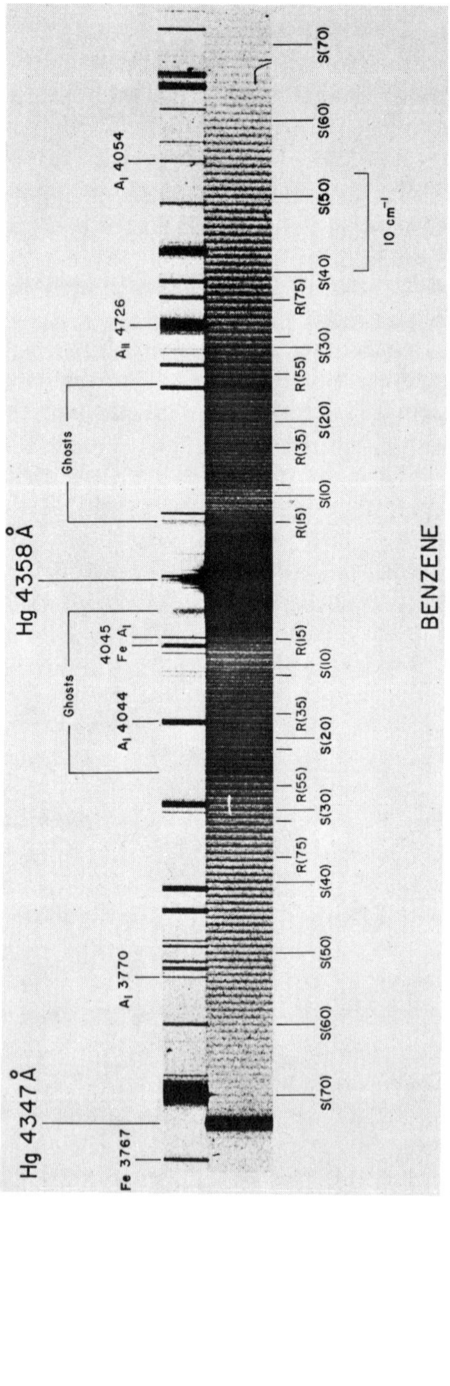

Fig. 4. Pure rotational Raman spectrum of benzene (Ref. (*131*)).

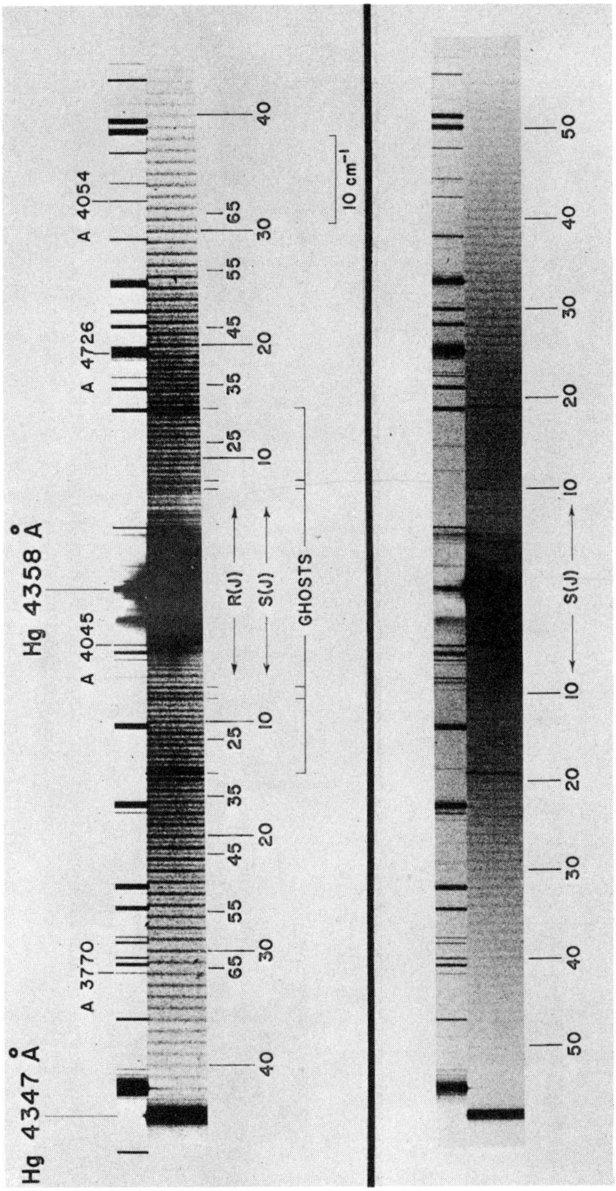

Fig. 5. Pure rotational Raman spectra of furan (top) and cyclopentene (bottom) [Ref. *(89)*].

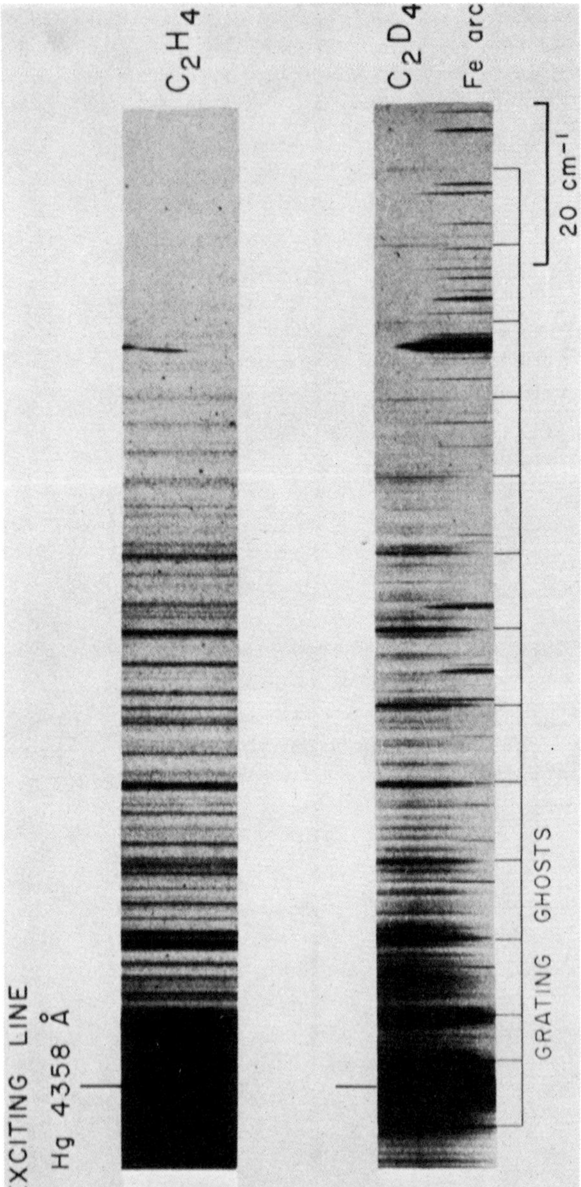

Fig. 6. Pure rotational Raman spectrum of ethylene. The irregularly spaced Raman lines of the asymmetric top spectrum occur between the Rowland ghosts [Ref. (*183*), with permission].

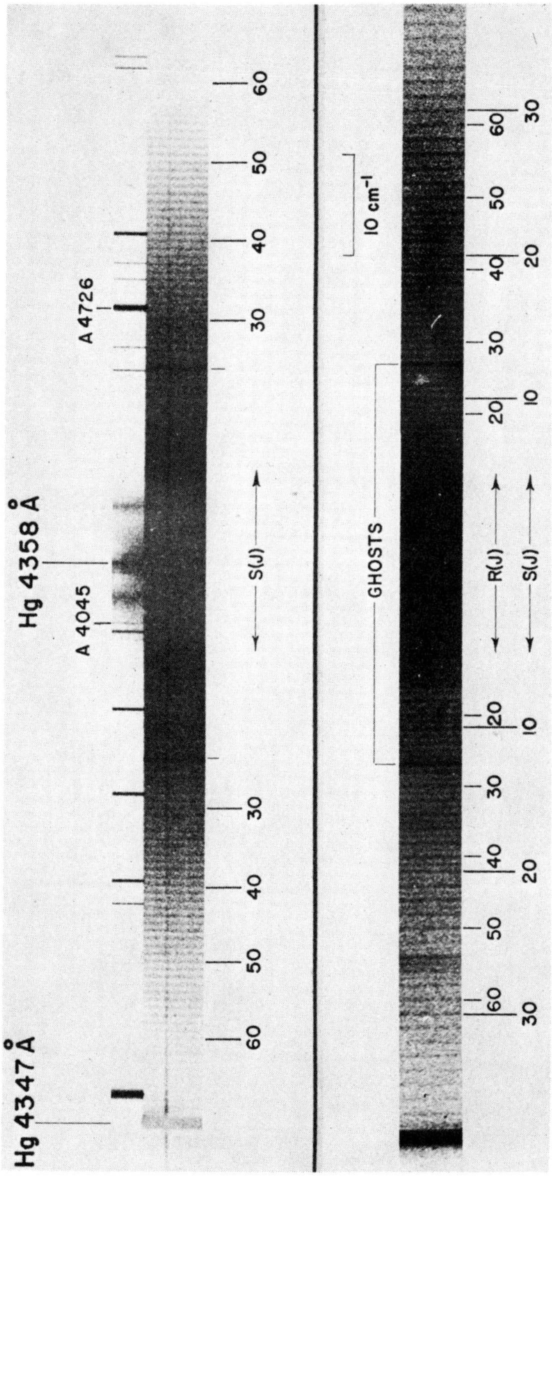

Fig. 7. Pure rotational Raman spectra of pyridine (top) and 1,1-difluoroethylene (bottom) [Ref. (*91*)].

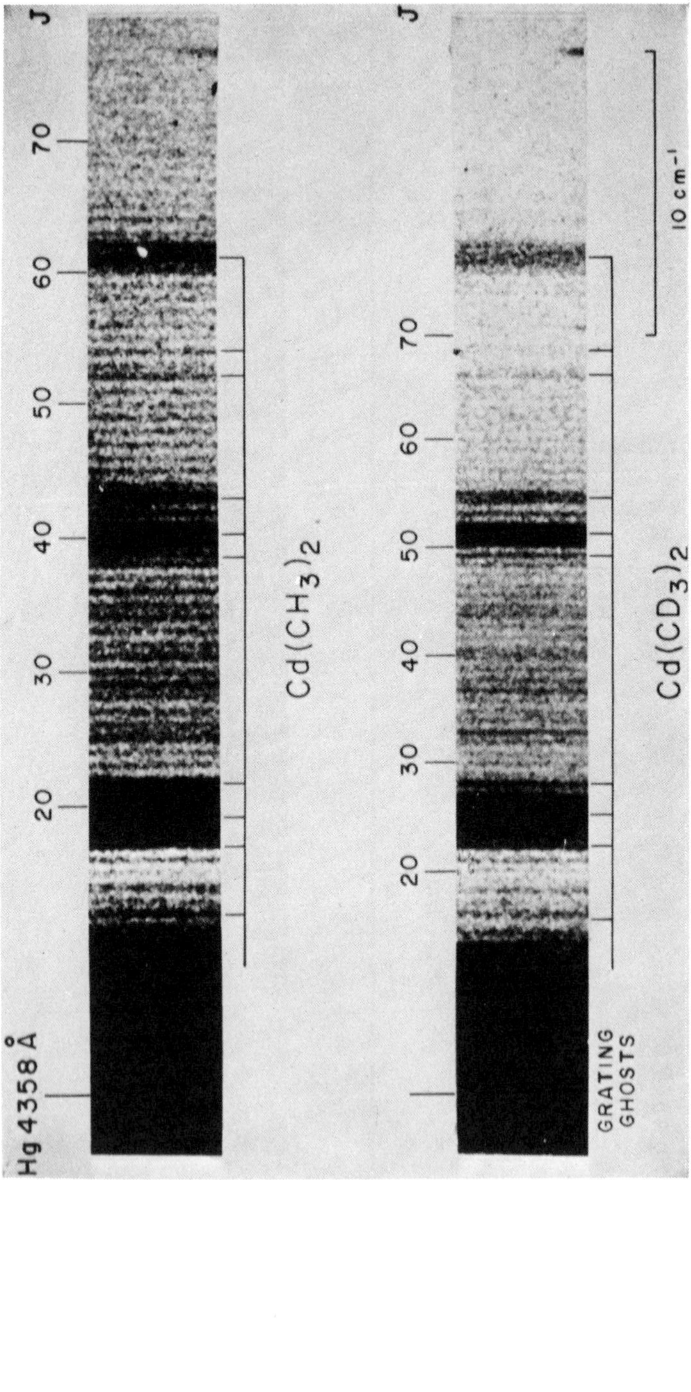

Fig. 8. The pure rotational Raman spectrum of dimethylcadmium (Ref. (*92*), with permission].

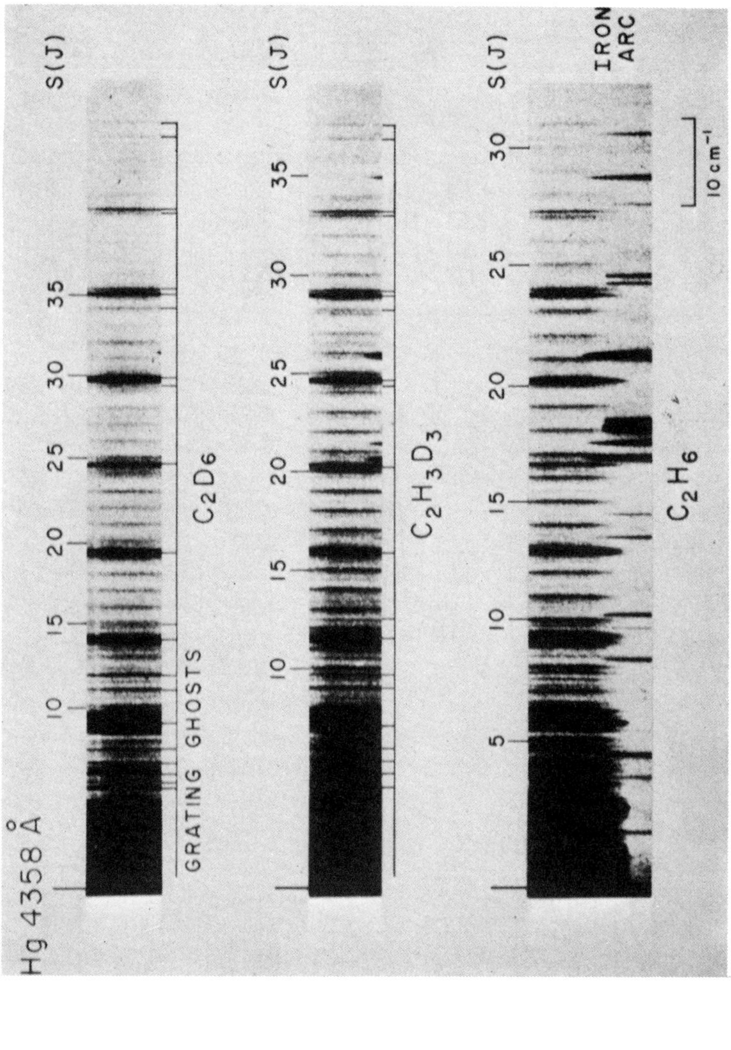

Fig. 9. The pure rotational Raman spectrum of ethane [Ref. (*93*) with permission]

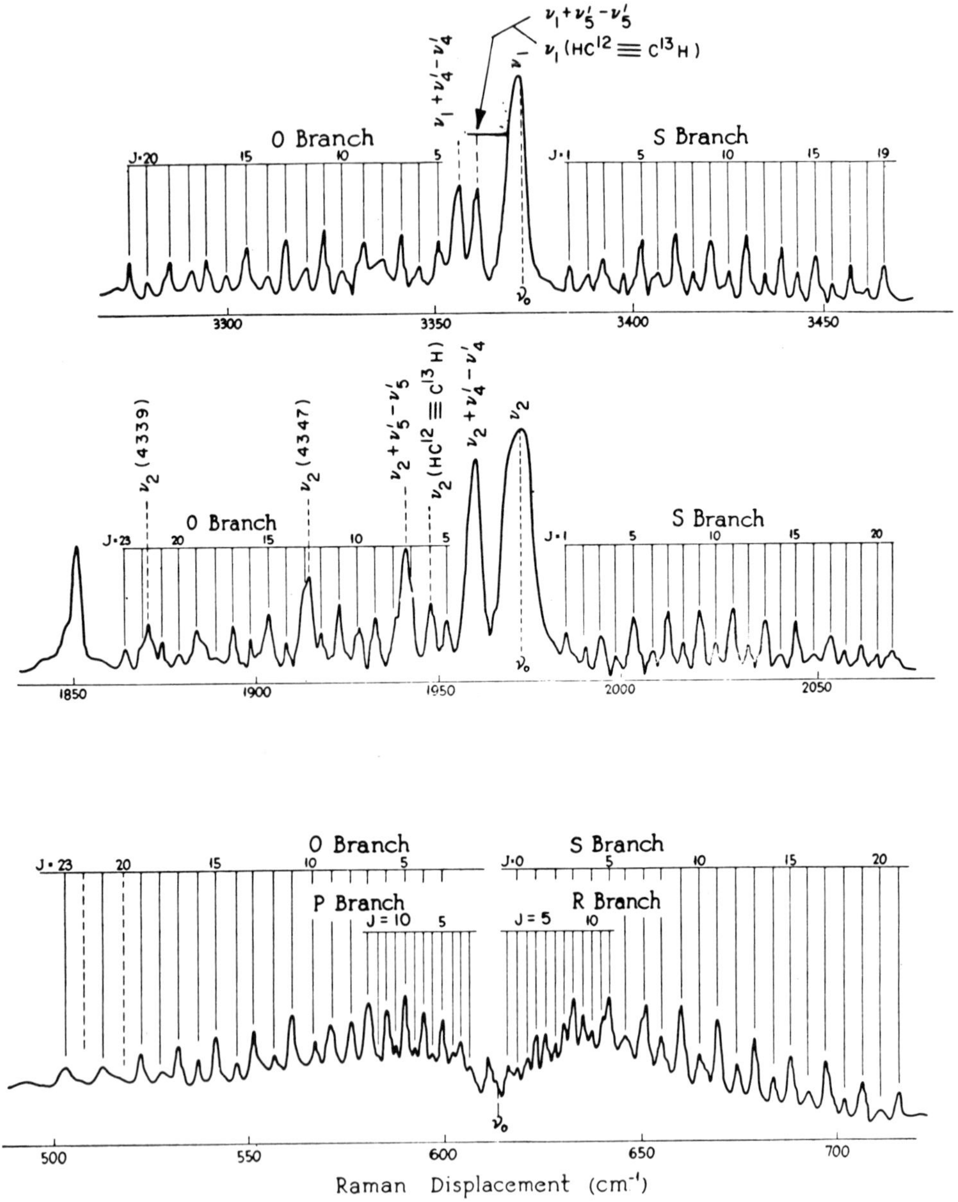

Fig. 10. The vibrational Raman bands of acetylene [Ref. (*116*), with permission].

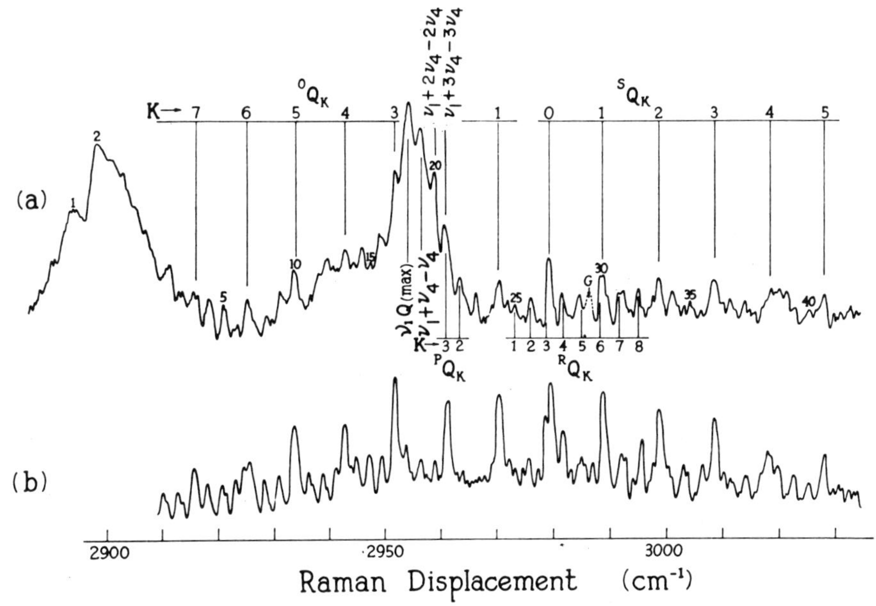

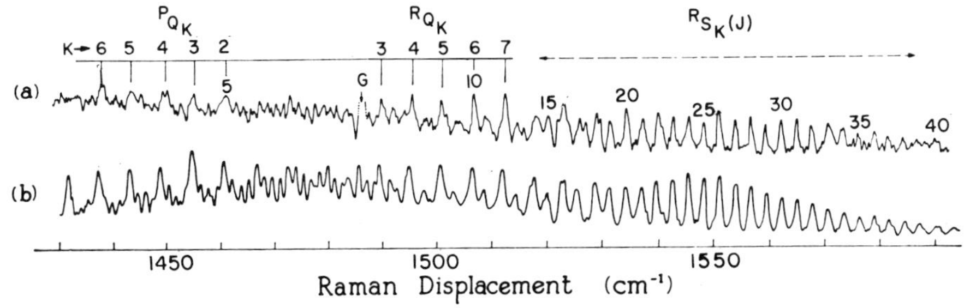

Fig. 11. The ν_{10} and ν_{11} Raman bands of ethane [Ref. *(94)*, with permission].

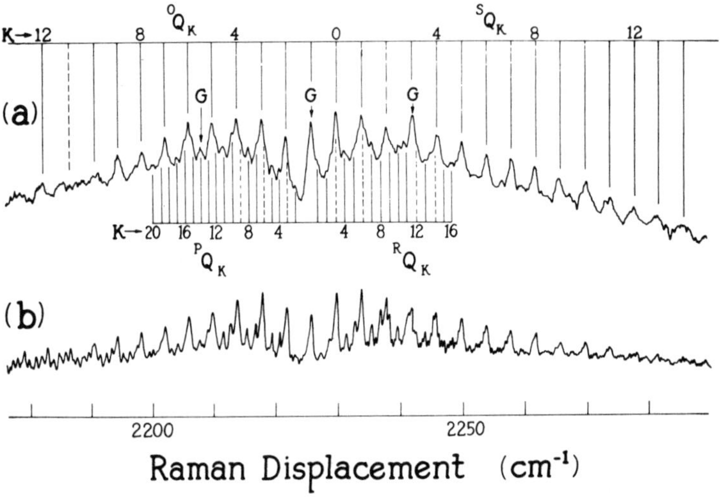

Fig. 12. The ν_{10} Raman band of ethane-d_6. (a) observed spectrum, (b) computed spectrum [Ref. (*95a*)]. The computed spectrum is not the same as that published in Ref. (*95*). For an explanation see Ref. (*94*), p. 2357. (The author is grateful to Dr. D. W. Lepard for calling this to his attention and for providing the figure).

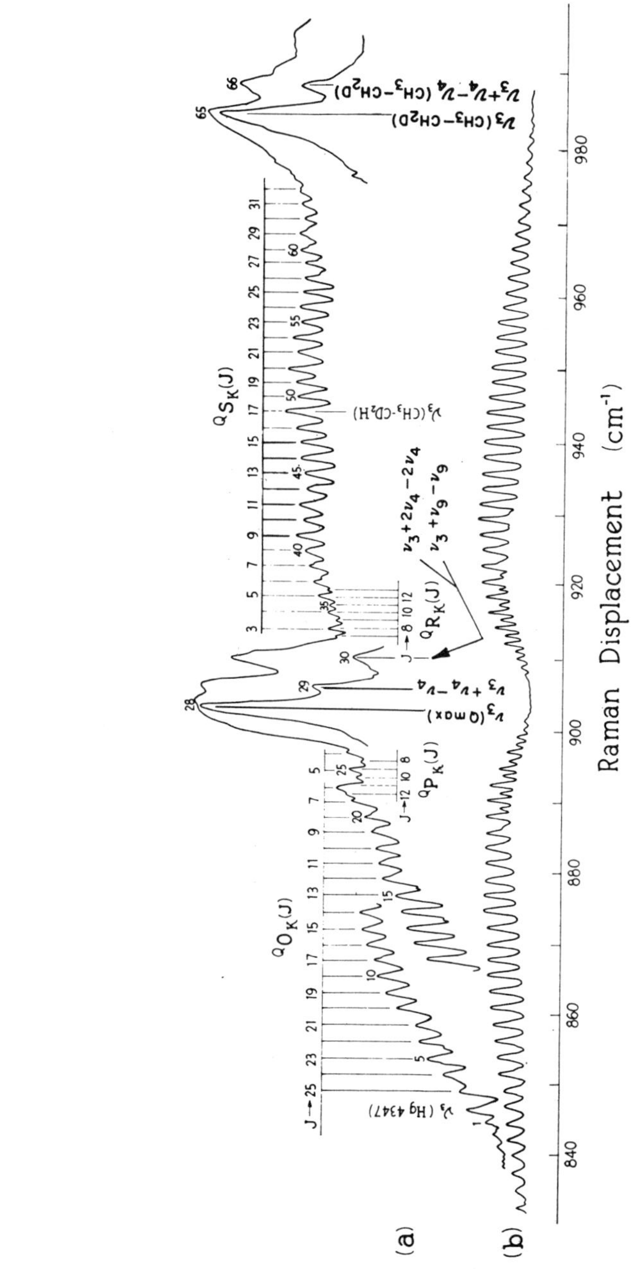

Fig. 13. The Raman spectrum of ethane-d_3 (CH_3-CD_3) in the 830–990 cm^{-1} region [Ref. *(96)*, with permission].

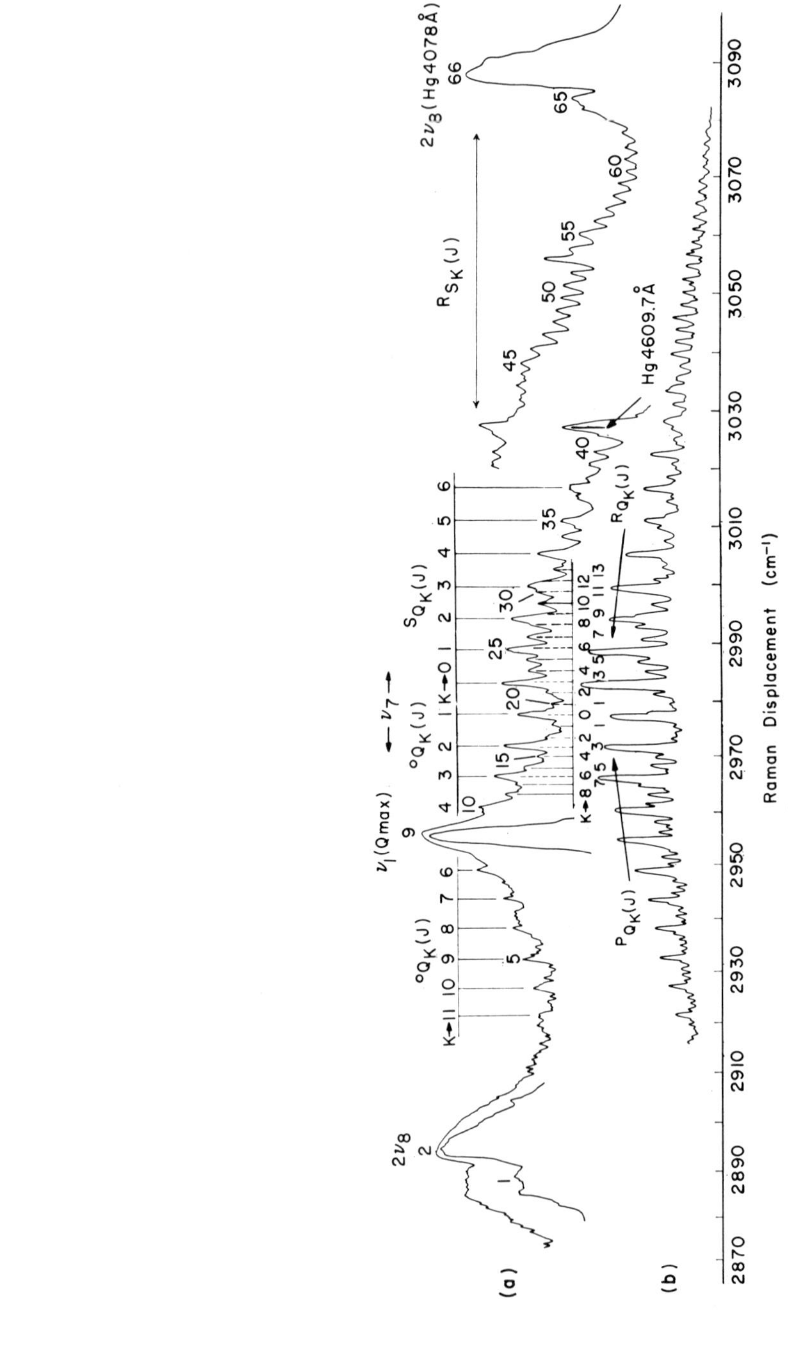

Fig. 14. The Raman spectrum of ethane-d_3 (CH_3-CD_3) in the 2870–3090 cm^{-1} region [Ref. *(96)*, with permission].

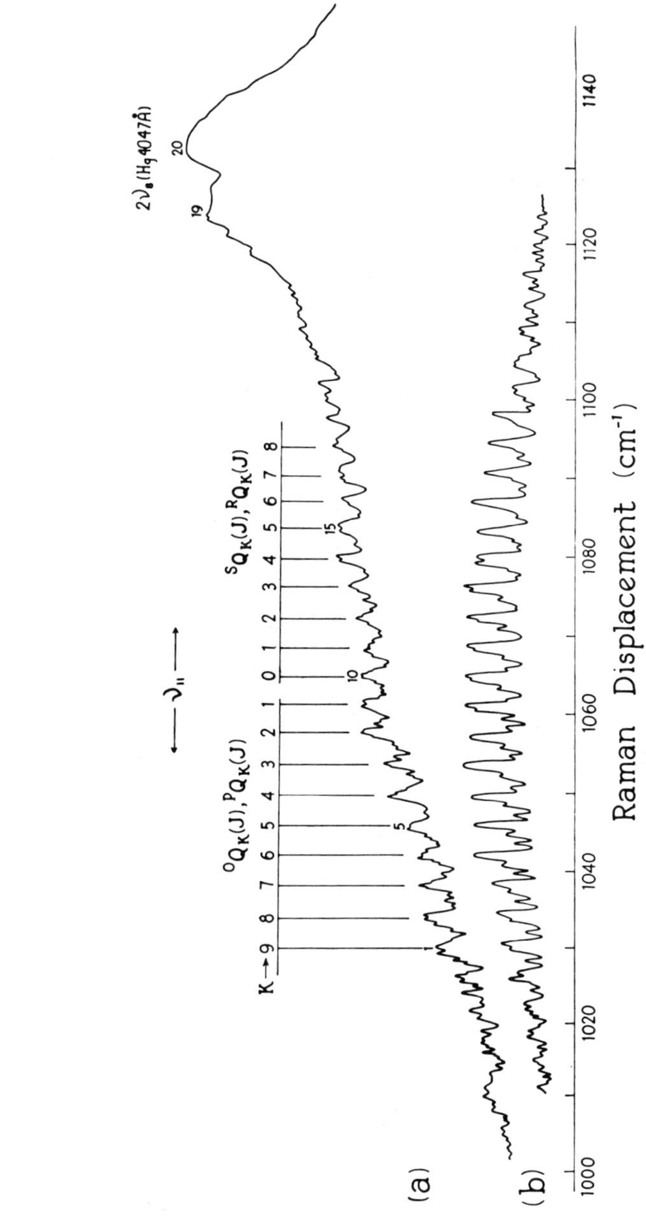

Fig. 15. The Raman spectrum of ethane-d_3 ($CH\text{-}CD_3$) in the 1000–1140 cm^{-1} region [Ref. (*96*), with permission].

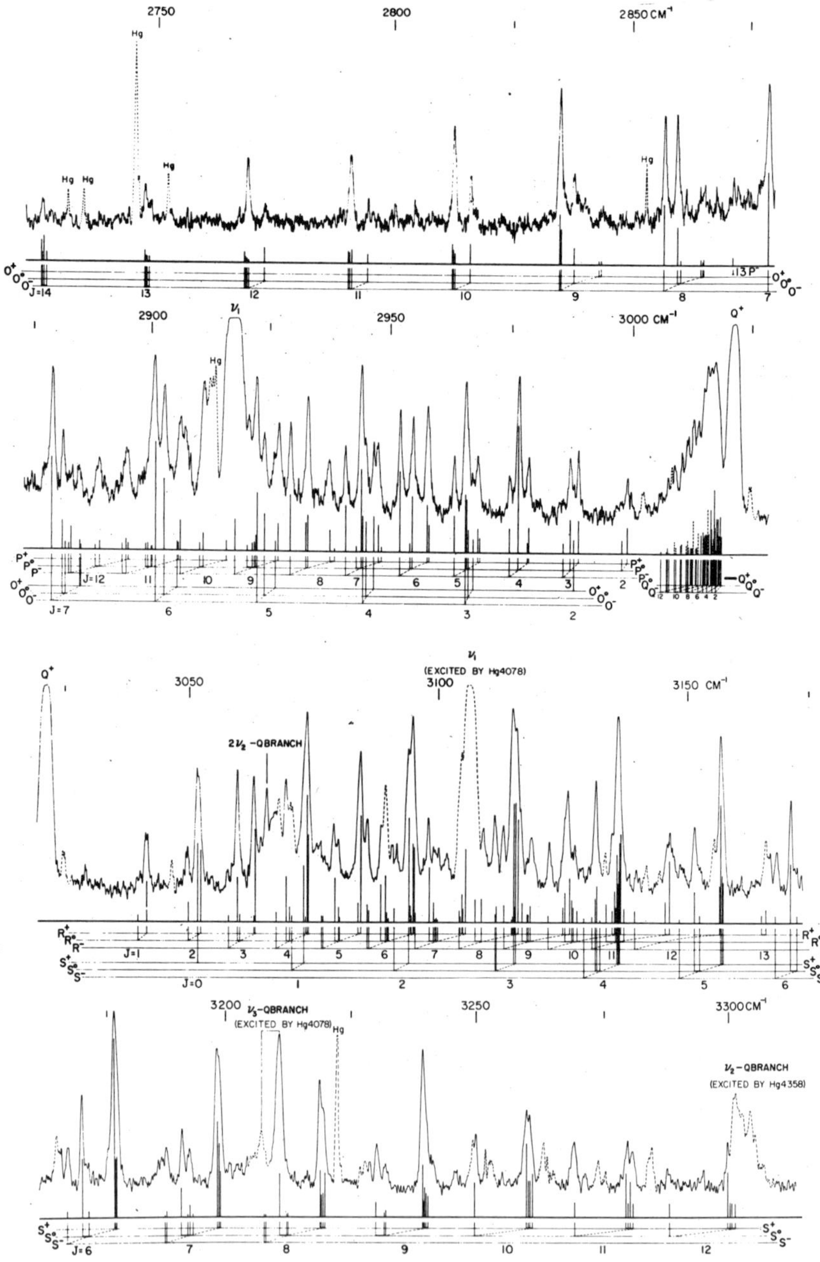

Fig. 16. The ν_3 Raman band of methane [Ref. (*62*), with permission].

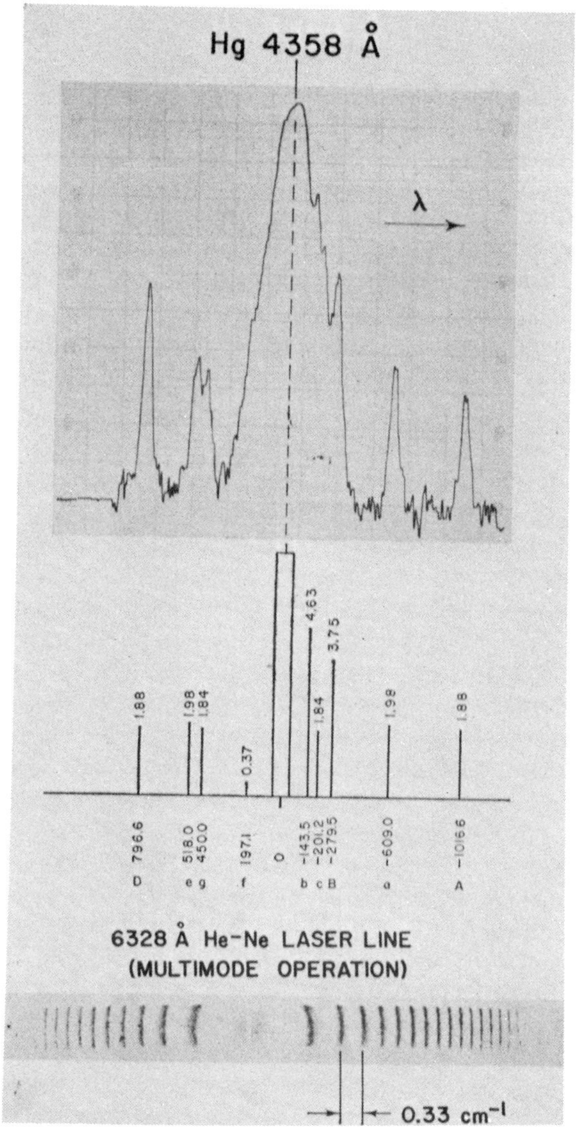

Fig. 17. Line profiles of the Hg 4358-Å and He-Ne 6328-Å laser radiations. (Top) Profile of the Hg 4358-Å line emitted by a water cooled low pressure mercury arc used to excite Raman spectra of gases. The width of the central unresolved structure is about 0.2 cm^{-1}. The values for the hyperfine structure separations, in mkayser, are taken from D. H. Rank, G. Skorinko, D. P. Eastman, G. D. Saksena, T. K. McCubbin, Jr., and T. A. Wiggins, *J. Opt. Soc. Am.* **50,** 1045 (1960). (Bottom) Fabry–Perot interferogram of 6328-Å radiation produced by a He-Ne laser. The interferogram was photographed during a Raman scattering experiment, using radiation reflected by one of the Brewster windows of the laser tube. Etalon spacer = 15.12 mm; the linewidth is less than 0.05 cm^{-1}.

(see Fig. 17 for an interferogram of the 6328 Å line emitted by a free running He-Ne laser) which opens the possibility of resolving finer details in a Raman spectrum but the high degree of collimation of laser beams suggests new approaches to the optical design of gas Raman cells. A variety of illumination systems are now in use depending on whether the gas sample is placed outside the laser cavity or within.

The simplest arrangement is of course a focused laser beam, with the focal region imaged onto the slit of the spectrograph. Photographic work with such an arrangement is prohibitively long in exposure time but photoelectrically recorded pure rotational spectra of simple gases are

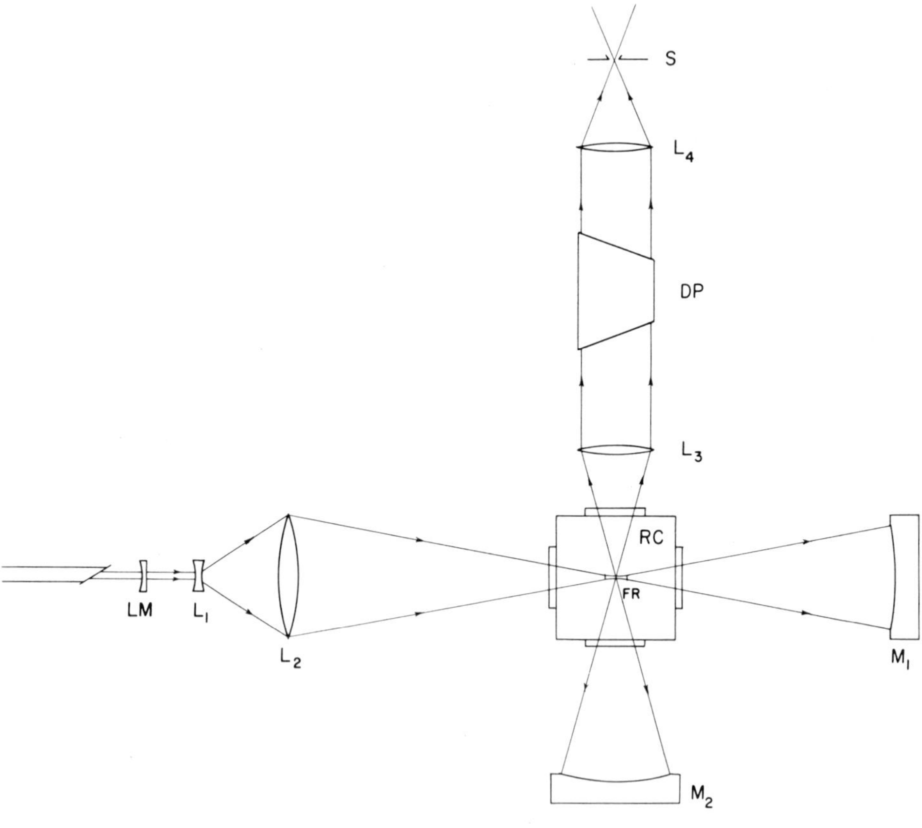

Fig. 18. Illuminating system for gas samples located outside the laser cavity; LM = laser dump mirror, L_1 = diverging lens, L_2 = focusing lens, M_1 = external resonating mirror, FR = focal region, M_2,L_3,L_4 = light collecting optics, DP = Dove Prism, S = spectrometer slit, RC = Raman cell.

easily obtained with fast spectrometers (*97*). Indeed, the pure rotational spectra of O_2 and N_2 in air may thus be used to provide a direct wave number calibration of the spectrometer for both the Stokes and anti-Stokes regions up to about 120 cm^{-1} away from the exciting line. A more efficient arrangement for working outside the laser cavity is suggested by Fig. 18. The laser beam that emerges from the laser "dump" mirror LM is rendered divergent by lens L_1 and then convergent by lens L_2 whose aperture ratio f/D is as small as possible. Mirror M_1 causes a near doubling of the intensity I_0 of the incident radiation in the focal region of L_2. This focal region FR is the effective scattering volume. Mirror M_3 doubles the amount of scattered radiation that is sent toward the spectrograph slit S by way of the transfer optics which consists of lenses L_3 and L_4. The focal region of lens L_2 is an approximately cylindrical volume element, so that if the scattering plane is horizontal, an image rotator consisting of a Dove prism DP or an equivalent refractive (Pechan prism, etc.) or reflective system is used to form an image of the scattering volume onto the spectrograph slit S which is nearly always vertical. A variation of the light collecting system shown in Fig. 18 is a system proposed by Plyler and Kostkowski (*98*) for the collection enhancement of infrared radiation emitted by a weak source. Thus, whereas in Fig. 18 only two solid angles (the "forward" angle subtended by lens L_3 at FR and the "reverse" angle subtended by M_2 at FR) contribute to the radiant flux collected by the spectrometer, the system shown in Fig. 19 has four solid angles (those subtended by L, M_3, M_4, and M_5 at FR) which contribute to the radiant flux collected by the spectrometer. With high reflectance mirrors a nearly fourfold gain is thus achieved. As pointed out by Plyler and Kostkowski, by using additional mirrors a sixfold and eightfold gain in the collected intensity is possible. These systems are particularly well suited for use with a scanning spectrometer of small f/D ratio. In its simpler form without mirrors M_2 and sometimes M_1 the system of Fig. 18 has been employed in several investigations (*97,99,100*). A particularly noteworthy aspect of these arrangements is the microsize of the scattering volume FR which has been estimated to be as low as $10^{-8} cm^3$ and thus contains as few as 10^{11} molecules at a pressure of 760 mm Hg (*99,100*).

By removing the laser dump mirror LM, the mirror M_1 of Fig. 18 becomes a fully reflecting laser resonator mirror and the gas sample is then situated inside the laser cavity. Very much higher incident intensities I_0 of the order of several tens of watts are thus available for the scattering experiment, in comparison to the former arrangement where the sample is outside the laser cavity. With such an arrangement and using an Ar^+-ion

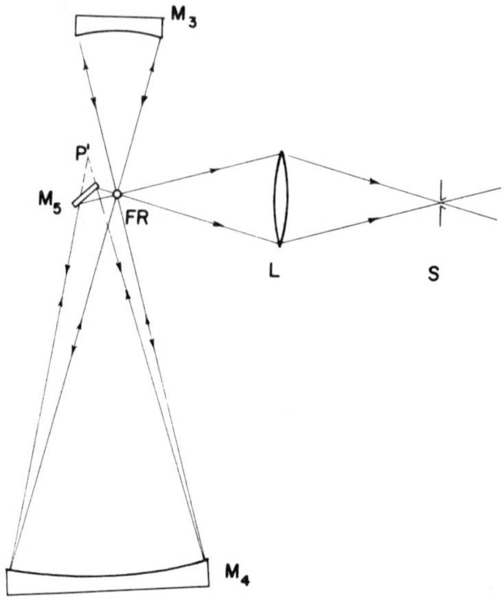

Fig. 19. Light collecting system for weak sources; from Plyler and Kostkowski [Ref. (98)]. FR = focal region of laser beam (see Fig. 18), mirrors M_3, M_4, and M_5 together with lens L constitute the light collecting system.

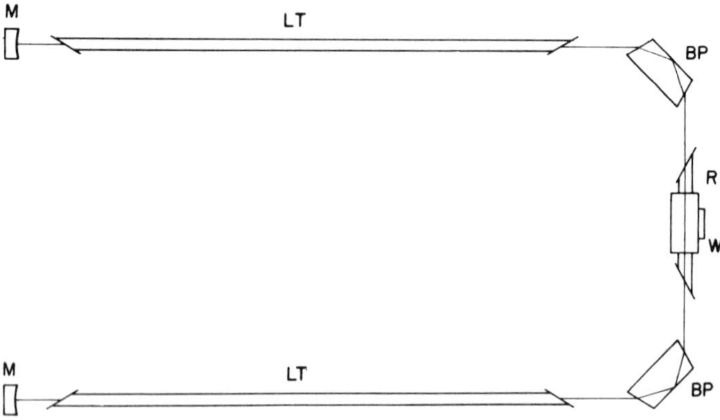

Fig. 20. Raman source system according to Fletcher et al. [Ref. (*101*)]. The gas cell is located in the focal region of the laser resonator. M_1, M_2 = fully reflecting laser mirrors.

laser Barrett and Adams (*99*) have successfully recorded the rotation vibration spectra of O_2, N_2, and CO_2 at atmospheric pressure and, Barrett and Rigden (*100*) have recorded the pure rotational Raman spectrum of CO_2 at a pressure of only 1 mm Hg.

A system suggested by Fletcher et al. (*101*) is shown in Fig. 20. Here two He-Ne laser tubes are placed in series, the resonator mirrors are mounted in the confocal configuration and the Raman sample is placed in the focal region.

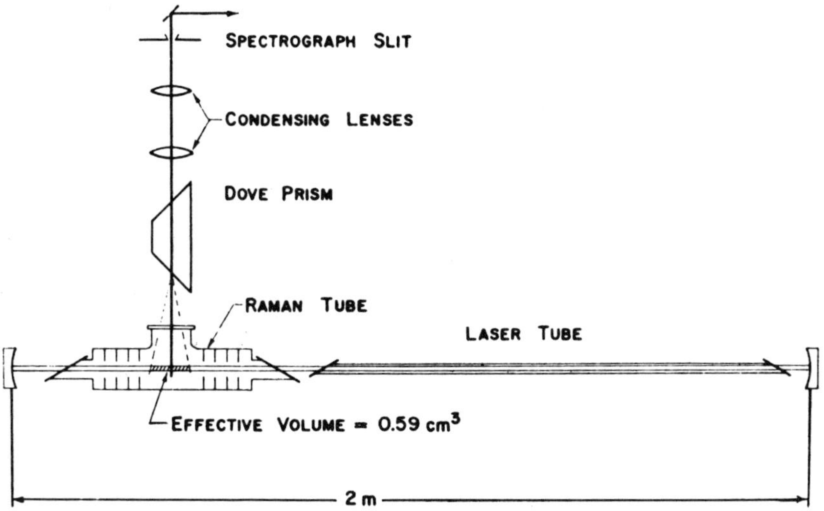

Fig. 21. Simple Raman excitation unit for gases [Ref. (*102*)].

The first laser-excited Raman spectrum of a gas was obtained with the simple arrangement shown in Fig. 21. The gas cell is part of the laser cavity and the effective scattering volume seen by the spectrograph was 0.59 cm^3. The laser beam traverses the cell through Brewster angle windows and no laser beam focusing devices were used. With a cylindrical lens placed in front of the photographic plate the pure rotational Raman spectrum of methylacetylene was photographed in 58 hrs. (*102*). A more luminous arrangement resulted by replacing the single traversal cell by a multiple traversal cell which is shown in Fig. 22. The laser beam multitraverses the cell by reflection off two parallel laser beam folding mirrors FM. These mirrors, as well as the entrance windows (either the Brewster angle windows shown or anti-reflection coated normal incidence windows), are part of the laser cavity and slight deterioration of the mirror coating has a disastrous effect on the performance. The number of passes that are possible is determined by the intrinsic gain per meter of the laser medium, the mirror reflectivity, radius of curvature of the fully reflecting laser mirrors and the overall (i.e. the unfolded) length of the laser cavity. With a He-Ne laser of 120 cm length, whose nominal output was 20 mW when operated in the confocal mode with 2 m radius mirrors (one of which was a "dump" mirror), up to 11 passes could be achieved through the cell when both laser resonator mirrors were coated for maximum reflectance. A system of concave spherical mirrors (CM) of the type described in Fig. 2

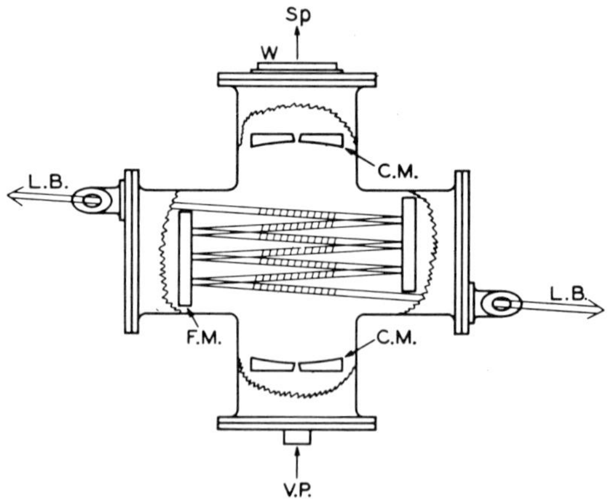

Fig. 22. Optical cross Raman cell suitable for work inside the laser cavity [Ref. (*83*)].

is used to collect the scattered radiation even though here this mirror system is not as efficient as when used in the long cylindrical gas cells (Fig. 2). Exactly the same system as shown in Fig. 22 has been proposed by Stenman (*103*), who demonstrated its usefulness with a pulsed ruby laser generating the Raman spectra of liquid substances.

Several other types of Raman sources have been suggested in the literature. Morét–Bailly and Berger (*103a*) place the Raman cell inside the laser cavity and observe the scattered radiation in a quasi-longitudinal mode; the scattered light is collected with a three mirror multiple reflection system. This arrangement is similar to the one originally proposed by Weber *et al.* (see Ref. *83*, Figure 2). Rich and Welsh (*103b*) place the typical four mirror multiple reflection Raman cell shown in Figure 2 outside the laser cavity. With a small right angle prism positioned centrally over the slot between the two front mirrors C and D (see figure 2), the laser beam is focussed to a point in the center of this slot whereupon it diverges and fills the two rear mirrors A and B. The mirror system now acts in "reverse" and a series of images of the focal spot is formed on the front mirrors C and D. The Raman radiation that is generated within the cell is then collected by the same mirror system which now operates in the "forward" direction and the collected Raman radiation emerges through the slot between the mirrors C and D. A novel system based on the principle of the light pipe has been suggested by Chapput, Delhaye, and Wrobel (*103c*). The Raman cell is a long tube placed outside the laser cavity. The laser beam passes through the tube axially and the Raman scattered radiation generated by the contained gas is conducted to the exit end of the tube (light pipe action) whence it is transferred to the spectrometer by means of conventional transfer optics. The quasi-longitudinal scattering mode of these three systems is of considerable usefulness, for in this mode the Raman line broadening due to the Doppler effect can be held to a minimum (see section VII, C).

The use of Brewster angle windows on laser tubes gives rise to linearly polarized light which can be used to considerable advantage. The very strong Rayleigh scattering has always caused a wide region near the exciting line to be severely overexposed and has produced strong ghosts near the exciting line (see Figs. 3–8). In regions far removed from the exciting line, rotation-vibration spectra could often not be observed due to severe "grass" type of grating ghosts which covered the whole region. One way out of this dilemma is to use a premonochromator before the main spectrograph to filter out the exciting line (*96*). A second method is based on the fact that the exciting laser radiation is linearly polarized. If the electric vector of the exciting radiation vibrates in the scattering plane and if, as is customary, the scattering angle is 90°, then the highly polarized, isotropically scattered Rayleigh radiation will have very low intensity. The degree of quenching of the Rayleigh line intensity depends on the value of its depolarization factor as well as the solid angle over which the scattered light is collected. This method is naturally limited to the study of the depolarized, anisotropically scattered radiation and would, thus, not be suitable in the study of the totally symmetric vibrations of molecules of tetrahedral and octahedral symmetry (i.e., CCl_4 and SF_6). Nevertheless, the degree of quenching is very striking as is shown in Fig. 23, which compares the pure rotational Raman spectrum of methylacetylene obtained with the "pre-laser" equipment with the spectrum obtained by means of the optical cross Raman cell (Fig. 22) and a He-Ne laser. Spectrum (a)

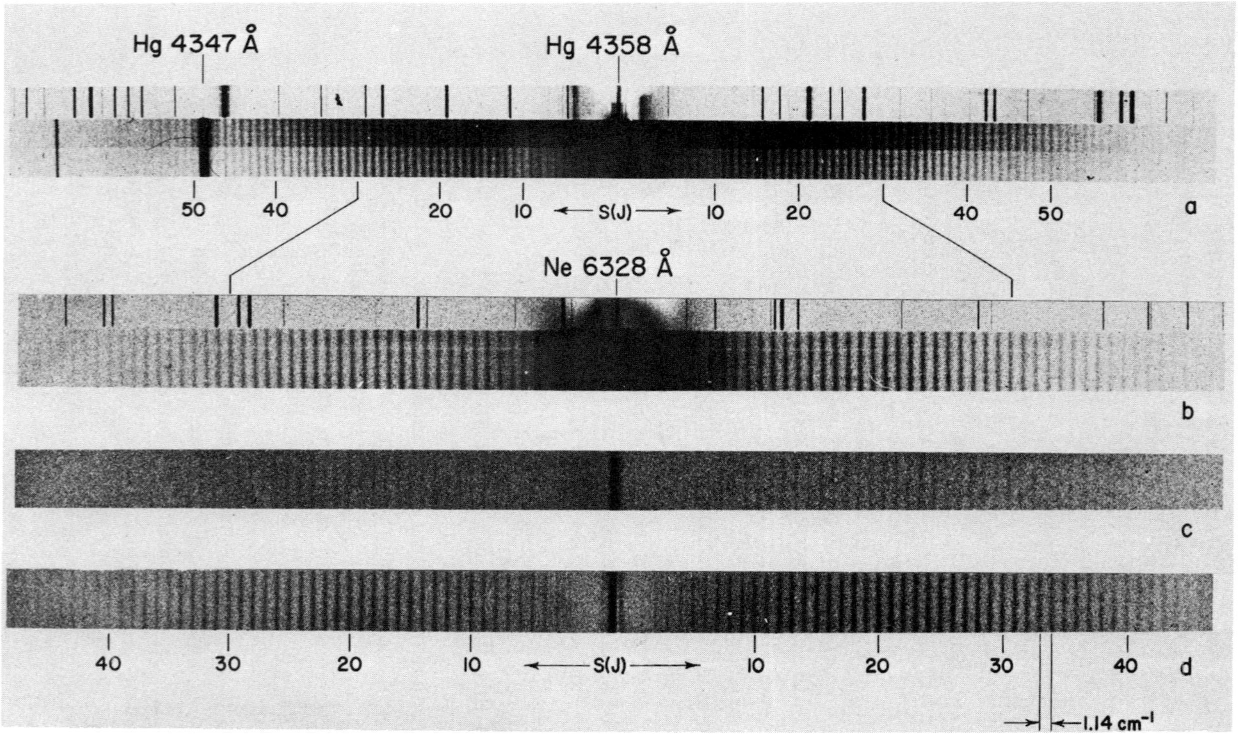

Fig. 23. Pure rotational Raman spectrum of methylacetylene at atmospheric pressure; (a) mercury arc excited spectrum using pre-laser techniques (Fig. 2). With four mercury arc lamps (5 kw each) illuminating a volume of 3000 cm^3 the spectrum was obtained on a Kodak 103a-0 plate in 14 hr. A 50% neutral density filter was placed over half of the slit. (b) Laser excited spectrum obtained with He-Ne laser (6328 Å exciting line) and equipment shown in Figs. 21 and 22 with the multiple pass cell adjusted for 9 passes inside the laser cavity. The spectrum was recorded on a Kodak 103a-E plate in 33 hr. The electric vector of the exciting radiation is perpendicular to the scattering plane. (c) Same conditions as for (b) but electric vector of exciting radiation lies in the scattering plane. (d) Same conditions as for (c) but recorded on Kodak Ia-E emulsion.

was obtained in 14 hr on a Kodak 103a-O plate with a 2 m Raman tube (Fig. 2) surrounded by four water cooled Hg-arc lamps (power consumption 5 kW each). Spectra (b) and (c) were obtained in 33 hr on Kodak 103a-E plates with the optical cross (Fig. 22) and a He-Ne laser rated at 20 mW. In (b) the electric vector of the exciting radiation vibrates perpendicular to the scattering plane whereas in (c) it vibrates in the scattering plane. Spectrum (d) was also obtained in 33 hr on the faster Kodak Ia-E emulsion. For all four spectra the gas pressure was 1 atm. Figures 24–27

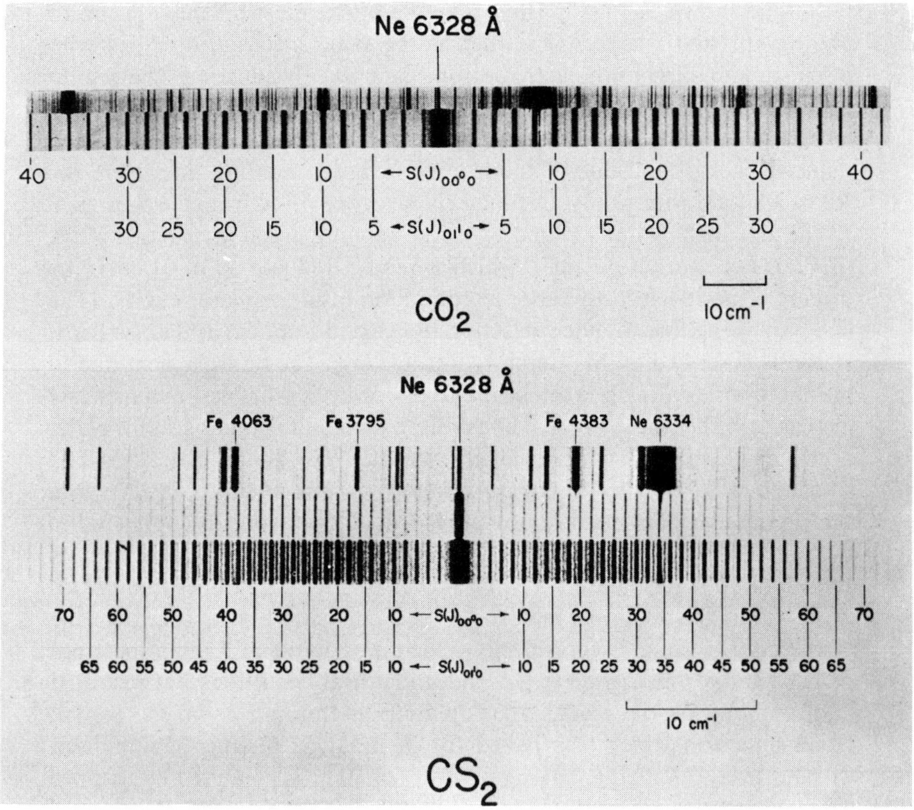

Fig. 24. Pure rotational spectra of CO_2 and CS_2 obtained with the multiple pass cell (Fig. 22, adjusted for 7 passes) and the arrangement shown in Fig. 21. Both spectra were recorded on Kodak Ia-E plates. Gas pressure and exposure times were, for CO_2, 1 atm and $51\frac{1}{2}$ hr; and for CS_2, 280 mmHg and 8 hr (top) and 44 hr (bottom). The electric vector of the exciting beam lies in the scattering plane. [Refs. (*55*, *111*)].

show similarly the superiority of the laser excitation technique over the pre-laser methods. Thus, with the pre-laser technique the pure rotation spectra of CO_2 and CS_2 in the 01^10 vibrationally excited state shown in Fig. 24 could not have been observed for, with the exposure times required to bring them out, they would have been masked by the ghost pattern produced by the overexposed exciting line and would also be overlapped by the 00^00 ground state pure rotation spectra excited by the hyperfine components of the Hg 4358 Å exciting line (see Fig. 17, components labeled A, D, a, e, and g) unless of course a single isotope lamp were used. The pure rotation spectrum of cyclohexane obtained with the pre-laser technique shown in Fig. 25 (top) was one of the most difficult spectra to photograph and analyze (*88*), whereas the same spectrum obtained with a free-running argon-ion laser (bottom) is markedly superior. The resolution is improved due to the lower pressure of the cyclohexane vapor, which results in a reduced pressure broadening of the Raman lines, and the reduced background due to the less overexposed exciting line. Here the *R*-branch (odd *J*-lines only, of course) is clearly resolved from the *S*-branch.

The λ = 4880 Å line emitted by a free-running argon laser has a width (*FWHH*) of nearly 0.15 cm^{-1} which is readily reduced to 0.001 cm^{-1} by placing a mode-selecting Fabry–Perot étalon inside the laser cavity. [The line narrowing due to mode selection by a tilted intra cavity Fabry–Perot étalon is described by M. Hercher, Ref. (*111a*)]. The improvement due to the narrower exciting line can be realized, however, only by simultaneously increasing either the reciprocal linear dispersion on the photographic plate, or by using fine grain plates. Until recently, the grainy Kodak 103a-J emulsion with a rather low plate resolving power of 56 to 68 lines/mm (*111b*) was the only emulsion employed in Raman spectroscopic studies in the blue-green region of the spectrum. The newer Kodak IIIa-J with its considerably higher plate resolving power of 136 to 225 lines/mm (*111b*) is, however, much slower than the 103a-J emulsion but its speed can be increased by baking. Figure 26 shows the pure rotational Raman spectrum of 1,3,5-trifluorobenzene excited under identical conditions but recorded in 30 minutes on the Kodak 103a-J emulsion and in 2 hr on the Kodak IIIa-J emulsion which was baked for $3\frac{1}{4}$ hr at 55°C and then exposed without delay. (Actually, baking at 50°C for 20 hr is now used by us since it gives more reproducible results.) Similarly, the spectra of cyanuric fluoride and hexafluorobenzene shown in Fig. 27 demonstrate the superiority of the baked IIIa-J emulsion. Although not indicated in Fig. 27, *R*-branch lines in the spectrum of hexafluorobenzene can be seen on the original spectrograms. The observed line spacing of

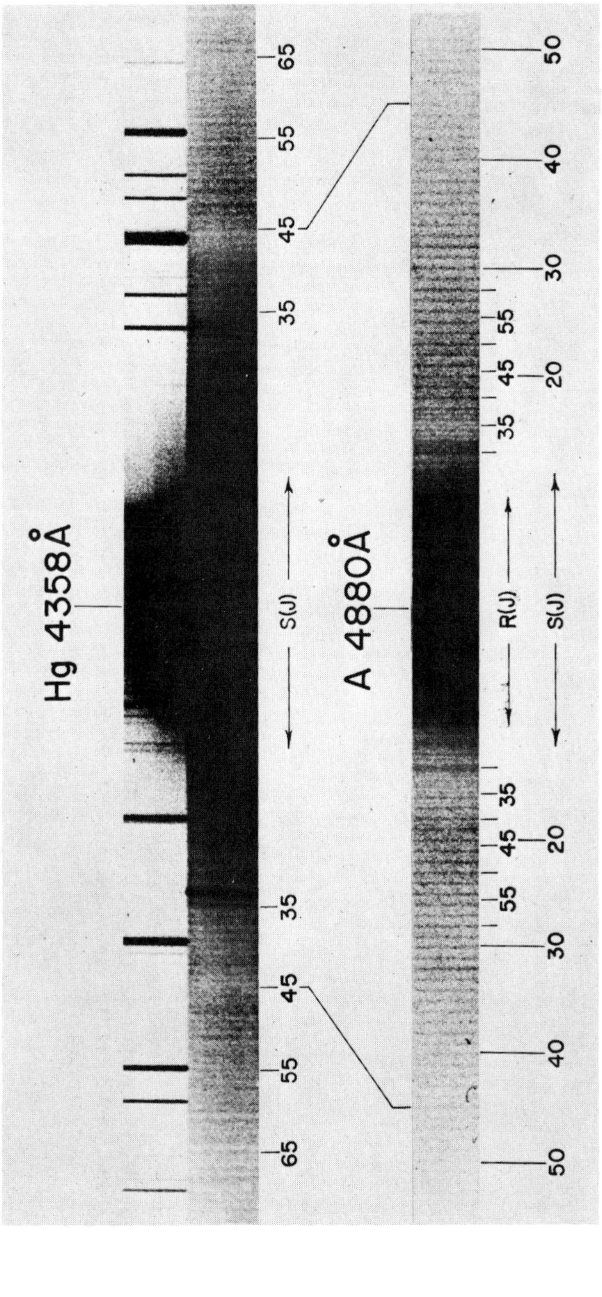

Fig. 25. Pure rotational spectrum of cyclohexane-d_0. Top: spectrum excited with pre-laser technique (see description for Fig. 23) using a pressure of $\frac{1}{2}$ atm and an exposure time of 40 hr (Kodak 103a-O plate). The bottom spectrum was obtained with the apparatus of Figs. 21 and 22 (cell adjusted for 9 passes located inside the laser cavity) and a free-running Carson Model 500 Argon laser (nominal output in the $\lambda = 4880$ Å line ~ 2 W). The spectrum was recorded on a Kodak 103a-J plate in 6 hr. The pressure of cyclohexane vapor was 61 mmHg [Refs. (*88*, *103d*)].

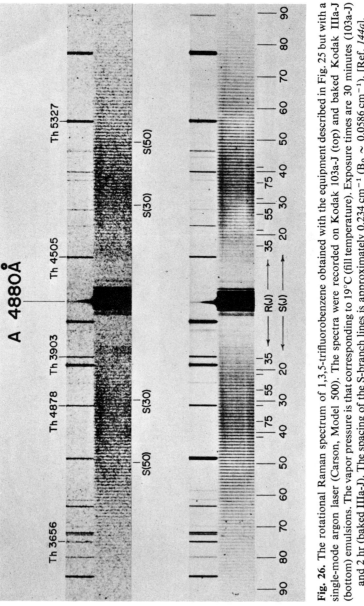

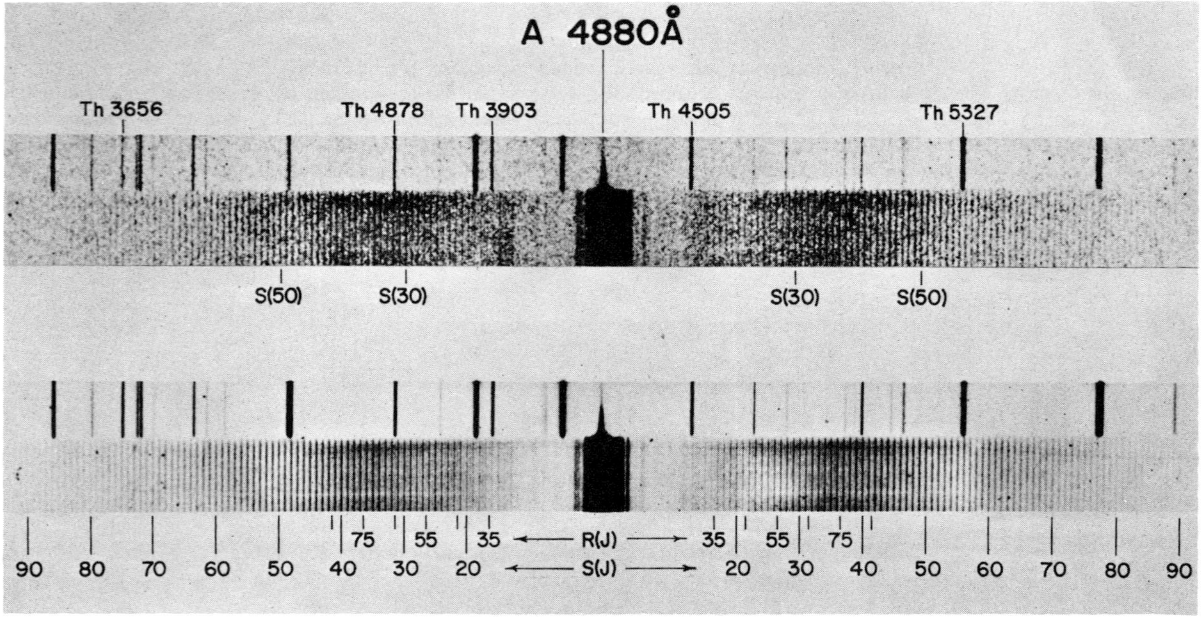

Fig. 26. The rotational Raman spectrum of 1,3,5-trifluorobenzene obtained with the equipment described in Fig. 25 but with a single-mode argon laser (Carson, Model 500). The spectra were recorded on Kodak 103a-J (top) and baked Kodak IIIa-J (bottom) emulsions. The vapor pressure is that corresponding to 19°C (fill temperature). Exposure times are 30 minutes (103a-J) and 2 hr (baked IIIa-J). The spacing of the S-branch lines is approximately 0.234 cm^{-1} ($B_0 \sim 0.0586\ cm^{-1}$). [Ref. *144a*].

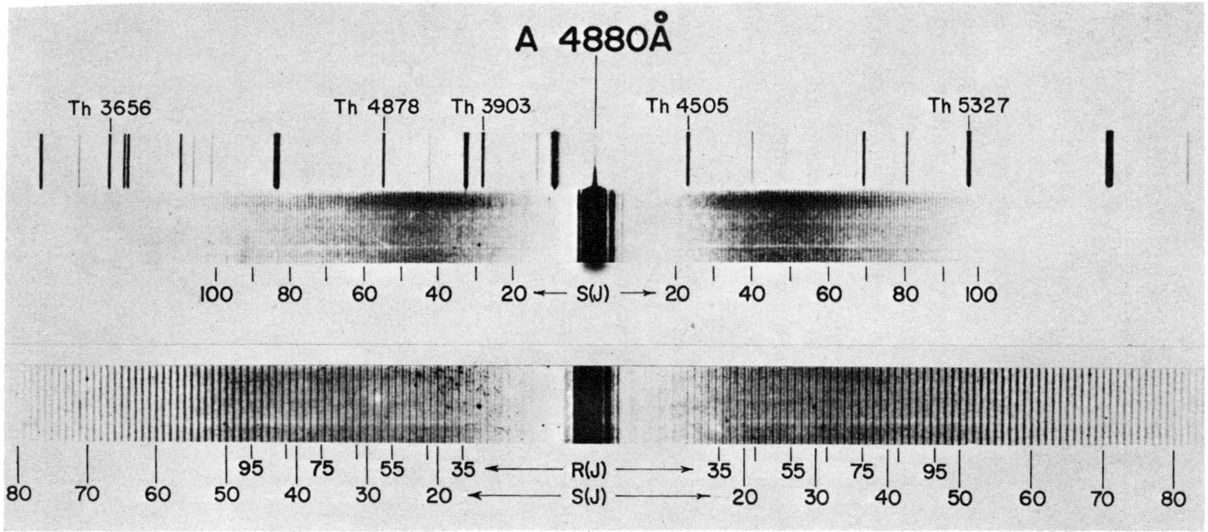

Fig. 27. The rotational Raman spectra of hexafluorobenzene (C_6F_6) (top) and cyanuric fluoride ($C_3N_3F_3$) (bottom) obtained with a single-mode argon laser on baked Kodak IIIa-J emulsions. Vapor pressure and exposure times are, for hexafluorobenzene 67 mmHg and $1\frac{3}{4}$ hr, and for cyanuric fluoride 70 mmHg and 6 hr. The cyanuric fluoride spectrum was photographed with a Corning 3-73 filter inside the cavity to prevent the ultraviolet radiation from entering the Raman cell. The spacing of the S-branch lines is approximately 0.2624 cm^{-1} ($B_0 \sim 0.0656$ cm^{-1}) for cyanuric fluoride and 0.137 cm^{-1} ($B_0 \sim 0.0343$ cm^{-1}) for hexafluorobenzene. R-branch lines with a spacing of $\sim$0.0686 cm^{-1} are visible on the original hexafluorobenzene spectrograms. [Ref. *144a,b*].

$2B = 0.0686\ \text{cm}^{-1}$ represents the highest resolution attained thus far in Raman spectroscopy ($\sigma/\Delta\sigma \approx 293{,}000$). [Note, however, that still higher resolutions are achieved when the "forward scattering" configuration with its attendant reduction in the Doppler broadening of Raman lines is used; see Refs. (*318–324*). This is discussed on pp. 729–733.] Additional spectra which have been obtained with these techniques (i.e., single-mode argon laser with polarization of the exciting radiation in the scattering plane, use of the multiple pass cell (Fig. 22), and photographic recording of the spectra on baked IIIa-J plates) are those of propane, *n*-butane, *n*-pentane, *n*-hexane, hexafluoroethane, and cycloheptane (*111c*). In addition to its use in these photographic studies, the multiple pass Raman cell has also been employed in a photoelectric study of the fine structure of the rotational lines of oxygen (*104*).

While nearly all recent investigations have been conducted with the aid of grating spectrographs or spectrometers, the small line width of the laser exciting radiation, particularly from a single-mode laser, and the small scattering volume suggests the use of interferometers as the high resolving power instrument. The obvious use of the plane parallel Fabry–Perot interferometer is based on the classic arrangement in which it is placed between the light source, which is here the scattering volume, and the spectrograph slit (see Fig. 28a). On the other hand the internally illuminated Fabry–Perot interferometer as described by Kastler (*105*) has been used in the two configurations (plane parallel and spherical) shown in Fig. 28b and c. With the plane parallel interferometer (Fig. 28b) the photographic exposure times are strictly comparable to those required with the multiple traversal Raman cell of Fig. 22 (*106*). Figure 28c shows the use of the internally illuminated spherical F-P. With piezoelectric scanning good pure rotational spectra can be recorded with an *FW*-130 photo-multiplier tube and the photon-counting technique (*107*). The problems which derive from pressure, and Doppler and natural line width must of course be considered when the full capabilities of the interferometric techniques are to be realized. Discussion of these problems will be deferred to section VII C.

In addition to these interferometric schemes, there are the methods of Fourier transform spectroscopy based upon the Michelson or the Fabry–Perot interferometer which may be considered. It appears to be the consensus that with the present state of the art the principal advantage of this technique is reserved for the infrared region of the spectrum, and no attempt has thus far been reported on the use of the Michelson interferometer for high resolution Raman spectroscopy. On the other hand,

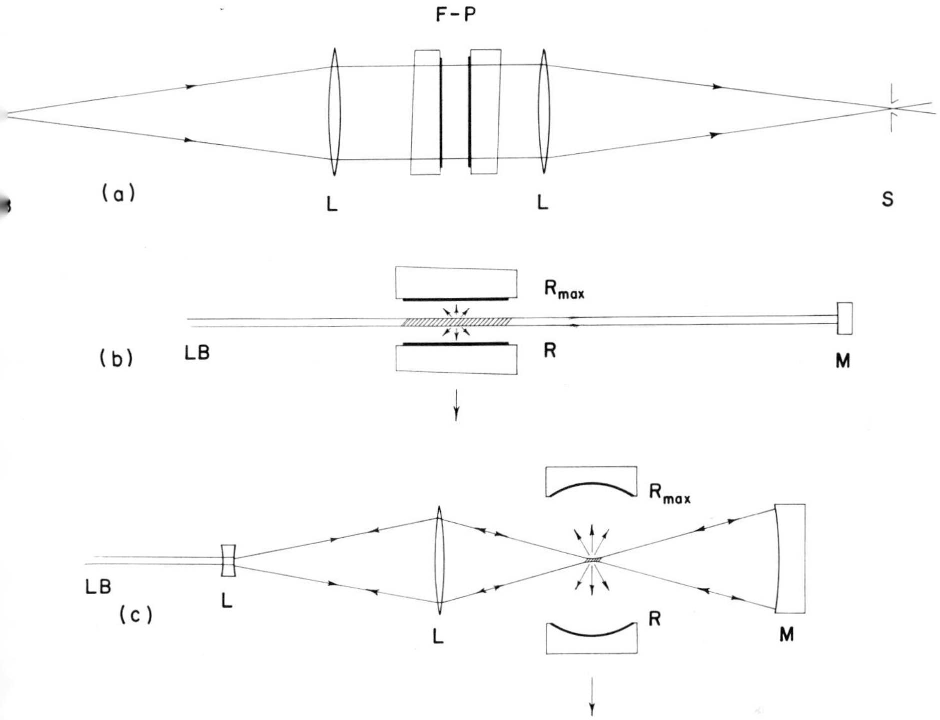

Fig. 28. Use of the Fabry–Perot interferometer. (a) Classic arrangement; (b) internally illuminated plane-parallel interferometer; (c) internally illuminated spherical interferometer.

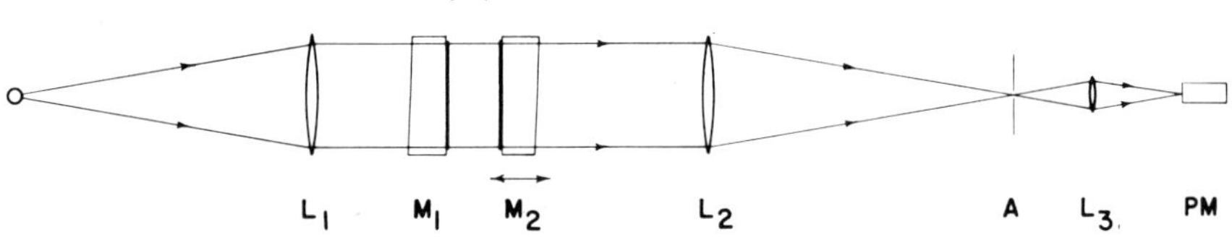

Fig. 29. Mechanically scanned Fabry–Perot interferometer for use in Raman spectroscopy [Ref. (*108*)].

Barrett (*108*) has successfully employed the Fabry–Perot interferometer in the classic scanning mode as depicted in Fig. 29. Here the Fabry–Perot mirror M_1 is held stationary and mirror M_2 is moved along accurate ways so as to either increase or decrease the gap between them in a smooth, linear manner and the Haidinger fringes are formed by lens L_2 on the plane of a pin hole aperture A, with the center of the ring system focused on the pin hole. As mirror M_2 is translated the signal picked up by the photomultiplier is modulated in intensity. As an example, if we consider that a pure rotational Raman spectrum is given whose frequencies are represented by

$$\nu = \nu_0 \pm 4B(J+\tfrac{3}{2})$$

where ν_0 is the frequency of the exciting radiation and centrifugal distortion effects are ignored, then the spectrum would appear as in Fig. 30 (top) which shows a series of lines with equal spacing ($= 4B$) disposed symmetrically about the exciting line, with the first two Raman lines occuring at an interval of $6B$ away from ν_0. Figure 30, middle, shows the transmission spectrum of the Fabry–Perot interferometer for a given plate separation d. For simplicity only a "line spectrum" at the transmission maxima instead of the complete Airy distribution function is shown. The spacing of the transmission "lines" is equal to the free spectral range $(2nd)^{-1}$ of the interferometer where d is the plate separation and n is the index of refraction. For the situation depicted all Raman frequencies coincide with the pass band frequencies of the interferometer, whereas the Rayleigh frequency does not. The photomultiplier will therefore detect a maximum signal which is due to the Raman radiation only. A slight displacement of mirror M_2 will destroy the register between Raman and pass band frequencies and the signal will decrease. A further displacement of mirror M_2 will cause the Rayleigh frequency to fall upon one of the interferometer pass bands and another maximum signal will be detected which is due to just the Rayleigh radiation. A continuous displacement of mirror M_2 does result in the interferogram shown in Fig. 30, bottom, consisting of the Rayleigh radiation fringes of constant intensity alternating with the weaker Raman radiation fringes, whose intensity varies due to the spectral distribution shown in the top, as well as to the nonequal Raman line spacing caused by the never-absent centrifugal distortion effect. The free spectral range of the interferometer and the Raman line spacing shown in Fig. 30 are both equal to $4B$. The "$4B$ interferogram" obtained by Barrett for nitrous oxide is shown in Fig. 31. The deduction of the molecular constants is made possible by continuously decreasing the mirror separation until a new configuration is attained in which the free spectral range of the interferometer is $6B$, so that every third Raman line is in register with the interferometer pass band thus giving rise to a "$6B$ interferogram." The number of Rayleigh line fringes between the intensity maxima of the $4B$ and $6B$ interferograms is directly related to the

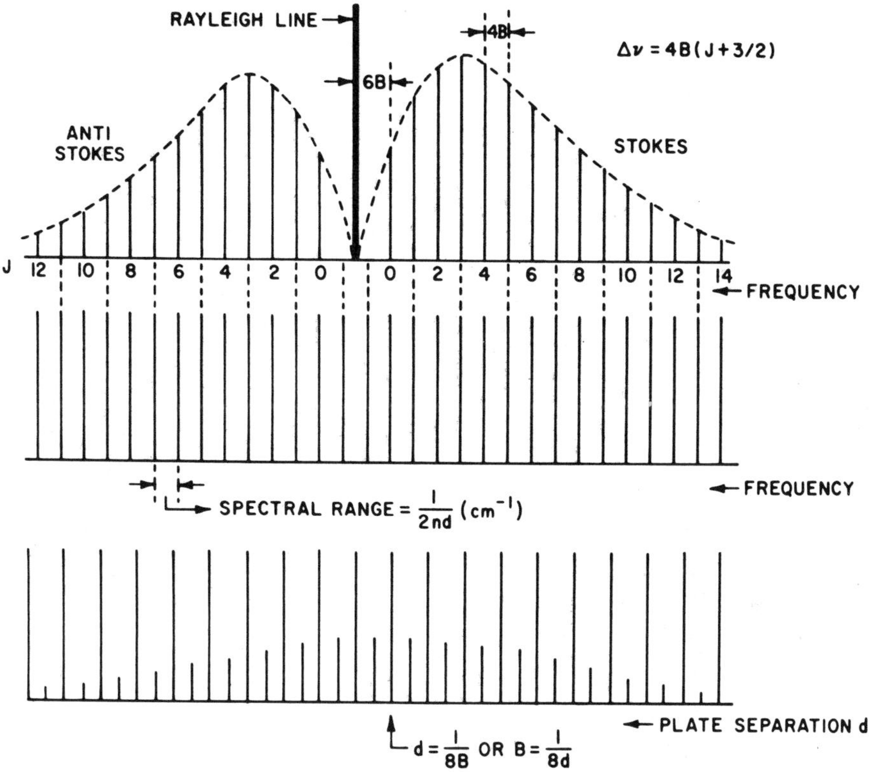

Fig. 30. Schematic representation of the Fabry–Perot interferogram of a rotational Raman Spectrum. (Top) Pure rotational Raman spectrum of a linear molecule without centrifugal distortion. (Middle) Fabry–Perot transmission spectrum. (Bottom) "$4B$-interferogram" of Raman spectrum [Ref. (*108*)].

molecular constants, and a knowledge of the order of interference of a given fringe or the corresponding interferometer thickness d is thus not necessary. A further reduction of the interferometer gap gives rise to an "$8B$-interferogram," etc. The effects of centrifugal distortion which have been ignored here, as well as the simultaneous presence of R- and S-

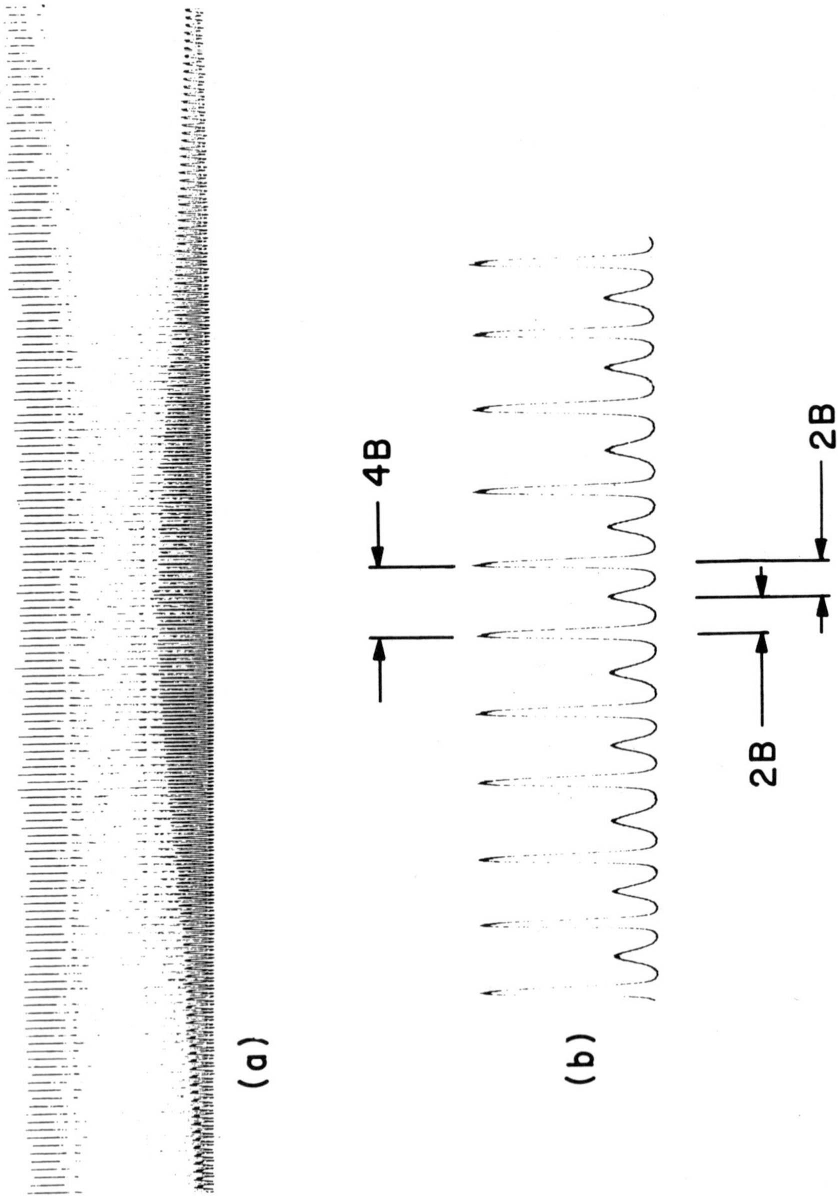

Fig. 31. The "$4B$-interferogram" of pure rotational Raman spectrum of nitrous oxide [Ref. (*108*)].

branches are easily included in the theory and give rise to no difficulty in the analysis. Rather difficult to ascertain, however, is the exact number of fringes that lie between the intensity maxima of the interferograms since, as seen from Fig. 31, these maxima are rather broad.

For simple spectra the molecular constants can be deduced very easily from the interferogram, but for complex spectra, i.e., asymmetric top pure rotation spectra as well as rotation-vibration bands, particularly of degenerate vibrations, the Fourier transform will have to be computed. Toward this end Röseler (*109*) has made an analytic study of the Fabry–Perot interferometer when employed as a Fourier transform spectrometer. His conclusion is that the amplitudes of the Fourier components in the interferogram of a two beam interferometer (i.e., Michelson interferometer) and those from a Fabry–Perot interferometer stand in the ratio $1:[2T^2R^k/(1-R^2)]$, where T and R are the transmissivity and reflectivity of the Fabry–Perot mirrors and k is the order number of a given Fourier component. The Fabry–Perot interferometer has therefore less luminosity in comparison to that of a two-beam interferometer and its only advantage lies in the simpler mechanical construction.

The resolution that is attainable in a Raman spectrum depends of course on the width of the Raman lines themselves. Whereas the limit of resolution in the pre-laser era was in practice determined by the width of the exciting radiation (i.e., 0.2 cm^{-1} for the 4358 Å line emitted by a low pressure, water-cooled mercury arc containing "natural" mercury) this is no longer the case with laser sources. The measurable widths of Raman lines (i.e., a single $J'' \leftarrow J'$ transition) are comprised mainly of pressure and Doppler broadening effects, in addition to the intrinsic, "natural" line width. Pressure broadening coefficients for a few gases (see pp. 733–740) have been measured and amount to roughly 0.06–0.30 cm^{-1}/atm for nonpolar gases (*110*) and 1 cm^{-1}/atm for polar gases (*28*). While this broadening effect is of intrinsic interest since it provides experimental data needed in the study of intermolecular forces, it obligates the investigator to work with gases at low pressures in order to achieve a desired limit of resolution.

The Doppler effect causes a further line broadening whose halfwidth value (= full width at half maximum intensity) is given by (see pp. 729–732):

$$\Delta\nu_{FWHH}^{D_0} = \frac{2\nu_0}{c}(2R\ln 2)^{1/2}(T/M)^{1/2} = 7.16\times 10^{-7}\nu_0(T/M)^{1/2}$$

where ν_0 is the center frequency of the line, T is the absolute temperature of the gas, and M is its molecular weight. As an example at room temperature (= 300°K) and with $\nu_0 = 20{,}000\ \mathrm{cm}^{-1}$ ($\lambda_0 = 5000$ Å), $\Delta\nu_{FWHH}^{D_0} =$ $0.045\ \mathrm{cm}^{-1}$ for ethane and $0.028\ \mathrm{cm}^{-1}$ for benzene. The observed Raman line profile is then a superposition of the effects of lifetime of excited states (natural width), Doppler and pressure broadening, as well as the instrumental line profile and finally the line shape of the exciting radiation itself. While the problems associated with these latter two contributions may be considered as solved via the availability of Fabry–Perot interferometers and single frequency laser sources, the problems due to the Doppler and pressure broadening effects have not been fully attended to as yet (see, however, Section VII, C).

IV. OBSERVED RAMAN SPECTRA

A. Introduction

The Raman spectra of slightly over 40 molecules (not counting the various isotopic species) have been studied thus far under the above conditions, and provide results to justify their inclusion in this report on "High Resolution Raman Studies." Nearly all these studies were performed with the "pre-laser" techniques and, since the vibration-rotation Raman spectra are much weaker than the pure rotation spectra, the bulk of these studies dealt with the pure rotation spectra only. Thus, of the 16 symmetric top molecules known to have been investigated, only four deal with vibration–rotation bands and of the 11 asymmetric top molecules studied, all but one study have been concerned with only the pure rotation spectra.

The problems that have been attacked thus far are mainly the determination of the molecular structure, deduced principally from the values of the rotation constants, the determination of the parameters that describe the dynamical behavior of molecules, these being primarily the Coriolis coupling coefficients, centrifugal distortion constants, and the harmonic and anharmonic force constants and, more recently, the molecular interactions as deduced from the pressure dependence of the frequency and half width of Raman lines.

The techniques that are used to deduce the rotational constants from a resolved spectrum are well known (*29,30,42*) and will not be elaborated here. For convenience as well as consistency, this section gives a brief presentation of the results deduced from the Raman spectra of linear, symmetric top, spherical top, and asymmetric top molecules.

B. Linear Molecules

The pure rotational Raman spectra of linear molecules are analyzed on the basis of Eq. (93) if the molecules are in a nondegenerate vibrational state ($l = 0$). This is the case for all linear molecules for which pure rotational spectra have been observed with the exception of CO_2, CS_2, O_2, and NO. For CO_2 and CS_2 the *S*-branch of the pure rotational transitions has also been observed for molecules in the $v_1 = 0, v_2 = 1^1, v_3 = 0$ excited vibrational state (*55,111*). Since this is a doubly degenerate state (species π_u) Eq. (99) with $l = 1$ is used to derive the molecular constants.

Figure 24 shows the pure rotational spectra of CO_2 and CS_2. The strong lines represent the pure rotational transitions in the vibrational ground state ($v_1 = v_2 = v_3 = 0$) with the selection rule $\Delta J = +2$. The weaker series of lines is interpreted as the pure rotational spectrum of these molecules in the 01^10 excited state, also with the selection rule $\Delta J = +2$. Figure 32 shows a rotational energy level diagram for these two vibrational states as well as the transitions that give rise to the pure rotational spectra. Since the ground electronic state of both CO_2 and CS_2 is ${}^1\Sigma_g{}^+$, both molecules are symmetric and possess a center of symmetry (point group $D_{\infty h}$), and since the spins of the equivalent nuclei are zero (we consider only the O^{16} and S^{32} isotopes since they are the most abundant), all rotational levels which are antisymmetric in the simultaneous exchange of equivalent nuclei are absent (*112,113*). For the vibrational ground state this results in the absence of all rotational levels with J = odd and the ground state pure rotational spectrum, therefore, consists of lines with J = even only, and with a line spacing equal to $8B(\sim 3.2\ \text{cm}^{-1}$ for CO_2 and $0.87\ \text{cm}^{-1}$ for CS_2).

In the degenerate vibrational state the rotation-vibration interaction causes a removal of the l-degeneracy with each rotational level J split into a doublet, one member of which is symmetric whereas the other member is antisymmetric in the nuclei. Therefore, in spite of the absence of the antisymmetric levels for CO_2 and CS_2 both even-J and odd-J rotational transitions occur in degenerate vibrational states. Since the difference in the B-values for the ground and the excited vibrational states is slight, the $\Delta J = 2$, even-J, transitions of molecules in the 00^00 and 01^10 vibrational states overlap and together constitute the strong spectrum seen in Fig. 24. The $\Delta J = 2$, odd-J, transitions in the 01^10 state, however, have no ground state counterpart and, thus, stand alone in the spectrum. Figure 24 shows only the *S*-branches ($\Delta J = +2$) of the pure rotation spectra. In the 01^10 state pure rotational transitions with $\Delta J = +1$ giving rise to an *R*-branch

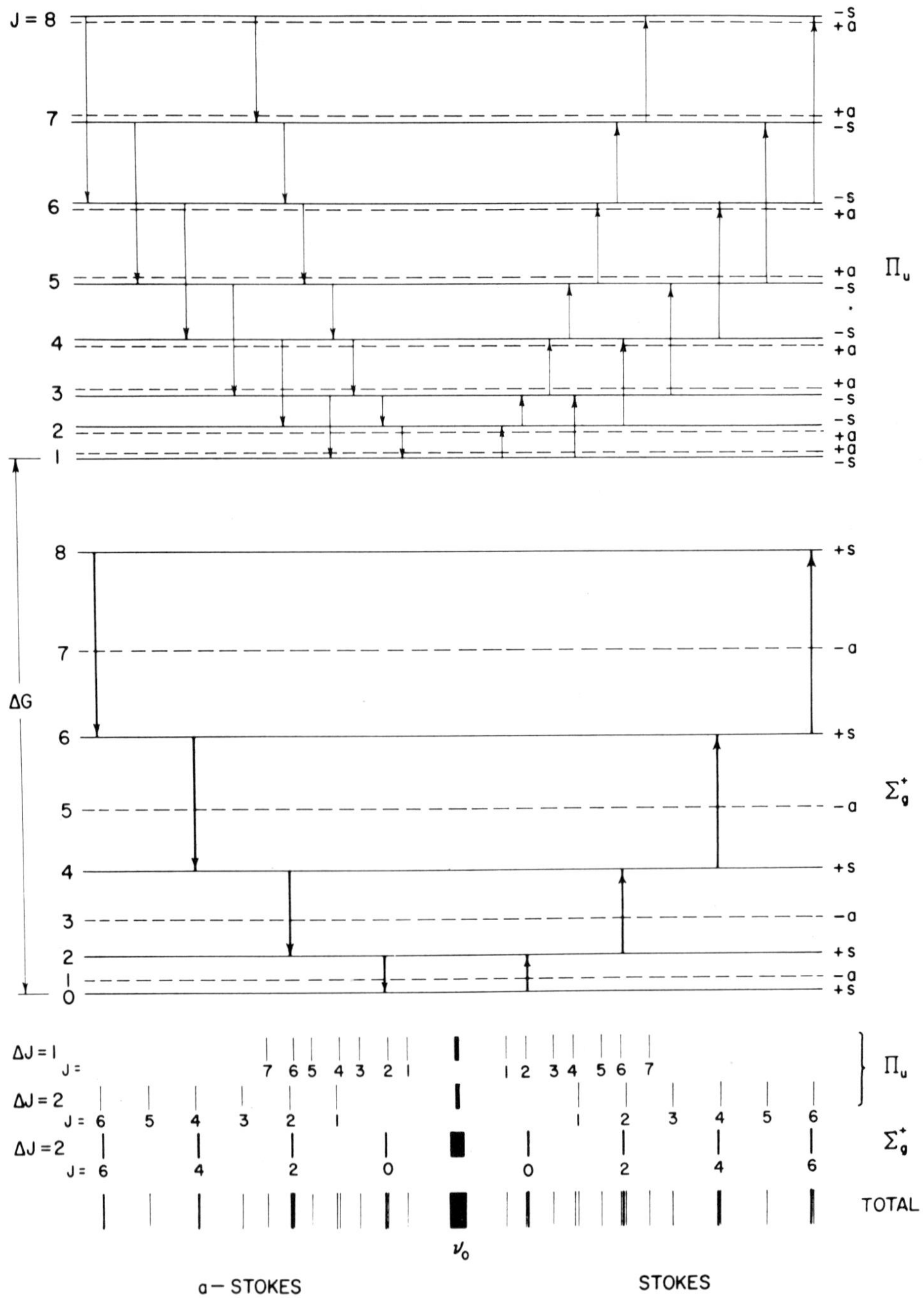

Fig. 32. Rotational energy levels and pure rotation spectrum for CO_2^{16} and CS_2^{32} in the 00^00 and 01^10 vibrational states. (s) = symmetric, (a) = antisymmetric.

with line spacing $2B$ are also allowed. However, as seen from Table 1, with $K = \ell = 1$, the R-branch intensity varies as J^{-1} and R-branch lines were barely noticeable for CO_2 (*55*).

Only the 00^00 and 01^10 states have been considered in this discussion since the population of the other vibrational states (10^00, 00^01, as well as the combination and overtone states) is small. [For CO_2 and CS_2, $\omega_2 = 667$ and $397\ cm^{-1}$ respectively. The relative populations of the ground (00^00) and first excited (01^10) vibrational states at room temperature (300°K) are then; for CO_2: 0.919 and 0.075; and for CS_2: 0.692 and 0.207, respectively.] On the other hand, the presence of the isotopic species $C^{32}S^{34}S$ may not be neglected and the molecular constants of CS_2 deduced from the pure rotational Raman spectrum must be viewed with caution.

For symmetric molecules ($D_{\infty h}$ point group) in which the equivalent nuclei do not have zero spin, both symmetric and antisymmetric levels are present and, in view of different statistical weights, the rotational Raman spectrum consists of even-J as well as odd-J transitions which appear with an intensity alternation which is determined by the value of the spin of the equivalent nuclei and the spin statistics obeyed by them (*112,113*). This characteristic intensity alternation has been observed in the spectra of N_2(*114*), F_2(*115*), C_2H_2(*116,117*) and C_2D_2(*118*), C_4H_2 and C_4D_2(*117*), and C_2N_2(*119*).

The rotational constants for linear molecules deduced from their Raman spectra are listed in Table 6. Not listed are the results of the earlier studies (i.e., before 1950) since they are of historical interest only (*120*).

Two additional cases merit special attention. The electronic ground state of oxygen is $^3\Sigma_g^-$ and the coupling between the electronic spin angular momentum with that of the overall rotation in space causes a splitting of the rotational levels into triplets (*121*). The pure rotational Raman spectrum shows, therefore, a complicated fine structure, which has eluded earlier observation (*29,80*). This fine structure has been partially resolved and shows an intensity distribution in good agreement with that predicted by theory (*104,110a*). Unlike all other stable diatomic molecules, nitric oxide (NO) has an electronic ground state with an electronic orbital angular momentum $\ell = 1$. The coupling between the electronic angular momentum and the overall molecular rotation causes a splitting of the ground electronic state into $^2\pi_{1/2}$ and $^2\pi_{3/2}$ states which are separated by $\sim 120\ cm^{-1}$. Each electronic state has its own set of vibration-rotational energies and pure rotation spectra with both $\Delta J = +1$ (R-branch) and $\Delta J = +2$ (S-branch) are allowed. In addition the Raman

TABLE 6

Rotational and Centrifugal Distortion Constants of Linear Molecules Determined from Pure Rotational Raman Spectra

Molecule		B_o (cm^{-1})	D_o (cm^{-1})	Reference
Hydrogen	H_2	59.3392[a]	0.04599[a]	(*124*)
	HD	44.6678[b]	0.02592[b]	(*124*)
	D_2	29.9105[c]	0.01134[c]	(*124*)
Nitrogen	N_2	1.98973[d]	6.1×10^{-6}	(*114*)
Oxygen	O_2	1.4378	5.6×10^{-6}	(*80*)
Fluorine	F_2	0.8828		(*115*)
Carbon dioxide	CO_2	0.39040[e]		(*29*)
		0.39027[e]	12.9×10^{-8}[e]	(*55*)
		0.39013[e]	10.0×10^{-8}[e]	(*85*)
		0.39065[f]	8.2×10^{-8}[f]	(*55*)
Carbon disulfide	CS_2	0.10910[g]	1.0×10^{-8}[g]	(*126*)
		0.10912[g]	0.83×10^{-8}[g]	(*111*)
		0.10935[h]	1.5×10^{-8}[h]	(*111*)
Acetylene	C_2H_2	1.1769	1.9×10^{-6}	(*117*)
	C_2D_2	0.8484	9.8×10^{-7}	(*118*)
Iodoacetylene	C_2HI	0.10622	3.9×10^{-8}	(*129*)
Cyanogen	C_2N_2	0.15752	4×10^{-8}	(*119*)
Diacetylene	C_4H_2	0.14689	3.2×10^{-8}	(*117*)
	C_4D_2	0.12767	2.3×10^{-8}	(*117*)

[a] $B_v = 60.8407 - 3.01774(v+\frac{1}{2}) + 0.02855(v+\frac{1}{2})^2$ cm^{-1};
$D_v = 0.046841 - 0.001706(v+\frac{1}{2}) + 0.0000308(v+\frac{1}{2})^2$ cm^{-1}; and
$H_v = 5.21 \times 10^{-5}$ cm^{-1}.

[b] $B_v = 45.6378 - 1.95004(v+\frac{1}{2}) + 0.01402(v+\frac{1}{2})^2$ cm^{-1};
$D_v = 0.026341 - 0.000857(v+\frac{1}{2}) + 0.000033(v+\frac{1}{2})^2$ cm^{-1}; and
$H_v = 2.24 \times 10^{-5}$ cm^{-1}.

[c] $B_e = 30.442$ cm^{-1}, $D_e = 0.01164$ cm^{-1}.

[d] $B_e = 1.99874$ cm^{-1}.

[e] Value for 00^00 state.

[f] Value for 01^10 state.

[g] Value for 00^00 state.

[h] Value for 01^10 state.

transition between the $^2\pi_{1/2}$ and $^2\pi_{3/2}$ electronic states has been observed (*110a,122,123,123a*).

The vibration-rotation Raman spectra of only a few linear molecules have thus far been observed under sufficient resolution and also intensity to display the rotational fine structure. Thus, for H_2, D_2, and HD only the resolved Q-branches have been observed by Stoicheff (*124*) and

Yoshino and Bernstein (*125*). For O_2 and N_2 the *O*- and *S*-branches have been observed with the pre-laser techniques (*77a*, *80*, *125*). They were also photoelectrically recorded with the focused laser technique by Barrett and Adams (*99*) requiring an effective scattering volume of only 10^{-8} cm^3, holding 10^{11} molecules at a pressure of 1 atm. These same workers also recorded the ν_1, $2\nu_2$ Fermi diad in CO_2. Stoicheff (*29,126*) was able to photograph the ν_1, $2\nu_2$ Fermi diad in both CO_2 and CS_2 and perform a detailed analysis of these spectra resulting in an accurate set of vibrational frequencies, anharmonicity constants, and the constants that describe the Fermi resonance (*127*).

The only other molecule for which a vibration-rotation Raman band has been resolved is acetylene, C_2H_2 as well as C_2D_2 (*116,118*). Figure 10 shows the microphotometer traces of the three fundamental Raman bands of C_2H_2. The two totally symmetric vibrations ν_1(C—H stretch) and ν_2(C≡C stretch) show the *O,Q,S*-branch structure typical for a linear molecule, with the (unresolved) *Q*-branch being the most prominent feature of the band. The frequencies of the lines in the *O*- and *S*-branches are given by Eq. (92). On the other hand, the intensity formula Eq. (88) for perpendicular bands predicts the appearance of five branches *O,P,Q,R,S* with the *Q*-branch intensity varying as J^{-1} (see Table 1, with $\Delta J = 0$, $K = \ell = 1$). The doubly degenerate ν_{4^1} bending mode shown in Fig. 10 is in full accord with this prediction. Also seen in the spectra is the 1:3 intensity alternation due to the spin of the hydrogen nuclei. The totally symmetric bands also show the *Q*-branches of "hot bands" as well as of the isotopic species $H^{12}C{\equiv}^{13}CH$. The assignment of these additional *Q*-branches has been modified by Yoshino and Bernstein (*125*) and by Schrötter and Bernstein (*128*) as a result of a careful study of the intensity distribution in the Raman spectrum of C_2H_2. The frequencies of the lines in the *P,R*- and *O,S*-branches are given by Eqs. (96) and (97), respectively. The ℓ-type doubling of the rotational levels in the degenerate upper state of the transition has as a consequence that the upper rotational levels of the *O*-, *Q*-, and *S*-branches are different from those of the *P*- and *R*-branches. One expects, therefore, that the upper state *B*-values provided by the analysis of the *P*- and *R*-branches via Eq. (96) to be different from those provided by the analysis of the *O*- and *S*-branches via Eq. (97). The accuracy of the available data (obtained with a prism spectrograph) is unfortunately not sufficient to detect this small effect of the ℓ-type doubling (*116,118*).

The molecular constants of the linear polyatomic molecules derived from their vibration-rotation spectra are listed in Table 7.

TABLE 7

Molecular Constants of Linear Molecules Determined from Vibration-Rotation Raman Spectra (in cm^{-1})

Molecule	Rotation constant	Vibrational frequencies	Rot.-Vibr. constants	Fermi resonance and anharmonic const.	Reference
H_2	*a*	*b*	*a*		(*124*)
HD	*c*	*d*	*c*		(*124*)
D_2	$B_1 = 28.8482$	$\Delta G_{\frac{1}{2}} = 2993.561$	$\alpha_e = 1.0623$		
			$\beta_e = 0.00059$		(*124*)
N_2		$\Delta G_{\frac{1}{2}} = 2329.66$ (Head)			(*114*)
O_2	$B_1 = 1.4220$	$\Delta G_{\frac{1}{2}} = 1556.26$ (Head)	$\alpha_e = 0.0158$		(*80*)
F_2		$\Delta G_{\frac{1}{2}} = 891.85$ (Head)			(*115*)
$C^{12}O_2$		$\nu_{10^\circ 0} = 1388.15$	$\alpha_1 = -0.00003$	$\delta = 15.8^e$	(*126*)
		$\nu_{02^\circ 0} = 1285.40$	$\alpha_2 = 0.00019$	$W = -50.7^e$	
CS_2		$\omega_1{}^0 = 661.11$		$x_{11} = -1.07, x_{12} = 7.56$	(*29*)
		$\omega_2{}^0 = 399.65$		$x_{22} = -1.56, x_{23} = -6.45$	
		$\omega_3{}^0 = 1542.24$		$x_{33} = -6.66, x_{13} = -8.10$	
				$g_{22} = -2.16$	
				$\delta = 126.0, \lvert W \rvert = 35.4$	
C_2H_2	$B_1 = 1.1699$	$\nu_1 = 3372.5$	$\alpha_1 = 0.007$	$x_{14} = -16.2, x_{24} = -12.9$	(*116, 125*)
	$B_2 = 1.1711$	$\nu_2 = 1973.5$	$\alpha_2 = 0.0058$	$x_{15} = -11.8, x_{25} \approx 7$	
	$B_4{}^1 = 1.1745$	$\nu_4{}^1 = 613.5$	$\alpha_4 = 0.0025$		
C_2D_2		$\nu_1 = 2703.8$ (Q max)		$x_{24} = -3.8$	
		$\nu_2 = 1764.2$ (Q max)		$x_{25} = -3.8$	(*118*)
		$\nu_4{}^1 = 511.12$	$\alpha_4 = -0.004$	$x_{44} = 0.61$	

[a] See footnote of Table 6.

[b] $G(v) = 4400.390(v+\frac{1}{2}) - 120.8148(v+\frac{1}{2})^2 + 0.72419(v+\frac{1}{2})^3$ cm^{-1}.

[c] See footnote of Table 6.

[d] $G(v) = 3811.924(v+\frac{1}{2}) - 90.7113(v+\frac{1}{2})^2 + 0.47759(v+\frac{1}{2})^3$ cm^{-1}.

[e] For $C^{13}O_2$, $\delta = 46.4$, and $\lvert W \rvert = 47.1$ cm^{-1}.

C. Symmetric Top Molecules

1. Pure Rotation Spectra

Of the 15 symmetric top molecules studied thus far only three have been subjected to an analysis of their vibration-rotation bands and only the pure rotational spectra were studied of the remaining 12 molecules. Figures 3 and 4 show the pure rotational spectra of the oblate symmetric top molecules cyclopentane and benzene and Figs. 8 and 9 show the spectra of dimethylcadmium and ethane, which are prolate symmetric top rotors. These spectra were obtained with the pre-laser technique and one notes the strongly exposed Rayleigh line which, together with the ghosts produced by it, obliterates a good portion of the region of small wave numbers and obscures the R-branch of the spectra. The intensity of the pure rotational Raman spectrum in relation to that of the Rayleigh line is determined by the ratio of the anisotropy δ^2 to the mean value α of the polarizability of a molecule in its ground vibrational state. For benzene and cyclopentane these values are (*87*): $\delta^2 = 33.1 \times 10^{-3}$ and 5.6×10^{-3}, and $\alpha = 98.7 \times 10^{-25}$ cm^3 and 88.9×10^{-25} cm^3, respectively. Similarly, using the data of LeFevre and LeFevre (*130*) we have for cyclohexane $\delta^2 = 3.9 \times 10^{-3}$ and $\alpha = 107 \times 10^{-25}$ cm^3 (*88*). Thus, while a relatively clean pure rotational spectrum of benzene which shows the odd-J R-branch lines is easily obtained with the pre-laser technique (*131*), the electrically more nearly spherical tops cyclopentane and cyclohexane exhibit a relatively "dirty" spectrum in which the grating ghosts are strongly blended with the Raman spectrum. The use of the laser technique (*83*) permits the recording of much cleaner spectra of which two are shown in Figs. 24 and 25. The contrast of the Ar^+-laser generated spectrum of cyclohexane photographed in 6 hr at a vapor pressure of 61 mm Hg with the pre-laser spectrum (40 hr and 380 mm Hg) is particularly striking.

The analysis of the pure rotational Raman spectra of symmetric tops is based on Eqs. (72′) and (73′). Both equations provide exactly the same constants and since the R-branch lines are at times not resolved from the S-branch we may limit our discussion of the analysis of pure rotation spectra to Eq. (72′) which gives the S-branch frequencies. Since the S-branch lines have nearly equal spacing the ratio of the Raman displacement of a line to the line spacing ($\sim 4B$) gives the assignment of the J-values in the spectrum. A least squares fit of the observed Raman displacement as function of J to Eq. (72′) then gives the molecular constants in the form of the coefficients $(4B - 6D_J - 4D_{JK}K^2)$ and $-8D_J$. An alternative procedure involves a graphical analysis in which the quotient

$(\Delta\nu_s)_{obs}/(J+\frac{3}{2})$ is plotted as function of $(J+\frac{3}{2})^2$. The slope and intercept of the resulting straight line are then $-8D_J$ and $(4B_0-6D_J-4D_{JK}K^2)$, respectively. Assuming that the contributions of the terms $6D_J$ and $4D_{JK}K^2$ to the value of the intercept are ignorable, the B_0-value is obtained without further ado. The pure rotational spectra of all symmetric top molecules that have been studied thus far in the Raman effect have been analyzed in this manner and the resulting B_0- and D_J- values are listed in the second and third columns of Table 8. Wherever possible the most recent values of these constants determined by other methods (infrared spectrum and microwave spectrum) are also listed for comparison.

The standard technique of analyzing pure rotational spectra is based on the use of several assumptions. We note, first, that it is assumed that the B-values for the low lying excited vibrational states of a molecule are the same, or nearly so, as those for the ground state, so that the pure rotational spectra of molecules in these excited states coincide with those produced by molecules in the ground state. That the excited state pure rotational spectrum cannot be ignored was shown to be the case for CO_2 and CS_2. Additional assumptions are based on the magnitude of the centrifugal distortion effect.

The centrifugal distortion constants D_J and D_{JK} are of the order 10^{-6} to 10^{-8} cm^{-1} for moderately heavy polyatomic molecules, whereas the B-values range typically from 0.03 to 1 cm^{-1} and higher (*132*). Ignoring the contributions of $6D_J$ and $4D_{JK}K^2$ to the value of the coefficient $(4B-6D_J-4D_{JK}K^2)$ causes an error in the B-value which, nevertheless, lies within the statistical range of error in the determination of the value of the coefficient itself. The smallness of the term $4D_{JK}K^2$ causes the various K-transitions associated with a given J-transition to nearly coincide to give the observed Raman "lines" of the pure rotational spectrum. A further assumption is that the maxima of these Raman "lines", whose $\Delta\nu$-values constitute the experimental data, occur all at the same K-value. Instead, the intensity maxima of the various Raman "lines" occur at K-values which are dependent on the quantum number J.

The intensity of a given totally symmetric Raman transition, and, thus, of the transitions that comprise the pure rotational spectrum, is given by Eq. (87). For pure rotational spectra in the ground state $G(v) = 0$ and ignoring the frequency dependence over the S-branch we note that the intensity is given by

$$I(0, J, K; 0, J+2, K) = Cg_{JK}b_{J,K;J+2,K}\exp\{-[BJ(J+1)+(A-B)K^2]\cdot[hc/kT]\} \qquad (106)$$

where all other quantities which are independent of J and K are included in the coefficient C, and the second order (i.e., centrifugal distortion) terms are ignored in the exponential. In addition to the factor 2 due to the two-fold degeneracy of the levels with $K > 0$, the dependence of the statistical weight g_{JK} on the quantum number K is due to the value of the spins as well as the spin statistics of the equivalent nuclei; this results in an intensity alternation of the various K-transitions.

The intensity profile of an S-branch "line" is therefore primarily determined by the line strength $b_{J,K;J+2,K}$ and the exponential factor. The b-coefficient is a decreasing function of K (see Table 1). For a prolate symmetric top, $A > B$, the exponential factor is then also a decreasing function of K and the maximum intensity in a Raman "line" will then occur at low K-values. For oblate tops, however, for which $A < B$, the exponential factor is an increasing function of K and the intensity maximum in a Raman "line" will occur at high K-values. For either case the intensity maxima for the various J-transitions occur at different K-values. The statistical weight g_{JK} is not a constant but varies with K and is also dependent on the spins of the equivalent nuclei as well as the statistics observed by them. For example, for molecules with a three-fold axis of symmetry (i.e. point groups C_3, C_{3v}, C_{3h}, D_3, D_{3d}, D_{3h}) in the ground vibrational state, the levels with K divisible by 3 have a greater statistical weight than those with K not divisible by 3. [See Ref. (*19*); Ref. (*42*), pp. 26–29 and Chapter IV, section 2a; Refs. (*47–49*); and Ref. (*50*), chapter 5]. Thus, differentiating Eq. (106) with respect to K while holding g_{JK} constant and setting the derivative equal to zero we see that the intensity maximum of a given S-branch Raman "line" will occur at a K-value which satisfies the equation

$$K_{\max}^4 - \left[(J+1)^2 + (J+2)^2 + \frac{2kT}{hc(A-B)}\right] K_{\max}^2 + (J+1)^2(J+2)^2 + [(J+1)^2 + (J+2)^2]\frac{kT}{hc(A-B)} = 0 \quad (107)$$

Ignoring, therefore, the K-structure of the observed Raman lines in a pure rotational spectrum, especially for an oblate symmetric top molecule, leads to an error in the values of the rotation constant B_0 as well as in the centrifugal distortion constant D_J. This problem is, of course, also present in the treatment of the pure rotational infrared absorption spectrum and has been discussed by various authors, notably Chantry et al. (*133*).

The degree to which our assumptions are justified in an individual case is hard to determine since the value of D_{JK} is not known and a judgment has to be rendered on the basis of the sharpness of the observed rotational lines. In any case, the molecular constants derived from a given pure rotational Raman spectrum must be considered as weighted averages and comparisons with the values of these constants obtained by the use of other techniques (i.e., microwave pure rotation spectrum, analysis of Raman as well as infrared vibration-rotation bands, centrifugal distortion constants computed from second-order theory of rotation-vibration interaction, etc.) must be undertaken with a grain of salt. However, the success of the Raman spectroscopic technique in providing highly accurate molecular structures (i.e., comparison of bond lengths deduced from pure rotational Raman spectra with those obtained with the electron diffraction technique) suggests that the errors due to the assumptions described above are not overly significant for most molecules studied thus far.

Nevertheless, an attempt to estimate the errors incurred through the neglect of the term $4D_{JK}K^2$ has recently been made by Tyulin and Tatevskii (*134*). Aliev et al. (*135*) have considered the nature of the centrifugal distortion constants D_J and D_{JK} in symmetric top molecules belonging to the C_{3v} and D_{3h} point groups. They find that a good estimate of D_{JK} can be had via the relations

$$D_{JK} \approx 2D_J[(I_{xx}^0/I_{zz}^0)^2 - 1] \tag{108}$$

for molecules belonging to the C_{3v} point group and

$$D_{JK} \approx 2D_J[(I_{xx}^0/I_{zz}^0)^4 - 1] \tag{109}$$

for planar molecules belonging to the D_{3h} and higher point groups, where I_{xx}^0 and I_{zz}^0 are the principal moments of inertia in the ground vibrational state. The constant D_J is always positive for symmetric top molecules (*135*), a fact which can also be understood classically since $D_J < 0$ implies a contraction of the molecular frame upon rotation as against a centrifugal expansion. For prolate symmetric tops belonging to the C_{3v} point groups $I_{xx}^0 > I_{zz}^0$ and D_{JK} is positive whereas for oblate symmetric tops $I_{xx}^0 < I_{zz}^0$ and D_{JK} is negative. For planar molecules belonging to D_{3h} and higher point groups D_{JK} is always negative since these molecules are oblate symmetric tops with $I_{xx}^0 < I_{zz}^0$. The estimates of D_{JK} obtained in this manner by Tyulin and Subbotin (*136*) are given in the fifth column of Table 8. These authors also computed corrected values of B_0 and D_J on the basis of Tyulin and Tatevskii's theory (*134*) and these values are given in the last two columns of the Table.

TABLE 8

Ground State Rotational Constants and Centrifugal Distortion Constants for Symmetric Top Molecules Deduced from Raman Spectra[a]

Molecule	Original analysis[b]			$D_{JK} \times 10^7$ (estimated)[c]	Corrected values[d]	
	B_o	$D_J \times 10^8$	Reference		B_o	$D_J \times 10^8$
PROLATE SYMMETRIC TOPS						
Ethane						
C_2H_6	$0.6621_5 \pm 0.0005$	94	93		0.66234	78
	0.66310 ± 0.00007[e]	70 ± 20[e]	138	(60 ± 30)[e]		
CH_3CD_3	$0.5486_2 \pm 0.0005$	42	93	50	0.5488_3	38
	0.5491 ± 0.0003[f]	27 ± 19[f]	96			
C_2D_6	$0.4591_5 \pm 0.0005$	34	93	40	0.4583_5	-32
	0.45973 ± 0.00008[g]	48 ± 14[g]	95			
	0.4596 ± 0.0005	18 ± 45	95			
Allene						
C_3H_4	$0.2965_3 \pm 0.00008$	11	140		0.2966_9	10.4
	$0.2963_2 \pm 0.00006$[h]	11.6 ± 2.4[h]	74	(46.0 ± 18)[h]		
H_2CCCD_2	$0.2619_0 \pm 0.0001$	7.0	140	36	0.2620_1	3.3
C_3D_4	$0.2323_0 \pm 0.0001$	7.5	140	28	0.2323_1	1.7
	$0.2321_4 \pm 0.00008$[h]	4.1 ± 1.9[h]	74			
Methyl-acetylene						
C_3H_4	$0.2850_7 \pm 0.0001_5$[i]	$-(2.7 \pm 3.7)$[i]	137		$0.2852_6 \pm 0.0001_5$[j]	$-(3.3 \pm 3.7)$[j]
	0.28506[k]	9.9[c]	137	(54.3)[k]		
C_3D_4	$0.2246_9 \pm 0.0001_8$[i]	$-(6.6 \pm 5.6)$[i]	137		$0.2248_8 \pm 0.0001_8$[j]	$-(8.3 \pm 5.7)$[j]
	0.22464[k]	7[k]	137	(30)[k]		
Dimethyl-acetylene						
C_4H_6	$0.1122_8 \pm 0.0002$	1.3	117	7	0.1122_3	1.0

TABLE 8 (*cont.*)

Molecule	Original analysis[b]			$D_{JK} \times 10^7$ (estimated)[c]	Corrected values[d]	
	B_o	$D_J \times 10^8$	Reference		B_o	$D_J \times 10^8$
Dimethyl-zinc						
$Zn(CH_3)_2$	$0.1347_8 \pm 0.0001$	5 ± 1	92	28	0.1349	4.8
$Zn(CD_3)_2$	$0.1048_5 \pm 0.0001$	4 ± 1	92	17	0.1047_1	−4.0
Dimethyl-cadmium						
$Cd(CH_3)_2$	0.11405 ± 0.0001	3 ± 1	92	22	0.1142_1	3.2
$Cd(CD_3)_2$	$0.0893_8 \pm 0.0001$	2 ± 1	92	12	0.0895_4	1.7
Dimethyl-mercury						
$Hg(CH_3)_2$	0.11620 ± 0.0001	2 ± 1	92	12	0.1162_2	0.8
$Hg(CD_3)_2$	$0.0912_0 \pm 0.0002$	2 ± 1	92	8	0.0913_2	1.6
OBLATE SYMMETRIC TOPS						
Cyclopropane						
C_3H_6	$0.6696_2 \pm 0.0002_0$	50 ± 10	141	—15	0.6697_6	75
	0.67024 ± 0.00015	82 ± 15[l]	141*a*			
C_3D_6	$0.4607_9 \pm 0.0001_5$	10 ± 10	141	−5	0.4610_3	24
Cyclobutane						
C_4H_8	$0.3548_0 \pm 0.0002$	~ 7	142	−3.8	0.3548_4	16
C_4D_8	$0.2559_5 \pm 0.0002$	~ 4	142	−3.2	0.2562_1	16
Cyclopentane						
C_5H_{10}	$0.2160_5 \pm 0.0001$	5 ± 1.4	87	−1.7	0.2160_5	7.3
C_5D_{10}	$0.1610_2 \pm 0.0001_2$	4 ± 2.2	87	−1.3	0.1610_3	6.6

Table 8 (*cont.*)

Molecule	Original analysis[b]			$D_{JK} \times 10_7$ (estimated)[c]	Corrected values[d]	
	B_o	$D_J \times 10^8$	Reference		B_o	$D_J \times 10^8$
Cyclohexane						
C_6H_{12}	0.143429 ± 0.000002	1.56 ± 0.03	103d			
C_6D_{12}	0.109469 ± 0.000001	0.61 ± 1.01	103d			
Benzene						
C_6H_6	0.18960 ± 0.00005	2.2 ± 1	143	-0.8	0.1896_2	3.6
sym$C_6H_3D_3$	$0.1716_5 \pm 0.0001$	1.3	144	-0.6	0.1716_5	2.2
C_6D_6	0.15681 ± 0.00008	0.8 ± 1.0	143	-0.4	0.1567_3	0.5
1,3,5-Trifluorobenzene						
$C_6H_3F_3$	$0.058651_7 \pm 0.0000021$	0.189 ± 0.015	144a			
Hexafluorobenzene						
C_6F_6	$0.034316_5 \pm 0.0000034$	0.07 ± 0.015	144a			
Cyanuric fluoride						
$C_3N_3F_3$	0.06561 ± 0.00001	0.32 ± 0.07	144b			
Sym-triazine						
$C_3N_3H_3$	$0.2146_0 \pm 0.00008$	~ 1.3	145	-0.8	0.2145_9	1.9
$C_3N_3D_3$	$0.1935_8 \pm 0.0001_5$	~ 2.5	145	-0.7	0.1935_6	3.5
Borazole						
$^{11}B_3N_3H_6$	0.1755_5	2.4	146[m], 146a			
$^{11}B_2{}^{10}BN_3H_6$	0.1776_4	7.4	146[m], 146a			

Table 8 (*cont.*)

Molecule	Original analysis[b]			$D_{JK}\times 10_7$ (estimated)[c]	Corrected values[d]	
	B_o	$D_J\times 10^8$	Reference		B_o	$D_J\times 10^8$
Chloroform						
$CHCl_3$	0.110141[n]	6.2 ± 2[o]	147		0.1098_8	4.0
		5.07 ± 0.03[p]	148	-0.83[p]		
	0.11015[q]	5.5 ± 0.8[q]	149			

[a] In cm^{-1}.

[b] Based on graphical analysis of original Raman data.

[c] Estimated on basis of theory of Ref. (*135*). Values given in parenthesis are experimental results.

[d] Based on least squares analysis of original Raman data and corrected according to the theory of Tyulin and Tatevskii (*134*).

[e] Based on an analysis of the infrared combination band $\nu_2+\nu_6$ by Lafferty and Plyler (*138*).

[f] This value derived by Shaw and Welsh (*96*) from an analysis of the ν_3 Raman band. From the observed microwave pure rotation spectrum of CH_3CD_3 Hirota (*96a*) deduces $B_o = 0.549523\ cm^{-1}$ by assuming Shaw and Welsh's (*96*) value $D_J = 2.7\times 10^{-8}\ cm^{-1}$ whereas $B_o = 0.549523\ cm^{-1}$ if Stoicheff's (*93*) value $D_J = 4.2\times 10^{-8}\ cm^{-1}$ is assumed. The dipole moment of CH_3CD_3 was found to be $\mu = 0.01078\pm 0.00009\,D$ (*96a*).

[g] Based on original data on the $\nu_9+\nu_{10}$ infrared band obtained by Allen and Plyler (*139*) and recalculated by Lepard, et al. (*95*).

[h] Based on an analysis of several infrared absorption bands by Maki and Toth (*74*).

[i] Based on least squares analysis of original data (*137*).

[j] Computed in Ref. (*137*).

[k] Microwave data quoted in Ref. (*137*).

[l] $|D_{JK}| < 15\times 10^{-7}$. From an analysis of the ν_6 infrared band by McCubbin et al., Ref. (*141a*).

[m] Report of average value for isotopic mixture containing naturally abundant boron isotopes.

[n] Microwave B_o-value for $CH^{35}Cl_3$.

[o] Raman spectrum of natural $CHCl_3$.

[p] Microwave value for $CHCl_3{}^{35}$, Ref. (*148*).

[q] From infrared absorption spectrum of natural $CHCl_3$, Ref. (*149*).

A comparison between the uncorrected B_0-values deduced from a graphical analysis (column 2) and the corrected B_0-values deduced from the original data with a least squares analysis and corrected according to Tyulin and Tatevskii (*134*) (column 6), shows that the correction is usually slight and is most often of the order of the originally quoted uncertainty in the B_0-value. The most significant changes occur for the constant D_J. The negative D_J-values shown in the last column are not due to the Tyulin and Tatevskii correction. Rather these negative values appear when the original data are subjected to a least squares analysis instead of the graphical analysis which provided positive values. This anomaly is suggested to be due to the omission of higher order terms in the rotational term expression $F(J, K)$ given by Eq. (62b) (Refs. *136* and *137*).

2. VIBRATION-ROTATION SPECTRA

The vibration-rotation Raman spectra of only ethane, allene, cyclopropane, and monodeuteromethane have thus far been investigated. Monodeuteromethane (CH_3D) is an isotopic variant of the spherical top molecule CH_4 and the discussion of its spectrum will be taken up in the next section. The Raman investigations of allene and cyclopropane are only partially complete and the available data for cyclopropane were obtained with a prism spectrograph under resolution and dispersion inferior to that of the more recently used grating spectrographs.

Due to the interesting problem of the nature of the internal rotation of the two methyl groups relative to one another about the C—C axis, as well as due to the uncertainty over the equilibrium configuration, the spectrum of ethane has received much attention over many years.

There are two plausible geometrical structures of the ethane molecule in the equilibrium configuration. In one, the two methyl groups eclipse one another when viewed along the C—C axis; the point group for this structure is D_{3h}. In the second structure the two methyl groups appear staggered when viewed along the C—C axis and the point group is D_{3d}. While the staggered model has been the favored one there has been no unambiguous demonstration of the correctness of this belief (*150*) until the observation of the resolved rotational fine structure of the doubly degenerate Raman active vibrations by Welsh and his coworkers (*94–96, 151*). The infrared and Raman vibrational selection rules for molecules belonging to the D_{3h} and D_{3d} point groups (*42,150*) together with the rotational selection rules for the infrared and Raman bands (see 563–564) indicate that an unambiguous proof of the D_{3h} or the D_{3d} structure for

TABLE 9

Selection Rules for the Normal Vibrations of Ethane, C_2H_6[a]

Mode	Description	D_{3h} (eclipsed model)		D_{3d} (staggered model)	
		Species	Selection rule	Species	Selection rule
ν_1	CH stretching	A_1'	$R, \Delta K = 0$	A_{1g}	$R, \Delta K = 0$
ν_2	CH_3 deformation	A_1'	$R, \Delta K = 0$	A_{1g}	$R, \Delta K = 0$
ν_3	C-C stretching	A_1'	$R, \Delta K = 0$	A_{1g}	$R, \Delta K = 0$
ν_4	Torsion	A_1''	Inactive	A_{1u}	Inactive
ν_5	CH stretching	A_2''	$I, \parallel, \Delta K = 0$	A_{2u}	$I, \parallel, \Delta K = 0$
ν_6	CH_3 deformation	A_2''	$I, \parallel, \Delta K = 0$	A_{2u}	$I, \parallel, \Delta K = 0$
ν_7	CH stretching	E'	$I, \perp, \Delta K = \pm 1; R, \Delta K = \pm 2$	E_u	$I, \perp, \Delta K = \pm 1$
ν_8	CH_3 deformation	E'	$I, \perp, \Delta K = \pm 1; R, \Delta K = \pm 2$	E_u	$I, \perp, \Delta K = \pm 1$
ν_9	Bending	E'	$I, \perp, \Delta K = \pm 1; R, \Delta K = \pm 2$	E_u	$I, \perp, \Delta K = \pm 1$
ν_{10}	CH stretching	E''	$R, \Delta K = \pm 1$	E_g	$R, \Delta K = \pm 1, \pm 2$
ν_{11}	CH_3 deformation	E''	$R, \Delta K = \pm 1$	E_g	$R, \Delta K = \pm 1, \pm 2$
ν_{12}	Bending	E''	$R, \Delta K = \pm 1$	E_g	$R, \Delta K = \pm 1, \pm 2$

[a] R = Raman active, I = Infrared active, $\parallel$ and $\perp$ designate parallel and perpendicular bands respectively. Raman bands with $\Delta K = 0$ are polarized while those with $\Delta K \neq 0$ are depolarized.

the ethane molecule is possible on the basis of the resolved rotational fine structure of the degenerate Raman active fundamentals. Table 9 gives these selection rules for the D_{3h} and D_{3d} point groups and their relation to the normal vibrations of ethane.

Whereas for the staggered model the rule of mutual exclusion insures that a given vibrational species can be active either in infrared absorption or the Raman effect, but not both, the vibrational selection rules for the eclipsed model permit the simultaneous infrared and Raman activity of the E' species, with the remaining species being either infrared or Raman active. The fact that no Raman bands corresponding to the observed infrared bands ν_7, ν_8, and ν_9 have been observed for gaseous ethane is not convincing enough to rule out the D_{3h} point group as describing the equilibrium configuration. The absence of Raman bands of the E' species in the gas may just be due to their intrinsic weakness which thus would render them unobservable. On the other hand weak Raman bands corresponding to ν_7, ν_8, and ν_9 have been observed in liquid ethane (*150*) and this fact may speak for the correctness of the D_{3h} model. It is plausible, however, that these weak Raman bands may be due to a breakdown of the vibrational selection rules of the D_{3d} point group (which holds only for free, isolated molecules) due to intermolecular interactions in the liquid.

The one unique feature that would allow an unambiguous choice between the staggered and the eclipsed models lies in the rotational fine structure of the ν_{10}, ν_{11}, and ν_{12} vibrations which are allowed as Raman bands in both models. For the D_{3h} point group (eclipsed model) the selection rule for the E'' species, $\Delta K = \pm 1$, allows for one series of Q-branches, ${}^{P}Q_K$ and ${}^{R}Q_K$ whose frequencies are given by Eqs. (82a)–(82c) and in which the Q-branches have a spacing which is approximately equal to $2[A'(1-\zeta)-B']$. On the other hand the rotational selection rule for the E_g species of vibration of the D_{3d} point group (staggered model) is $\Delta K = \pm 1$ and ± 2, so that two series of Q-branches are allowed namely; ${}^{P}Q_K$ and ${}^{R}Q_K$ for $\Delta K = \pm 1$, with frequencies given by Eqs. (82a)–(82c), as well as ${}^{0}Q_K$ and ${}^{S}Q_K$ for $\Delta K = \pm 2$, with frequencies given by Eqs. (85a, b) and (84c). The spacing of the Q-branches is approximately $2[A'(1-\zeta)-B']$ for the ${}^{P,R}Q_K$-branches and $4[A'(1+\frac{1}{2}\zeta)-B']$ for the ${}^{O,S}Q_K$-branches. Therefore the presence of just one, or two sets of Q-branches would give a unique proof for the D_{3h} or D_{3d} model, respectively.

The original high resolution Raman study of ethane (*151*) suffered from a lack of sufficient resolution and only one series of Q-branches was observed in the ν_{10} and ν_{11} bands that were studied. In addition the superposition of the strong totally symmetric ν_1 band on the weak doubly, degenerate ν_{10} band obscured a significant portion of the latter band. A reinvestigation of the Raman spectrum of C_2H_6 (*94,95a*) in addition to the study of the isotopic variants C_2D_6 (*95,95a*) and CH_3CD_3 (*96*) with superior techniques has resulted in an unambiguous solution of this structure problem. The microphotometer traces of some of the Raman bands are reproduced in Figs. 11–15. The spectrograms were obtained typically at a pressure of 1 atm and with exposures ranging up to 185 hr in duration. A compilation of the fundamental vibrations for the three molecules is given in Table 10 (*96*).

Figure 11, trace *a*, shows the observed profile for the ν_{10} and ν_{11} bands of C_2H_6 respectively. We see the superposition of the strong *Q*-branches of the totally symmetric fundamental mode ν_1 as well as of the hot bands $\nu_1+\nu_4-\nu_4$, $\nu_1+2\nu_4-2\nu_4$, and $\nu_1+3\nu_4-3\nu_4$ on the ν_{10} band. Less serious is the appearance of the bands near 2900 cm^{-1} which are identified as the overtones $2\nu_8$ and $2\nu_{11}$. To assist in the analysis of the ν_{10} and ν_{11} bands a computation of the relative intensities (*82,94*), shown in trace *b*, was performed. The excellent agreement between the calculated and observed profile for the regions without overlap points to the correctness of the assignments. The ν_{10} band of C_2D_6 (*95,95a*) shown in Fig. 12 is not blended with the ν_1 band and the appearance of the $\Delta K = \pm 1$ and $\Delta K = \pm 2$ transitions is unquestionable. The staggered equilibrium configuration of ethane (D_{3d} point group) is thereby undisputably established.

The CH_3–CD_3 molecule no longer possesses the symmetry D_{3d} of C_2H_6 or C_2D_6 but has the lower symmetry C_{3v}. Only two vibrational species occur, the totally symmetric species A_1 with selection rule $\Delta K = 0$, and the doubly degenerate species *E* with the Raman selection rule $\Delta K = \pm 1, \pm 2$ in addition to the selection rule on *J*. Figure 13 shows the totally symmetric ν_3 band of CH_3–CD_3. The *P*- and *R*-branches as well as the *O*- and *S*-branches are well developed, and the *Q*-branch of ν_3 together with the *Q*-branches of the hot bands $\nu_3+\nu_4-\nu_4$, $\nu_3+2\nu_4-2\nu_4$, and $\nu_3+\nu_9-\nu_9$ is the most prominent feature of the band. The computed profile of the rotational structure due to the anisotropic part of the polarizability, trace *b*, is an excellent match to the observed spectrum. Figures 14 and 15 show similarly the doubly degenerate ν_7 and ν_{11} bands, in the latter of which the ${}^{P,R}Q_K$-branches are not resolved from the ${}^{O,S}Q_K$-branches. The complexity of the observed spectrum due to overlapping bands, hot bands, and bands due to isotopic molecules as well as limited resolution makes for considerable difficulties in the analysis of the spectra. The use of computed intensity profiles to assist in the analysis seems to be mandatory in such cases.

TABLE 10

The Normal Vibrations of C_2H_6, C_2D_6, and CH_3CD_3[a]

Mode	Description[b]	D_{3d} Species	D_{3d} Selection rule	Observed frequencies[c] C_2H_6	Observed frequencies[c] C_2D_6	C_{3v} Species	C_{3v} Selection rule	Observed frequencies CH_3CD_3
ν_1	CH stretching			(2953.7)	(2083.0)		$I, \Delta K = 0$	(2955.5)
ν_2	CH_3 deformation	A_{1g}	$R, \Delta K = 0$	(1388.4)	1154.50	A_1	$R, \Delta K = 0$	(1388)
ν_3	C—C stretching			994.8	842.97			904.66
ν_4	Torsion	A_{1u}	Inactive	(289)	(200)	A_2	Inactive	(245)
ν_5	C—D stretching			2895.79	2087.40		$I, \Delta K = 0$	(2121)
ν_6	CD_3 deformation	A_{2u}	$I, \Delta K = 0$	1379.19	(1077.1)	A_1	$R, \Delta K = 0$	(1125)
ν_7	CH stretching			2995.48	(2236)			2976.62
ν_8	CH_3 deformation	E_u	$I, \Delta K = \pm 1$	1472.2	1081.30			(1469)
ν_9	Bending			821.60	593.78		$I, \Delta K = \pm 1$	(685)
ν_{10}	C—D stretching			2968.69	2225.65	E	$R, \Delta K = \pm 1,$	(2238)
ν_{11}	CD_3 deformation	E_g	$R, \Delta K = \pm 1, \pm 2$	1468.1	1041		± 2	1062.59
ν_{12}	Bending			(1190)	(970)			(1080)

[a] In cm^{-1}; from the compilation of Shaw and Welsh (*96*).
[b] Description is given for the modes of CH_3CD_3. For C_2H_6 and C_2D_6 replace D by H and H by D respectively.
[c] Unbracketed frequencies are derived from rotational analysis.

Although the resolution of detail that has been achieved in these studies is considerable (the limit of resolution is about 0.3 cm^{-1}) many significant details of the bands remain unresolved. Thus, for the totally symmetric vibrations the Q-branches [see Eq. (71)] are unresolved, as are the "lines" in the O,S- and P,R-branches whose frequencies are represented by Eqs. (72) and (73), respectively. The lack of a resolved K-structure, therefore, brings with it the same assumptions regarding the position of the intensity maximum as a function of the quantum number K for a given rotational "line" that were discussed for pure rotation spectra. The frequencies of the observed rotational lines are then fitted to Eqs. (72) and (73) in which the K-dependent terms are omitted.

Similarly, for the doubly degenerate bands the lack of resolution of the Q-branches into their J-structure usually justifies the omission of the J-dependent terms given by Eqs. (82c) and (84c) and the observed Q-branch frequencies are fitted to the equations for the sub-bands, given by Eqs. (82b) and (85b). However, through the use of the computed intensity profile (*95*) it was found that a better match between the observed and computed profiles can be had by retaining the term $(B'-B'')J(J+1)$ in the expression for the Q-branch frequencies, and by assuming that the observed frequency of any Q-branch corresponds to the J-value with maximum intensity as calculated from the line strengths $b_{J,K';J,K''}$ (Table 1). Centrifugal distortion terms, however, are omitted, undoubtedly in view of the limited accuracy of the data. The Q-branch frequencies, therefore, were fitted to the expression

$$Q_K(J) = \nu^{\text{sub}} + (B'-B'')J(J+1) \qquad J \geqq K$$

where, for the ${}^{P,R}Q_K$-bands with $\Delta K = \pm 1$

$$\begin{aligned}\nu^{\text{sub}}({}^{P,R}Q_K) = \nu_0 &+ [A'(1-2\zeta)-B'] \\ &\pm 2[A'(1-\zeta)-B']K \\ &+ [(A'-B')-(A''-B'')]K^2\end{aligned} \tag{110}$$

and for the ${}^{O,S}Q_K$-bands with $\Delta K = \pm 2$

$$\begin{aligned}\nu^{\text{sub}}({}^{O,S}Q_K) = \nu_0 &+ 4[A'(1+\zeta)-B'] \\ &\pm 4[A'(1+\tfrac{1}{2}\zeta)-B']K \\ &+ [(A'-B')-(A''-B'')]K^2\end{aligned} \tag{111}$$

The computations are best carried out by the method of least squares using the convenient formulation of Brodersen and Richardson (*152*). The molecular constants derived with these techniques from the Raman data are given in Table 11.

TABLE 11

Molecular Constants of C_2H_6, C_2D_6, and CH_3CD_3 Derived from Vibration-Rotation Raman Bands[a]

Constant	C_2H_6[b]		
ν_i	$\nu_3 = 994.8 \pm 0.2$	$\nu_{10} = 2968.69 \pm 0.005$	$\nu_{11} = 1468.1 \pm 0.2$
B''	(0.66310)[e]		
B'	0.6551		
A''		2.671 ± 0.005	(2.671)[f]
A'		2.711 ± 0.005	2.663 ± 0.007
D_J''	(7.0×10^{-7})[e]		
D_J'			
ζ_i		$\zeta_{10} = 0.223 \pm 0.002$	$\zeta_{11} = -0.330 \pm 0.007$

Constant	C_2D_6[c]			
ν_i	$\nu_2 = 1154.50 \pm 0.05$	$\nu_3 = 842.97 \pm 0.06$	$\nu_{10} = 2225.65 \pm 0.03$	$\nu_{11} = 1041.0 \pm 3$
B''	(0.45973)[g]	(0.45973)[g]	(0.45973)[g]	
B'	0.4592 ± 0.0002	0.4573 ± 0.0003	0.45874	
A''			$1.341_6 \pm 0.0009$	
A'			$1.345_6 \pm 0.0008$	
D_J''	(4.8×10^{-7})[g]	(4.8×10^{-7})[g]		
D_J'	$(3.0 \pm 2.0) \times 10^{-7}$	$(1.1 \pm 3.0) \times 10^{-7}$		
ζ_i			$\zeta_{10} = 0.161_2 \pm 0.0009$	$\zeta_{11} = \begin{Bmatrix} -0.36 \\ -0.29 \end{Bmatrix}$[h]

TABLE 11 (*cont.*)

Constant		CH_3CD_3[d]	
ν_i	$\nu_3 = 904.66$	$\nu_7 = 2976.62 \pm 0.03$	$\nu_{11} = 1062 \pm 3.8$
B''	0.5491 ± 0.0003	$(0.5491)^i$	
B'	0.5463 ± 0.0004	0.5481	
A''	$(A' - A'')$	1.7809 ± 0.0016	1.806
A'	$= 0.0018 \pm 0.0005$	1.7927 ± 0.00019	
D_J''	$(2.7 \pm 1.9) \times 10^{-7}$		
D_J'	$(6.9 \pm 2.0) \times 10^{-7}$		
ζ_i		$\zeta_7 = 0.179 \pm 0.001$	$\zeta_{11} = -0.344$

[a] In cm^{-1}; Zeta constants are dimensionless.
[b] From Lepard, Shaw, and Welsh (*94*).
[c] From Lepard, Sweeney, and Welsh (*95*).
[d] From Shaw and Welsh (*96*).
[e] Infrared value from Lafferty and Plyler (*138*).
[f] Value derived from ν_{10} band.
[g] Infrared value from Allen and Plyler (*139*) as recomputed by Lepard, Sweeney, and Welsh (*95*).
[h] Assuming $A' = A''$, $B' = B''$, and line maxima assigned to ${}^{P,R}Q_K$ branches gives $\zeta_{11} = -0.36$; line maxima assigned to ${}^{O,S}Q_K$ branches gives $\zeta_{11} = -0.29$.
[i] Value derived from ν_3 band.

Since for light molecules it is possible to resolve most of the rotational fine structure in a Raman band a rather detailed and direct derivation of the molecular constants is possible. For moderately heavy molecules, however, the rotational fine structure may not be resolved and only band contours would be observed. An attempt to derive molecular constants from unresolved Raman bands has been made by Mathai, Shepherd, and Welsh (*153*) who photographed the Raman spectrum of cyclopropane with a prism spectrograph providing a reciprocal linear dispersion of 10 cm^{-1}/mm and a resolving limit of about 1 cm^{-1}. Except for the pure rotation spectrum, which was photographed without the use of a cylindrical lens, only unresolved bands were observed in exposures ranging up to 100 hr in duration at a gas pressure of 3 atm. For the doubly degenerate bands an attempt was made to deduce the Coriolis coupling coefficients from the spacing of the intensity maxima of the unresolved wings of the E' bands which are made up of the closely spaced ${}^{O}Q_K$- and ${}^{S}Q_K$-branches, as well as of the wings of the E'' bands comprised of the ${}^{P}Q_K$- and ${}^{R}Q_K$-branches. A computed intensity profile for the unresolved wings provides an equation for the separation of the intensity maxima of these unresolved wings in which the Coriolis constant for the given vibration appears as a parameter. Using the observed separation of the intensity maxima, the Coriolis constants for the respective bands can be obtained. A comparison of the Coriolis constants obtained in this manner with those computed by means of a normal coordinate analysis by Guenthard, Lord, and McCubbin (*154*) indicated a limited applicability of the band contour analysis when the intensity maxima are closely spaced. It is very likely, however, that the limited success of this technique for cyclopropane was due to insufficient resolution provided by the spectrograph used in this study and a reinvestigation of this problem would seem to be indicated.

The vibration-rotational Raman spectrum of allene (C_3H_4) was photographed by Brodersen and Richardson (*77*) at a gas pressure of 1 atm, a reciprocal linear dispersion of 5 to 3 cm^{-1}/mm, and a practical limit of resolution of 0.4 cm^{-1}. Allene belongs to the point group D_{2d} and all fundamental vibrations ($3A_1+B_1+3B_2+4E$) are Raman active but only the B_2 and E species fundamentals are allowed in the infrared. The three totally symmetric vibrations ν_1, ν_2, ν_3 as well as the doubly degenerate vibration ν_8 were observed in the Raman study. The analysis of the totally symmetric bands was straightforward and the molecular constants for these vibrations deduced by means of a least squares analysis of the data are given in Table 12.

For the degenerate vibration ν_8 (species E) the rotational selection rule

TABLE 12

Molecular Constants of Allene, C_3H_4, Deduced from Vibration-Rotation Raman Spectra[a]

Constant	A_1			E
	ν_1	ν_2	ν_3	ν_8[b]
ν_i	3015.0 (Q_{max})	1442.64 ± 0.03	1072.582 ± 0.002	3085.6 ± 0.1
B''		0.2959 ± 0.0006	0.2960 ± 0.0001	0.2965 ± 0.0001[c]
$B' - B''$		-0.0005 ± 0.0001	-0.00040 ± 0.00004	
A''				4.816 ± 0.005
				4.807 ± 0.008[d]
				4.82 ± 0.01[e]
A'				4.797 ± 0.0005
D_J''		$(-1 \pm 7) \times 10^{-7}$	$(11 \pm 5) \times 10^{-8}$	
$D_J' - D_J''$		$(-2 \pm 2) \times 10^{-7}$	$(2 \pm 2) \times 10^{-8}$	
ζ_i				$\zeta_8 = -0.0005 \pm 0.001$
				-0.0067 ± 0.0015[d]
				$+0.00_2$[e]
x_{ij}		$x_{2,11} = 0.7$	$x_{3,11} = 2.7$	
			$x_{3,10} = -2.2$	

[a] In cm^{-1}; Zeta constant is dimensionless. Quoted probable errors are from least squares analysis.
[b] Calculated by Mills (*43*) from combined Raman (*77*) and infrared (*155*) data.
[c] Stoicheff's (*140*) value from pure rotation spectrum (see Table 10).
[d] Computed by Maki and Toth (*74*) from their infrared and Brodersen and Richardson's (*77*) Raman data on ν_8.
[e] Computed by Mills, Smith, and Duncan (*156*) from infrared data on ν_8 (*155*), ν_9 and ν_{10} (*156*), and ν_{11} (*157*) bands, and Zeta sum rule.

on K is $\Delta K = \pm 1$ for both the infrared as well as the Raman transitions. The ν_8 band was also observed in the infrared by Overend and Thompson (*155*) and a comparison between the wave numbers of the Q-branches in the Raman and infrared spectra reveals slight differences among them. Both the infrared and Raman data were originally analyzed on the basis of Eq. (82b) without the centrifugal distortion terms. Mills (*43*) derived the selection rules for the degenerate vibrations of a symmetric top molecule in which the $+l$ and $-l$ components are split due to the Coriolis interaction. This work also showed that for D_{2d} molecules the Raman selection rules for the degenerate vibrations differ from the infrared selection rules in that $\Delta K = \pm 1$ for the transition $E(-l) \leftarrow A_1$ whereas for the infrared spectrum the selection rule is $\Delta K = \pm 1$ for $E(+l) \leftarrow A_1$. The infrared and Raman transitions involve therefore different l-levels in the degenerate upper state. The infrared bands are, therefore, described by Eqs. (82a–c) whereas the Raman bands are described by Eqs. (83a, b) and (82c). A reevaluation of the infrared and Raman data for the ν_8 band by Mills yields the constants given in Table 12. It is noted that the low value $\zeta_8 = -0.0005$ for the Coriolis coefficient is responsible for the near coincidence of the infrared and Raman wavenumbers of the ${}^{P,R}Q_K$-branches and that the ground state value $A'' = 4.816$ for C_3H_4 is almost equal to the corresponding value found in ethylene (see Table 18). This suggests that the geometry of the CH_2 groups in these two molecules is identical to within the accuracy of the experimental data. The ν_8 band is observed to be afflicted with a rotational perturbation in the high ${}^{R}Q_K$ bands. In the infrared spectrum this perturbation occurs around $K = 7$ or 8 whereas in the Raman spectrum it occurs around $K = 9$ or 10. The nature of this perturbation was treated by Mills, Smith, and Duncan (*156*) who also studied the ν_9 and ν_{10} bands in an independent infrared investigation which provided a check on the A''-value by not using the Raman data. Thus, using only their infared data on the ν_9 and ν_{10} bands, the data of Overend and Thompson (*155*) and Rao and Palik (*157*) on the ν_8 and ν_{11} bands respectively, as well as the zeta sum rule $\zeta_8+\zeta_9+\zeta_{10}+\zeta_{11}=1-(B/2A)$, they find that $A'' = 4.82\ \text{cm}^{-1}$ and $\zeta_8 = +0.00_2$. The agreement among the different A'' and zeta values (Table 12) is remarkably good considering the accuracy of the data and the assumptions used in their analysis.

D. Spherical Top Molecules

1. Pure Rotation Spectra

Since spherical top molecules ($I_A = I_B = I_C$) have a ground state polarizability tensor which is spherically symmetric they do not exhibit a pure rotational Raman spectrum. In addition, it has been noted that several molecules which are mechanically symmetric ($I_A \neq I_B = I_C$), or even asymmetric tops ($I_A \neq I_B \neq I_C$), namely, BF_3, SO_2, and H_2S, do not generatc purc rotational Raman spectra even after long exposures (*158*). For these molecules it must be concluded that their electric charge distribution and their polarizability tensor is spherically symmetric, or nearly so.

2. Vibration-Rotation Spectra

The only spherical top molecule for which a resolved vibration-rotation Raman spectrum has been observed is methane, both CH_4 and CD_4, as well as for CH_3D which is mechanically a symmetric top but which has a polarizability which is spherically symmetric, at least as long as one considers the charge distribution to be unaffected by isotopic substitution. In addition, low resolution spectra which reveal the band contours only have been observed for the heavier molecules CF_4 (*159*) and SF_6 (*160*). [Note added in proof. Resolution of some of the vibration-rotation bands of CF_4 and SF_6 has been achieved in recent work in the author's laboratory.]

Methane (CH_4 and CD_4) belongs to the T_d point group and has four fundamental vibrations: one totally symmetric $\nu_1(A_1)$, one doubly degenerate $\nu_2(E)$, and two triply degenerate modes $\nu_3(F_2)$ and $\nu_4(F_2)$. All vibrations are allowed in the Raman effect but only the two triply degenerate modes are infrared active. However, due to the strong Coriolis interaction between ν_2 and ν_4 the doubly degenerate fundamental $\nu_2(E)$ of methane is observed weakly in the infrared spectrum. The isotopic variant CH_3D belongs to the C_{3v} point group and has six fundamental vibrations: three totally symmetric $\nu_1(A_1)$, $\nu_2(A_1)$, and $\nu_3(A_1)$, and three doubly degenerate modes $\nu_4(E)$, $\nu_5(E)$, and $\nu_6(E)$, all of which are allowed in both infrared absorption and the Raman effect. The fundamental vibrations for CH_4, CD_4, and CH_3D are listed in Table 13.

Although it is a very simple, highly symmetric molecule, methane exhibits an exceedingly complex vibration-rotation spectrum and for this reason it has been the subject of numerous investigations over the past 40 years. Although the ν_3 band of CH_4 was one of the first Raman bands whose rotational structure was resolved (*14*) most of the experimental investigations as well as the associated theoretical developments focused on the triply degenerate ν_3 and ν_4 bands in the infrared, which were studied over the years with consistently improving resolution and accuracy of

TABLE 13

Fundamental Vibrations of CH_4, CD_4, and CH_3D[a]

Mode	CH_4	Reference	CD_4	Reference	Mode	CH_3D	Reference
$\nu_1\ (A_1)$	2916.7	*(76)*	2908.9 (Q_{max})	*(163)*	$\nu_1\ (A_1)$	~ 2969.7	*(82)*
$\nu_2\ (E)$	1533.32 ± 0.08	*(167)*	1091.63 ± 0.08	*(167)*	$\nu_2\ (A_1)$	2200.038 ± 0.003[b]	*(82)*[b]
$\nu_3\ (F_2)$	$3019.49_3 \pm 0.05$	*(62)*	2259.30	*(164)*	$\nu_3\ (A_1)$	1300	*(169)*
	3019.48 ± 0.02	*(168)*			$\nu_4\ (E)$	3016.59 ± 0.02	*(82)*
					$\nu_5\ (E)$	1471	*(169)*
$\nu_4\ (F_2)$	1305.9		996.0	*(166)*	$\nu_6\ (E)$	1155	*(169)*

[a] In cm^{-1}.

[b] Calculated by Richardson et al. *(82)* from the data of Allen and Plyler *(170)*.

wave number determination. After the initial work by Dickinson, Dillon, and Rasetti (*14*) high resolution Raman investigations of methane (CH_4 and CD_4) were resumed in the 1950's by Prof. Welsh and his co-workers at the University of Toronto (*76,161–164*). The main conclusion of these studies was that the then available theory of vibration-rotation energy levels for methane was inadequate to satisfactorily account for the observed features in the spectrum. Similar conclusions were drawn from the study of the infrared spectrum (*165,166*).

The theory of vibration-rotation spectra for tetrahedral XY_4 molecules has since been extended to higher (i.e., third and fourth) orders by Louck (*58*), Hecht (*59*), Moret-Bailly (*60*), and Herranz (*61*) with the result that the observed details in the spectrum, as regards to both the frequencies and the intensities of the transitions, are now well understood. Thus, on the basis of the more complete theory Herranz et al. (*167*) analyzed the doubly degenerate ν_2 bands of CH_4 and CD_4 observed in the infrared under high resolution, and they were able to account for all observed features using only six molecular constants, whereas a total of nine constants was needed to explain the stronger lines of the ν_2 Raman band of CD_4 on the basis of the older theory (*163,164*). Similar success was had in the analysis of the ν_3 infrared band of CH_4 by Hecht (*59*), the ν_4 infrared band of CH_4 by Moret-Bailly (*60*), and the ν_3 infrared bands of $^{12}CH_4$ and $^{13}CH_4$ by McDowell (*168*).

The availability of the improved theory of vibration-rotational energy levels prompted Herranz and Stoicheff to reinvestigate the triply degenerate ν_3 Raman band of CH_4 (*62*). The spectrum was photographed in the second order of a 21-foot concave grating arranged in the Eagle mounting. With a cylindrical lens placed in front of the photographic plate and a gas pressure of 2 atm two spectra were photographed in 12 and 16 hr. The effective limit of resolution was 0.4 cm^{-1} and the absolute as well as the relative wave number accuracy was ± 0.05 cm^{-1}. The microphotometer trace of the ν_3 band is shown in Fig. 16 and the band is seen to extend over nearly 600 cm^{-1}. The analysis of this band was performed on the basis of Eqs. (*102*) and (*103*) for the ground and excited states respectively.

The selection rules are that $\Delta J = 0, \pm 1, \pm 2$ with $J' + J'' \geqq 2$. The complete band therefore consists of 15 branches (five branches, O,P,Q,R,S, connecting the ground state to each of the three upper states F^+, F^0, F^-, respectively) whose respective intensities are determined by the quantities $\beta_{\mathscr{L}}{}^2$ and $(b_J^i)_{nT,n'T'}$ given in Tables 4 and 5. The integral coefficients of the factors (Table 4) represent the intensities of the branches for the limiting case of high J. Thus, the relative intensities of the branches for high J are:

$$S^+:S^0:S^- = O^-:O^0:O^+ = 15:5:1$$
$$R^+:R^0:R^- = P^-:P^0:P^+ = 10:8:3$$
$$Q^+:Q^0:Q^- = 6:9:6$$

as was originally quoted by Teller (*63*). The highest intensities in the outer regions (large J) of the band are therefore to be found in the S^+ and O^- branches and inspection of Fig. 16 bears this out. As seen from the spectrum many of the lines are sharp and, even though they often are composites of several transitions between groups of sublevels in the upper and lower states, these were used in the determination of the molecular constants.

The molecular constants for the ground and excited states were obtained using the method of combination differences and graphical analysis. They are listed in Table 14 together with the results obtained by McDowell (*168*) from an analysis of the infrared ν_3 bands for $^{12}CH_4$ and $^{13}CH_4$, using the least squares technique. The Raman and infrared results are seen to be in good agreement. Table 15 gives the molecular constants of CH_4 and CD_4 from the analysis of the infrared ν_2 band by Herranz et al. (*167*). These results supersede those previously obtained from the Raman analysis of the ν_2 Raman band (*162,164*).

The isotopic variant CH_3D is a symmetric top molecule and as such is not afflicted with the strong interactions found in CH_4 and CD_4 as a result of their higher symmetry. The fundamental vibrations of CH_3D are also listed in Table 13. The Raman spectrum of CH_3D was photographed by Richardson et al. (*82*) who observed extensive rotational structure in the ν_2 and ν_4 bands (Table 13). Partially resolved Q-branches were recorded for ν_1, $2\nu_5$ and $2\nu_6$ while the three remaining fundamentals were not observed. The totally symmetric ν_2 band at 2200 cm^{-1} is associated with the C–D stretching mode. This band was also recorded in the infrared by Allen and Plyler (*170*) with a resolution of 0.05 cm^{-1} whereas the resolution in the Raman studied was about 0.5 cm^{-1}. It thus serves as a check on the reliability of the Raman results which, although of lesser accuracy, are derived not only from the P- and R-branches as in the case of the infrared results, but also from O- and S-branches which extend over twice the frequency range of the infrared band. Partial resolution of the K-structure was achieved (which is probably the only recorded case of such resolution in a Raman spectrum) which allows the determination of the centrifugal distortion constant D^{JK}. The molecular constants deducted from the analysis of the ν_2 and ν_4 bands are given in Table 16. The infrared results listed in the table have been recomputed from the original

TABLE 14

Molecular Constants of $^{12}CH_4$ and $^{13}CH_4$ Determined from ν_3 Raman and Infrared Bands[a]

	Constant[b]	$^{12}CH_4$ Raman[c]	$^{12}CH_4$ Infrared[d]	$^{13}CH_4$ (Infrared)[d]
Ground state	$B'' = B_o$	5.2412 ± 0.0005	$[5.2412 \pm 0.0005]^e$	$[5.2412 \pm 0.0005]^e$
($v_1 = v_2 = v_3 = v_4 = 0$)	$D_J'' = D_o^J$	$(1.12 \pm 0.02) \times 10^{-4}$	$(1.14 \pm 0.06) \times 10^{-4}$	$(1.14 \pm 0.06) \times 10^{-4}$
	$D_o^{J\tau}$	$(0.3\ \pm 0.10) \times 10^{-4}$	$(0.46 \pm 0.18) \times 10^{-4}$	$(0.46 \pm 0.18) \times 10^{-4}$
Upper state	ν_3	$3019.49_3 \pm 0.05$	3019.48 ± 0.02	3009.53 ± 0.03
($v_3 = 1, v_1 = v_2 = v_4 = 0$)	$B_{eff}^{\pm}(= B_1 - \beta_3)$	5.2027 ± 0.0005	5.2019 ± 0.0009	5.2026 ± 0.0010
	$B_{eff}^{0}(= B_1 + 2\beta_3)$	5.1936 ± 0.0005	5.1941 ± 0.0008	5.1968 ± 0.0006
	B_1	5.1996 ± 0.0005	5.1993 ± 0.0007	5.2006 ± 0.0008
	β_3	-0.0030 ± 0.0003	-0.0026 ± 0.0003	-0.0019 ± 0.0003
	α_3	0.0416 ± 0.0010	0.0419 ± 0.0005	0.0406 ± 0.0006
	D_1^J	$(0.97 \pm 0.02) \times 10^{-4}$	$(0.94 \pm 0.06) \times 10^{-4}$	$(0.94 \pm 0.06) \times 10^{-4}$
	$2B_e\zeta_3$	$0.578_5 \pm 0.003$	0.5760 ± 0.0016	0.4834 ± 0.0016
	ζ_3	0.0552 ± 0.0005	0.0550 ± 0.0005	0.0461 ± 0.0005
	δ_3	0.058 ± 0.005	0.055 ± 0.004	0.046 ± 0.005
	$d^{J\tau}$	$(0.55 \pm 0.10) \times 10^{-4}$	$(0.65 \pm 0.15) \times 10^{-4}$	$(0.54 \pm 0.17) \times 10^{-4}$

[a] In cm^{-1}.

[b] The constants B_o, D_o^J, $B_1(= B_o - \alpha_3)$, D_1^J and ζ_3 have the usual meaning. Other constants are higher order coefficients in Eqs. (102) and (103) as defined by Herranz (*61,62*). The Zeta constant is dimensionless.

[c] From analysis of the ν_3 Raman band by Herranz and Stoicheff (*62*).

[d] From analysis of the ν_3 infrared band by McDowell (*168*).

[e] Assumed Raman value (column 2).

TABLE 15

Molecular Constants of CH_4 and CD_4 Derived from Infrared ν_2 Band[a]

	Constant[b]	CH_4	CD_4
Ground state			
$(v_1 = v_2 = v_3 = v_4 = 0)$	$B'' = B_o$	$[5.2412 \pm 0.0005]^c$	$2.634_0 \pm 0.001_0$
	$D_J'' = D_o^J$	$(1.12 \pm 0.02) \times 10^{-4c}$	$(0.45 \pm 0.1_0) \times 10^{-4}$
	$D_0^{J\tau}$	$(0.3_0 \pm 0.1_0) \times 10^{-4c}$	$(0.3_0 \pm 0.2_0) \times 10^{-4}$
Upper state			
$(v_2 = 1, v_1 = v_3 = v_4 = 0)$	ν_2	1533.32 ± 0.08	1091.63 ± 0.08
	$B' = B_2$	5.324 ± 0.003	2.701 ± 0.002
	$D_J' = D_2^J$	$(1.4_5 \pm 0.2_5) \times 10^{-4}$	$(0.8_6 \pm 0.2_5) \times 10^{-4}$
	b_2	$(3.7_0 \pm 0.3_0) \times 10^{-2}$	$(2.55 \pm 0.06) \times 10^{-2}$
	d_2	$(-2.25 \pm 0.0_3) \times 10^{-3}$	$(-1.5_9 \pm 0.1_1) \times 10^{-3}$
	$D_2^{J\tau}$	$(4.1 \pm 0.8) \times 10^{-4}$	$(1.1 \pm 0.3) \times 10^{-4}$

[a] In cm^{-1}; from Herranz, Morcillo, and Gomez, Ref. (*167*).

[b] The constants B_o, D_o^J, B_2, D_2^J, and ν_2 have the usual meaning. Other constants are higher order coefficients as defined by Herranz (*61,62*).

[c] Assumed values, taken from analysis of ν_3 Raman band, Table 14.

data of Allen and Plyler (*170*). Except for the constants D_0^{JK} and D_1^{JK}, the agreement between the infrared and Raman results for the ν_2 band is remarkably good considering the lesser resolution available in the Raman work. The resolution of the *K*-structure was not sufficient to have resulted in more accurate D^{JK} values.

The method of band contour analysis, first used by Mathai *et al.* (*153*) in their study of cyclopropane (see above, p. 645) has been developed more fully for spherical top molecules by Masri and Fletcher (*170a*). These authors use both the spherical top theory of Herranz and Stoicheff (*62*) as well as the spherical top limit of Placzek and Teller's theory of the symmetric top (*19*) to compute the intensity of the band contours. Both approaches give the same results for the separation of the maxima of the composite O+P and S+R branches (called "P-R separation" by Masri

TABLE 16

Molecular Constants of CH_3D from ν_2 and ν_4 Bands[a]

	$\nu_2(A_1)$		$\nu_4(E)$
Constant	Infrared[b]	Raman[c]	(Raman)[c]
ν_i	2200.038±0.003	2200.00±0.02	3016.59±0.02
B_0	3.8804±0.0002	3.878±0.001	3.877±0.001
B_1	3.8381±0.0002	3.836±0.001	3.863±0.001
A_0			5.243±0.002
A_1			5.223±0.003
(A_1-B_1) $-(A_0-B_0)$	0.0373±0.0002	0.041±0.002	−0.0058±0.0011
ζ_i			0.0775±0.0002
$D_0{}^J\times 10^5$	5.2±0.2	4.6±0.4	4.7±0.9
$D^J\times 10^4$	5.6±0.1	5.2±0.4	5±1
$D_0{}^{JK}\times 10^5$	12.8±0.3	0±3	3±3
$D_1{}^{JK}\times 10^5$	12.3±0.3	6±4	−27±3
$D_0{}^K\times 10^5$			−5±2
$D_1{}^K\times 10^5$			18±3
$(D_1{}^K-D_0{}^K)\times 10^5$	−(0.2±0.2)		

[a] In cm^{-1}; zeta constant is dimensionless. For the totally symmetric ν_2 band the zeta value is zero. All constants derived from least squares analysis of data.

[b] Constants recomputed by Richardson et al. (*82*) from original data of Allen and Plyler (*170*)

[c] From Richardson et al. (*82*).

and Fletcher). Comparison of the theoretically predicted spacing of these maxima with the observed values in CF_4 (*159*) and SF_6 (*160*) as well as in UF_6 indicates satisfactory agreement for some of the bands but not for others. It is very likely that the existing data, obtained with pre-laser techniques, are of insufficient accuracy to allow a critical evaluation of the theoretical expressions. Further experimental work with laser excitation is indicated.

E. Asymmetric Top Molecules

1. Pure Rotation Spectra

The pure rotational Raman spectra of linear and symmetric top molecules are characterized by regularly spaced series of lines corresponding to the transition with $\Delta J = +1, +2$ and $\Delta K = 0$. The basic expression for the term value of the symmetric top rotor, Eq. (62a), shows that the energy is a function of two quantum numbers, J and K which are the quantum numbers of the total angular momentum and its projection onto the symmetry axis of the top respectively, and that for $K > 0$ each term is doubly degenerate. For an asymmetric top molecule $I_A \neq I_B \neq I_C$ with the principal moments of inertia ordered, such that for the rotation constants $A > B > C$, this double degeneracy is lifted and to each value of J there are associated $2J+1$ distinct energy levels. The symmetric top quantum number K has no longer any meaning and the $2J+1$ sublevels of each J-state are labeled by a pseudoquantum number τ which ranges in integral steps from $\tau = -J$ for the lowest energy to $\tau = +J$ for the highest energy of the sublevels belonging to J.

The expression for the rotational term value is now

$$F_0(J_\tau) = \tfrac{1}{2}(A+C)J(J+1)+\tfrac{1}{2}(A-C)E_\tau^{\,J}(\kappa) \tag{112}$$

where $E_\tau^{\,J}(\kappa)$ is a numerical coefficient whose value must be determined for each individual value of J and κ. The quantity κ is Ray's (*66*) asymmetry parameter which is defined by

$$\kappa = \frac{2B-A-C}{A-C} \tag{113}$$

and which has the limiting values $\kappa = -1$ for the prolate top with $A > B = C$ and $\kappa = +1$ for the oblate top with $A = B > C$. For the most asymmetric case $B = \tfrac{1}{2}(A+C)$ and $\kappa = 0$ (Refs. *64–71*). For given J and κ the quantity $E_\tau^{\,J}(\kappa)$ assumes $2J+1$ different values which are the roots of a secular determinant of degree $2J+1$. Numerical values of $E_\tau^J(\kappa)$ have been tabulated for values of κ ranging in steps of 0.01 from $\kappa = 0$ to $\kappa = 1$ and for J up to 12 [see, for instance, Townes and Schawlow, Ref. (*64*), Appendix IV]. A finer grained compilation with κ changing in steps of 0.001 and for J up to 20 is now available (*171*). The centrifugal distortion effects which are not accounted for in the term expression given by Eq. (112) are included in Nielsen's general theory of vibration-rotation spectra (*172*). A very convenient form of the energies of a nonrigid asymmetric top rotor has been developed by Kivelson and Wilson (*173*) according to which

$$F(J_\tau) = F_0 + A_1 F_0^2 + A_2 F(J)J(J+1) + A_3 J^2(J+1)^2 + A_4 J(J+1)\langle P_z^2\rangle + A_5\langle P_z^4\rangle + A_6 F_0\langle P_z^2\rangle \qquad (114)$$

The first term F_0 is the term value of the rigid asymmetric top given by Eq. (112) and the other six terms describe the centrifugal distortion. The generalized centrifugal distortion coefficients A_n are given in terms of the symmetric top constants D_J, D_{JK}, and D_K as well as three additional constants R_5, R_6, and δ_J which vanish in the symmetric top limit. The quantity $\langle P_z^2\rangle$ is the expectation value of P_z^2, where P_z is the component of the angular momentum operator lying along the z-axis of the limiting symmetric top.

The analysis of the rotational Raman spectrum on the basis of either Eq. (112) or (114) and with the aid of a tabulation of $E_\tau^J(\kappa)$ values is thus in principle a straightforward procedure. The selection rules permit transitions for $\Delta J = 0, \pm 1$ and ± 2 but the selection rule on the symmetric top quantum number K is now replaced by more general statements involving the symmetry properties of the rotational sublevels J_τ. The rotational energy levels of an asymmetric top are distinguished according to the behavior (+ or −) of the rotational eigenfunctions with respect to the three operations C_2^a, C_2^b, C_2^c which are twofold (180°) rotations about the principal axes *a,b,c* of the top. Since one of these is equivalent to the other two carried out in succession the behavior with respect to only two, usually C_2^c and C_2^a is specified [Herzberg, Ref. (*42*), pp. 50–55]. There are thus four different species of rotational levels designated by $++$, $+-$, $-+$, and $--$ where the first sign indicates the behavior under the operation C_2^c and the second gives the behavior under C_2^a. The general selection rule for the Raman effect is that transitions between levels of any of the four symmetry species are allowed subject to the rule that $\Delta J = 0, \pm 1, \pm 2$ with $J'+J'' \geqq 2$. The resulting spectrum is, therefore, expected to be exceedingly complex. However, for molecules which possess at least one twofold axis of symmetry (point groups C_{2v}, D_2, or V_h) the principal axes of the moment of inertia ellipsoid coincide with those of the polarizability ellipsoid and the selection rules are more restrictive: only levels of the same species may combine with one another, or

$$++ \leftrightarrow ++, \quad +- \leftrightarrow +-, \quad -+ \leftrightarrow -+, \quad -- \leftrightarrow --$$

Therefore, for molecules which belong to the C_{2v} point group and which thus have a pure rotational infrared spectrum, for example H_2O, H_2CO, CH_2Cl_2, transitions which may occur in the Raman effect are forbidden in the infrared and vice versa.

Of the asymmetric top molecules that have been studied thus far in the Raman effect unfortunately all but two exhibit a pure rotation spectrum in which none of the splittings appear resolved. The spectra look very much like those generated by symmetric top molecules showing well developed R- and S-branches according to the selection rule $\Delta J = +1$ and $+2$ respectively. Figures 5, and 7 are typical of such cases and the only indication of an asymmetric top character is that the Raman lines are somewhat broader than in the spectrum of a comparable symmetric top. These molecules are approximate symmetric tops in which the quantum number K has an approximate validity and the selection rule $\Delta K = 0$ holds approximately. Therefore lines with given J and different K ($\leqq J$) fall closely together thus giving the R- and S-branch structure in the spectrum. The equation for the rotational Raman shifts, Eqs. (72′) and (73′) are then applicable provided that the rotation constant B is replaced by an average of the two approximately equal rotation constants B and C or $\tilde{B} = \frac{1}{2}(B+C)$ for the prolate top. The ground state $\tilde{B}_0$ as well as the approximate D_J values for a number of asymmetric top molecules that have been determined in this manner are given in Table 17. Whenever possible the corresponding values obtained from microwave spectra are listed for comparison. The agreement among the $\tilde{B}_0$ values is in these cases only fair.

Since K is only approximately defined, pure rotational transitions with $\Delta K = 1$ and 2 are also permitted in addition to those with $\Delta K = 0$. The only such case that has been reported thus far is for the pure rotation spectrum of formaldehyde-d_1 which is satisfactorily described by the accidentally symmetric top approximation with the strong Raman lines corresponding to transitions with $\Delta J = 0$, $\Delta K = +2$ (*174*). The Raman shifts for this case are then $\Delta\nu = 4(A'' - \tilde{B}'')(K+1)$ if centrifugal distortion is ignored.

After the original work by Lewis and Houston (*16*) the rotational Raman spectrum of ethylene, C_2H_4, was reinvestigated by Romanko et al. (*182*), by Dowling and Stoicheff who studied both C_2H_4 and C_2D_4 (*183*), and by Van Riet and de Hemptinne who investigated C_2H_3D (*187*). Under moderate resolution and dispersion the rotational spectrum of C_2H_4 consists of three branches, an R-branch ($\Delta J = +1$), an S-branch ($\Delta J = +2$) and an S'-branch ($\Delta J = +2$) whose lines go in and out of step with those of the S-branch (*182*). The R- and S-branches are the symmetric top features of the spectrum while the S'-branch is an indication of the deviation of the molecule from the exact symmetric top. While the assignment of the R- and S-branch lines was straightforward the lines of the S'-branch were assigned only after an approximate calculation of the relative intensities showed that they correspond to transitions involving the two lowest τ levels in each J state; for these sublevels the energy eigenvalues of the asymmetric top deviate most from those of the symmetric top.

For the high τ sublevels the rotational term value of the rigid prolate asymmetric top is approximately given by the symmetric top form

$$F_{\text{prolate}}(J, K) = \tfrac{1}{2}(B+C)J(J+1)+[A-\tfrac{1}{2}(B+C)]K^2, \quad K \leqq J, J = 0, 1, 2, \ldots \tag{115}$$

while for the two lowest τ sublevels (J_{-J} and J_{-J+1}) of an oblate top the average rotational terms are approximately given by Mecke's expression [Herzberg, Ref. (*42*), p. 49]

$$\tfrac{1}{2}[F(J_{-J})+F(J_{-J+1})] = CJ^2+\tfrac{1}{2}(A+B)J - \tfrac{1}{8}(A-B)J\left(\frac{2J-1}{J-1}\right)b^*\left(1+\frac{b^{*2}}{4}\right) \tag{116}$$

where

$$b^* = \frac{B-A}{2[C-\tfrac{1}{2}(A+B)]} \tag{117}$$

Although Mecke's approximation is derived for an oblate top, Romanko et al. showed it to be applicable to prolate tops for high J values. From Eq. (116) we obtain with $\Delta J = +2$ for the Raman shifts of the lines in the S' branch

$$\Delta\nu_{S'} = 4C(J+1)+(A-B)-\tfrac{1}{2}(A-B)b^*\left(1+\frac{b^{*2}}{4}\right) \tag{118}$$

for the high J limit. The spacing of the S'-branch lines is thus $4C$, (centrifugal distortion is neglected). A graph of $\Delta\nu$ versus $(J+1)$ gives a straight line with slope $4C$ and intercept $[(A-B)-\tfrac{1}{2}(A-B)b^*(1+b^{*2}/4)]$.

TABLE 17

Ground State Rotation and Centrifugal Distortion Constants for Asymmetric Top Molecules Deduced from Rotational Raman Spectra[a]

Molecule		Structure	Rotation constant[b]	$D_J \times 10^8$	Reference
Formaldehyde-d$_1$	HDCO	C_s	$A_o - \tilde{B}_o = 5.46 \pm 0.4$[c]		(174)
Ethylene		V_h	see Table 18		
1,1-Difluoroethylene	$C_2H_2F_2$	C_{2v}	$\tilde{B}_o = 0.35660 \pm 0.00035$	4.85 ± 1.1	(91)
			0.357407 (Microwave)		(91a)
Allene-1,1-d$_2$	$C_3H_2D_2$	C_{2v}	$\tilde{B}_o = 0.2619_0 \pm 0.0001$	7.0	(104)
Trans-2-butene	C_4H_8	C_{2h}	$\tilde{B}_o = 0.1206$		(29)
Trans-1,3-butadiene	C_4H_6	C_{2h}	$\tilde{B}_o = 0.1413 \pm 0.0002$	~ 1	(175)
			$A_o = 1.370 \pm 0.011$[d]		
	C_4D_6		$\tilde{B}_o = 0.1155 \pm 0.0002$	~ 1	(175)
Butatriene	C_4H_4	V_h	$\tilde{B}_o = 0.1314_1 \pm 0.0001$	1	(176)
Vinylacetylene	C_4H_4	V_s	$\tilde{B}_o = 0.1512_5 \pm 0.0002$ (*S*-branch)	3 ± 2	(177)
			$0.1514_1 \pm 0.0003$ (*R*-branch)	13 ± 6	
			0.15135_0 (microwave value)[e]		
			$C_o = 0.143_4 \pm 0.001$ (*S'*-branch)[e]	3 ± 8	
			$H = 1.07 \pm 0.11$		
			$H = 0.92$ (microwave value)[e]		
Furan	C_4H_4O	C_{2v}	$\tilde{B}_o = 0.31154 \pm 0.00006$ (*S*-branch)	12.5 ± 2.5	(89)
			$= 0.31160 \pm 0.00010$ (*R*-branch)	7 ± 3	
			$= 0.31178$ (microwave value)[f]	10.01	(178)
Pyridine	C_5NH_5	C_{2v}	$\tilde{B}_o = 0.19692 \pm 0.0001$	1.87 ± 1.41	(91)
			0.19676 ± 0.00012 (infrared)	0.5	(91b)
			0.19754 (microwave)[g]	6.25	(178)

TABLE 17 (*cont.*)

Molecule		Structure	Rotation constant[b]	$D_J \times 10^8$	Reference
Cyclopentene	C_5H_8	C_{2v}	$\tilde{B}_o = 0.24165 \pm 0.00005$	3.75 ± 1.25	(*89*)
			$0.2419_4 \pm 0.00015$	1.4 ± 4	(*179*)
			0.24227 (microwave)[h]		(*180*)
1,4-Cyclohexadiene	C_6H_8	C_s	$\tilde{B}_o = 0.1671_1 \pm 0.00006$	2.1 ± 0.4	(*90*)
1,3,5-Cyloheptatriene	C_7H_8	C_s	$\tilde{B}_o = 0.1226_4 \pm 0.00005$	1.4 ± 0.5	(*90*)
			0.12290 (microwave)[i]	2.2	(*181*)

[a] In cm^{-1}.

[b] Microwave $\tilde{B}_o$ values are computed from $\tilde{B}_o = \frac{1}{2}(B_o + C_o)$ for prolate tops and $\tilde{B}_o = \frac{1}{2}(A_o + B_o)$ for oblate tops. The value $c = 2.997930 \times 10^{10}$ cm/sec was used in the computations.

[c] $(A_o - \tilde{B}_o)$ value determined directly from pure rotation spectrum, $\Delta J = 0, \Delta K = 2$ (Ref. (*174*).

[d] A_o value computed using $A_o - \tilde{B}_o = 1.229 \pm 0.01\ cm^{-1}$ determined from infrared absorption spectrum, Ref. (*175*). Cole et al. Ref. (*175a*) find, however, $A_o - \tilde{B}_o = 1.245 \pm 0.002\ cm^{-1}$ so that using the Raman value for $\tilde{B}_o$ and assuming the molecule to be planar, $A_o = 1.3868 \pm 0.002\ cm^{-1}$, and $C_o = 1341 \pm 0.0002\ cm^{-1}$.

[e] Microwave values are $A_o = 1.683_3$, $B_o = 0.15828$, $C_o = 0.14442\ cm^{-1}$ as computed by Gribova et al., Ref. (*177*). The value of H was calculated from the formula $H = (A+B) - \frac{1}{2}(A-B)b(1+b/4)$, where $b = (B-A)/(2C-A-B) = 0.982$.

[f] Microwave values are $A_o = 0.3151222$, $B_o = 0.3084384$, $C_o = 0.1558023$, $D_J = 10.01 \times 10^{-8}$, $D_{JK} = -17.95 \times 10^{-8}$, and $D_K = 8.466 \times 10^{-8}\ cm^{-1}$.

[g] Microwave values are $A_o = 0.201449$, $B_o = 0.193632$, $C_o = 0.0987091$, $D_J = 6.25 \times 10^{-8}$, and $D_K = 2.33 \times 10^{-8}\ cm^{-1}$.

[h] Microwave values are $A_o = 0.243452$, $B_o = 0.241085$, $C_o = 0.131717\ cm^{-1}$.

[i] Microwave values are $A_o = 0.123289$, $B_o = 0.122487$, $C_o = 0.0677901$, $D_J = 2.2 \times 10^{-8}$, $D_{JK} = -34.0 \times 10^{-8}$, $D_K = 1.8 \times 10^{-8}\ cm^{-1}$.

While the results for ethylene obtained by Romanko et al. (*182*) have been superseded by those obtained by Dowling and Stoicheff (*183*), the analysis of rotational Raman spectra of slightly asymmetric top molecules, based on the observation of S and S' series, may be applicable in heavier molecules. Thus, the rotational Raman spectrum of vinylacetylene was analyzed by Gribova et al. (*177*) on the basis of this technique. Vinylacetylene approximates a symmetric top even more closely than does ethylene (for ethylene $b^* = 0.910$, for vinylacetylene $b^* = 0.982$, prolate symmetric top $b^* = 1$). Moreover, since the rotational constants for this molecule have been obtained with the technique of microwave spectroscopy, another check on the usefulness of the technique can be made. The results of the Raman investigation of vinylacetylene are given in Table 17 where they are compared with the corresponding microwave results.

In a rather elegant study of the ethylene rotation spectrum [Fig. 6] Dowling and Stoicheff (*183*) were able to resolve considerably more detail than was possible in the work of Romanko et al. (*182*). Over 120 pairs of Raman lines each were observed for C_2H_4 and C_2D_4 respectively and their assignments were facilitated by an approximate spectrum computed with the constants determined by Romanko et al., supplemented by a computation of the relative intensities based on the symmetric top theory. Most of the observed lines turned out to be blends or unresolved superpositions of several transitions and only 14 lines in the spectrum of C_2H_4 and 9 in the spectrum of C_2D_4, all S-branch lines, were found to be single. Their wave numbers were fitted to the equation for the S-branch transitions

$$\Delta\nu_S = S(J) = (A_0 + C_0)(2J+3) + \tfrac{1}{2}(A_0 - C_0)[E_{\tau'}^{J+2}(\kappa) - E_{\tau}^{J}(\kappa)] \quad (119)$$

which involves three unknowns, A_0, C_0, and κ. The values of A_0, B_0 and κ that give the best fit are given in Table 18 for both C_2H_4 and C_2D_4. The value of B_0 is determined from Eq. (113) for the asymmetry parameter. The accuracy of the data warranted the inclusion of the centrifugal distortion effects in the analysis. These were estimated using centrifugal distortion constants calculated according to Kivelson and Wilson's theory (*173*); these constants are also given in Table 18.

An independent determination of the rotational constants B_0 and C_0 was made by Allen and Plyler (*184*) who studied the ν_{11} parallel bands of C_2H_4 and C_2D_4 in the infrared, while Smith and Mills (*185*) determined an A_0 value for C_2H_4 from a study of the ν_7 and ν_{10} perpendicular bands. The difference between the infrared and Raman A_0 values is not understood as yet. On the other hand the B_0 and C_0 values determined by Allen and Plyler are close to the Raman values but the small differences between

TABLE 18

Molecular Constants for C_2H_4 and C_2D_4 Deduced from the Pure Rotational Raman Spectrum[a]

Constant	C_2H_4	C_2D_4
A_o	4.828 ± 0.009	2.432 ± 0.008
	4.861 ± 0.005[b]	
B_o	1.0012 ± 0.0009	0.7369 ± 0.0012
	0.9998 ± 0.0002[c]	0.7334 ± 0.00[c]
C_o	0.8282 ± 0.0004	0.5630 ± 0.0006
	0.8294 ± 0.0002[c]	0.5636 ± 0.00[c]
κ	-0.9135 ± 0.0003	-0.8139 ± 0.0005
D_J	1.143×10^{-6}	6.651×10^{-7}
D_{JK}	2.148×10^{-5}	5.822×10^{-6}
D_K	7.960×10^{-5}	1.916×10^{-5}
R_5	-5.028×10^{-6}	-1.634×10^{-6}
R_6	-1.788×10^{-8}	-2.249×10^{-8}
δ_J	2.112×10^{-7}	1.961×10^{-7}

[a] In cm^{-1}. From Dowling and Stoicheff, Ref. (*183*). The asymmetry parameter κ is dimensionless. Centrifugal distortion constants are theoretically computed values.

[b] From analysis of ν_7 and ν_{10} infrared bands by Smith and Mills (*185*).

[c] From analysis of ν_{11} parallel bands of C_2H_4 and C_2D_4 by Allen and Plyler (*184*).

them nevertheless suggests that a significant discrepancy exists between the infrared and Raman results. Since ethylene is a planar molecule (point group $V_h = D_{2h}$) the moments of inertia I_a, I_b, I_c for the rigid molecule are related such that $I_c = I_a + I_b$. This relation does not hold, however, for the vibrating molecule (zero point oscillations in the ground vibrational state!) and the difference $\Delta = I_c - I_a - I_b$ for the ground state constants is known as the "inertial defect." In a theoretical study of the inertial defect for ethylene Kuchitsu, Oka and Morino (*186*) find that Dowling and Stoicheff's rotational constants are essentially correct and suggest that further spectroscopic work be done to remove the discrepancy between the infrared and Raman results.

The work by Van Riet and de Hemptinne (*187*) on the rotational Raman spectrum of C_2H_3D provided only the value $\tilde{B}_0 = 0.8249\ cm^{-1}$ since they observed only the symmetric top like *R*- and *S*-branches in the spectrum.

2. Vibration-Rotation Spectra

Ethylene is the only known asymmetric top molecule for which a resolved vibration-rotational Raman band has been reported and analyzed. Of the 12 fundamental vibrations of C_2H_4 six are active in the Raman effect ($3A_{1g}$, $2B_{1g}$, B_{2g}) five are active in infrared absorption (B_{1u}, $2B_{2u}$, $2B_{3u}$) and one (A_u) is inactive. Since ethylene has a center of symmetry the Raman and infrared activities are mutually exclusive. The fundamental modes of vibration of C_2H_4 are listed in Table 19 together with the rotational

TABLE 19

Fundamental Vibrations of Ethylene[a]

Mode	Species	Selection rule	Frequency (cm^{-1})	Reference
ν_1	A_{1g}	R, $\Delta K = 0$	3026.4 (ν_0)	(*189*)
ν_2	A_{1g}	R, $\Delta K = 0$	1622.6 (Q_{max})	(*189*)
ν_3	A_{1g}	R, $\Delta K = 0$	1342.2 (ν_0)	(*189*)
ν_4	A_u	Inactive	1023 ± 3	(*185*)
ν_5	B_{1g}	R, $\Delta K = \pm 2$	3102.5 (ν_0)	(*189*)
ν_6	B_{1g}	R, $\Delta K = \pm 2$	1222.0	(*185*)
ν_7	B_{1u}	I, $\Delta K = \pm 1$	949.3	(*185*)
ν_8	B_{2g}	R, $\Delta K = \pm 1$	950.0	(*188*)
ν_9	B_{2u}	I, $\Delta K = \pm 1$	3105.5	(*190*)
ν_{10}	B_{2u}	I, $\Delta K = \pm 1$	826.0	(*185*)
ν_{11}	B_{3u}	I, $\Delta K = 0$	2988.7	(*184*)
ν_{12}	B_{3u}	I, $\Delta K = 0$	1443.5	(*190*)

[a] Adapted from Smith and Mills, Ref. (*185*).

selection rules. The spectrum of the gas was photographed by Stoicheff (*188*) at low resolution while Feldman et al. (*189*) observed extensive rotational structure in the totally symmetric ν_1 and ν_3 bands and a series of ${}^{O,S}Q_K$ branches in the nontotally symmetric ν_5 band. The ν_3 band showed the characteristic O,P,Q,R,S branches of a totally symmetric vibration of a symmetric top molecule and in addition showed O'- and S'-branches with $\Delta J = -2$ and $+2$ respectively of the asymmetric top, similar to the case of the pure rotation spectrum. The ν_1 and ν_5 bands overlap considerably and only the O-branch of ν_1 as well as the ${}^{O}Q_K$- and ${}^{S}Q_K$-branches of ν_5 were discernible. The spectrum was obtained with a prism spectrograph of moderate resolving power and a reinvestigation with currently available high resolution grating spectrographs would seem to be indicated.

V. DETERMINATION OF MOLECULAR STRUCTURE

A. Introduction

Thc previous section reviewed the body of data that has been collected thus far with the technique of high resolution Raman spectroscopy. These data consist of a set of rotational and centrifugal distortion constants for the ground and some excited vibrational states of molecules, as well as Coriolis coupling coefficients for some of the degenerate vibrations of symmetric and spherical top rotors. The purpose of the Raman investigations is, of course, the determination of the structure and the dynamical parameters of these molecules with an independent spectroscopic technique so as to complement the information that is gathered with the infrared, and microwave absorption, and the electron diffraction methods.

In the determination of a molecular structure we may distinguish between two kinds of data. Customarily, it is understood that the structure of a molecule is known when all the internuclear distances or, alternatively, all bond lengths and interbond angles for the rigid molecule have been determined. This "static" structure of the molecule presupposes the knowledge of a geometrical model, which information is obtained largely from the study of the vibrational infrared and Raman spectra and their interpretation with the aid of group theory [see Herzberg, Ref. (*42*), Chapts. 2 and 3]. An analysis based on the vibrational spectrum alone is not always conclusive and recourse is then taken to other information such as dipole moment and heat capacity data and others, including the rotational fine structure of vibrational bands (see, for example, the discussion on ethane, pp. 637–644). From the observed values of the ground state rotational constants A_0, B_0, and C_0 one obtains "effective" moments of inertia I_a^0, I_b^0, and I_c^0 of the molecule and its various isotopic species, from which one computes the bond lengths and interbond angles.

One of the most important assumptions of this method is that the molecule is "rigid" although this is known not to be the case. Indeed, the effective moments of inertia are determined by the dynamical properties of the molecule which are described by the force constants, both harmonic and anharmonic, the vibrational normal coordinates, the Coriolis coefficients, as well as the centrifugal distortion constants. These dynamical parameters, which constitute the second kind of the above mentioned data, are needed to correctly ascertain the equilibrium values of the bond lengths and angles from the observed data. Unfortunately only for a few (i.e., about a dozen or so) polyatomic molecules is sufficient data available for the determination of their equilibrium structures and it is, therefore, customary to just report the ground state structures which, luckily, are quite adequate for many purposes.

Nevertheless, the high accuracy of microwave and modern infrared rotational constants has forced the experimental spectroscopist to pay careful attention to the physical significance of the experimentally determined rotational constants and the molecular structures derived from them. Since the desirable "equilibrium" structure of a molecule is difficult to obtain due to the lack of a sufficient amount of empirical data, several approaches which give different types of structures have been developed: an ideal "r_e" structure, which is the equilibrium structure, the "r_0", "r_s", and "average" structures, all four of which are derivable from spectroscopic data, and the "r_g" structure which is derived from electron diffraction data.

After a review of the principles of the different structure calculations we present the "r_0" structures for those molecules that have been studied thus far by means of the Raman spectroscopic technique.

B. The "Effective" Moment of Inertia

Spectroscopic measurements do not provide the value for a moment of inertia averaged over a given vibrational state. Instead, the measurements give an average of a reciprocal moment of inertia. Consider, for simplicity, the case of the diatomic molecule. The rotational constant

$$B_v = \frac{h}{8\pi^2 c}\left\langle \frac{1}{I} \right\rangle_v \tag{120}$$

is a function of the vibrational state and is called the "effective" rotation constant. The quantity $\langle I^{-1}\rangle_v$ is the average of the reciprocal moment of inertia over the vibrational state v. An "effective" moment of inertia I^v for the vibrational state v may be defined by Eq. (121) and, thus, Eq. 122.

$$B_v = \frac{h}{8\pi^2 c}\frac{1}{I^v} \tag{121}$$

$$I^v = \langle I^{-1}\rangle_v^{-1} \tag{122}$$

The rotation constant B_v may be written to a high degree of approximation as

$$B_v = B_e - \alpha_e(v+\tfrac{1}{2}) \tag{123}$$

where B_e is the rotation constant for the equilibrium state

$$B_e = \frac{h}{8\pi^2 c}\frac{1}{I^e} \tag{124}$$

where $I^e = \mu r_e^2$ is the moment of inertia in the equilibrium configuration and μ is the reduced mass of the molecule. The rotation-vibration interaction constant α_e can be calculated theoretically with results that depend on the form of the vibrational potential energy function. Thus, for an anharmonic oscillator with a potential given by $U(r-r_e) = f(r-r_e) - g(r-r_e)^3$ where f and g are the harmonic and anharmonic potential constants, respectively

$$\alpha_e = 24\frac{B_e^3 r_e}{\omega_e}g - 6\frac{B_e^2}{\omega_e} \tag{125a}$$

where ω_e is the harmonic frequency. On the other hand, for the Morse potential, $U(r-r_e) = D_e\{1-\exp[-\beta(r-r_e]\}^2$

$$\alpha_e = \frac{6(\omega_e x_e B_e^3)^{1/2}}{\omega_e} - 6\frac{B_e^2}{\omega_e} \tag{125b}$$

where $\omega_e x_e$ is the first order anharmonic coefficient in the vibrational term value expression [see Herzberg, Ref. (*113*), p. 108]. Since $g > 0$ as well as $\omega_e x_e > 0$ we have that for most cases $B_v < B_e$ so that the moment of inertia in any vibrational state v is greater than in the equilibrium state. We also note that even for the harmonic oscillator for which $g = \omega_e x_e = 0$ and for which the potential function is symmetric with respect to the equilibrium distance between the nuclei r_e, α_e does not vanish and indeed has the negative value $\alpha_e = -6B_e^2/\omega_e$. While the effects of the vibration-rotation interaction are easily accounted for in the case of a diatomic molecule, this becomes exceedingly difficult and involved even for the simplest polyatomic molecules.

For a polyatomic molecule the rotation constant B_v (and similarly the rotation constants A_v and C_v) is represented by

$$B_v = B_e - \sum_i \alpha_i(v_i + \tfrac{1}{2}d_i) \tag{126}$$

where v stands for the totality of the vibrational quantum numbers $v_1, v_2, v_3, \ldots, v_{3N-6}$, v_i and d_i are the vibrational quantum number and degree of degeneracy of the ith vibrational state respectively, and the summation is taken over all vibrational states. The vibration rotation interaction constants α_i may be either positive or negative. Theoretical expressions for the α_i's have been obtained for a number of molecular models (*172*). They are exceedingly complex and one relies on the empirically determined values of the α_i to determine the equilibrium constant B_e. Unfortunately a complete set of the α_i constants is available for only a few molecules for which an equilibrium structure can then be determined. Several empirical techniques are used which give acceptable approximations to the equilibrium structure.

C. The "r_o" Structure

We define a moment of inertia $I_b{}^0 = \sum_i m_i r_{oi}^2$ for the ground vibrational state, where r_{oi} is the distance of the ith nucleus of mass m_i from the b axis (principal axis) of the molecule, by means of the relation

$$B_o = \frac{h}{8\pi^2 c}\left\langle \frac{1}{I_b} \right\rangle_0 \equiv \frac{h}{8\pi^2 c}\frac{1}{I_b{}^o} \tag{127}$$

where $\langle I_b^{-1}\rangle_o$ is the average of the instantaneous reciprocal moment over the ground state. Then

$$I_b{}^o = \sum_i m_i r_{o_i}^2 = \frac{h}{8\pi^2 c}\frac{1}{B_o} \tag{128}$$

gives the moment of inertia in terms of the experimental datum B_o. For each experimentally determined ground state rotation constant (A_o, B_o, C_o) one such equation may be set up. Since the number of structural parameters usually exceeds the number of measured rotation constants, use is also made of the rotation constants for the isotopic variants of the "parent" molecule to provide additional data together with the assumption that the bond lengths are unaffected by isotopic substitution. Simultaneous solution of the moment of inertia equations then gives the bond lengths and interbond angles. The structure determined by this technique is called the "r_o" structure.

D. The "r_s" Structure

An exact solution of the molecular structure problem which gives the coordinates of the individual atoms in the principal axis system of the molecule has been developed by Kraitchman (*191*). The technique is based on the following arguments.

Let the position of the center of mass of the molecule from an arbitrary coordinate origin be given by **r** and let the position of the ith atom with respect to the arbitrary origin and the center of mass be given by $\mathbf{r}_i$ and $\mathbf{r}_i^c$ respectively. Then

$$\mathbf{r} = \mathbf{r}_i - \mathbf{r}_i^c \tag{129}$$

and the center of mass conditions are shown by Eqs. (130) and (131):

$$\sum_i m_i \mathbf{r}_i^c = 0 \tag{130}$$

$$\mathbf{r} = \frac{\sum_i m_i \mathbf{r}_i}{\sum_i m_i} \tag{131}$$

where the summations extend over all the atoms in the molecule. The moment of inertia tensor with respect to an arbitrary origin is given in dyadic form by (*192*)

$$\mathbf{I} = \sum_i m_i (r_i^2 \mathbf{1} - \mathbf{r}_i \mathbf{r}_i) \tag{132}$$

where $\mathbf{1}$ is the unit tensor. Using Eqs. (*129*)–(*131*) the inertia tensor for the equilibrium configuration and referred to the center of mass origin is then

$$I^e = \sum_i m_i (r_i^2 \mathbf{1} - \mathbf{r}_i \mathbf{r}_i) - \frac{1}{M}\left[\left(\sum_i m_i \mathbf{r}_i\right)\cdot\left(\sum_i m_i \mathbf{r}_i\right)\mathbf{1} - \left(\sum_i m_i \mathbf{r}_i \sum_i m_i \mathbf{r}_i\right)\right] \tag{133}$$

where $M = \sum_i m_i$ is the mass of the molecule. In the principal axis system the elements of this tensor are (x,y,z = cyclic)

$$I_{xx}^e = \sum m_i (y_i^2 + z_i^2)$$

and (134)

$$I_{xy}^e = 0$$

For an isotopic variant of the "parent" molecule the inertia tensor, in the (principal) coordinate system of the "parent" molecule, has elements

$$I_{xx}^{e'} = I_{xx}^e + \Delta m(y^2 + z^2) - \frac{1}{M + \Delta m}\,[(y \cdot \Delta m)^2 + (z \cdot \Delta m)^2]$$

or

$$I_{xx}^{e'} = I_{xx}^e + \mu(y^2 + z^2)$$

as well as

$$I_{xy}^{e'} = -\mu xy \tag{135}$$

where Δm is the change in mass of the molecule due to the isotopic substitution at the point (x,y,z) and $\mu = M\Delta m/(M+\Delta m)$ is the reduced mass of the substituted molecule. From these equations the coordinates x,y,z of the substitution atom can then be determined.

As an example consider a linear molecule whose z axis lies along the figure axis and for which $I_{xx}^{e'} = I_{yy}^{e'}$, $I_{xx}^{e} = I_{yy}^{e}$ and $I_{zz}^{e} = I_{zz}^{e'} \approx 0$ (neglecting the contributions of the electrons). The x and y coordinates of all atoms are zero. Substituting these values into Eq. (135) we have

$$I_{xx}^{e'} = I_{xx}^{e} + \mu z_e^{2}$$

so that

$$z_e^{2} = (I_{xx}^{e'} - I_{xx}^{e})/\mu = \Delta I_{xx}^{e}/\mu \tag{136}$$

The z-coordinate of each atom in the molecule can thus be determined. Since, however, the equilibrium moments of inertia are mostly unavailable, effective moments are used to give

$$z_s^{2} = (I_{xx}^{o'} - I_{xx}^{o})/\mu = \Delta I_{xx}^{o}/\mu \tag{137}$$

The molecular structure derived by this substitution method is called the "r_s" structure and was suggested by Costain (*193*) who showed on the hand of available "r_e" structures that the "r_s" values give an acceptable approximation to the r_e values, and that they have greater consistency when overdetermined than the r_o values. The determination of the "r_s" structures is of course not limited to linear molecules and special cases of only partial substitution, substitution near a principal axis etc. are dealt with by several authors (*194*).

E. Relationship between "r_o" and "r_e" Structures

The "r_o" and "r_s" structures described in the foregoing are defined only operationally and the question arises as to how they relate to the equilibrium, or "r_e" structure. The basic connection between the "r_o" and "r_e" structures is contained in Nielsen's general theory of the vibration-rotation spectra of polyatomic molecules (*172*). Recently several workers, notably Oka and his collaborators (*195–199*), and Herschbach and Laurie (*200,201*), have reinvestigated this problem and have suggested alternative structures which are more amenable to a direct comparison with the "r_g" structure derived from electron diffraction studies. The starting point of these investigations is the Wilson-Howard form of the Hamiltonian for a vibrating-rotating polyatomic molecule namely (*202*),

$$\mathscr{H} = \tfrac{1}{2}\sum_{\alpha,\beta} \mu^{1/4}(P_\alpha - p_\alpha)\mu_{\alpha\beta}\mu^{-1/2}(P_\beta - p_\beta)\mu^{1/4} + \tfrac{1}{2}\mu^{1/4}\sum_{s} p_s\mu^{-1/2}p_s\mu^{1/4} + V \tag{138}$$

Here the P_α are the components of the rotational angular momentum along the molecule fixed axes $\alpha,\beta,\gamma(= x,y,z)$, which are defined by the Eckart conditions (*203*), the p_α are the components of the vibrational angular momenta which are related to the vibrational momenta p_s by means of the relation

$$p_\alpha = -\sum_s \sum_{s'} \zeta_{ss'}^{(\alpha)} Q_s p_{s'} \tag{139}$$

where the Q_s are the normal coordinates of the sth vibration and $\zeta_{ss'}^{\alpha}$ is the Coriolis coupling coefficient. The quantities $\mu_{\alpha\beta}$ are the elements of the inverse moment of inertia tensor of the instantaneous molecular configurations and μ is the determinant of this (inverse) tensor. Due to the vibrations of the nuclei both the $\mu_{\alpha\beta}$ and μ are functions of the nuclear coordinates and may be expanded in terms of the vibrational normal coordinates Q_s. Including second order terms the expansion about the equilibrium configurations gives

$$\mu_{\alpha\beta} = \mu_{\alpha\beta}^{(e)} - \mu_{\alpha\alpha}^{(e)}\mu_{\beta\beta}^{(e)}\left\{ \sum_s a_s^{(\alpha\beta)} Q_s + \sum_s \sum_{s'} \left[\left(A_{ss'}^{(\alpha\beta)} - \sum_{s''} \zeta_{ss''}^{(\alpha)}\zeta_{s's''}^{(\beta)} \right) - \sum_\xi \mu_{\xi\xi}^{(e)} a_s^{(\alpha\xi)} a_{s'}^{(\beta\xi)} \right] Q_s Q_{s'} \right\} \tag{140}$$

$$\mu = \mu^{(e)}\left\{ 1 - \sum_s \sum_\alpha \mu_{\alpha\alpha}^{(e)} a_s^{(\alpha\alpha)} Q_s + \sum_s \sum_{s'} \left[\sum_{\beta\gamma} \mu_{\beta\beta}^{(e)}\mu_{\gamma\gamma}^{(e)} a_s^{(\beta\gamma)} a_{s'}^{(\beta\gamma)} - \sum_\alpha \mu_{\alpha\alpha}^{(e)} \left(A_{ss'}^{(\alpha\alpha)} - \sum_{s''} \zeta_{ss''}^{(\alpha)} \zeta_{s's''}^{(\alpha)} \right) \right] Q_s Q_{s'} \right\} \tag{141}$$

where the $a_s^{(\alpha\beta)}$ and $A_{ss'}^{(\alpha\beta)}$ are the expansion coefficients of the moment of inertia $I_{\alpha\beta}$ about the equilibrium configuration

$$I_{\alpha\beta} = I_{\alpha\beta}^{(e)} + \sum_s a_s^{(\alpha\beta)} Q_s + \sum_s \sum_{s'} \left\{ A_{ss'}^{(\alpha\beta)} - \sum_{s''} \zeta_{ss''}^{(\alpha)} \zeta_{s's''}^{(\beta)} \right\} Q_s Q_{s'} \tag{142}$$

The potential energy V is similarly given up to second order terms in the Q_s by

$$V = \tfrac{1}{2}\sum_s \lambda_s Q_s^2 + hc \sum_s \sum_{s'} \sum_{s''} k_{ss's''} q_s q_{s'} q_{s''} + hc \sum_s \sum_{s'} \sum_{s''} \sum_{s'''} k_{ss's''s'''} q_s q_{s'} q_{s''} q_{s'''} \tag{143}$$

where the dimensionless normal coordinates q_s are related to the Q_s by $Q_s = (\hbar^2/\lambda_s)^{1/4} q_s$, where $\lambda_s = 4\pi^2 c^2 \omega_s{}^2$, and where the vibrational frequency ω_s and the anharmonic constants $k_{ss's''}$ and $k_{ss's''s'''}$ are given in cm^{-1}. Substitution of Eqs. (140), (141), and (143) into the expanded form of the Wilson-Howard Hamiltonian yields

$$\mathscr{H} = \mathscr{H}^{(0)} + \mathscr{H}^{(1)} + \mathscr{H}^{(2)} \tag{144}$$

where $\mathscr{H}^{(0)}$ is the zero order harmonic oscillator, rigid rotor Hamiltonian and the first and second order parts $\mathscr{H}^{(1)}$ and $\mathscr{H}^{(2)}$ comprise a perturbation on the zero order part. The perturbation calculation is facilitated by a contact transformation of the Hamiltonian $\mathscr{H}$ by means of which terms which are of second order in the vibrational quantum number v are removed and a separation of the new Hamiltonian $\mathscr{H}'$ into a vibrational and a rotational part is accomplished (*172*)

$$\mathscr{H}' = \mathscr{H}_v{}' + \mathscr{H}_R{}' \tag{145}$$

The rotational part is given by

$$\mathscr{H}_R{}' = \mathscr{H}_R^{(0)\prime} + \mathscr{H}_R^{(2)\prime} \tag{146}$$

where the zero order part is

$$\mathscr{H}_R^{(0)\prime} = \tfrac{1}{2} \sum_\alpha (P_\alpha{}^2 / I_{\alpha\alpha}^{(e)}) \tag{147}$$

and the second order part is (*196,197*)

$$\begin{aligned}\mathscr{H}_R^{(2)\prime} = \sum_{\alpha,\beta} \sum_s \Bigg\{ & \frac{1}{4\pi} \sqrt{\frac{h}{c}} \left[\frac{3k_{sss}}{\omega_s^{3/2}} a_s^{(\alpha\beta)} + \sum_{s'}{}' \frac{k_{sss'}}{\omega_{s'}^{3/2}} a_{s'}^{(\alpha\beta)} \right] \\ & + \frac{h}{2\pi^2 c} \left[\sum_{s'} \frac{\omega_{s'}^2}{\omega_s(\omega_s{}^2 - \omega_{s'}^2)} \zeta_{ss'}^{(\alpha)} \zeta_{ss'}^{(\beta)} + \frac{3}{4} \frac{A_{ss}^{(\alpha\beta)}}{\omega_s} \right] \Bigg\} \frac{P_\alpha P_\beta}{I_{\alpha\alpha}^{(e)} I_{\beta\beta}^{(e)}} (v_s + \tfrac{1}{2}) \\ & + \tfrac{1}{4} \sum_{\alpha,\beta,\gamma,\delta} \tau_{\alpha\beta\gamma\delta} P_\alpha P_\beta P_\gamma P_\delta \end{aligned} \tag{148}$$

$\mathscr{H}_R^{(0)\prime}$ is the zero order Hamiltonian which gives the rotational energies of the rigid molecule in its equilibrium configuration. The first order perturbation Hamiltonian vanishes except for a degenerate vibration in which case it is nonzero due to the Coriolis interaction between the normal coordinates of the vibration. The second order perturbation $\mathscr{H}_R^{(2)\prime}$ causes the rotational energies to be modified and gives rise to an "effective" moment of inertia $(I_{\alpha\alpha})_{\mathrm{eff}}$ which differs from the equilibrium moment $I_{\alpha\alpha}^{(e)}$. This difference is due to the following effects as explained on hand of the various terms that comprise $\mathscr{H}_R^{(2)\prime}$.

The first two terms involve the anharmonic constants k_{sss} and $k_{sss'}$. They modify the rotational energy on account of the change in the equilibrium position of the nuclei produced by the anharmonic potential. The third term gives the Coriolis interaction and the fourth term represents the mean square amplitude of vibration. The last term gives the centrifugal distortion where the $\tau_{\alpha\beta\gamma\delta}$ are the centrifugal distortion constants which have to be evaluated for each type of rotator.

Treating, therefore, the centrifugal distortion term in a formal manner we may write the rotational Hamiltonian as

$$\mathscr{H}_R' = \mathscr{H}_R^{(0)\prime} + \mathscr{H}_R^{(2)\prime} = \tfrac{1}{2} \sum_\alpha \frac{P_\alpha^{\,2}}{(I_{\alpha\alpha})_{\rm eff}} \tag{149}$$

where the "effective" moment of inertia $(I_{\alpha\alpha})_{\rm eff}$ follows in a straightforward manner from Eqs. (147) and (148), namely,

$$\begin{aligned}(I_{\alpha\alpha})_{\rm eff} = I_{\alpha\alpha}^{(e)} - \sum_s (v_s + \tfrac{1}{2}) \Bigg\{ &\frac{1}{2\pi}\sqrt{\frac{h}{c}} \left[\frac{3k_{sss}}{\omega_s^{\,3/2}} a_s^{(\alpha\alpha)} + \sum_{s'}{}' \frac{k_{sss'}}{\omega_{s'}^{3/2}} a_{s'}^{(\alpha\alpha)} \right] \\ &+ \frac{h}{\pi^2 c} \left[\sum_{s'} \frac{\omega_{s'}^{\,2}}{\omega_s(\omega_s^{\,2} - \omega_{s'}^2)} (\zeta_{ss'}^{(\alpha)})^2 + \frac{3}{4} \frac{A_{ss}^{(\alpha\alpha)}}{\omega_s} \right] \Bigg\} \\ &+ \text{centrif. dist.}\end{aligned} \tag{150}$$

For the special case of planar molecules the centrifugal distortion correction is given by *(195,197)*

$$\text{centrif. dist.} = -\frac{h^3}{8\pi^2} C_\alpha I_{\alpha\alpha}^2 \tau_{zxzx} \tag{151}$$

with $C_x = C_z = -2$ and $C_y = 3$. In general, to second order of approximation, the centrifugal distortion correction is independent of the vibrational states. The vibration-rotation interaction constant α_s [called α_i in Eq. (126)] is the coefficient of $(v_s + \frac{1}{2})$ in Eq. (150) or

$$\begin{aligned}\alpha_s = &\frac{1}{2\pi}\sqrt{\frac{h}{c}} \left[\frac{3k_{sss}}{\omega_s^{\,3/2}} a_s^{(\alpha\alpha)} + \sum_{s'}{}' \frac{k_{sss'}}{\omega_{s'}^{3/2}} a_{s'}^{(\alpha\alpha)} \right] \\ &+ \frac{h}{\pi^2 c} \left[\sum_{s'} \frac{\omega_{s'}^2}{\omega_s(\omega_s^{\,2} - \omega_{s'}^2)} (\zeta_{ss'}^{(\alpha)})^2 + \frac{3}{4} \frac{A_{ss}^{(\alpha\alpha)}}{\omega_s} \right]\end{aligned} \tag{152}$$

[Here $(\alpha\alpha) = (xx), (yy), (zz)$ is not to be confused with the interaction constant α_s.] The equilibrium moment of inertia is thus modified by the vibrational anharmonicities (first two terms) and the harmonic contributions due to the Coriolis interactions (third term) and the mean square amplitudes of vibration (fourth term), in addition to the centrifugal distortion. For symmetric top molecules the centrifugal distortion contribution is separable from the rigid rotor terms and appears in the form of the constants D_J, D_{JK}, and D_K of Eq. (62b). For the nonrigid asymmetric top rotor the energy can not be written as the sum of a rigid rotor term plus the centrifugal stretching terms. However, the first order calculation of centrifugal distortion effects due to Kivelson and Wilson (*173*) allows this separation [see Eq. (114)] with a good deal of accuracy and the majority of the centrifugal distortion calculations that have been performed were made with the aid of their formalism. The "r_o" structure derived from the ground state moments of inertia $I_a^{\,0}$, $I_b^{\,0}$, $I_c^{\,0}$ thus contains the harmonic and anharmonic contributions of Eq. (152) produced by each vibrational state and the relationship to the "r_e" structure is thus seen to be quite complicated.

F. The "r_z" Structure

Since the anharmonic terms of Eq. (152) describe real shifts of the positions of the nuclei while the harmonic terms do not, Oka et al. (*195–199*) suggest the use of a ground state moment of inertia $I_{\alpha\alpha}^{\text{zero}}$ which is obtained by subtracting the harmonic contribution from the effective moment of inertia $(I_{\alpha\alpha})_{\text{eff}}$, i.e.,

$$I_{\alpha\alpha}^{z} = I_{\alpha\alpha}^{(e)} - \sum_{s} (v_s + \tfrac{1}{2}) \cdot \frac{1}{2\pi}\sqrt{\frac{h}{c}} \times \left\{ \frac{3k_{sss}}{\omega_s^{3/2}}\, a_s^{(\alpha\alpha)} + \sum_{s'} \frac{k_{sss'}}{\omega_{s'}^{3/2}}\, a_{s'}^{(\alpha\alpha)} \right\} \tag{153}$$

The structure derived from $I_{\alpha\alpha}^{z}$ is called the "r_z" structure.

The usefulness of the "r_z" structure lies in the fact that it represents a structure which is an average over the ground vibrational state. If $\alpha_i (= x_i, y_i, z_i)$ represents the Cartesian coordinate of the ith atom then its average value $\langle \alpha_i \rangle$ is given by (*199*)

$$\langle \alpha_i \rangle = \alpha_i^{e} - \sum_{s} \frac{l_{is}^{(\alpha)}}{\sqrt{m_i}} \left(\frac{h}{4\pi^2 c \omega_s} \right)^{1/2} \times \frac{1}{\omega_s} \left\{ 3k_{sss}(v_s + \tfrac{1}{2}) + \sum_{s'}{}' \, k_{sss'}\,(v_s + d_s/2) \right\} \tag{154}$$

where $\alpha_i^{\,e}$ is the equilibrium value of α_i, m_i is the mass of the ith atom, $l_{is}^{(\alpha)}$ is the transformation coefficient that links the Cartesian displacement coordinate of the ith atom $\Delta\alpha_i$ to the normal coordinate Q_s and d_s is the degeneracy of the vibration ($d_s = 1, 2$ for nondegenerate and doubly degenerate vibrations respectively). If these average Cartesian coordinates are used to calculate the moment of inertia from the relation $I^z_{\alpha\alpha} = \sum_i m_i[\langle\beta_i\rangle^2 + \langle\gamma_i\rangle^2]$ the result is the same as that given by Eq. (153) if fourth-order terms are neglected. The "r_z" structure, therefore, gives the molecular configuration averaged over the ground vibrational state, with the neglect of the angular momentum of the degenerate vibrations. Using a slightly different procedure Herschbach and Laurie (*200*) arrived at the same conclusion and also demonstrated the usefulness of the structure (called "average," or $\langle r\rangle$, structure by them) on hand of specific examples (*201*).

G. The "r_g" Structure

Advances in the electron diffraction technique of determining molecular structures have paralleled those of the spectroscopic technique. These advances also caused parallel difficulties in the interpretation of the electron diffraction results. While the spectroscopic technique is in principle capable of providing the r_e structure from spectroscopic data only (to be sure, these must be the ground state rotation constants and the vibration-rotation interaction constants for all fundamental vibrations, a complete set of which is very difficult to obtain), the interatomic distances derived from electron diffraction studies are not r_e-values, but are some average distances which are modified by the effect of thermal motions. Several distance parameters are, therefore, used in electron diffraction analyses: $r_{\max}$, which is the distance derived from the peak maxima of the radial distribution curve; $r_g(1)$, which is the distance derived from the centers of gravity of the peaks of the radial distribution curve; and $r_g(0)$, henceforth simply called r_g, which is obtained from the centers of gravity of the peaks of the probability distribution curve (*204,205*).

If Δx, Δy, and Δz are the instantaneous relative displacements of two atoms which form a bond and the z axis of the Cartesian coordinates is taken along the equilibrium positions of the nuclei then the average value of the instantaneous distance between the nuclei (the bond length) taken over the probability distribution function is given by (*198*)

$$r_g \equiv \langle r\rangle = r_e + \delta r + \langle\Delta z\rangle + \frac{1}{2r_e}[\langle\Delta x^2\rangle + \langle\Delta y^2\rangle] + \dots \qquad (155)$$

where δr represents a contribution due to centrifugal distortion. Since the Cartesian displacement coordinates of the ith atom $\Delta\alpha_i (= \Delta x_i, \Delta y_i, \Delta z_i)$

are linearly related to the normal coordinate Q_s of the sth mode of vibration, viz., $\sqrt{m_i}\Delta\alpha_i = \sum_s l_{is}^{(\alpha)} Q_s$ where m_i is the mass of the ith atom and $l_{is}^{(\alpha)}$ is the transformation coefficient, and since $\langle Q_s \rangle = 0$ for harmonic oscillator wave functions, it is seen that the quantity $\langle \Delta z \rangle$ is determined by the anharmonic part of the vibrational potential. The quantities $\langle \Delta x^2 \rangle$ and $\langle \Delta y^2 \rangle$, however, do not vanish for harmonic oscillator wavefunctions. Thus, while $\langle \Delta z \rangle$ modifies the bond length due to the vibrational anharmonicity, $\langle \Delta x^2 \rangle$ and $\langle \Delta y^2 \rangle$ come from the motions of the atoms perpendicular to the bonds by which the mean positions of the nuclei do not change. The harmonic contributions are readily assessed since quadratic force constants are usually available. The "r_g" structure is then easily compared to the "r_z" structure derived from spectroscopic data. Bartell and co-workers (*204–209*) have performed detailed calculations of the anharmonic effects as well as the effects produced by isotopic substitution on the "r_g" structure derived from diffraction data.

H. The "r_o" Structures of Molecules Derived from Raman Spectra

The previous sections dealt briefly with the different types of structural data that are now found in the literature. Typically the infrared and Raman spectroscopic method give "r_o" structures since a complete set of vibration-rotation interaction constants necessary for the determination of the equilibrium moments of inertia and hence the "r_e" structure is not available. Similarly the "r_s" structure is primarily derived through microwave spectroscopic data.

From the observed rotation constant, say B_o, one obtains

$$I_b{}^0 = \frac{27.9890}{B_o} \times 10^{-40} \text{g cm}^2 \tag{156}$$

when B_o is given in cm^{-1}. Similar expressions are given also for $I_a{}^0$ and $I_c{}^0$ in terms of the A_o and C_o rotation constants. Table 20 lists the r_o bond lengths of linear molecules obtained from the B_o values in Table 6. In some cases equilibrium values are also given. Invariably these were obtained by combining the Raman data with those obtained by the infrared and microwave techniques.

Table 21 gives the r_o structures for most of the molecules whose ground state B_o values are listed in Tables 8, 14, and 17. Here additional complications arise in that more structural parameters are to be determined than the number of available rotation constants permits. Recourse is then had to specific assumptions or the structure is only partially determined.

An assumption that is customarily made is that C—H and C—D bond lengths in a molecule and its isotopic variants are the same. The degree to which this assumption is justified in deducing the r_o structure is best exemplified by methane CH_4 and its isotopic variants CD_4 and CH_3D, and by ethane, both C_2H_6 and C_2D_6. For CH_4 and CD_4 r_o(C—H) > r_o(C—D) by 0.002 Å which is outside the error limits given

TABLE 20

Bond Lengths for Linear Molecules Studied in the Raman Effect[a]

Molecule	Parameter	r_e	r_o	Reference
H_2	(H—H)	0.74173	0.75105	(*124*)
HD	(H—D)	0.74173	0.74973	(*124*)
D_2	(D—D)	0.74165	0.74820	(*124*)
N_2	(N≡N)	1.0975_8	1.1000_6	(*114*)
F_2	(F—F)		1.418	(*115*)
CO_2	(C=O)	1.1600[b]	1.162	(*29*)
CS_2	(C=S)	1.5529 ± 0.0005[c]	1.5545 ± 0.0003	(*125*)
C_2H_2	(C—H)	1.0585	1.061	(*117*)
	(C≡C)	1.2047	1.207	
C_2HI	(C—H)		1.055 (assumed)	(*129*)
	(C—I)		1.988 ± 0.002	
	(C≡C)		1.203 (assumed)	
C_2N_2	(C≡N)		1.157 (assumed)	(*119*)
(cyanogen)	(C—C)		1.380[d]	
C_4H_2	(C—H)		1.046 ± 0.009	(*117*)
(diacetylene)	(C—C)		1.376 ± 0.002	
	(C≡C)		1.205 (assumed)	

[a] In Å; only principal reference on Raman work is cited in last column.
[b] Obtained by C. Courtoy, Ref. (*210*), from study of infrared vibration-rotation spectrum.
[c] Quoted by Stoicheff, Ref. (*211*).
[d] Electron diffraction value $r_g = 1.38 \pm 0{,}02$ Å, Ref. (*212*).

for these bond lengths. The same holds true for C_2H_6 and C_2D_6 where the bond lengths are obtained subject to the assumption that the angles $\angle$HCH = $\angle$DCD. On the basis of these differences it is probably safe to state that C—H bond lengths that are derived from ground state rotation constants for several isotopic species of a molecule cannot be more accurately determined than within 0.002 Å which is most often less than the quoted error.

TABLE 21

Molecular Structures of Polyatomic Molecules Studied in the Raman Effect[a]

Molecule	Parameter	r_o	Ref.	r_g	Ref.
CH_4	r(C—H)	1.09397 ± 0.00005	(*62*)	1.106_8	(*206*)
CD_4	r(C—D)	1.0918 ± 0.0003	(*164*)	1.102_7	
CH_3D	r(C—H)	1.0937 ± 0.002	(*82*)		
	r(C—D)	1.0928 ± 0.002			
	∠HCD	assumed tetrahedral			
C_2H_6,C_2D_6	r(C—H)	1.095 ± 0.002	(*213*)	1.1122 ± 0.0012	(*214*)
(ethane)[b]	r(C—D)	1.093 ± 0.001		1.107 ± 0.0012	
	r(C–C)	1.534 ± 0.002		1.5340 ± 0.0011	
	∠HCH	107.8° ± 0.2°		*c*	
	∠DCD	= ∠HCH (assumed)		*c*	
C_2H_4,C_2D_4	r(C—H)	1.086 ± 0.003	(*180*)	1.103_0 ± 0.002	(*215*)
(ethylene)[d]		1.086 ± 0.003	(*184*) IR		
	r(C—D)	assumed = r(C—H)		1.099 ± 0.003	
	r(C=C)	1.339 ± 0.002	(*180*)	1.336 ± 0.002[e]	
		1.337 ± 0.003	(*184*) IR	1.338 ± 0.003[f]	
	∠CCH	121.2° ± 0.25°	(*180*)	120.7° ± 0.6°	
		121.3° ± 0.5°	(*184*) IR		
	∠CCD	assumed = ∠CCH		120.9° ± 0.8°	
C_3H_4,C_3D_4	r(C=C)	1.308_8 ± 0.001	(*140*)	1.312[g]	(*217*)
(allene)		1.308_4 ± 0.003	(*74*) IR		(*218*)
	r(C—H)	1.07 ± 0.01	(*140*)	1.082[g]	
		1.087_2 ± 0.0013	(*74*) IR		
	∠HCH	117° ± 1.5°	(*140*)	120.8°[g]	
		118.2° ± 0.2°	(*74*) IR		
C_4H_6,C_4D_6	r(C—C)	1.476 ± 0.01[h]	(*175*)	1.467_2[j]	(*219*)[j]

TABLE 21 (*cont.*)

Molecule	Parameter	r_o	Ref.	r_g	Ref.
(1,3-*trans*-butadiene)		1.464 ± 0.003	(*175a*)		
	r(C=C)	(assumed)[h,i]		1.343_4[j]	
	r(C—H)			1.094_4[j]	
	∠C=C—C	$122.9° \pm 0.5°$[h]	(*175*)	$122.8_6° \pm 0.5°$[j]	
		$123.2° \pm 0.2°$[i]	(*175a*)		
	∠H—C=C			$119.5° \pm 1.0°$[j]	
C_4H_4	r(=C=C=)	1.284 ± 0.006[k]	(*176*)	1.238 ± 0.005	(*220*)
(butatriene)	r(—C=C=)	(assumed)[k]		1.318 ± 0.005	
	r(C—H)	(assumed)[k]		1.083 ± 0.005	
$Zn(CH_3)_2$,$Zn(CD_3)_2$	r(Zn—C)[l]	1.929 ± 0.004	(*92*)		
(dimethylzinc)	r(C—H)	1.09 ± 0.02 (assumed)			
	∠HCH	$107.7° \pm 1.0°$			
$Cd(CH_3)_2$,$Cd(CD_3)_2$	r(Cd—C)[m]	2.111 ± 0.004	(*92*)		
(dimethylcadmium)	r(C—H)	1.09 ± 0.02 (assumed)			
	∠HCH	$108.4° \pm 1.0°$			
$Hg(CH_3)_2$,$Hg(CD_3)_2$	r(Hg—C)[n]	2.094 ± 0.005	(*92*)		
(dimethylmercury)	r(C—H)	1.09 ± 0.02 (assumed)			
	∠HCH	$109.3° \pm 1.0°$			
C_3H_6,C_3D_6	r(C—C)	1.514 ± 0.002[o]	(*141*)	$1.509_6 \pm 0.003$[p]	(*221*)
(cyclopropane)	r(C—H)	1.082 ± 0.003		$1.088_8 \pm 0.003_2$	
	∠HCH	$116.2° \pm 0.3°$ (assumed)		$115.1_2° \pm 1.0_1°$	
	∠CCH			$117.6_8° \pm 0.4_2°$	
C_4H_8,C_4D_8	r(C—C)	1.558 ± 0.003[q]	(*142*)	1.548 ± 0.003[s]	(*222*)
(cyclobutane)	r(C—H)	1.097[r]		1.092 ± 0.010[s]	
	∠HCH	$116 \pm 2°$			
C_5H_{10},C_5D_{10}	r(C—C)	$1.537_0 \pm 0.002$[t]	(*87*)	1.539 ± 0.003[v]	(*222*)
(cyclopentane)	r(C—H)	*u*		1.095 ± 0.010[v]	

C_6H_{12},C_6D_{12}	r(C—C)	[illegible]	[illegible]	[illegible]	[illegible]
(cyclohexane)				1.53 ± 0.01[y]	(224)
	r(C—H)	x		1.104 ± 0.005[y]	(223)
				1.09 ± 0.02[y]	(224)
	∠CCC	111.55° (assumed)		111.55° ± 0.15°[y]	(223)
				111.5° ± 1.5°[y]	(224)
	∠CCH			107° ± 2°[y]	(224)
C_6H_6,C_6D_6	r(C═C)	$1.397_3 \pm 0.001$	(143)	1.4000	(225)
(benzene)	r(C—H)	1.084 ± 0.006		1.0897	
$C_6H_3F_3$					
(1,3,5-trifluorobenzene)	r(C—F)	1.304[z]	(144a)	1.305 ± 0.010	(225a)
	r(C═C)			1.402 ± 0.005	
C_6F_6					
(hexafluorobenzene)	r(C—F)	1.321[aa]	(144a)	1.324 ± 0.006	(225a)
	r(C═C)			1.408 ± 0.006	(225a)
$C_3N_3H_3,C_3N_3D_3$	r(C—H)	1.084 ± 0.009(ass.)[ab]	(145)		
(sym-triazine)	r(C═N)	$1.338_1 \pm 0.001$			
	∠NCN	126.8° ± 0.4°			
	∠CNC	113.2° ± 0.4°			
$C_3N_3F_3$					
(cyanuric Fluoride)	r(C—F)	1.271[ac]	(144b)	1.310 ± 0.008	(225a)
	r(C═N)			1.333 ± 0.009	

[a] Bond lengths are given in Å. r_0 values are determined from Raman or IR = infrared spectroscopy. r_g values are determined with the electron diffraction technique. Rotation constants A_0, B_0, C_0 are listed in Tables 8, 14, and 17.

[b] Rotation constants for CH_3CD_3 were judged not to be of sufficient accuracy to be useful for a more refined analysis (*96*).

[c] ∠CCH = ∠CCD = 111.0 ± 0.2° from Electron Diffraction, (*214*).

[d] Structures reported are derived from rotational Raman Spectrum (*180*), infrared vibration-rotation spectrum (*184*), and electron diffraction (*215*) data. The average, r_z structure of ethylene has been computed by Kuchitsu (*216*) by correcting the r_g values of Bartell *et al*. (*215*) for the effect of atomic displacements perpendicular to the equilibrium bond directions and the centrifugal distortion, and also by correcting the spectroscopic r_0 structure for the vibration-rotation interaction. The structure thus obtained is: r_z(C═C = 1.335 ± 0.003 Å, r_z(C—H = 1.090 = 0.003 Å, $\angle_z$CCH = 121.7° ± 0.4° and $\angle_z$HCH = 116.6° ± 0.8. The $r_\alpha{}^0$ structure suggested by Morino *et al*. (*198*) is found from the electron diffraction (r_g) data of Bartell (*215*) to be $r_x{}^0$(C═C) = $1.335_6 \pm 0.002$ Å, $r_\alpha{}^0$(C—H) = $1.089_8 \pm 0.002$ Å, and $\angle_\alpha{}^0$HCH = 121.4° ± 0.6°.

[e] Value determined for C_2H_4.

[f] Value determined for C_2D_4.

[g] These values are r_{max} values, determined from the peaks of the radial distribution curve. The value r_g(=C=C=) = 1.3128 ~ 1.3114 Å has been computed by Morino *et al.* (*218*) by correcting the r_{max} values for the Bastiansen-Morino shrinkage effect.

[h] Structure calculated from Raman and infrared data under the following assumptions: (1) Molecule is planar and $I_c = I_a + I_b$; (2) all r(C—H) = 1.085 Å; and (3) the angles ∠HCH = ∠CCH = 120° and r(C=C) = 1.337±0.005 Å from electron diffraction (*219a*).

[i] Structure calculated from Raman and infrared data assuming that r(C=C) = 1.338 Å from electron diffraction, and ∠H—C—H = 118°.

[j] Recently Kuchitsu, Fukuyama, and Morino (*219b*) determined the r_α^0 and r_{ave} structures for butadiene. Their results are, for the r_α^0 and r_{ave} structures respectively: r(C—C) = 1.4626 and 1.4627 Å, r(C=C) = 1.3419 and 1.3405 Å, r(C—H) = 1.093 and 1.0904 Å; and for the angles ∠(C=C—C)=123.63° and 123.33°, ∠(H—C=C)^{trans} = 120.9° and 122.4°, ∠(H—C=C)^{cis} = 120.9° and 120.0°, and ∠(H—C=C)$_{H\text{-atom geminal to C-atom}}$ = 120.9° and 123.0°.

[k] Values r(C—H) = 1.07±0.01 Å, r(H_2C=C=) = 1.309±0.003 Å, and ∠HCH = 117±1.5° assumed from Raman results on Allene (*140*).

[l] Value of r(Zn—C) is obtained independent of assumed r(C—H) value.

[m] Value of r(Cd—C) is obtained independent of r(C—H) value.

[n] Value of r(Hg—C) is obtained independent of assumed r(C—H) value.

[o] r(C—C) is independent of assumed value for r(C—H).

[p] The electron diffraction values, called r_a-values by Bastiansen *et al.* (*221*), are derived from intensity curves using least squares refinement.

[q] r(C—C) is independent of assumed value for r(C—H) and is the same for both D_{4h} and D_{2d} symmetry.

[r] For an assumed D_{4h} structure and empirical relationship between average CH stretching frequency and CH bond length given by Bernstein, (*226*).

[s] Not r_g values. Values were determined from intensity and radial distribution curves (*222*).

[t] r(C—C) is independent of assumed r(C—H) value.

[u] For an assumed value of r(C—H) = 1.09 Å; ∠HCH = 113°.

[v] Not r_g values. Values were determined from intensity and radial distribution curves (*222*). Recent electron diffraction studies by Wade J. Adams, Ph.D. Thesis, University of Michigan, 1969, gave the following results: r_g(C—H) = $1.113_5 \pm 0.001_5$ Å, r_g(C—C) = $1.546 \pm 0.001_2$ Å, ∠CCH = 111.7±0.2°, and for the ring puckering amplitude, q_H = $0.43_5 \pm 0.01$ Å.

[w] r(C—C) is independent of assumed r(C—H) value but depends on the assumed value for the CCC angle (111.55°).

[x] The C—H bond length is functionally related to the HCH angle. Using the electron diffraction value r(C—H) = 1.104 Å, then ∠HCH = 102°.

[y] Not r_g values. Determined from maxima of radial distribution curve.

[z] Computed assuming D_{3h} point group and with r_0(C—C) and r_0(C—H) values of benzene (*143*).

[aa] Computed assuming D_{6h} point group and with r_0(C—C) value of benzene (*143*).

[ab] Value of r(C=N) is only slightly dependent on the assumed value of r(C—H). Both angles ∠CNC and ∠NCN depend strongly on assumed value of r(C—H). Quoted parameters are the result of combined Raman spectroscopic and X-Ray diffraction data.

[ac] Computed assuming D_{3h} point group and using values of C—N ring parameters of sym-triazine (*145*).

Even with the assumption that both the bond lengths and the interbond angles for the isotopic molecules are the same most often there are more structural parameters to be determined than there are independently determined rotation constants. Thus, for dimethyl-zinc, -cadmium, and -mercury r(C-metal), r(C—H), and $\angle$HCH are to be determined and similarly for the cyclic molecules cyclopropane, cyclobutane, cyclopentane and cyclohexane the bond lengths r(C—C), r(C—H) and the angles $\angle$HCH and $\angle$HCC as well as $\angle$CCC are to be determined from only two rotation constants, for the parent molecule and the fully deuterated molecule. For these cases the carbon-metal and carbon-carbon bond length can be determined uniquely but the carbon-hydrogen bond length and the HCH angle are related to one another. Thus, for example, the moment of inertia I_b^{H} of cyclopentane, C_5H_{10}, about an axis lying in the plane of the carbon ring (D_{5h} symmetry is assumed) is given by (*87,131*)

$$I_b^{\mathrm{H}} = ar(\mathrm{C{-}C})^2 + br(\mathrm{C{-}H})^2 + c.r(\mathrm{C{-}H})r(\mathrm{C{-}C}) \qquad (157a)$$

where

$$a = 2m_{\mathrm{C}}(\sin^2\beta + 0.25) + 4m_{\mathrm{H}}(\sin^2\beta + 0.25) \qquad (157b)$$

$$b = m_{\mathrm{H}}[10\sin^2\alpha + 16\cos^2\alpha\cos^2\beta\,(\sin^2\beta + 0.25)] \qquad (157c)$$

and

$$c = 16m_{\mathrm{H}}\cos\alpha\cos\beta\,(\sin^2\beta + 0.25) \qquad (157d)$$

Here m_{H} and m_{C} are the masses of the hydrogen and carbon atoms, respectively, and $2\alpha = \angle$HCH and $2\beta = \angle\mathrm{CCC} = 108°$ (for a regular pentagon). The same expressions are obtained for I_b^{D}, the moment of inertia of the fully deuterated molecule C_5D_{10}, by substituting for m_{H} the mass of the deuterium atom m_{D}. Without any further assumptions as regards the C—H bond length and the HCH angle, the C—C bond length can then be computed from the relation

$$r(\mathrm{C-C}) = \left[\frac{\mu I_b^{\mathrm{H}} - I_b^{\mathrm{D}}}{2(\mu - 1)m_{\mathrm{C}}(\sin^2\beta + 0.25)}\right]^{1/2} \qquad (158)$$

where $\mu = M_{\mathrm{D}}/M_{\mathrm{H}}$. Using the B_o values for C_5H_{10} and C_5D_{10} given in Table 8 and relation (156) one then obtains the result r(C—C) = $1.537_0 \pm 0.0024$ Å. This value of r(C−C) when substituted into Eq. (157a) provides a rather complicated relation between r(C—H) and the angle $\angle$HCH and use is now made of plausibility arguments on the value of $\angle$HCH in order to obtain an r(C—H) value or vice versa. Thus, if the methylene group angle is taken to be tetrahedral ($\angle$HCH = 109°28′) then r(C—H) = 1.083 Å whereas if we assume that r(C—H) = 1.09 Å then $\angle$HCH = 113°. This latter result seems to be more plausible since it is more consistent with the electron diffraction values of r(C—H) obtained for cyclobutane, cyclopentane, and cyclohexane.

For more complicated situations, structures have been derived by combining data from vibration-rotation bands, from electron and X-ray diffraction work as well as from microwave studies. Thus, the structure of trans-butadiene is derived by combining the pure rotational Raman result for $\tilde{B}_0$ (Table 17) with the value for $(A_0 - B_0)$ derived from the out-of-plane wagging vibration (A_u species) of the C—CH_2 groups observed in the infrared spectrum at 908 cm^{-1} (*175,175a*), and the (old) electron diffraction value r(C=C) = 1.338 Å derived from the maxima of the radial distribution curve (*219a*). For cyclobutane it was necessary to utilize the empirical relationship between the average C—H stretching frequency and the C—H bond length given by Bernstein (*226*) to obtain the values for the C—H bond length and the HCH angle for an assumed D_{4h} model of the molecule.

A comparison of the spectroscopic r_0 values with the structures derived from the electron diffraction analyses is not easy. As described in the previous sections the r_0 structures are not strictly comparable to the r_g structures and the agreement or disagreement between them must be taken with a grain of salt. The most accurately determined structures are those of methane, ethane and ethylene and here the comparison shows that for the carbon-hydrogen bond $r_g = r_0 + 0.014$ Å on the average while for the C—C and C=C bonds $r_g = r_0$ within the quoted errors.

The body of structural data that has thus far been accumulated has been reviewed by Stoicheff (*211*) who finds that the carbon-carbon bond lengths in open chain molecules can be represented by empirical formulae which take into account the variation of bond length with environment. For carbon-carbon single and double bonds these relations are

$$r(\text{C—C}) = 1.299 + 0.040n, \qquad n = 2, 3, \ldots, 6, \tag{159}$$

$$r(\text{C=C}) = 1.226 + 0.028n, \qquad n = 2, 3, 4 \tag{160}$$

where n is the number of adjacent bonds. These relations give most of the bond lengths to ± 0.005 Å.

VI. DYNAMICAL ASPECTS OF STRUCTURE DETERMINATION

A. Introduction

The static parameters of a molecular structure, viz, the bond lengths and the interbond angles, are determined by the electron distribution in the molecule which also governs the dynamics of vibration and rotation. The vibrational force constants are intimately related to the centrifugal distortion and Coriolis coupling effects and these relationships have often proven to be useful in structure analysis. Thus, the structure determinations by means of microwave spectroscopy usually rely on the frequencies of low-J transitions in which the centrifugal distortion effects are assumed to be ignorable and the centrifugal distortion constants are then not determined. The availability of these experimentally determined constants would, however, aid in establishing a reliable force field for the molecule. Wherever theoretically computed centrifugal distortion constants have been compared with the experimentally determined values the agreement has generally been good. On the other hand significant disagreements, as in chloroform, indicated a discrepancy in the analysis of the microwave data. The pure rotational Raman spectrum provides a reasonably accurate value for the D_J constant since transitions with J ranging up to 100 can be observed for heavy molecules.

The analysis of the pure rotational spectrum as well as of the totally symmetric vibration-rotation bands of symmetric top molecules provides only the moment of inertia I_b about an axis perpendicular to the symmetry axis of the molecule. The determination of A-values and hence the moment of inertia I_a about the symmetry axis is possible through the analysis of the doubly degenerate vibration-rotation bands. Thus, the spacing of the pertinent Q-branch transitions (see Table 3) is determined by the A-value which can be determined by combining the Q-branch spacings for the $\Delta K = \pm 1$ and $\Delta K = \pm 2$ transitions. It is seen that these expressions also contain the Coriolis coefficients ζ which are then determined simultaneously with the A-values. In practice, however, the spectra are often incomplete and poorly resolved and thus do not lend themselves to an unambiguous analysis. Moreover, since the doubly degenerate bands occur in the infrared with the more restrictive selection rule $\Delta K = \pm 1$ the A and ζ values cannot be determined individually. Recourse is therefore often had to the zeta sum rules to reduce the number of independent constants that must be determined. In addition, individual zeta constants can be computed theoretically from the vibrational normal coordinates and their incorporation into the body of known data is of assistance in the analysis. For bands which are not resolved into their Q-branch structure calculations of the intensity profile have been performed in an attempt to deduce the ζ value for that band (see the discussion on cyclopropane, Sec. IV, C, 2). More fruitful were the intensity calculations for the degenerate bands of ethane C_2H_6, C_2D_6, and CH_3CD_3 (see the discussion on pp. 637-644 and

Figs. 11,12,14, and 15) which materially aided in the interpretation of the spectra and the determination of the molecular structure. As these problems are part and parcel of the analysis of a vibration-rotation Raman spectrum we briefly discuss in this section the theory of the centrifugal distortion and Coriolis coupling effects to the extent that they can be described by a harmonic force field. Since both the centrifugal distortion and the Coriolis coupling are governed by the vibrational force field a discussion of these effects must be preceded by a normal coordinate analysis which is outlined below.

B. Normal Coordinate Analysis

For polyatomic molecules the *FG* matrix method of normal coordinate analysis developed by Wilson (*227,228*) has proven to be exceedingly successful. Using the intuitively understood valence internal coordinates, the most common of which are the changes in the chemical bond lengths, interbond angles, and the angles which describe the torsion about a bond and the out-of-plane displacements of an atom, the method enables the construction of the kinetic energy function in a routine manner while at the same time allowing a physical meaning to be given to at least the principal force constants in the potential energy function. The calculation of the centrifugal distortion and Coriolis coupling effects in terms of the *FG* matrix formalism is now universal for all those problems which can be treated within the framework of the harmonic oscillator approximation.

Let x_a represent the Cartesian displacement coordinates of an atom of mass m_a, where the index $a = 1, 2, 3, \ldots, 3N$ and where N is the number of atoms comprising the molecule. In terms of the mass reduced displacement coordinates

$$q_a = \sqrt{m_a} x_a \qquad (a = 1, 2, 3, \ldots, 3N) \tag{161}$$

the kinetic energy is given by

$$2T = \sum_{a,b}^{3N} \dot{q}_a \dot{q}_b \, \delta_{ab} \qquad (a, b = 1, 2, \ldots 3N) \tag{162}$$

Of the $3N$ degrees of freedom there are $(3N-6)$ degrees which describe the internal, relative, motions of the atoms to one another while the remaining six degrees of freedom describe the overall translations and rotations of the rigid molecule in space. We define a set of $(3N-6)$ internal coordinates S_i by means of the transformation

$$S_i = \sum_{a}^{3N} D_{ia} q_a \qquad (i = 1, 2, 3, \ldots, 3N-6) \tag{163}$$

where the coefficients D_{ia} form a $(3N-6)\times 3N$ rectangular matrix. The six coordinates T_x, T_y, T_z, and R_x, R_y, R_z which describe the translations and rotations respectively with reference to the three coordinate axes may be added to the internal coordinates S_i to give a generalized displacement vector of $3N$ components, the transpose of whose matrix is

$$\tilde{\mathbf{S}} = \mathbf{S}(S_1, S_2, S_3, \ldots S_{3N-6}, T_x, T_y, T_z, R_x, R_y, R_z) \qquad (164)$$

The displacement vector **S** is then given in terms of the mass reduced Cartesian displacement coordinates q by means of the transformation

$$S_b = \sum_a^{3N} D_{ba} q_a \qquad (b = 1, 2, 3, \ldots 3N) \qquad (165)$$

where the D_{ba} form a $3N \times 3N$ matrix. The x, y, z coordinate system that is used here must be such that the interaction between vibration and rotation is minimized. This is assured by means of the Eckart conditions (*203*) which require that $T_x = T_y = T_z = R_x = R_y = R_z = 0$. Since the coordinates q_a and S_b are independent, the transformation D is nonsingular and we may express the q_a's in terms of the S_b's. Using two indexes $i = 1, 2, 3, \ldots 3N-6$ and $p = 3N-5, \ldots 3N$ to replace the single index $a(= 1, 2, \ldots 3N)$ in order to separate out the internal, vibrational coordinates from the external rigid body translation and rotational coordinates we have for the Cartesian displacements

$$q_a = \sum_i^{3N-6} (D^{-1})_{ai} S_i \qquad (166)$$

since the $S_p(= T_x, \ldots, R_z) = 0$. Equation (162) for the kinetic energy then becomes in the internal coordinates

$$2T = \sum_{a,b}^{3N} \dot{q}_a \dot{q}_b \, \delta_{ab} = \sum_{i,j}^{3N-6} (g^{-1})_{ij} \, \dot{S}_i \dot{S}_j \qquad (167)$$

where the metric coefficients $(g^{-1})_{ij}$ are given by

$$(g^{-1})_{ij} = \sum_{a,b}^{3N} (D^{-1})_{ai} (D^{-1})_{bj} \, \delta_{ab} \qquad (168)$$

Polo (*229*) has given a method for the calculation of the elements of the D^{-1} matrix but it is more convenient to write the kinetic energy in terms of the momenta conjugate to the internal coordinates. First, however, we want to introduce the Wilson **s**-vector which materially facilitates the computations.

Let the instantaneous position of the nth atom ($n = 1, 2, \ldots, N$) in the molecule with respect to the center of mass be given by

$$\mathbf{r}_n = \mathbf{r}_n^{\,e} + \mathbf{d}_n \tag{169}$$

where $\mathbf{r}_n^{\,e}$ is the position vector of the atom for the equilibrium configuration and $\mathbf{d}_n$ is the displacement away from equilibrium. The unit vectors along the Cartesian coordinates are designated by $\mathbf{e}_\alpha(\alpha = x, y, z)$. Splitting now the index $a(= 1, 2, \ldots 3N)$ into two indexes $n(= 1, 2, \ldots N)$ and $\alpha(= x, y, z)$ we have for the Cartesian displacement x_a of Eq. (161)

$$x_{n\alpha} = \mathbf{e}_\alpha \cdot \mathbf{d}_n \tag{170}$$

and the internal coordinates S_i are then, from Eq. (163)

$$S_i = \sum_{n,\alpha=x,y,z}^{N} D_{i,n\alpha} q_{n\alpha} = \sum_{n,\alpha=x,y,z}^{N} D_{i,n\alpha} \sqrt{m_n} x_{n\alpha} \tag{171}$$

or

$$S_i = \sum_{n}^{N} \mathbf{s}_{in} \cdot \mathbf{d}_n \tag{172}$$

where the Wilson s-vector is

$$\mathbf{s}_{in} = \sum_{\alpha=x,y,z} D_{i,n\alpha} \sqrt{m_n}\, \mathbf{e}_\alpha \tag{173}$$

As was shown by Malhiot and Ferigle (*230*) these s-vectors have the property that

$$\sum_{n}^{N} \mathbf{s}_{in} = 0 \tag{174}$$

and

$$\sum_{n}^{N} \mathbf{r}_n^{\,e} \times \mathbf{s}_{in} = 0 \tag{175}$$

These relations express the Eckart conditions and insure that the coupling between rotation and vibration is minimized when generalized internal rather than Cartesian coordinates are used to describe the motions of the molecule.

Turning now to the kinetic energy we have from Eq. (162) for the momenta

$$p_a = \frac{\partial T}{\partial \dot{q}_a} = \dot{q}_a \tag{176}$$

so that

$$2T = \sum_{a,b}^{3N} p_a p_b \delta_{ab} \tag{177}$$

On the other hand using Eq. (163) for the relation between the internal and mass reduced Cartesian coordinates we have

$$p_a = \frac{\partial T}{\partial \dot{q}_a} = \sum_b^{3N} \frac{\partial T}{\partial \dot{S}_b} \frac{\partial \dot{S}_b}{\partial \dot{q}_a} = \sum_i^{3N-6} \frac{\partial T}{\partial \dot{S}_i} \frac{\partial \dot{S}_i}{\partial \dot{q}_a}$$

or

$$p_a = \sum_i P_i D_{ia} \tag{178}$$

where

$$P_i = \frac{\partial T}{\partial \dot{S}_i} \tag{179}$$

is the momentum conjugate to the internal coordinate S_i. The kinetic energy then takes on the form

$$2T = \sum_{i,j}^{3N-6} g_{ij} P_i P_j \tag{180}$$

where the coefficients g_{ij} are given by

$$g_{ij} = \sum_{a,b}^{3N} D_{ia} D_{jb} \delta_{ab} \tag{181}$$

Using Eq. (173) for the **s**-vectors the elements of the $(3N-6) \times (3N-6)$ g-matrix are

$$g_{ij} = \sum_n \frac{1}{m_n} \mathbf{s}_{in} \cdot \mathbf{s}_{jn} \tag{182}$$

An explicit derivation of the **s**-vectors for the four common internal coordinates-changes in bond length, interbond angle, torsion angle, and out-of-plane displacement, has been presented by Malhiot and Ferigle *(231)* and convenient tabulations of the g-matrix elements are now available *(232)*.

In the internal coordinates the potential energy is given by

$$2V = \sum_{i,j}^{3N-6} f_{ij} S_i S_j \tag{183}$$

or, in matrix form,

$$2V = \tilde{\mathbf{S}} \mathbf{f} \mathbf{S} \tag{184}$$

where **S** is a $(3N-6) \times 1$ column matrix, $\tilde{\mathbf{S}}$ is its transpose, and **f** is the

$(3N-6)\times(3N-6)$ force constant matrix. The kinetic energy is similarly given by

$$2T = \tilde{\dot{\mathbf{S}}}\mathbf{g}^{-1}\dot{\mathbf{S}} \tag{185}$$

We introduce normal coordinates Q_s by means of the transformation

$$\mathbf{S} = \mathbf{LQ} \tag{186}$$

such that the potential and kinetic energies are simultaneously diagonal, namely,

$$2V = \tilde{\mathbf{Q}}\mathbf{\Lambda}\mathbf{Q} \tag{187}$$

and

$$2T = \tilde{\dot{\mathbf{Q}}}\dot{\mathbf{Q}} \tag{188}$$

where $\mathbf{\Lambda}$ is a diagonal matrix with elements $\lambda_s = 4\pi^2c^2\omega_s{}^2$, where ω_s is the frequency in cm^{-1} of the s th mode of vibration. Using Eq. (186) to substitute for $\mathbf{S}$ and $\dot{\mathbf{S}}$ in Eqs. (184) and (185) and comparing with Eqs. (187) and (188) we have the relations

$$\tilde{\mathbf{L}}\mathbf{fL} = \mathbf{\Lambda} \tag{189}$$

and

$$\tilde{\mathbf{L}}\mathbf{g}^{-1}\mathbf{L} = \mathbf{E} \tag{190}$$

where $\mathbf{E}$ is the $(3N-6)\times(3N-6)$ unit matrix. From the last two equations we obtain

$$\mathbf{fL} = \mathbf{g}^{-1}\mathbf{L\Lambda} \tag{191}$$

whence

$$\mathbf{gfL} = \mathbf{L\Lambda} \tag{192}$$

where the elements of $\mathbf{g}$ are given by Eq. (182). Since $\mathbf{\Lambda}$ is a diagonal matrix we may write the last equation as

$$(\mathbf{gf}-\mathbf{\Lambda})\mathbf{L} = 0 \tag{193}$$

This matrix equation represents a set of $(3N-6)$ homogeneous algebraic equations in the unknown coefficients L_{is} and a nontrivial solution for these requires that the determinant formed by the coefficients of L_{is} vanishes. The roots λ_s of the secular determinant

$$|\,\mathbf{gf}-\mathbf{\Lambda}\,| = 0 \tag{194}$$

give the vibrational frequencies ω_s for each mode ($\lambda_s = 4\pi^2c^2\omega_s{}^2$ for ω_s expressed in cm^{-1}). Each column of the matrix $\mathbf{L}$ comprises one eigenvector $\mathbf{L}_s$ that belongs to the sth vibrational mode. The components of the vector $\mathbf{L}_s$ are obtained by simultaneous solution of the $3N-6$ mode equations for each value λ_s. The matrix representation of this problem is

$$(\mathbf{gf}-\lambda_s\mathbf{E})\mathbf{L}_s = 0 \tag{195}$$

where $\mathbf{L}_s$ is a $(3N-6)\times 1$ column matrix. The vectors $\mathbf{L}_s$ are normalized in such a way that

$$\mathbf{L}\tilde{\mathbf{L}} = \mathbf{g} \tag{196}$$

as can be seen from Eq. (190).

The normal coordinate computations are simplified by utilizing the point group symmetry of the molecule under study. Instead of solving for the roots λ_s of the $(3N-6)\times(3N-6)$ secular determinant, Eq. (194), and for the $(3N-6)$ eigenvectors $\mathbf{L}_s$ by Eq. (195), the vibration problem may be set up in terms of symmetry coordinates which causes the secular determinant to appear in block-diagonal form. Starting with a set of generalized coordinates S_j (internal coordinates are commonly employed but it is obvious that these constitute only a special set of generalized coordinates) it is possible to form linear combinations $\mathscr{S}_i$

$$\mathscr{S}_i = \sum_j U_{ij}S_j \tag{197}$$

which transform according to the irreducible representations of the group which describes the symmetry of the molecule. Each set of the coordinates $\mathscr{S}_i$ thus formed belongs to a given vibrational species. The coefficients U_{ij} constitute a unitary transformation. If further the sets of coordinates $\mathscr{S}_i$ of the same degenerate symmetry species have the same transformation coefficients then the $\mathscr{S}_i$ are said to be symmetry coordinates. Using the matrix form

$$\mathscr{S} = \mathbf{US} \tag{198}$$

and substituting for $\mathbf{S}$ and $\dot{\mathbf{S}}$ into Eqs. (184) and (185) it is seen that the potential and kinetic energies are given by

$$2V = \tilde{\mathscr{S}}\mathscr{F}\mathscr{S} \tag{199}$$

$$2T = \tilde{\dot{\mathscr{S}}}\mathscr{G}^{-1}\dot{\mathscr{S}} \tag{200}$$

where

$$\mathscr{F} = \mathbf{Uf}\tilde{\mathbf{U}} \tag{201}$$

$$\mathscr{G}^{-1} = \mathbf{Ug}^{-1}\tilde{\mathbf{U}} \tag{202}$$

are symmetrized matrices of the force constants and the metric coefficients.

The same steps that lead to Eq. (180) for the kinetic energy in terms of the momenta yields also the result that

$$\mathscr{G} = \mathbf{U}\mathbf{g}\tilde{\mathbf{U}} \tag{203}$$

and that the secular determinant is in the form

$$| \mathscr{G}\mathscr{F} - \mathbf{\Lambda} | = 0 \tag{204}$$

which is block diagonal (*233*) with each block representing the secular determinant for the vibrations of a given species and where blocks are repeated twice or three times for doubly and triply degenerate species. The construction of symmetry coordinates from the a-priori generalized coordinates, the treatment of redundant coordinates and special methods for evaluating the secular determinant and fuller expositions of the theory of normal coordinate analyses of polyatomic molecules are available in Refs. (*37*) and (*234–238*), and detailed applications of group theory to molecular structure problems are given by Ferraro and Ziomek (*239*).

C. Coriolis Coupling

The most widely used theory of Coriolis coupling is that developed by Meal and Polo (*240*) within the framework of Wilson's *FG* matrix method of normal coordinate analysis. A lesser used theory of Coriolis interaction is that of Boyd and Longuet-Higgins (*241*). Following Meal and Polo we consider the kinetic energy of a vibrating-rotating polyatomic molecule in the form

$$2T = \tilde{\boldsymbol{\omega}}\mathbf{A}\boldsymbol{\omega} + 2\tilde{\boldsymbol{\omega}}\mathbf{B}\dot{\mathbf{S}} + \tilde{\dot{\mathbf{S}}}\mathbf{g}^{-1}\dot{\mathbf{S}} \tag{205}$$

where the first term on the right hand side represents the kinetic energy of the rigid rotor, the third term represents the kinetic energy of vibration [Eq. (185)] and the mixed term

$$2T_{\text{int}} = 2\tilde{\boldsymbol{\omega}}\mathbf{B}\dot{\mathbf{S}} \tag{206}$$

represents the vibration-rotation interaction. Here $\dot{\mathbf{S}}$ is a column matrix of ($3N$) rows where the $\dot{\mathbf{S}}_i$ are the generalized velocities and $\boldsymbol{\omega}$ is the column matrix of the angular velocities. For small displacements from equilibrium the elements of the matrix $\mathbf{B}$ which couples the rotation to the vibration are given by (*242*)

$$B_{\alpha j} = B^0_{\alpha j} + \sum_{j'} B_{\alpha j j'} S_{j'} \tag{207}$$

where the $S_{j'}$ comprise the set given by Eq. (164). The Eckart conditions require that $B^0_{\alpha j} = 0$ and the coefficient $B_{\alpha j j'}$ is given by (*242*)

$$B_{\alpha j j'} = \boldsymbol{\varepsilon}_\alpha \cdot \sum_n m_n\, \mathbf{d}_{nj'} \times \mathbf{d}_{nj} \tag{208}$$

where $\boldsymbol{\varepsilon}_\alpha (\alpha = x, y, z)$ is the unit vector along the molecule fixed system of axes (defined by the Eckart conditions) and the $\mathbf{d}_{nj}$'s give the displacements of the nth atom according to

$$\mathbf{d}_n = \sum_j \mathbf{d}_{nj} S_j \tag{209}$$

The interaction energy is then given by

$$\begin{aligned} T_{\text{int}} &= \sum_{\alpha j,j'} \omega_\alpha \boldsymbol{\varepsilon}_\alpha \cdot \left(\sum_n m_n \, \mathbf{d}_{nj'} \times \mathbf{d}_{nj}\right) S_{j'} \dot{S}_j \\ &= \sum_{n,\alpha} \omega_\alpha \boldsymbol{\varepsilon}_\alpha \cdot (m_n \, \mathbf{d}_n \times \dot{\mathbf{d}}_n) \\ &= \sum_\alpha \omega_\alpha \Omega_\alpha \end{aligned} \tag{210}$$

where

$$\Omega_\alpha = \sum_n m_n \boldsymbol{\varepsilon}_\alpha \cdot (\mathbf{d}_n \times \dot{\mathbf{d}}_n) \tag{211}$$

Introducing the mass reduced Cartesian displacements q_n and using Eqs. (161) and (170) we may write

$$\Omega_\alpha = \sum_n \boldsymbol{\varepsilon}_\alpha \cdot (\mathbf{q}_n \times \dot{\mathbf{q}}_n) \tag{212}$$

which assumes the matrix form

$$\Omega_\alpha = \mathbf{q} \, \mathbf{M}^\alpha \dot{\mathbf{q}} \tag{213}$$

where the matrices M^α are, for each atom n,

$$(M^x)_n = \begin{pmatrix} 0 & 0 & 0 \\ 0 & 0 & 1 \\ 0 & -1 & 0 \end{pmatrix}, \quad (M^y)_n = \begin{pmatrix} 0 & 0 & -1 \\ 0 & 0 & 0 \\ 1 & 0 & 0 \end{pmatrix}, \quad (M^z)_n = \begin{pmatrix} 0 & 1 & 0 \\ -1 & 0 & 0 \\ 0 & 0 & 0 \end{pmatrix} \tag{214}$$

Introducing now the normal coordinates Q_s which form the components of a $3N$ dimensional vector $\mathbf{Q}$

$$\mathbf{Q} = (Q_1, Q_2, \ldots, Q_{3N-6}, R_x, R_y, R_z, T_x, T_y, T_z) \tag{215}$$

where $Q_1, Q_2, \ldots Q_{3N-6}$ describe the internal vibrations (genuine vibrations) and the remaining six normal coordinates $R_x, \ldots, T_z$ describe the rigid body rotations and translations (nongenuine vibrations) of the molecule. These are related to the mass reduced Cartesian coordinates q_{nt}

$$\mathbf{q} = (q_{1x}, q_{1y}, q_{1z}, q_{2x}, q_{2y}, q_{2z}, \ldots q_{Nx}, q_{Ny}, q_{Nz})$$

by means of the orthogonal transformation

$$\mathbf{Q} = \mathbf{l}\mathbf{q} \tag{216}$$

in which

$$\mathbf{l}\mathbf{l}^{-1} = \mathbf{l}\tilde{\mathbf{l}} = \mathbf{E} \tag{217}$$

is a $3N \times 3N$ unit matrix. Both $\mathbf{Q}$ and $\mathbf{l}$ may be partitioned into submatrices $\mathbf{Q}_v$, $\mathbf{l}_v$ and $\mathbf{Q}_r$, $\mathbf{l}_r$ for the vibrational motions and the infinitesimal rigid motions respectively. Thus,

$$\mathbf{Q} = \begin{pmatrix} \mathbf{Q}_v \\ \mathbf{Q}_r \end{pmatrix} \quad \text{and} \quad \mathbf{l} = \begin{pmatrix} \mathbf{l}_v \\ \mathbf{l}_r \end{pmatrix} \tag{218}$$

Using Eqs. (216) and (217) we may rewrite Eq. (213) in the form

$$\Omega_\alpha = \mathbf{Q}\boldsymbol{\zeta}^\alpha \mathbf{Q} \tag{219}$$

where the $3N \times 3N$ Coriolis matrix $\boldsymbol{\zeta}^\alpha$ is

$$\boldsymbol{\zeta}^\alpha = \mathbf{l}\mathbf{M}^\alpha\tilde{\mathbf{l}} = \mathbf{l}\mathbf{M}^\alpha\mathbf{l}^{-1} \tag{220}$$

Similar to the partitioning of the normal coordinates given by Eq. (218) we may write for the generalized coordinates S_i the matrix equation

$$\mathbf{S} = \begin{pmatrix} \mathbf{S}_v \\ \mathbf{S}_r \end{pmatrix} = \begin{pmatrix} \mathbf{L}_v & 0 \\ 0 & \mathbf{L}_r \end{pmatrix} \begin{pmatrix} \mathbf{Q}_v \\ \mathbf{Q}_r \end{pmatrix} = \begin{pmatrix} \mathbf{D}_v \\ \mathbf{D}_r \end{pmatrix} \mathbf{q} \tag{221}$$

where use has been made of Eqs. (161), (171), and (186). Here, since the Eckart conditions require that $S_r = Q_r = 0$ the matrix $\mathbf{L}_r$ is a 6×6 unit matrix. Using Eq. (216) we then have that

$$\mathbf{D} = \mathbf{L}\mathbf{l} \tag{222}$$

and

$$\mathbf{D}\mathbf{D} = \mathbf{L}\mathbf{L} = \mathbf{g} = \begin{pmatrix} \mathbf{g}_v & 0 \\ 0 & \mathbf{g}_r \end{pmatrix} \tag{223}$$

where $\mathbf{g}_v$ is the $\mathbf{g}$-matrix whose elements are given by Eq. (182) and $\mathbf{g}_r$ is a 6×6 unit matrix. Using Eq. (222) we obtain for the zeta matrix associated with the (genuine) vibrations

$$\boldsymbol{\zeta}_v^\alpha = \mathbf{L}_v\bar{\mathbf{C}}_v^\alpha\mathbf{L}_v = (\mathbf{L}^{-1})_v\mathbf{C}_v^\alpha(\mathbf{L}^{-1})_v \tag{224}$$

where

$$\mathbf{C}_v^\alpha = \mathbf{D}_v\mathbf{M}^\alpha\mathbf{D}_v \tag{225}$$

and

$$\bar{\mathbf{C}}_v^\alpha = (\mathbf{D}^{-1})_v\mathbf{M}^\alpha(\mathbf{D}^{-1})_v \tag{226}$$

The elements of the $\mathbf{D}_v$ matrix are given in terms of the **s**-vectors by Eq. (173), or

$$\mathbf{s}_{in} = \mathbf{D}_{in}\sqrt{m_n} \tag{227}$$

or

$$D_{in\alpha} = m_n^{-\frac{1}{2}}\mathbf{s}_{in}\cdot\boldsymbol{\varepsilon}_a \tag{228}$$

The elements of the $\mathbf{C}_v^\alpha$ matrix are, therefore, given by

$$C_{ij}^\alpha = \sum_n (\mathbf{D}_{in}\times\mathbf{D}_{jn})\cdot\boldsymbol{\varepsilon}_\alpha = \sum_n m_n^{-1}(\mathbf{s}_{in}\times\mathbf{s}_{jn})\cdot\boldsymbol{\varepsilon}_\alpha \tag{229}$$

and are, thus, as easily evaluated as the elements of the g-matrix given by Eq. (182). The C-matrix elements for various types of internal coordinates have been tabulated *(243)* in a manner similar to the tabulations of the g-matrix elements, with the results given in terms of the angles between the bonds and between the bonds and the α-axis of coordinates. The elements of the Coriolis matrix ζ_v^α are then computed by Eq. (224) using the eigenvectors $\mathbf{L}_s$ obtained through the normal coordinate analysis by means of Eq. (195).

Using Eqs. (189) and (190) together with the second of Eq. (224) we obtain the following two relations, namely,

$$(\tilde{\mathbf{L}})_v(\mathbf{g}^{-1})_v\mathbf{C}_v^\alpha(\tilde{\mathbf{L}})_v^{-1} = \zeta_v^\alpha \tag{230}$$

and

$$\tilde{\mathbf{L}}_v\mathbf{f}\mathbf{C}_v^\alpha(\tilde{\mathbf{L}})_v^{-1} = \boldsymbol{\Lambda}\zeta_v^\alpha \tag{231}$$

Equation (230) shows that ζ_v^α and $(\mathbf{g}^{-1})_v\mathbf{C}_v^\alpha$ are related by a similarity transformation and thus have the same roots. Since $(\mathbf{g}^{-1})_v\mathbf{C}_v^\alpha$ depends only on the atomic masses and the geometry of the molecule then the roots of ζ_v^α are independent of the force field. Similarly, the roots of $\mathbf{f}\mathbf{C}_v^\alpha$ are the same as those of $\boldsymbol{\Lambda}\zeta_v^\alpha$. The secular equations that follow from Eqs. (229) and (230) are

$$|\,(\mathbf{g}^{-1})_v\mathbf{C}_v^\alpha - \sigma\mathbf{E}\,| \equiv |\,\zeta_v^\alpha - \sigma\mathbf{E}\,| = 0 \tag{232}$$

$$|\,\mathbf{f}\mathbf{C}_v^\alpha - \gamma\mathbf{E}\,| \equiv |\,\boldsymbol{\Lambda}\zeta_v^\alpha - \gamma\mathbf{E}\,| = 0 \tag{233}$$

Comparing the coefficients in the two polynomials allows one to set up some useful relations, the most important ones of which are the zeta-sum rules.

The use of the molecular symmetry brings about a factorization of the zeta matrix in a manner similar to the factorization of the normal coordinate problem discussed in the previous section. All of the above relations which are written out in terms of the base of the generalized coordinates S_i hold, *mutatis mutandis*, for the symmetry coordinate base. The symmetry properties exhibited by the $\mathbf{M}^\alpha$, $\mathbf{C}^\alpha$, and ζ^α matrices allow considerable simplifications of the computations. The most important of these properties is known as Jahn's Rule (*244*) which specifies between which vibrational states Coriolis coupling can occur. Thus, if Q_i and Q_j are the normal coordinates for the ith and jth normal modes of vibration then ζ_{ij}^α is different from zero only if the direct product $\Gamma(Q_i) \times \Gamma(Q_j)$ of the representations to which the coordinates Q_i and Q_j belong contains the representation $\Gamma(R_\alpha)$ for the rotation about the α-axis of coordinates.

The Coriolis coupling is usually small as long as the vibrations have significantly different frequencies. For symmetric top molecules, however, the Coriolis coupling is especially strong among the two components of a degenerate pair of vibrations and gives rise to a first order splitting of the energies.

Using Eqs. (186) and (198) we have for the symmetry coordinates

$$\mathscr{S} = \mathbf{US} = \mathbf{ULQ} = \mathscr{L}\mathbf{Q} \tag{234}$$

where

$$\mathscr{L} = \mathbf{UL} \tag{235}$$

is a nonsingular eigenvector matrix. Therefore

$$\mathbf{L}^{-1} = \mathscr{L}^{-1}\mathbf{U} \tag{236}$$

and we have from Eq. (224) for the zeta matrix

$$\zeta_v^\alpha = \mathscr{L}_v^{-1}\mathscr{C}_v^\alpha(\tilde{\mathscr{L}}_v^{-1}) \tag{237}$$

where the symmetrized $\mathbf{C}_v^\alpha$ matrix, $\mathscr{C}_v^\alpha$, is given by

$$\mathscr{C}_v^\alpha = \mathbf{UC}_v^\alpha\tilde{\mathbf{U}} \tag{238}$$

The $\mathscr{C}_v^\alpha$ matrix has the same block diagonal form as the $\mathscr{G}_v$ matrix [Eq. (203)], with each block corresponding to one of the vibrational species. For the doubly degenerate (type E) species of vibrations of symmetric top molecules the $\mathscr{L}_v$, $\mathscr{F}$ and $\mathscr{G}_v$ matrices are of the form

$$\mathscr{L}_v = \begin{pmatrix} \mathscr{L}_a & 0 \\ 0 & \mathscr{L}_b \end{pmatrix}, \quad \mathscr{F} = \begin{pmatrix} \mathscr{F}_a & 0 \\ 0 & \mathscr{F}_b \end{pmatrix},$$
$$\mathscr{G}_v = \begin{pmatrix} \mathscr{G}_a & 0 \\ 0 & \mathscr{G}_b \end{pmatrix} \tag{239}$$

where the subscripts a and b label the components of the degenerate pair.

The $\mathscr{C}_v^{\alpha}$ and ζ_v^{α} matrices for the doubly degenerate species are thus of the form

$$(\mathscr{C}_v^{z})_E = \begin{pmatrix} 0 & \mathscr{C}_{ab}^z \\ -\mathscr{C}_{ab}^z & 0 \end{pmatrix}, \quad (\zeta_v^{z})_E = \begin{pmatrix} 0 & \zeta_{ab}^z \\ -\zeta_{ab}^z & 0 \end{pmatrix} \tag{240}$$

(since the $\mathbf{C}_v^{\alpha}$ and hence $\mathscr{C}_v^{\alpha}$ is skew-symmetric and $\alpha = z$), and where

$$\zeta_{ab}^z = \mathscr{L}_a^{-1}\mathscr{C}_{ab}^z\widetilde{(\mathscr{L}_b^{-1})} \tag{241}$$

Here $\mathscr{C}_{ab}^z$ is a symmetric matrix. The diagonal elements of the matrix ζ_{ab}^z, i.e., $\zeta_{ia,ib}^z = \zeta_i$ for brevity, are the Coriolis coupling coefficients that appear in the rotational term value given by Eq. (77) and the subsequent equations for the frequencies of the various transitions, Eqs. (82a)–(85b), and Table 3. For spherical top molecules, however, Jahn's Rule indicates that the Coriolis coupling does not modify the term values for the doubly degenerate vibrations. Instead, only the triply degenerate (F species in tetrahedral, octahedral, and icosahedral point groups) and the five-fold degenerate (H species in icosahedral point groups) terms are split by the Coriolis interaction.

Some useful relations for symmetric top molecules may be obtained by combining Eqs. (190) and (230), and Eqs. (189) and (231), respectively, and transforming to symmetry coordinates. Thus,

$$\mathbf{E}-\zeta = \mathscr{L}^{-1}(\mathscr{G}-\mathscr{C})(\tilde{\mathscr{L}})^{-1} \tag{242}$$

$$\boldsymbol{\Lambda}(\mathbf{E}-\zeta) = \tilde{\mathscr{L}}\mathscr{F}(\mathscr{G}-\mathscr{C})(\tilde{\mathscr{L}})^{-1} \tag{243}$$

Since Eq. (243) represents a similarity transformation the traces of $\boldsymbol{\Lambda}(\mathbf{E}-\zeta)$ and $\mathscr{F}(\mathscr{G}-\mathscr{C})$ are equal. The trace of $\mathscr{F}(\mathscr{G}-\mathscr{C})$ is a linear function of the force constants, with coefficients that depend only on the geometry of the molecule and the masses of the atoms. This relationship, if explicitly written out for a given molecular model, is useful to incorporate observed ζ-values into the determination of the molecular force constants. For all symmetric top molecules except those belonging to the S_4 and D_{2d} point groups the matrix $(\mathscr{G}-\mathscr{C})$ has elements which are independent of the atoms located on the symmetry axis. If the atoms located off the symmetry axis are all identical then all elements of $(\mathscr{G}-\mathscr{C})$ will have the common factor m_n^{-1} where m_n is the mass of the off-axis atoms. Therefore, taking the trace of Eq. (243) and multiplying by m_n gives the relation

$$m_n \sum_i \omega_i^2(1-\zeta_i) = k, \tag{244}$$

where ω_i is the frequency of the ith mode, the summation is taken over all modes that belong to a given degenerate species and k is a constant for isotopic molecules.

In addition to the isotope rule, Eq. (244), Meal and Polo derived the zeta rules for the degenerate vibrations of symmetric top molecules. Of the several techniques that have been employed to derive the zeta sum rules, including the use of the trace of Eq. (230), the most elegant and general method is that based on the properties of the ζ_v^α matrices. Meal and Polo showed that the eigenvalues of the ζ_v^α matrix are $+1, 0, -1$ and $B/2A$ where A and B are the rotation constants. Explicitly,

> the number of roots equal to -1 is equal to one half the number of doubly degenerate degrees of freedom associated with the x- and y-directions contributed by the off-axis atoms to the irreducible representation in question. The number of roots equal to $+1$ is equal to the number of roots equal to -1 plus the number of doubly degenerate degrees of freedom contributed by axial atoms of the same symmetry. If one of these is a rotation, there will also be a root equal to $B/2A$.

TABLE 22

Zeta Sum Rules for the Doubly Degenerate Fundamental Vibrations of Symmetric Top Molecules[a]

Point group	Species	Nongenuine modes	$(\Sigma_i \zeta_i)^b$
C_{nh} and D_{nh}, n odd	E_1'		
(1) C_{nh} and D_{nh}, n even; S_{2n} and D_{nd}, n odd	E_{1u}	(T_x, T_y)	$N_p - 1 + \delta$
C_{nh} and D_{nh}, n odd	E_1''		
(2) C_{nh} and D_{nh}, n even; S_{2n} and D_{nd}, n odd	E_{1g}	(R_x, R_y)	$N_p - 1 + B/2A$
(3) C_n, D_n, and C_{nv}	E_1	(T_x, T_y) and (R_x, R_y)	$N - 2 + B/2A$
(4) S_{2n} and D_{nd}, n even	E_1	(T_x, T_y)	$N_p - 1 + \delta$
(5) S_{2n} and D_{nd}, n even	E_{n-1}	$(R_x, -R_y)$	$-(N_p - 1 + B/2A)$
(6) S_4 and D_{2d}	E	(T_x, T_y) and $(R_x, -R_y)$	$\delta - B/2A$
(7) All symmetric-top point groups	All other degenerate symmetry species	—	0

[a] Adapted from Lepard, Ref. (*246*).

[b] N_p = number of pairs of axial atoms, $\delta = 1$ or 0 according as there is an atom at the center or not, and $N = 2N_p + \delta$ = number of axial atoms. The summation Σ_i is only over the genuine vibrations.

The zeta sum rules for the different vibrational species of the various symmetric top point groups then follow immediately. Using the approach developed by Boyd and Longuet-Higgins (*241*), Lepard (*246*) derived the sum rules including those for the D_{2d} point group about which there was some earlier confusion. Lepard's results are presented in Table 22 and include the results of earlier derivations by Meal and Polo (*240*), Boyd and Longuet-Higgins (*241*), and Lord and Merrifield (*245*). For spherical top molecules first order Coriolis coupling occurs among the components of the triply and fivefold degenerate vibrations. The zeta sum rules for the

TABLE 23

Zeta Sum Rules and Limiting Values for the Triply Degenerate Fundamental Vibrations of Spherical Top Molecules[a]

Point group	Species	$(\Sigma_i \zeta_i)$[b]	Limits of ζ: If one or more sets of eight equivalent nuclei are present	Limits of ζ: Otherwise
T	F	$N_0+N_3-3/2$		$-\frac{1}{2} \leqq \zeta \leqq +1$
T_h	F_g	$N_3-\frac{1}{2}$	$-\frac{1}{2} \leqq \zeta \leqq +1$	$-\frac{1}{2} \leqq \zeta \leqq +\frac{1}{2}$
	F_u	N_0+N_3-1	$-\frac{1}{2} \leqq \zeta \leqq +1$	$-\frac{1}{2} \leqq \zeta \leqq +1$
T_d	F_1	$\frac{1}{2}(N_3-1)$		$-\frac{1}{2} \leqq \zeta \leqq +\frac{1}{2}$
	F_2	$N_0+\frac{1}{2}N_3-1$		$-\frac{1}{2} \leqq \zeta \leqq +1$
O	F_1	$N_0+N_3+N_4-3/2$	$-\frac{1}{2} \leqq \zeta \leqq +1$	$-\frac{1}{2} \leqq \zeta \leqq +1$
	F_2	N_3-N_4	$-\frac{1}{2} \leqq \zeta \leqq +1$	$\zeta = -\frac{1}{2}$
O_h	F_{1g}	$\frac{1}{2}(N_3+N_4-1)$	$\zeta = +\frac{1}{2}$	$\zeta = +\frac{1}{2}$
	F_{1u}	$N_0+\frac{1}{2}(N_3+N_4)-1$	$-\frac{1}{2} \leqq \zeta \leqq +1$	$-\frac{1}{2} \leqq \zeta \leqq +1$
	F_{2g}	$\frac{1}{2}(N_3-N_4)$	$-\frac{1}{2} \leqq \zeta \leqq +1$	$\zeta = -\frac{1}{2}$
	F_{2u}	$\frac{1}{2}(N_3-N_u)$	$-\frac{1}{2} \leqq \zeta \leqq +\frac{1}{2}$	$\zeta = -\frac{1}{2}$
I	F_1	$N_0+N_3+N_5-3/2$		
I_h	F_{1g}	$\frac{1}{2}(N_3+N_5-1)$		
	F_{1u}	$N_0+\frac{1}{2}(N_3+N_5)-1$		

[a] Adapted from McDowell, Refs. (*247,247a*).

[b] N_0 is the number of nuclei lying on all elements of symmetry ($N_0 = 1$ if a central atom is present, $N_0 = 0$ otherwise); N_3, N_4, and N_5 are the number of sets equivalent nuclei lying on threefold, fourfold, and fivefold axes respectively, but not on all symmetry elements.

triply degenerate vibrations only have been derived by McDowell (*247*) and they are given in Table 23. McDowell (*247a*) has also derived the upper and lower limiting values of the zetas for tetrahedral and octahedral molecules; these are shown in columns 4 and 5 of Table 23. It is to be noted that according to Jahn's rule not only are the $\zeta_i^\alpha = 0$ for the doubly degenerate vibrations of the tetrahedral and octahedral molecules, but also for the F_2 triply degenerate species of icosahedral molecules. Finally, we want to mention that zeta sum rules also exist for asymmetric top molecules and that Nemes (*248*) derived such rules for planar asymmetric top rotators.

The evaluation of the Coriolis coupling has been carried out for a number of molecules. Cyvin (*228*) lists the algebraic formulations of the normal coordinate and zeta constant calculations for a number of molecular models and detailed numerical computations for many other molecules are to be found in the literature. Of direct interest to the present discussion are the dynamical analyses of those molecules that have been subjected to a Raman spectroscopic study in the gaseous phase. These are ethane, allene, cyclopropane, and cyclobutane, with methane representing a somewhat special case. To illustrate the interplay between the empirical analysis of the observed spectrum, i.e., the assignment of the rotational transitions and the determination of the molecular constants, and the calculation of normal coordinates and zeta constants we discuss briefly the work done on the above four symmetric top molecules.

Duncan (*249*) calculated the force constants of ethane by using all available vibrational frequencies and zeta values. These are shown in columns 2 and 5 of Table 24 for C_2H_6 and C_2D_6, respectively. The quality of the force field thus obtained is judged by a comparison of the then computed frequencies and zeta constants which are given in columns 3 and 6. The calculated and observed frequencies agree to better than 1.3% and the calculated and observed zeta values for the infrared active E_u vibrations agree to within 0.01 unit. For the Raman active E_g vibrations the calculated value for $\zeta_{10} = 0.10$ is in considerable disagreement with the observed value of 0.256 which is believed to be accurate to within ± 0.05 while for ζ_{11} the difference between the calculated and observed values lies within the uncertainty of ζ_{11} which is also ± 0.05. Columns 4 and 7 list the more recently obtained frequencies and zeta constants. In these columns the unbracketed frequencies were derived from the analysis of the respective resolved vibration-rotation bands.

The difference between the newer, and also more accurate, frequencies and the older values in columns 2 and 5 is probably insufficient to re-

TABLE 24

Observed and Calculated Fundamental Frequencies and Coriolis Coupling Constants for C_2H_6 and C_2D_6[a]

		C_2H_6			C_2D_6		
Mode		Obs[b]	Calc[c]	Obs[d]	Obs[b]	Calc[c]	Obs[d]
A_{1g}	ν_1	2920	2915	(2953.7)	2100	2104	(2083)
	ν_2	1400	1407	(1388.4)	1158	1151	1154.50
	ν_3	995	1000	994.8	852	847	842.97
A_{2u}	ν_5	2910	2914	2895.79	2095	2092	2087.40
	ν_6	1379	1393	1379.19	1077	1065	(1077.1)
E_u	ν_7	2958	2998	2995.48	2236	2226	(2236)
	ν_8	1472	1483	1472.2	1082	1074	1081.30
	ν_9	821	822	821.60	594	594	593.78
	ζ_7	0.10	0.10		(0.24)[e]	0.22	
	ζ_8	−0.33	−0.33		−0.42	−0.41	
	ζ_9	0.24	0.23		0.18	0.19	
E_g	ν_{10}	2950	2967	2968.69	2225	2213	2225.65
	ν_{11}	1469	1475	1468.1	1055	1050	1041
	ν_{12}	1190	1201	(1190)	970	960	(970)
	ζ_{10}	0.256	0.10	0.223		0.24	0.161
	ζ_{11}	−0.36	−0.33	−0.330		−0.39	−0.36
	ζ_{12}	(0.238)[e]	0.36	(0.231)[e]		0.33	(0.270)[e]

[a] Frequencies are in cm^{-1} and zeta constants are dimensionless. The inactive $\nu_4(A_{1u})$ mode is not listed.

[b] Observed data used by Duncan, Ref. (*249*), to establish the force field.

[c] Calculated by Duncan, Ref. (*249*).

[d] Observed data taken from Tables 10 and 11.

[e] Zeta constants given in parentheses are derived through the use of the zeta sum rules.

determine the force field and the interest in the comparison lies in the newly determined zeta values of the vibrations and those predicted on the basis of the calculations. For both C_2H_6 and C_2D_6 the computed and observed values of ζ_{10} are in severe disagreement while the difference in the values of ζ_{11} is within the experimental uncertainty. For C_2H_6 the old value $\zeta_{10} = 0.256$ was derived from a poorly resolved band whereas the newer value $\zeta_{10} = 0.223$ was derived from a much better resolved spectrum whose analysis was verified by a critical intensity profile calculation as shown in Fig. 11. Similarly the value of $\zeta_{11} = -0.330$ seems to be established without a doubt. The difficulty of analyzing the ν_{10} band of C_2H_6 no longer exists for C_2D_6 for which, as is seen in Fig. 12, the ν_{10} band is a textbook example of a doubly degenerate Raman band of a symmetric top molecule, from which $\zeta_{10} = 0.161$ is undisputably established. However, the value $\zeta_{11} = -0.36$ for C_2D_6 is less certain (see Table 11, footnote *h*).

The zeta sum rules and the isotope rule [Eq. (244)] constitute additional relations which serve as a check on the analysis or for the evaluation of zeta constants which cannot be determined from the spectrum. For the infrared active E_u species the sum rule (Table 22) is $\zeta_7+\zeta_8+\zeta_9 = 0$. For C_2H_6 the experimental zeta constants (column 2) satisfy this rule within the experimental uncertainty of the zeta values. That the computed zeta constants (column 3) satisfy the sum rule exactly is of course not surprising and only tells that there are no arithmetical errors in the computations. The unknown value of ζ_7 for C_2D_6 when determined from the sum rule agrees favorably with the computed value. For the Raman active E_g vibrations the situation is less satisfactory. Here the sum rule states that $\zeta_{10}+\zeta_{11}+\zeta_{12} = B/2A$ where, using the data from Table 11, $B/2A = 0.124$ for C_2H_6 and 0.171 for C_2D_6. Using the newer data in columns 4 and 7 one then obtains the listed values of $\zeta_{12} = 0.231$ and 0.270 for C_2H_6 and C_2D_6, respectively.

The isotope rule, however, provides a better test of the zeta values. Using the observed data in columns 2 and 5 we have for the E_u species $m_n \sum_{i=7}^{9} \nu_i^2(1-\zeta_i) = 11.27 \times 10^6$ for C_2H_6 and 11.50×10^6 for C_2D_6, which agreement is quite satisfactory. Using the observed data from columns 4 and 7 we have for the E_g vibrations $m_n \sum_{i=10}^{12} \nu^2(1-\zeta_i) = 10.90 \times 10^6$ for C_2H_6 and 12.72×10^6 for C_2D_6. It is difficult to establish the source of this large difference. The calculated ζ_{10} values suggest that the observed values are not correct yet the painstaking analysis of the ν_{10} bands of C_2H_6 and C_2D_6 (see Sec. IV, C, 2) does not permit such a conclusion. On the other hand the computed zeta constants are extremely sensitive to the values of the off-diagonal force constants as was noted by Clark (*250*) in his work on a series of ethane type molecules. Some further work on the E_g vibrations of ethane seems to be indicated.

Like ethane the allene molecule (point group D_{2d}) has been intensively studied in the past and the apparent discrepancies between the infrared and Raman results for the doubly degenerate band were not resolved until Mills' study of the Raman selection rules (see page 566). A further discrepancy was found to be due to the use of an incorrect zeta sum rule for the degenerate species of the D_{2d} point group. Curiously enough the discovery of this fact by Mills and Duncan (*251*) was brought about through the use of the zeta sum rule to check the accuracy of the values of the zeta constants calculated from an assumed force field and the method of Meal and Polo described in this section. The calculated zetas ($\zeta_8, \zeta_9, \zeta_{10}, \zeta_{11}$) added up to a value of 0.97 whereas the sum rule $\sum_i \zeta_i = 1+B/2A$ which was believed to be correct until the time of their work implies a value of 1.03 (from Table 12, $A'' = 4.816\ \text{cm}^{-1}$, and $B'' = 0.2965\ \text{cm}^{-1}$). The correct sum rule derived by Mills and Duncan (*251*) for allene is $\sum_i \zeta_i = 1-B/2A$ (see Table 22, rule 6). While Mills and Duncan thought that this result is due to the freakish nature of the D_{2d} point group in that it is the only symmetric top point group that does not include a symmetry operation C_m with $m > 2$, Lepard (*246*) showed that it is only a special case of a more general sum rule (rules 4 and 5, Table 22). In addition Mills showed that the type E infrared and Raman transitions obey different selection rules so that for $\Delta K = \pm 1$ different frequency expressions must be used in the analysis of the vibration-rotation bands (see pp. 645–647 for a discussion of the observed Raman spectrum). Furthermore, in their calculation of the normal coordinates and Coriolis constants Nemes, Duncan, and Mills (*252*) noted another result due to the peculiar nature of the D_{2d} point group namely that, contrary to the original statement (*240*), the matrix $(\mathscr{G}-\mathscr{C})$ is such that its elements are not independent of the atoms located on the symmetry axis. In consequence the isotope rule given by Eq. (244) holds for all symmetric tops except those that belong to the D_{2d} or S_4 point groups.

In their calculations Nemes et al. restricted themselves to the degenerate vibrations only and used the observed wave numbers for C_3H_4, C_3D_4, and H_2CCCD_2, the five observed Coriolis constants for C_3H_4 and C_3D_4 as well as the zeta sum and the product rules to account for the one unobserved zeta constant and unobserved wave numbers. A total of 21 input parameters was thus used to derive a most general force field of 10 parameters, subject to one constraint, by means of a refinement procedure. The resulting force field was then used to compute the complete ζ^z-matrix for allene-1,1-d_2 and hence the rotational structures of the perpendicular bending vibrations for this molecule. The good agreement between the computed and observed spectrum of allene-1,1-d_2 speaks for the reliability of the force field.

Allene is one of the few molecules for which a Coriolis coupling between two different vibrational levels of the same degenerate species both of which are active in combination with the ground state has been observed (in the infrared) and analyzed (*156*). The modes in question are $\nu_9 = 999\ \text{cm}^{-1}$ and $\nu_{10} = 841\ \text{cm}^{-1}$ of C_3H_4. Both are of species E, the direct product $E \times E = A_1 + A_2 + B_1 + B_2$, and the A_2 species is the representation of R_z, the rotation about the figure axis (*253*). Jahn's Rule thus allows the Coriolis interaction, and the proximity of the fundamentals (841 and 999 cm^{-1}) as well as the large A-value ($= 4.82\ \text{cm}^{-1}$) and zeta value that couples these two modes ($|\zeta_{9,10}| = 0.56_3$) render the effect large. This problem as well as that of the associated intensity perturbation has been treated in detail by Mills et al. (*156,254*). The ability of the derived force field to satisfactorily account for the observed intensity perturbation is further evidence for its reliability. Unfortunately the ν_9 and ν_{10} bands were not observed by Brodersen and Richardson (*77*) in their study of the Raman spectrum. A further study of the Raman spectrum of allene to investigate this interesting problem seems to be indicated.

Simultaneous to the publication of the force field calculations by Nemes et al. (*252*) an independent calculation was published by Andersen et al. (*255*). These investigators used only the observed wave numbers of allene, allene-d_4, and allene-1,1-d_2 to derive the force field which was then used to compute the Coriolis coefficients for allene and allene-d_4. The rather substantial differences between the observed and calculated zeta values points to their extreme sensitivity to the values of the force constants.

As discussed on p. 645 an attempt was made by Mathai et al. (*153*) to derive the Coriolis coupling coefficients for cyclopropane (D_{3h} point group) from the spacing of the intensity maxima of the unresolved profiles of the E' and E'' degenerate bands. Of the four E' vibrations they observed ν_8, ν_9, and ν_{11}. The spacing of the maxima of the band profiles and thus the zeta values that could be derived from these spacings were found to be inconsistent with the zeta values computed by Guenthard et al. (*154*) and this fact is believed to be due to the small spacing of the profile maxima. The three E'' fundamentals of cyclopropane are only Raman active and all were observed by Mathai et al. For these bands the spacings of the profile maxima is greater than that for the E' bands. The results of the profile analyzes were the following: $\nu_{12} = 3082.2$, $\nu_{13} = 1188.0$, and $\nu_{14} = 738.8\ \text{cm}^{-1}$ and for the Coriolis constants $\zeta_{12} = 0.29$, $\zeta_{13} = 0.63$, and $\zeta_{14} = -0.86$. The value $\zeta_{14} = -0.86$ was chosen over an equally allowed value (-0.29) through the use of the zeta sum rule for the E'' vibrations according to which $\zeta_{12} + \zeta_{13} + \zeta_{14} = -1 + B/2A = -0.21$. The observed zeta sum is $+0.06$ or $+0.63$ according as ζ_{14} is taken as -0.86 or -0.29 hence the value -0.86 was chosen for ζ_{14}. The discrepancy between the observed and predicted zeta sums is a measure of the accuracy of the technique of obtaining Coriolis coupling coefficients from band profile analyses.

A reinvestigation of the infrared spectra of cyclopropane, C_3H_6 as well as C_3D_6, by Duncan and Burns (*256*) culminated in a comprehensive determination of the force field using the most recently determined values for the fundamental frequencies and Coriolis constants, including two of the three E'' zeta constants, ζ_{13} and ζ_{14}, determined by Mathai et al. Their Raman value $\zeta_{12} = 0.29$ was, however, rejected in view of the inadequate satisfaction of the zeta sum rule (see above) and the fact that it did not even approximately agree with the calculated value.

The observed and calculated frequencies and Coriolis constants are shown in Table 25. We note that for C_3H_6 the calculated value $\zeta_{12} = -0.018$ is indeed far off the experimental value of $+0.29$. Even though the Raman spectrum of gaseous C_3D_6 has not been observed as yet the force field for cyclopropane and therefore the values of the Coriolis constants not experimentally determined may be considered as established. The accuracy of the force field was given an independent test by Duncan and Burns (*256*) by computing (a) the fundamental frequencies of cyclopropane-d_5, (b) the intensity perturbation arising from Coriolis interaction between the ν_{10} and ν_{11} (species E') fundamental vibrations of C_3D_6, as well as (c) the centrifugal distortion constants (see next section) for C_3H_6 (calculated values are, in units of cm^{-1}; $D_J = 9.5 \times 10^{-7}$ and $D_{JK} = -8.3 \times 10^{-7}$; observed values from Table 8 are $D_J = (8.2 \pm 1.5) \times 10^{-7}$ and $|D_{JK}| < 1{\cdot}5 \times 10^{-7}$). Similar to the case of allene, the Raman spectrum of C_3D_6 ought to be investigated to study the intensity perturbation due to the Coriolis interaction between the ν_{10} and ν_{11} fundamentals for which $|\zeta_{10a,11b}| = 0.51$ as calculated from the force field.

As a last example we wish to mention the cyclobutane molecule, C_4H_8 and C_4D_8. From the pure rotational Raman spectrum alone it is not possible to determine whether this molecule has a configuration described by the D_{2d} or D_{4h} point group since for either point group it is a symmetric top rotator (*142*). The vibration-rotation spectra of C_4H_8 and C_4D_8 are only partially known but are nevertheless of sufficient extent to permit the performance of a normal coordinate analysis. Using only the observed and estimated values of the fundamental frequencies Lord and Nakagawa (*257*) calculated the force constants and the eigenvectors of the normal vibrations for an assumed structure of D_{4h} symmetry. Using these results they then computed the zeta constants for the E_g and E_u species of vibrations of the (assumed) D_{4h} model. The zeta constants for the E_g species

TABLE 25

Observed and Calculated Fundamental Frequencies and Coriolis Coupling Coefficients for Cyclopropane-d_0 and Cyclopropane-d_6[a]

Mode[b]		C_3H_6 Obs	C_3H_6 Calc	C_3D_6 Obs	C_3D_6 Calc
A_1'	ν_1	3038.0	3058.4	2242.0	2225.8
	ν_2	1479.0	1482.0	1275.0	1272.5
	ν_3	1188.0	1190.8	956.0	953.6
A_1''	ν_4	1126.0	1128.2	800.0	798.0
A_2'	ν_5	1070.0	1071.5	870.0	868.8
A_2''	ν_6	3101.7	3119.1	2336.9	2323.5
	ν_7	854.0	855.0	614.5	614.2
E'	ν_8	3024.4	3036.5	2209.0	2199.6
	ν_9	1437.7	1441.6	1071.5	1068.3
	ν_{10}	1028.4	1029.3	886.5	885.3
	ν_{11}	868.5	873.1	717.0	715.9
	ζ_8	−0.04	−0.045	−0.05	−0.058
	ζ_9	+0.105	+0.100	+0.033	+0.034
	ζ_{10}	−0.073	−0.069	−0.44	−0.452
	ζ_{11}	−0.96	−0.986	−0.515	−0.524
E''	ν_{12}	3082.0	3094.3	2335.0	2325.5
	ν_{13}	1188.0	1187.7	945.0	950.1
	ν_{14}	739.0	740.2	526.0	525.3
	ζ_{12}		−0.018		−0.027
	ζ_{13}	+0.63	+0.666		+0.589
	ζ_{14}	−0.86	−0.851		−0.841

[a] Taken from Duncan and Burns, Ref. (*256*). Frequencies are in cm^{-1}, zeta constants are dimensionless.

[b] The A_1', E', and E'' species are Raman active, the A_2'' and E' species are infrared active and the A_1'' and A_2' species are forbidden in both infrared absorption and the Raman effect.

were found to be of the correct magnitude but of opposite sign as inferred from the contours of the observed infrared bands assigned to the degenerate vibrations. As predicted by Mills and Duncan (*251*) in their work on the Coriolis coupling in molecules having D_{2d} symmetry (i.e. allene) such a sign change is to be expected when the molecular structure is actually of D_{2d} symmetry. A subsequent calculation of the zeta constants by Lord and Nakagawa for the D_{2d} symmetry gave results which were not only consistent with the normal contours of the observed infrared bands but which also accounted for the unusual shapes of the 749 cm^{-1} band of C_4H_8 and the 556 cm^{-1} band of C_4D_8. For the various arguments involved and details of the calculations reference is made to the original work (*257*).

D. Centrifugal Distortion

The presence of centrifugal distortion is easily recognized in vibration-rotation spectra, especially so in the totally symmetric bands. For symmetric top molecules the empirical distortion constants are the quantities D_J, D_{JK}, and D_K which are given as combinations of the coefficients $\tau_{\alpha\beta\gamma\delta}$ of the quartic term of the angular momentum operators in Eq. (148). For asymmetric top molecules additional empirical constants are needed to adequately describe the energies. Since the molecular force constants determine the value of the centrifugal distortion constants these latter constants are in turn additional empirical data which are used to determine the force constants. There are two theoretical formulations which give the relationship between the force constants and the centrifugal distortion constants, the first order theory of centrifugal distortion by Kivelson and Wilson (*173*) and the all inclusive second order theory of Nielsen (*172*).

As shown by Wilson and Howard (*202*) the Hamiltonian for the non-rigid rotator may be written in the form

$$\mathscr{H} = \tfrac{1}{2}\sum_{\alpha} \sigma_{\alpha\alpha} P_{\alpha}^{2} + \tfrac{1}{4} \sum_{\alpha\beta\gamma\delta} \tau_{\alpha\beta\gamma\delta} P_{\alpha} P_{\beta} P_{\gamma} P_{\delta} \tag{245}$$

where the τ's are given by

$$\tau_{\alpha\beta\gamma\delta} = \sum_{v'}{}' \frac{\langle v \mid \mu_{\alpha\beta} \mid v' \rangle \langle v' \mid \mu_{\gamma\delta} \mid v \rangle}{E_v - E_{v'}} \tag{246}$$

Here E_v is the energy of the vibrational state v, the summation extends over all vibrational states with $v' \neq v$ and v as well as v' stand, as usual, for the totality of the vibrational quantum numbers. The elements of the inverse inertia tensor $\mu_{\alpha\beta}$ are related to the equilibrium moments of inertia as shown in Eq. (140). In his original work on the subject Wilson (*258*) has evaluated the τ's by expanding the $\mu_{\alpha\beta}$ directly in normal coordinates about the equilibrium configuration, retaining only the linear terms. Since the centrifugal distortion correction to the rigid rotor energy is a second order effect anyway its approximation by harmonic terms is deemed adequate.

A more convenient method to evaluate the τ's has been developed by Kivelson and Wilson (*173*) who expand the $\mu_{\alpha\beta}$'s in the internal coordinates

S_i and then transform to normal coordinates. Thus, following Kivelson and Wilson

$$\mu_{\alpha\beta} = \mu_{\alpha\beta}^{e} + \sum_i \mu_{\alpha\beta}^{(i)} S_i \tag{247}$$

where higher order terms in the coordinates S_i are assumed to be negligible and where the constant coefficients $\mu_{\alpha\beta}^{e}$ and

$$\mu_{\alpha\beta}^{(i)} = \left(\frac{\partial\, \mu_{\alpha\beta}}{\partial\, S_i}\right)_e \tag{248}$$

are evaluated for the equilibrium configuration of the molecule. The matrix elements in Eq. (246) are then given by

$$\begin{aligned}\langle v \mid \mu_{\alpha\beta} \mid v' \rangle &= \sum_i \mu_{\alpha\beta}^{(i)} (v \mid S_i \mid v') \\ &= \sum_i \mu_{\alpha\beta}^{(i)} \sum_s L_{is} (v \mid Q_s \mid v')\end{aligned} \tag{249}$$

where the transformation to normal coordinates, Eq. (186), as well as the fact that $\langle v \mid \mu_{\alpha\beta}^{e} \mid v' \rangle = 0$ for $v \neq v'$ have been employed. The τ's, therefore, become

$$\begin{aligned}\tau_{\alpha\beta\gamma\delta} = \sum_{ij} \mu_{\alpha\beta}^{(i)} \mu_{\gamma\delta}^{(j)} \sum_s L_{is} L_{js} \Bigg[&\frac{\langle n_s \mid Q_s \mid n_s + 1 \rangle \langle n_s + 1 \mid Q_s \mid n_s \rangle}{E_s - E_{s+1}} \\ &+ \frac{\langle n_s \mid Q_s \mid n_s - 1 \rangle \langle n_s - 1 \mid Q_s \mid n_s \rangle}{E_s - E_{s-1}} \Bigg]\end{aligned} \tag{250}$$

since the only nonvanishing matrix elements of Q_s for $\Delta v \neq 0$ are those for which $\Delta v = \Delta n_s = \pm 1$ where n_s is the quantum number associated with the normal coordinate Q_s. Using now the expressions

$$\left.\begin{aligned}\langle n_s \mid Q_s \mid n_s + 1 \rangle &= \left(\frac{h}{8\pi^2 c \omega_s}\right)^{1/2} (n_s + 1)^{1/2} \\ \text{and} \quad \langle n_s \mid Q_s \mid n_s - 1 \rangle &= \left(\frac{h}{8\pi^2 c \omega_s}\right)^{1/2} (n_s)^{1/2}\end{aligned}\right\} \tag{251}$$

where ω_s is the vibrational frequency in cm^{-1} of the s th harmonic oscillator, and using $E_s - E_{s\pm 1} = \mp hc\omega_s$ we obtain for the $\tau_{\alpha\beta\gamma\delta}$

$$\begin{aligned}\tau_{\alpha\beta\gamma\delta} &= \sum_{ij} \mu_{\alpha\beta}^{(i)} \mu_{\gamma\delta}^{(j)} \sum_s L_{is} L_{js} \left(\frac{1}{8\pi^2 c^2 \omega_s^{\,2}}\right) [-(n_s + 1) + n_s] \\ &= -\tfrac{1}{2} \sum_{ij} \mu_{\alpha\beta}^{(i)} \mu_{\gamma\delta}^{(j)} \sum_s L_{is} L_{js} \lambda_s^{-1} \\ &= -\tfrac{1}{2} \sum_{ij} \mu_{\alpha\beta}^{(i)} \mu_{\gamma\delta}^{(j)} (f^{-1})_{ij}\end{aligned} \tag{252}$$

where the last step is obtained by means of Eq. (189) according to which

$$(f^{-1})_{ij} = \sum_s L_{is} L_{js} \lambda_s^{-1} \tag{253}$$

The derivatives of the components of the inverse inertia tensor with respect to the internal coordinates, $\mu_{\alpha\beta}^{(i)}$, are easily evaluated by rewriting them in terms of the derivatives of the inertia tensor itself. Thus, expanding the inertia tensor **I** in a Taylor's series about the equilibrium configuration we have, to terms linear in the coordinates S_i

$$\mathbf{I} = \mathbf{I}^e + \sum_i \mathbf{J}^{(i)} S_i \tag{254}$$

where the tensor $\mathbf{I}^e$ and the derivative

$$\mathbf{J}^{(i)} = \left(\frac{\partial \mathbf{I}}{\partial S_i}\right)_e \tag{255}$$

are evaluated at equilibrium. Since, by definition, the tensor $\boldsymbol{\mu}$ is inverse to **I**, we have, by multiplying Eq. (254) by the tensor form of Eq. (247) and retaining only linear terms in the S_i

$$\mathbf{I}\boldsymbol{\mu} = \mathbf{E} = \mathbf{I}^e \boldsymbol{\mu}^e + \mathbf{I}^e \sum_i \boldsymbol{\mu}^{(i)} S_i + \sum_i \mathbf{J}^{(i)} S_i \boldsymbol{\mu}^e \tag{256}$$

where **E** is the unit tensor, or

$$0 = \sum_i [\mathbf{I}^e \boldsymbol{\mu}^{(i)} + \mathbf{J}^{(i)} \boldsymbol{\mu}^e] S_i \tag{257}$$

If the S_i are independent coordinates then it follows that

$$\boldsymbol{\mu}^{(i)} = -\boldsymbol{\mu}^e \mathbf{J}^{(i)} \boldsymbol{\mu}^e \tag{258}$$

or, for the $\alpha\beta$ component

$$\mu_{\alpha\beta}^{(i)} = -\frac{J_{\alpha\beta}^{(i)}}{I_{\alpha\alpha}^e I_{\beta\beta}^e} \tag{259}$$

where

$$J_{\alpha\beta}^{(i)} = \left(\frac{\partial I_{\alpha\beta}}{\partial S_i}\right)_e \tag{260}$$

The τ's are, therefore, given by

$$\tau_{\alpha\beta\gamma\delta} = -\frac{1}{2}\frac{1}{I_{\alpha\alpha}^e I_{\beta\beta}^e I_{\gamma\gamma}^e I_{\delta\delta}^e} \sum_{ij} J_{\alpha\beta}^{(i)} J_{\gamma\delta}^{(j)} (f^{-1})_{ij} \tag{261}$$

For the various valence internal coordinates that are customarily used the derivatives $J_{\alpha\beta}^{(i)}$ may be evaluated according to the method of Kivelson and

Wilson who also discuss the utilization of the molecular symmetry to simplify the calculations. The τ-coefficients are seen to be a function of the molecular force constants but, except in very simple molecules, the relationship is a rather complicated one. The elements $(f^{-1})_{ij}$ of the inverse force constant matrix are called the compliances. Decius (*259*) has discussed the various properties of the compliance matrix $\mathbf{f}^{-1}$ and has shown how the formulation of the vibration problem in terms of it offers certain advantages.

The calculation of the energy levels of the Hamiltonian given by Eq. (*245*) has been performed by Kivelson and Wilson to first order of approximation. Their result for the general asymmetric top rotator is given by Eq. (114) which contains six distortion coefficients $A_1, \ldots, A_6$ which are functions of the $\tau_{\alpha\beta\gamma\delta}$. However, as was shown by Watson (*260*) only five of these coefficients are independent. For symmetric top molecules the number of independent coefficients is three, these being D_J, D_{JK}, and D_K which appear in Eq. (62b). In terms of the τ's the empirical constants are, in energy units,

$$D_J = -\tfrac{1}{32}(3\tau_{xxxx}+3\tau_{yyyy}+2\tau_{xxyy}+4\tau_{xyxy})\hbar^4 \tag{262a}$$

$$D_K = D_J-\tfrac{1}{4}(\tau_{zzzz}-\tau_{zzxx}-\tau_{yyzz}-2\tau_{xzxz}-2\tau_{yzyz})\hbar^4 \tag{262b}$$

$$D_{JK} = -D_J-D_K-\tfrac{1}{4}\tau_{zzzz}\hbar^4 \tag{262c}$$

For planar molecules Dowling (*261*) has demonstrated the existence of relationships between the τ's thus reducing the number of independent parameters. In particular, for planar symmetric top molecules (point group D_{3h} or higher) Dowling showed that

$$D_J = -\tfrac{1}{4}\tau_{xxxx}\hbar^4 \tag{263a}$$

$$D_{JK} = \tfrac{1}{2}(\tau_{xxxx}-2\tau_{zzzz})\hbar^4 \tag{263b}$$

$$D_K = -\tfrac{1}{4}(\tau_{xxxx}-3\tau_{zzzz})\hbar^4 \tag{263c}$$

of which only two are independent since now $D_{JK} = -\tfrac{2}{3}(D_J+2D_K)$.

The centrifugal distortion constants may also be computed by the general method developed by Nielsen (*172*). In this method the instantaneous moments of inertia are expanded in normal coordinates about the equilibrium configuration, only linear terms are retained and a second order perturbation calculation is performed. In Nielsen's notation

$$I_{\alpha\alpha} = I^e_{\alpha\alpha}+\sum_{s\sigma} a^{\alpha\alpha}_{s\sigma} Q_{s\sigma}+\ldots \tag{264a}$$

$$I_{\alpha\beta} = \sum_{s\sigma} a^{\alpha\beta}_{s\sigma} Q_{s\sigma}+\ldots \tag{264b}$$

where the expansion coefficients are given by

$$a_{s\sigma}^{\alpha\alpha} = 2\sum_i M_i^{-\frac{1}{2}}(\beta_i'^0 l_{i,s\sigma}^{(\beta)} + \gamma_i'^0 l_{i,s\sigma}^{(\alpha)}) \tag{265a}$$

and

$$a_{s\sigma}^{\alpha\beta} = -\sum_i M_i^{-\frac{1}{2}}(\alpha_i'^0 l_{i,s\sigma}^{(\beta)} + \beta_i'^0 l_{i,s\sigma}^{(\alpha)}) \tag{265b}$$

In these expressions $\alpha_i'^0$, $\beta_i'^0$, $\gamma_i'^0$ are the Cartesian coordinates of the ith nucleus at equilibrium in the molecule fixed coordinate system defined by the Eckart conditions, the $l_{i,s\sigma}^{(\alpha)}$ are the transformation coefficients which relate the normal coordinates $Q_{s\sigma}$ to the Cartesian displacements $\delta\alpha_i'$ of the ith nucleus

$$M_i^{\frac{1}{2}}\delta\alpha_i' = \sum_{s\sigma} l_{i,s\delta}^{(\alpha)} Q_{s\sigma} \tag{266}$$

and where the double index $s\sigma$ is used to label the eigenvalue λ_s and the component of the vibration, with $\sigma = 1, 2, 3$ according to whether the vibration is nondegenerate, twofold, or threefold degenerate (262). [In our previous discussion the degeneracy index was not explicitly written out. Note also that the transformation given by Eq. (266) is the inverse of that given by Eq. (216).]

As was shown by Walsh (*243*) the coefficients $a_{s\sigma}^{\alpha\alpha}$ and $a_{s\sigma}^{\alpha\beta}$ may be expressed in terms of the Wilson **s**-vector and thus their evaluation may be formally incorporated into the *FG* matrix scheme of normal coordinate analysis. Thus, in terms of our notation, but using the index σ as well, the a's are given by (*243*)

$$a_{s\sigma}^{\alpha\alpha} = 2\sum_{n,it} m_n^{-\frac{1}{2}}[\mathbf{s}_{in}\cdot(\beta_n{}^e\boldsymbol{\varepsilon}_\beta + \gamma_n{}^e\boldsymbol{\varepsilon}_\gamma)]U_{ti}(\mathscr{L}^{-1})_{s\sigma,t} \tag{267a}$$

$$a_{s\sigma}^{\alpha\beta} = -\sum_{n,it} m_n^{-\frac{1}{2}}[\mathbf{s}_{in}\cdot(\alpha_i{}^e\boldsymbol{\varepsilon}_\beta + \beta_i{}^e\boldsymbol{\varepsilon}_\alpha)]U_{ti}(\mathscr{L}^{-1})_{s\sigma,t} \tag{267b}$$

where m_n is the mass of the nth nucleus, $\mathbf{s}_{in}$ is the Wilson **s**-vector, $\boldsymbol{\varepsilon}_\alpha$ is the unit vector along the α-axis of the molecule fixed Cartesian coordinates, U_{ti} is the transformation from the generalized to the symmetry coordinates, Eq. (198), and $(\mathscr{L}^{-1})_{s\sigma,t}$ is the transformation from symmetry to normal coordinates, Eq. (234). These expressions may be conveniently written as [see Ref. (*264*)]

$$a_{s\sigma}^{\alpha\alpha} = 2\sum_t (\mathscr{L}^{-1})_{s\sigma,t} W_t^{\alpha\alpha} \tag{268a}$$

$$a_{s\sigma}^{\alpha\beta} = -\sum_t (\mathscr{L}^{-1})_{s\sigma,t} W_t^{\alpha\beta} \tag{268b}$$

where

$$W_t^{\alpha\alpha} = \sum_i U_{ti} V_i^{\alpha\alpha} \tag{269a}$$

$$W_t^{\alpha\beta} = \sum_i U_{ti} V_i^{\alpha\beta} \tag{269b}$$

in which

$$V_i^{\alpha\alpha} = \sum_n m_n^{-\frac{1}{2}} \mathbf{s}_{in} \cdot (\beta_n{}^e \boldsymbol{\varepsilon}_\beta + \gamma_n{}^e \boldsymbol{\varepsilon}_\gamma) \tag{270a}$$

$$V_i^{\alpha\beta} = \sum_n m_n^{-\frac{1}{2}} \mathbf{s}_{in} \cdot (\alpha_n{}^e \boldsymbol{\varepsilon}_\beta + \beta_n{}^e \boldsymbol{\varepsilon}_\alpha) \tag{270b}$$

The quantities $W_t^{\alpha\alpha}$ and $W_t^{\alpha\beta}$ are simple algebraic expressions whose computation is eased by the fact that $V_i^{\alpha\alpha}$ is invariant under rotations about the α-axis, reflection in a plane containing the α-axis, inversions through the origin, and reflections in a plane perpendicular to the α-axis; $V_i^{\alpha\beta}$ is invariant under inversion, simultaneous reflection in the $\alpha\gamma$- and $\beta\gamma$-planes and reflection in the $\alpha\beta$-plane, whereas it changes sign under reflection in the $\alpha\gamma$-plane or in the $\beta\gamma$-plane (*264*). These symmetry properties shorten the calculations and also provide checks on their accuracy. With the eigenvectors $(\mathscr{L}^{-1})_{s\sigma,t}$ that are obtained through the solution of the normal coordinate problem the coefficients $a_{s\sigma}^{\alpha\alpha}$ and $\alpha_{s\sigma}^{\alpha\beta}$ are then obtained numerically. The symmetric top centrifugal distortion constants D_J, D_{JK}, and D_K are then computed by the expressions derived by Nielsen (*263*) accurate to second order. According to Nielsen

$$D_J = \frac{h^3}{512\pi^6 c^3} \sum_{s\sigma} \frac{1}{8\omega_s{}^2} \left[3\frac{(a_{s\sigma}^{xx})^2}{(I_{xx}^e)^4} + 3\frac{(a_{s\sigma}^{yy})^2}{(I_{yy}^e)^4} + 2\frac{a_{s\sigma}^{xx}a_{s\sigma}^{yy} + 2(a_{s\sigma}^{xy})^2}{(I_{xx}^e)^2(I_{yy}^e)^2} \right] \tag{271}$$

$$D_L = \frac{h^3}{64\pi^6 c^3} \sum_{s\sigma} \frac{1}{8\omega_s{}^2} \left[\frac{(a_{s\sigma}^{zz})^2}{(I_{zz}^e)^4} \right] \tag{272}$$

$$D_{JL} = \frac{h^3}{64\pi^6 c^3} \sum_{s\sigma} \frac{1}{8\omega_s{}^2} \left[\frac{a_{s\sigma}^{zz}a_{s\sigma}^{xx} + 2(a_{s\sigma}^{xz})^2}{(I_{xx}^e)^2(I_{zz}^e)^2} + \frac{a_{s\sigma}^{yy}a_{s\sigma}^{zz} + 2(a_{s\sigma}^{yz})^2}{(I_{yy}^e)^2(I_{zz}^e)^2} \right] \tag{273}$$

The empirical coefficients D_{JK} and D_K are then obtained from

$$D_{JK} = D_{JL} - 2D_J \tag{274}$$

$$D_K = D_L - D_{JL} + D_J \tag{275}$$

The two methods outlined here for the calculation of centrifugal distortion constants are equivalent. Most computations performed thus far have been based on the Kivelson-Wilson technique but the incorporation of the *FG* matrix formalism into the Nielsen expressions makes the latter attractive for the calculations particularly since the $W_t^{\alpha\alpha}$ and $W_t^{\alpha\beta}$ are easily evaluated and since the eigenvector matrices $\mathscr{L}^{-1}$ are also used in the computation of the Coriolis zeta matrices. Computations based on this method have been performed by Walsh (*243*) and Clark (*250*).

Let us now consider the empirical data which are presented in the various Tables. We note first that with the exception of CH_3D only the constant D_J has been determined through the Raman investigations and that its value is afflicted with a considerable error. Moreover the accuracy of the D_J values deduced from infrared vibration rotation bands is most often not much better, the exception being those simple molecules (CO_2, CS_2, HCN, N_2O, NH_3, and others) which have been very extensively studied over many years. This fact makes the direct utilization of centrifugal distortion constants deduced from infrared and Raman spectra for the determination of the molecular force field questionable. The fact that the constant D_{JK} has thus far not been determined from a pure rotation spectrum has thrown some doubts on the accuracy of the B_0-values. Using estimates of D_{JK} obtained via Eqs. (108) and (109) Tyulin and Tatevskii (*134*) suggest improved values for both B_0 and D_J for a number of symmetric top molecules (see Table 8). In a few cases they find that the D_J-values are negative, i.e., for ethane-d_6, methylacetylene-h_4 and -d_4, and zincdimethyl-d_6. Since the constant D_J cannot be negative they suggest that the Hamiltonian given by Eq. (245), and thus also the term value expression Eq. (62b), is inadequate and that terms of higher order in the angular momentum operators are needed to account for the observed spectrum.

In only a few cases has it thus far been possible to assess the reliability of the D_J values for symmetric top molecules determined from the Raman spectrum. For chloroform, $CHCl_3^{35}$, the value $D_J = 1.44$ kc/sec $= 4.80 \times 10^{-8}$ cm^{-1} calculated by Dowling et al. (*265*) from Eq. (302) was in disagreement with the experimental value determined from microwave work. This prompted a study of the pure rotational Raman spectrum of chloroform. Since rotational transitions with J ranging as high as 80–100 are commonly observed in the rotational Raman spectra of heavy molecules it was believed that a reliable D_J value might be obtained. In spite of the fact that due to presence of various isotopic species of chloroform the rotational spectrum was one of the most difficult ones to analyze, the Raman result $D_J = (6.2 \pm 2) \times 10^{-8}$ cm^{-1} suggests that the value computed by Dowling et al. is correct. An independent and contemporaneous microwave investigation of $CHCl_3{}^{35}$ by Favero and Mirri (*148*) gave the result $D_J = (5.07 \pm 0.03) \times 10^{-8}$ cm^{-1} and a later study of the infrared vibration-rotation spectrum of naturally abundant chloroform by Antilla (*149*) yielded $D_J = (5.5 \pm 0.7) \times 10^{-8}\ \text{cm}^{-1}$. Similarly, the original microwave analysis of the slightly asymmetric top molecule cyclopentene gave centrifugal distortion constants which were shown to be erroneous by means of the rotational Raman spectrum (*89*) and this was corroborated by a reanalysis of the microwave spectrum (*180*).

For the few asymmetric top molecules (Table 17) for which microwave and Raman D_J values are available the comparison indicates fair agreement among them. In a study of the determination of centrifugal distortion constants from microwave spectra of asymmetric tops Sørensen (*178*) concludes that quite reliable D_J values may be provided by the Raman spectroscopic technique. On the other hand Petzuch (*266*) computes D_J, D_{JK}, and D_K for cyclopentene from normal coordinates. The calculated value $D_J = 7.9 \times 10^{-8}\ \text{cm}^{-1}$ is higher than the available experimental value $(3.75 \pm 1.25) \times 10^{-8}$ [Ref. (*89*)] and a comparison with the value $(30 \pm 50) \times 10^{-8}$ [Ref. (179)] is not meaningful.

Petzuch's calculations also show that the centrifugal distortion constants are determined primarily by the carbon ring vibrations but that otherwise they are quite insensitive to changes in the assignment of the vibrational frequencies and thus to the computed normal coordinates. This finding substantiates the earlier empirical result (*87–89,90,91,143,145*) that for planar cyclic molecules the constant D_J is given to a good approximation by Kratzer's formula for diatomic molecules, namely,

$$D_J = \frac{4B^3}{\omega^2} \tag{276}$$

if the frequency of the totally symmetric ring breathing vibration is used for ω. Indeed, for cyclopentene using $\omega = 900\ \text{cm}^{-1}$ and $B_0 = 0.24165\ \text{cm}^{-1}$ (Table 17) we have from Eq. (276) $D_J = 7.0 \times 10^{-8}\ \text{cm}^{-1}$ which agrees exceedingly well with the value calculated by Petzuch. Similarly for cyclopropane (which is not a planar molecule) using $\omega = 1188\ \text{cm}^{-1}$ (Table 25) and $B_0 = 0.6692\ \text{cm}^{-1}$ (Table 8) Kratzer's formula gives $D_J = 8.48 \times 10^{-7}\ \text{cm}^{-1}$ whereas the value calculated by Duncan and Burns (*254*) from normal coordinates is $9.5 \times 10^{-7}\ \text{cm}^{-1}$. The experimental values for D_J are $(5 \pm 1) \times 10^{-7}$ [Raman, Ref. (*141*)], $(6.3 \pm 1) \times 10^{-7}$ [Raman, Ref. (*88*)] and $(8.2 \pm 1.5) \times 10^{-7}\ \text{cm}^{-1}$ [infrared, Ref. (*141a*)]. One would expect that Kratzer's formula would be more appropriate for linear molecules but in the few cases examined, namely cyanogen (*119*) and diacetylene (*117*) this expectation is not born out.

Only for acetylene (*117*) is the agreement between the observed and calculated values good. Somewhat more disturbing, however, is the fact that for cyanogen and diacetylene the constant D_J computed from normal coordinates based on a general force field agrees well with the approximate value determined from Eq. (276) but is in decided disagreement with the observed Raman value (*117,119*).

E. Summary

In the preceding we discussed the normal coordinate, Coriolis coupling, and centrifugal distortion calculations more or less independently of one another. It is, therefore, appropriate to conclude this section on Dynamical Aspects of Structure Determination with a brief summary in which we mention a few aspects of this topic which have bearing on all three types of computations as well as other sources of empirical data which are useful in structure determination.

The techniques discussed in this section are based on the harmonic oscillator model for the vibrating molecule. The basic observational data that go into the calculation of the vibrational normal coordinates are the vibrational frequencies as determined from the infrared and Raman spectra. The observed fundamental frequencies ν_s differ from the harmonic frequencies ω_s by amounts which are determined by the anharmonic portion of the potential energy. Although it is possible in principle to deduce the harmonic frequencies from the observed spectrum provided that sufficient data on overtone and combination vibrations have been collected, this has in practice been accomplished for only a very few molecules. For the vast majority of cases only the observed, anharmonic, frequencies ν_s of the fundamental vibrations are available. The normal coordinate calculations based on such frequencies are, therefore, afflicted with an error which is propagated into the calculation of Coriolis and centrifugal distortion constants. Similarly the zeta sum rules and the isotope rule, Eq. (244) hold only for a harmonic force field and deviations between the observed and predicted values of the sums may be attributable to the anharmonicities. A method to at least partially remedy this deficiency is an approximation suggested by Dennison (*267*). If the relation between ν_s and ω_s is assumed to be of the form

$$\nu_s = \omega_s(1 - x_s) \tag{277}$$

where x_s is an anharmonicity constant and if the same relation is assumed to hold for the frequencies $\nu_s^{(i)}$ and $\omega_s^{(i)}$ and for the constant $x_s^{(i)}$ of the isotopic variants of the molecule then according to Dennison

$$\frac{x_s^{(i)}}{x_s} = \frac{\omega_s^{(i)}}{\omega_s} \approx \frac{\nu_s^{(i)}}{\nu_s} \tag{278}$$

Eqs. (277) and (278) together with the Teller-Redlich product rule (*268*) often allow a good approximation to the harmonic frequencies to be obtained.

From Eqs. (271)–(273) we see that the centrifugal distortion correction to the energy is independent of the vibrational states, a result which is accurate to second order. The improved accuracy of modern data obtained from infrared spectra shows however a slight dependence of the centrifugal distortion constants upon the vibrational states and a higher order theory of vibration-rotation spectra has subsequently been developed (*269*). Furthermore the discussion of the Coriolis coupling and centrifugal distortion effects presented in the above makes it appear that these two effects are quite independent of one another. This is of course not the case and has been discussed by Aliev and Aleksanyan (*270*) who show that the relation between the Coriolis and centrifugal distortion coefficients is

$$\sum_{\alpha\gamma} [(I_{\alpha\alpha}^e)^2 I_{\gamma\gamma}^e]\tau_{\alpha\gamma\alpha\gamma} = -4\sum_s \lambda_s^{-1}\{1-\tfrac{1}{2}\sum_\alpha\sum_j (\zeta_{sj}^\alpha)^2\} \tag{279}$$

which is independent of the force field or the form of the vibrations. For a linear molecule Aliev and Aleksanyan show that with the substitutions $B = 1/2I$ and $D_J = -\frac{1}{4}\tau_{xxxx}$ Eq. (279) becomes

$$D_J = 4B^3\{\sum_s \lambda_s^{-1}[1-\sum_j (\zeta_{sj})^2]\} \tag{280}$$

The integration of vibrational frequencies, Coriolis constants and centrifugal distortion constant data into the determination of the molecular force field has been attempted by several investigators. While Daykin et al. (*271*) utilize only the centrifugal distortion constants as additional data, the full utilization of Coriolis and centrifugal distortion constants as independent parameters in addition to the vibrational frequencies has been developed by Mills, Duncan, and their co-workers (*272*) who have also treated the specific cases of ethane, allene and cyclopropane discussed earlier in this section.

A dynamical effect which has bearing on the direct comparison of molecular structures determined from electron diffraction and spectroscopic methods is the so called Bastiansen-Morino shrinkage effect. If, for example, in a linear triatomic molecule *ABC* the internuclear distances *r*(*A*–*B*), *r*(*B*–*C*) and *r*(*A*- - -*C*) are determined by the electron diffraction technique it will be found that $r(A\text{---}C) < r(A\text{–}B)+r(B\text{–}C)$. This "shrinkage" effect is due to the fact that at a temperature $T > 0$ the molecules are distributed over the various vibrational states. The effect can be theoretically assessed by calculating the "mean square amplitudes" of vibration which depend very much on the vibrational normal coordinates. Thus, the C—C and C—H bond lengths in benzene determined from electron diffraction work have been corrected in this manner by Brooks et al. (*225*). The corrected values (Table 21) are r(C—C) = 1.4000 Å and r(C—H) = 1.0897 Å. In turn, the mean square amplitudes of vibration can be directly determined from electron diffraction studies and thus take their place along side the Coriolis and centrifugal distortion constants as independent parameters for the determination of a molecular force field. As an example of such a calculation we may cite the work on PCl_3 done by Hedberg and Iwasaki (*273,274*). In this work the structure of PCl_3 was determined by electron diffraction from the vapor at 300° and 505°K. Both the size and the mean square amplitudes of vibration of the molecule are greater at the higher temperature. Thus, at 300° and 505°K the results are, respectively, r(P—Cl) = 2.039 ± 0.0014 Å and= 2.045 ± 0.0016 Å for the bond length, $<$Cl—P—Cl = $100.27 \pm 0.09°$ and $100.40 \pm 0.16°$ for the pyramidal angles, and l(P—Cl) = 0.0501 ± 0.0013 Å and 0.0594 ± 0.0017 Å for the mean square amplitudes of vibration. The bond length r(P—Cl) at 300° and 505°K is greater than the equilibrium value by 0.0054 and 0.0076 Å respectively. The experimental mean square amplitudes together with the observed fundamental frequencies of vibration were then used to derive a set of force constants for the molecule. Since the mean square amplitudes are functions of the temperature then the force constants derived in this manner are similarly dependent on the temperature. It is interesting to point out that the force constants that describe the bond stretching vibrations are quite sensitive to the value of the mean square amplitudes, i.e. the temperature, but that the bending vibrations force constants are quite insensitive to the temperature. A more inclusive treatment has been presented by Papoušek and Plíva (*275*) who use the mean square amplitudes and centrifugal distortion constants to obtain the force field by means of a least squares procedure.

The formalism of mean square amplitude analysis has been fully developed in terms of the Wilson *FG* matrix method. A full treatment of this special area including especially the Coriolis interactions into the calculations has recently been published by S. J. Cyvin (*228*) which is to be consulted for the details of the algebraic calculations and numerical results for many molecular models.

There are additional experimental sources of data which have been utilized in the solution of molecular structure problems (dipole moment, thermodynamic functions, and others) but the last topic that we wish to discuss and that is especially germane to our subject is the problem of the intensities of Raman lines. This is taken up in the next section.

VII. INTENSITIES, LINE WIDTHS, AND RELATED PROBLEMS

A. Introduction

The problem of molecular spectroscopy is twofold: the determination of the energy levels and the determination of the transition probabilities for a molecular system. In the foregoing sections we dealt exclusively with the first of these two problems and showed how the structure of a molecule can be determined from the analysis of the rotational fine structure of the vibration-rotation Raman and also infrared bands and how the dynamics of the molecular vibration, rotation and their interactions play a decisive role in these endeavors. However, except for the derivation of the Raman selection rules and reference to an occasional computation of the intensity distribution in a Raman band no attention has been paid thus far to the intensities and widths of the Raman transitions.

It is a well known fact of spectroscopy that the analyses of the energy levels have been performed to a high degree of success and satisfaction but that the study of the intensities leaves a lot to be desired. There are two reasons for this. It is extremely difficult to make measurements of intensities which give the absolute values of the transition probabilities with an uncertainty of less than, say, 10%, and these experimental difficulties are matched by the complexity of the theory of radiative transitions. Nevertheless, a considerable body of data has been collected on the Raman intensities of some polyatomic molecules. In this section we wish to describe very briefly the state of affairs regarding the determination of the mean value and the anisotropy of the molecular polarizability, the depolarization factors, and the Raman line widths insofar as these pertain to our subject of high resolution studies.

B. Raman Intensities

From Eqs. (14) (42) (43) (61a), and (61b) we have for the scattered power produced by a single Raman transition between states v, S and v', S' (v, v' = totality of vibrational quantum numbers, S, S' = totality of rotational quantum numbers)

$$I(v, S; v', S') = \bar{Q}_{v,S;v',S'} I_0 \tag{281}$$

where I_0 (in ergs/sec-cm^2) is the intensity of the unidirectionally incident beam of exciting radiation and $\bar{Q}_{v,S;v',S'}$ is the molecular scattering cross section averaged over all orientations in space. The cross section is given by

$$\bar{Q}_{v,S;v',S'} = \frac{2^7\pi^5}{9}\frac{(\nu_0+\nu')^4}{c^4}[G^{(0)}_{v,S;v',S'} + G^{(1)}_{v,S;v',S'}] \tag{282}$$

where

$$G^{(0)}_{v,S;v',S'} = 3(2J+1)\mid a_{vSO;v'S'O}\mid^2 \tag{283a}$$

and

$$G^{(1)}_{v,S;v',S'} = (2J+1)\sum_{\lambda\mu}\mid (\alpha^{(1)}_{\lambda\mu})_{vSO;v'S'(\lambda+\mu)}\mid^2 \tag{283b}$$

are the frequency independent [i.e., independent of the $(\nu_0+\nu')^4$ dependence] isotropic and anisotropic parts of the scattering cross section, in which a is the mean value of the polarizability and $\alpha^{(1)}_{\lambda\mu}$ is the $\lambda\mu$-component ($\lambda\mu$ = space fixed circular coordinates) of the anisotropic portion of the polarizability [see Eqs. (20–22) and (35) and (36)]. If the total cross section given by Eq. (282) is summed over all initial and final rotational states Placzek and Teller (*19*) have shown that the total scattered power produced in a vibrational transition $v' \leftarrow v$ is the same as the power scattered by a vibrating, nonrotating molecule held fixed in space but averaged over all possible orientations. The corresponding sum rule is that the isotropic and anisotropic contributions to the scattering cross section are given by

$$G^{(0)}_{vv'} = 3\mid a_{vv'}\mid^2 \tag{284a}$$

$$G^{(1)}_{vv'} = \sum_{\lambda'\mu'}\mid (\alpha^{(1)}_{\lambda'u'})_{vv'}\mid^2 \tag{284b}$$

where $a = \frac{1}{3}Tr\boldsymbol{\alpha} = \frac{1}{3}(\alpha_{xx}+\alpha_{yy}+\alpha_{zz}) = \frac{1}{3}(\alpha_{00}+2\alpha_{1-1})$ is the mean value of the tensor (x, y, z and $\lambda'\mu'$ = Cartesian and circular, molecule fixed coordinates, respectively). It is more convenient to express the intensity formulas in terms of the anisotropy γ of the polarizability rather than in terms of the quantity $G^{(1)}$.

It is well known that a second rank tensor possesses three invariants namely the trace, the sum of the determinants of the three 2×2 minors taken along the principal diagonal, and the determinant. [This is easily demonstrated in terms of the principal axes transformation which diagonalizes the (symmetric) polarizability tensor. The three invariants are the coefficients in the cubic secular equation which gives the principal values of the tensor.] The anistropy of the polarizability tensor, γ, is defined by

$$\gamma^2 = \tfrac{1}{2}[3G - | Tr\boldsymbol{\alpha} |^2] \tag{285}$$

[see Eqs. (53) and (54)]. In Cartesian coordinates γ^2 is then of the form

$$\gamma^2 = \tfrac{1}{2}[(\alpha_{xx}-\alpha_{yy})^2+(\alpha_{yy}-\alpha_{zz})^2+(\alpha_{zz}-\alpha_{xx})^2+6(\alpha_{xy}^2+\alpha_{yz}^2+\alpha_{zx}^2)] \tag{286a}$$

while in the circular coordinate representation we have

$$\gamma^2 = | \alpha_{00}-\alpha_{1-1} |^2+6 | \alpha_{01} |^2+3 | \alpha_{11} |^2 \tag{286b}$$

The polarizability tensor was decomposed into an isotropic, a symmetric, and an antisymmetric part, the last of which is zero. The symmetric part $\boldsymbol{\alpha}^{(1)}$ has a zero trace so that the quantity $G_{vv'}^{(1)}$ may be replaced by the square of the anisotropy, γ^2, or from Eqs. (284b) and (285)

$$G_{vv'}^{(1)} = \tfrac{2}{3} | \gamma_{vv'} |^2 \tag{287}$$

For the total vibrational scattering cross section we then have

$$Q_{vv'} = \frac{2^7\pi^5}{9}\frac{(\nu_0+\nu')^4}{c^4}[3 | a_{vv'} |^2+\tfrac{2}{3} | \gamma_{vv'} |^2] \tag{288}$$

For an ensemble of N molecules which at temperature T are distributed over the various vibrational states we have for the total scattered power

$$\begin{aligned} I(v, v') &= I_0 \sum_v \frac{N_v}{N} Q_{vv'} \\ &= I_0 \frac{2^7\pi^5}{9}\frac{(\nu_0+\nu')^4}{c^4}\frac{\sum_v[3 | a_{vv'} |^2+\tfrac{2}{3} | \gamma_{vv'} |^2]\, e^{-E_v/kT}}{\sum_v e^{-E_v/kT}} \end{aligned} \tag{289}$$

One of the quantities that is most important in the assignment of the observed Raman bands of liquids to the normal modes of vibration is the depolarization factor. To be sure, the rotational structure of the Raman band of gases is more useful in this respect, but even for gases, the depolarization factor is another important datum (see the following). For linearly polarized unidirectionally incident light and orthogonal observation direction (see Fig. 1), the depolarization factor ρ is defined to be ratio of the minimum scattered power to maximum scattered power. Thus,

$$\rho = \frac{I_\perp}{I_\parallel} = \frac{I_y}{I_z} = \frac{| C_y |^2}{| C_z |^2} \tag{290}$$

where $I_\perp$ and $I_\parallel$ is the power radiated by an induced dipole that oscillates perpendicular and parallel to the direction of vibration of the incident electric vector.

Since $C_y = -i(C_{+1} - C_{-1})/\sqrt{2}$, $I_y = \text{const} \sum_M |(\alpha_{10})_{vSM;v'S'(M+1)}|^2 = \text{const} \{\frac{1}{10} G^{(1)}_{vS;v'S'}\}$ and similarly $I_z = \text{const} \sum_M |(\alpha_{00})_{vSM;v'S'M}|^2 = \text{const} \{\frac{1}{3} G^{(0)}_{vS;v'S'} + \frac{2}{15} G^{(1)}_{vS;v'S'}\}$ in view of Eq. (60.) The depolarization factor is then given by

$$\rho = \frac{3G^{(1)}_{vS;v'S'}}{10G^{(0)}_{vS;v'S'} + 4G^{(1)}_{vS;v'S'}} . \tag{291}$$

If one invokes the sum rules Eq. (284) and also uses Eq. (287) one obtains instead Eq. (291)

$$\rho = \frac{3\,|\gamma_{vv'}|^2}{45\,|a_{vv'}|^2 + 4\,|\gamma_{vv'}|^2} \tag{292}$$

which is the ratio of intensities integrated over the whole vibration-rotation band. Equations (289) and (292) are experimentally measurable quantities from which the molecular parameters $a_{vv'}$ and $\gamma_{vv'}$ can be determined. A host of experimental investigations based on these two equations has been directed toward the evaluation of these invariants and the older work has been summarized in the books by Bhagavantam (*276*), Stuart (*277*), and Fabelinskii (*278*). The older work was performed primarily with natural, i.e., unpolarized, incident radiation. The depolarization factors ρ for linearly polarized and ρ_n for natural incident light are related by

$$\rho_n = \frac{2\rho}{1+\rho} \tag{293}$$

Since the rotational transitions, $\Delta J \neq 0$, are determined only by $G^{(1)}_{vS;v'S'}$ the depolarization factor for a rotational line is always 3/4 (6/7 for natural light). For the Q-branches for which $\Delta J = 0$, however, both the isotropic and the anisotropic parts of the polarizability determine the intensity and depolarization factor, both of which are in general functions of the quantum number J, with different results being obtained for the various special cases. Thus, limiting ourselves to the Q-branches of the totally symmetric vibrations of symmetric top molecules, Eq. (87) gives only the anisotropic contribution to the intensity. To this has to be added the contribution due to the isotropic scattering which is determined by

$\frac{1}{3}G_{vv'}^{(0)} = (2J+1) \mid a_{vv'} \mid^2$. Thus, using Eq. (68a) and summing over K we have from Eq. (291)

$$\rho^Q(J) = \frac{3[\frac{3}{2} \sum_K g_{JK} b_{JK,JK} \mid (\alpha_{oo})_{vv'} \mid^2 \exp(-[G(v)+F(J,K)]hc/kT)]}{\sum_K \{10(3 \mid a_{vv'} \mid^2 + 4[\frac{3}{2} b_{JK,JK} \mid (\alpha_{oo})_{vv'} \mid^2]\} g_{JK} \cdot \exp(-[G(v)+F(J,K)]hc/kT)}$$

$$= \frac{3 \mid \gamma_{vv'} \mid^2 \sum_K g_{JK} b_{JK,JK} \exp(-[G(v)+F(J,K)]hc/kT)}{\sum_K [45 \mid a_{vv'} \mid^2 + 4 \mid \gamma_{vv'} \mid^2 b_{JK,JK}] g_{JK} \exp(-[G(v)+F(J,K)]hc/kT)} \tag{294}$$

where the intensity factor $b_{JK,JK}$ is given in Table 1, and where the substitution $\gamma = \frac{3}{2}\alpha_{oo}$ (valid only for the symmetric top) has been made. For diatomic and linear polyatomic molecules there is no K-dependence so that

$$\rho^Q(J) = \frac{3 \mid \gamma_{vv'} \mid^2 f(J)}{45 \mid a_{vv'} \mid^2 + 4 \mid \gamma_{vv'} \mid^2 f(J)} \tag{295a}$$

where

$$f(J) = \frac{J(J+1)}{(2J-1)(2J+3)} \tag{295b}$$

If the Q-branch is not resolved into its individual transitions, both numerator and denominator of Eq. (294) have to be summed over J as well. For unresolved bands Placzek and Teller (*19*) have performed this calculation. If the fractional contribution of the Q-branch to the anisotropic part of the intensity is denoted by c_Q then the depolarization factor for the unresolved Q-branch is given by

$$\rho^Q = \frac{3 \mid \gamma_{vv'} \mid^2 c_Q}{45 \mid a_{vv'} \mid^2 + 4 \mid \gamma_{vv'} \mid^2 c_Q} \tag{296}$$

where, in the classical, high temperature, limit,

$$c_Q = \frac{1}{8}\left[\left(2+\frac{21}{\beta}+\frac{27}{\beta^2}\right)-\left(\frac{12}{\beta}+\frac{27}{\beta^2}\right)(1+\beta^2)^{1/2}\frac{\text{arc sinh}\sqrt{\beta}}{\sqrt{\beta}}\right] \tag{297a}$$

in which

$$\beta = \left(\frac{B}{A}-1\right) = \left(\frac{I_A}{I_B}-1\right) \tag{297b}$$

(A and B are the rotation constants, see p. 559). For diatomic and linear polyatomic molecules $\beta = \infty$ so that $c_Q = \frac{1}{4}$. Thus, for these molecules,

$$\rho^Q = \frac{3 \mid \gamma_{vv'} \mid^2}{180 \mid a_{vv'} \mid^2 + 4 \mid \gamma_{vv'} \mid^2} \tag{298}$$

This relation holds also for the Rayleigh line ($v = v'$) and was derived from classical theory by Cabannes and Rocard (*279*), Bhagavantam (*280*), and Born (*281*) and (*282*). This result is, however, not valid for hydrogen at room temperature since due to its small moment of inertia the assumptions which underly the derivations of Eqs. (296–298) are not fulfilled. Thus, at room temperature ($T = 300°$K), using the constants given in Table 6, and with g_{JK} replaced by $(2J+1)g_I$ where g_I is the statistical weight factor due to the nuclear spin (*278a*) we find from direct evaluation of Eq. (294) and comparison with Eq. (296) that $c_Q = 0.3221$, 0.2705, and 0.2518 for H_2, HD, and D_2, respectively, which values differ from the classical limiting value of 0.2500 by 28%, 8.2%, and 0.72%, respectively. The classical limit $c_Q = 0.25$ may, therefore, be safely used for all linear and diatomic molecules other than hydrogen and its isotopes unless the gas is at very low temperature.

Using Eqs. (292) and (296) we may relate the depolarization factor for the total band with the depolarization factor for the unresolved Q-branch. Thus,

$$\rho^Q = \frac{\rho c_Q}{1-\frac{4}{3}(1-c_Q)\rho} \tag{299}$$

(For natural light the coefficient 4/3 in the denominator is replaced by 7/6.) For the classical limiting case of a linear molecule we then have

$$\rho^Q = \frac{1}{4}\frac{\rho}{1-\rho}$$

as has also been shown in an independent classical derivation by Rowell, Aval, and Barrett (*288*).

The use of the polarizability invariants $a_{vv'}$ and $\gamma_{vv'}$ in molecular structure studies is well known. In particular for Rayleigh scattering, ($v = v'$, $v' = 0$) this use is well described by Stuart (*277*) and Wolkenstein (*283* and *284*). The most recent experimental work in this area (*83,285–288*) has been directed to obtain reliable values of the Rayleigh line depolarization factors for a number of gases using the most modern techniques. Particular attention is being paid to the degree of collimation of the incident and scattered beams and the rejection of the Raman scattered radiation, both pure rotation and vibration-rotation Raman bands, by means of narrow band pass interference filters or a grating monochromator. Critical experiments on the dependence of the Rayleigh line intensity, width, and depolarization factor, on the scattering angle, wavelength of exciting radiation and gas pressure are now capable of being performed and the results collected thus far supersede those obtained by the older techniques. It should be remarked here that, with the exception of hydrogen, all so called "Rayleigh line" intensities and depolarization factors which are reported in the older literature refer to the composite of Rayleigh line, $\Delta v = \Delta J = 0$, and the pure rotational Raman spectrum (Stokes and anti-Stokes parts) which flanks it. It would be more appropriate to designate this composite unresolved "line" as the Rayleigh band. Table 26 lists the most recent results for the depolarization factors of the Rayleigh band and the Rayleigh line for a number of diatomic and linear triatomic molecules.

TABLE 26

Depolarization Factors for the Rayleigh Band and the Rayleigh Line of Some Linear Molecules for Linearly Polarized Incident Light

Molecule	Rayleigh band $\rho \times 100$			Rayleigh line $\rho^Q \times 100$			
	a (4880 Å)	*b* (6328 Å)	*c* (White)	*a* (4880 Å)	*b* (6328 Å)	*d* (4880 Å)	*e* (6943 Å)
H_2	0.95	0.80		0.25	0.32		0.34
N_2	1.08	1.018	1.15	0.31		1.2	0.59
O_2	2.91	3.02	3.35	0.78	1.4		
CO	0.59	0.480		0.18			
CO_2	3.8	4.03	4.21	1.01	2		
N_2O	5.5	5.96		1.54			4.7

[a] Rowell, Barrett, and Aval, Ref. (*288*).
[b] Bridge and Buckingham, Ref. (*285*).
[c] Gucker et al., Ref. (*287*).
[d] Weber et al., Ref. (*83*).
[e] Rudder and Bach, Ref. (*286*).

To evaluate the polarizability invariants $a_{vv'}$ and $\gamma_{vv'}$ for vibration-rotation bands it is convenient to expand the polarizability tensor $\boldsymbol{\alpha}$ in a power series in vibrational normal coordinates Q_S about the equilibrium configuration. Keeping only linear terms we have,

$$\alpha_{xy} = \alpha_{xy}^e + \sum_s \alpha_{xy;s} Q_S + \ldots \tag{300}$$

where $\alpha_{xy}^{(e)}$ and

$$\alpha_{xy;S} = \left(\frac{\partial \alpha_{xy}}{\partial Q_S}\right)_e \tag{301}$$

are evaluated at equilibrium. In the harmonic oscillator approximation the nonvanishing matrix elements are

$$\langle n_S \mid \alpha_{xy} \mid n_S \rangle = \alpha_{xy}^{(e)}$$

$$\langle n_S \mid \alpha_{xy} \mid n_S+1 \rangle = (n_S+1)^{1/2}\left(\frac{h}{8\pi^2 \nu_S}\right)^{1/2} \alpha_{xy;S}$$

$$\langle n_S \mid \alpha_{xy} \mid n_S-1 \rangle = (n_S)^{1/2}\left(\frac{h}{8\pi^2 \nu_S}\right)^{1/2} \alpha_{xy;S} \tag{302}$$

In this approximation the Rayleigh scattered power is given by

$$I(\nu_0) = \frac{2^7\pi^5}{9}\frac{\nu_0{}^4}{c^4}\{3 \mid a^{(e)} \mid^2 + \tfrac{2}{3} \mid \gamma^{(e)} \mid^2\}I_O \tag{303}$$

For the Stokes Raman scattering ($n_S \rightarrow n_S+1$, $\nu' = -\nu_S$) we then have from Eq. (289)

$$I(\nu_0-\nu_S) = I_0 \frac{2^7\pi^5}{9}\frac{(\nu_0-\nu_S)^4}{c^4}$$

$$\times \frac{\sum_{n_S}[3 \mid \langle n_S \mid a \mid n_S+1\rangle \mid^2 + \frac{2}{3} \mid \langle n_S \mid \gamma \mid n_S+1\rangle \mid^2] \times \exp(-E(n_S)/kT)}{\sum_{n_S}\exp(-E(n_S)/kT)}$$

$$= I_0 \frac{2^7\pi^5}{9}\frac{(\nu_0-\nu_S)^4}{c^4}[3 \mid a_S \mid^2 + \tfrac{2}{3} \mid \gamma_S \mid^2]b_S{}^2$$

$$\times \frac{\sum_{n_S}(n_S+1)\exp(-(n_S+\frac{1}{2})h\nu_S/kT)}{\sum_{n_S}\exp(-(n_S+\frac{1}{2})h\nu_S/kT)}$$

$$= I_0 \frac{2^7\pi^5}{9}\frac{(\nu_0-\nu_S)^4}{c^4}[3 \mid a_S \mid^2 + \tfrac{2}{3} \mid \gamma_S \mid^2]\frac{g_S\, b_S{}^2}{1-\exp(-h\nu_S/kT)} \tag{304}$$

For the anti-Stokes Raman scattering ($n_S \rightarrow n_S-1$, $\nu' = \nu_S$) we obtain similarly

$$I(\nu_0+\nu_S) = I_0 \frac{2^7\pi^5}{9}\frac{(\nu_0+\nu_S)^4}{c^4}[3 \mid a_S \mid^2 + \tfrac{2}{3} \mid \gamma_S \mid^2]\frac{g_S\, b_S{}^2}{\exp(h\nu_S/kT)-1} \tag{305}$$

where $b_S = [h/8\pi^2\nu_S]^{1/2}$ is the zero point amplitude of vibration of the normal coordinate Q_S, g_S is the degeneracy of the s th vibration (228a) and where a_S and γ_S are the mean value and the anisotropy of the tensor $(\partial \boldsymbol{\alpha}/\partial Q_S)_e$, i.e.,

$$a_S = \frac{1}{3}\left\{\left(\frac{\partial \alpha_{xx}}{\partial Q_S}\right)_e + \left(\frac{\partial \alpha_{yy}}{\partial Q_S}\right)_e + \left(\frac{\partial \alpha_{zz}}{\partial Q_S}\right)_e\right\} \tag{306}$$

$$\begin{aligned} |\gamma_S|^2 = \frac{1}{2}\Bigg\{&\left[\left(\frac{\partial \alpha_{xx}}{\partial Q_S}\right)_e - \left(\frac{\partial \alpha_{yy}}{\partial Q_S}\right)_e\right]^2 + \left[\left(\frac{\partial \alpha_{yy}}{\partial Q_S}\right)_e - \left(\frac{\partial \alpha_{zz}}{\partial Q_S}\right)_e\right]^2 \\ &+ \left[\left(\frac{\partial \alpha_{zz}}{\partial Q_S}\right)_e - \left(\frac{\partial \alpha_{xx}}{\partial Q_S}\right)_e\right]^2 \\ &+ 6\left[\left(\frac{\partial \alpha_{xy}}{\partial Q_S}\right)_e^2 + \left(\frac{\partial \alpha_{yz}}{\partial Q_S}\right)_e^2 + \left(\frac{\partial \alpha_{zx}}{\partial Q_S}\right)_e^2\right]\Bigg\} \end{aligned} \tag{307}$$

Equations (303)–(305) give the total radiation of the respective types that is scattered into a solid angle 4π, produced by a linearly polarized, unidirectionally incident beam of frequency ν_0. For specific scattering configurations these expressions are modified as follows. For z-polarized incident light traveling along the y-direction and scattered light observed along the x-direction without an analyzer (see Fig. 1) the coefficient of $|\gamma^{(e)}|^2$ or $|\gamma_S|^2$ is 7/15 instead of 2/3, whereas for x-polarized light the coefficient becomes 6/15. For unpolarized incident light the coefficient of $|\gamma^{(e)}|^2$ or $|\gamma_S|^2$ is 13/15 instead of 2/3.

The determination of absolute intensities of the Raman bands of a variety of polyatomic molecules has been performed by a number of investigators notably Woodward, Long, Bernstein, Brandmüller, Holzer, and their coworkers. Their results, obtained with the older mercury arc technique have been collated in a review paper by Murphy, Holzer, and Bernstein (*79*) which is also to be consulted for the original literature of the experimental investigations.

Although it is possible in principle to calculate both the mean value and the anisotropy of $\boldsymbol{\alpha}$ and $\partial \boldsymbol{\alpha}/\partial Q_S$, such calculations have been performed only for hydrogen (*289,290,290a*) and nitrogen (*291*) and these results have had the unique application of estimating the amounts of Rayleigh and Raman scattering of Lyman-α radiation by molecular hydrogen and nitrogen in interstellar space (*291,292*). A more down-to-earth application is the use of the theoretical value of γ^2 for the ground state of H_2 to establish the absolute values of $|a_{vv'}|^2$ and $|\gamma_{vv'}|^2$ for the observed Raman bands of other molecules. This is done by comparison of the measured intensity of the $J = 3 \leftarrow J = 1$ pure rotational transition in $H_2(\Delta\nu = 597\ cm^{-1})$ with the measured intensities of the "unknown" Raman bands of the molecules (*79,293,294*). The reliability of the theoretical values of hydrogen is rather substantial as can be inferred from a comparison of the theoretically predicted and observed values of the parameters that determine the Rayleigh and Raman scattering. Table 27 presents such a comparison for hydrogen (*290*).

The relationship between the tensor invariants a and γ and the molecular structure is buried in the complicated formulae of the dispersion theory and the polarizability approximation. These quantities must therefore of necessity be considered as empirical parameters which may contribute to the elucidation of the molecular structure. To this end the so-called valence—optical scheme has been proposed according to which the electrical properties of a molecule, i.e., the dipole moment and the polarizability, are simple sums of dipole moments and polarizabilities associated with each valence bond of a molecule (*297*). The bond polarizability concept, according to which bonds have different polarizabilities along their lengths and along directions transverse to the bond, was suggested first by Meyer and Otterbein and was developed quantitatively by Sachse, Wang, and Denbigh (*298*). The usefulness of the concept lies in the expectation that if the principal values of the bond polarizabilities, say, for the C—C and C—H bonds are known, it should be possible to compute on the basis of a conformational model the invariants a and γ for any alkane molecule and hence the depolarization factor for the Rayleigh line or band. Comparison of the thus computed depolarization factor with the experimentally determined value then gives some clues as to the correctness of the assumed molecular structure. Although the value of the bond polarizability concept, at least in its more rudimentary form, has been called into question (*299*) it has had sufficient success to have merited considerable attention over the years. A recent review of the subject by LeFévre (*300*) delves critically into the various aspects of the subject. Jernigan and Flory (*301*) have computed the depolarization factor for the n-alkanes and find that the agreement between the calculated and experimental values of the anisotropy leaves much to be desired. It is likely that these discrepancies are largely due to the limited accuracy of the experimental results but intrinsic limitations of the bond-polarizability concept and local field effects (*302*) due to neighboring molecules may also play a significant role.

The intensities of the vibration-rotation Raman bands are determined not by the invariants of the tensor $\boldsymbol{\alpha}$ but rather by those of the tensor

TABLE 27

Rayleigh and Raman Scattering Parameters for H_2[a]

Parameter[b]	Zero frequency value[c]	λ(A)	Measured	Predicted
$a(\omega)$	0.8023			
	0.8045[d]	5462	0.827[e]	0.823
		4358	0.840[e]	0.834
		4047	0.845[e]	0.838
		3342	0.865[e]	0.855
$\gamma(\omega)$	0.2999			
	0.3017[d]	6328	0.314[f]	0.309
$a_{01}(\omega)$	0.1095	4358		0.116
			0.114[g]	
		4047		0.118
$\gamma_{01}(\omega)$	0.09034	4358		0.0996
		4047		0.101
$\gamma_{01}(\omega)/a_{01}(\omega)$	0.8250	4358		0.856
			0.775[g], 0.76[h]	
		4047		0.857
$(a_{01}/a)^2$	0.01863	3358		0.0195
			0.0155[h]	
		4047		0.0197
γ^2	0.08994	6328	0.0986[f]	0.0955
κ	0.1246	6328	0.128[f]	0.126
$\rho_n^{\text{Rayl}}(\omega)$	0.01823	4358		0.0188
			0.0159[h]	
		4047		0.0190
ρ_n^{Ram}	0.08207	4358		0.0882
			0.070[h], 0.073[g]	
		4047		0.0877

[a] From Victor, Browne and Dalgarno, Ref. (*290*). A more recent computation of the dynamical dipole polarizability of H_2 by Victor and Dalgarno, Ref. (*290a*), improves the agreement between the observed and computed polarizability, especially in the ultraviolet region of the spectrum. These authors also give computed values of the anisotropy, Rayleigh line depolarization factor, Rayleigh scattering cross section and Verdet constant at selected wavelengths from $\lambda = 1212$ Å to $\lambda = 6328$ Å.

[b] The polarizability invariants are in units of Å^3. $a(\omega)$ and $\gamma(\omega)$ are the mean value and the anisotropy of the ground state polarizability; $a_{01}(\omega)$ and $\gamma_{01}(\omega)$ are the mean value and anisotropy of the derived tensor $\partial\alpha/\partial Q$; $\kappa = \gamma(\omega)/3a(\omega)$ = measure of molecular anisotropy; $\rho_n^{\text{Ray}}(\omega)$ depolarization factor for Rayleigh band, at frequency ω; ρ_n^{Ram} depolarization factor for Raman band for unpolarized incident light.

[c] Zero frequency values computed by Kolos and Wolniewicz (*289*).

[d] The values refer to a temperature of 293°K. All other values refer to the zero rotational state.

[e] Determined from index of refraction data, Ref. (*295*).

[f] Bridge and Buckingham, Ref. (*285*).

[g] Golden and Crawford, Ref. (*293*).

[h] Yoshino and Bernstein, Ref. (*296*).

$\partial \boldsymbol{\alpha}/\partial Q_S$. Wolkenstein (*303*) and Wolkenstein and Eliashevich (*304,305*) have, therefore, proposed a bond polarizability theory for the Raman intensities which is based on the following assumptions; (1) Each bond polarizability $\boldsymbol{\alpha}^{(n)}$ is a tensor, one of whose principal axes coincides with the direction of the bond and the other two principal axes are perpendicular to the bond. The bonds are assumed to be cylindrically symmetric so that for the principal values $\alpha_{n1} \neq \alpha_{n2} = \alpha_{n3}$ where n denotes the bond; (2) the bond polarizabilities change when the bond length changes; and (3) the bond polarizabilities are independent of changes in the valence angles. This theory has been reformulated in terms of the Wilson *FG* matrix scheme by Long (*306*) and Ferigle and Weber (*307*). Sverdlov (*308*) and Long et al. (*309*) generalized the formulation so that the third of the Wolkenstein assumptions is now removed from the theory. Furthermore Sverdlov and Prokofeva (*310*) have discussed the necessity of also including in the theory the derivatives of the polarizability of a given bond with respect to changes in the lengths and angles of the other bonds of the molecule.

Critical tests of the theory are difficult to carry out in view of the complexity of the calculations and the uncertainties in the experimental data. In one of the earliest investigations of the intensities of Raman bands of gases Welsh et al. (*26*) found serious deficiencies in the original bond polarizability model of Wolkenstein. Similarly, it was found by Ferigle, Weber, and Krupp (*311,312*) that the computed depolarization factors for the totally symmetric Raman bands of CCl_3X and CBr_3X molecules were generally in good agreement with the observed values only for the ν_1-vibrations, whereas for the ν_2- and ν_3-vibrations the agreement was poor. However, using the modified Wolkenstein theory as well as its first order extension (*308,310*), numerous computations of Raman intensities and depolarization factors, albeit for liquid substances only, have been performed with a good deal of success by Soviet investigators (*313*).

Recent work on a test of the bond polarizability theory through the study of Raman spectra of gases was undertaken by Long et al. (*309*) and by Holzer (*314,315*). Holzer computed the intensities of the totally symmetric Raman bands of a whole series of CX_3Y molecules with and without taking into account the contributions to $\partial \boldsymbol{\alpha}/\partial Q_S$ due to the derivatives of the bond polarizabilities with respect to changes in the valence angles. With the modified Wolkenstein model very good agreement with the observed intensities was obtained for the CH vibrations of the methyl halides and the agreement was as good as could be expected for most of the other lines. For the CCl and CBr vibrations the agreement is not as good and it was suggested that the CCl bond polarizability is higher in CCl_4 than in CH_3Cl and $CHCl_3$. The situation here is quite similar to that mentioned before in regard to the depolarization factor of the Rayleigh bands. The source of the discrepancies between the experimentally determined and theoretically computed intensities and depolarization factors of the Raman bands may be due to an intrinsic inadequacy of the bond polarizability theory or insufficient or inaccurate data. The question is still open.

The foregoing discussion of the theory of Raman intensities is based on the intensity formulae given by Eqs. (304) and (305). These are based on a harmonic oscillator, rigid-rotor model and differences between predicted and observed intensities must not only be viewed in terms of a possible inadequacy of the polarizability approximation, but one must also consider the discrepancies introduced into the intensity formulae through the neglect of vibrational anharmonicities and vibration-rotation interaction. Very little work has been done on this subject. Most informative, therefore, is the work of James and Klemperer (*316*) on the effect of the vibration-rotation interaction on the Raman line intensities for diatomic molecules. According to their work, the vibration-rotation interaction changes the relative intensities of the pure rotational Raman lines of hydrogen by 5% for $J = 3$, whereas its effect should be quite ignorable in the pure rotational spectra of other diatomic molecules. On the other hand they find that in the vibration-rotation spectra the intensity ratio I^S/I^0 of the lines in the *S*- and *O*-branches, as computed from the uncorrected theory, is modified by a factor $R \approx 1-8\chi\gamma J(J+1)$ due to the vibration-rotation interaction, where, in the notation of James and Klemperer, $\gamma = (2B_e/\omega_e) \approx (D_e/B_e)^{1/2}$ measures the vibration-rotation interaction and $\chi = [\beta(r_e)/\beta_1 \cdot r_e]$ in which $\beta(r_e) = (\alpha_{\parallel}-\alpha_{\perp})_{r=r_e}$ is the anisotropy of the ground state polarizability evaluated at $r = r_e$ and $\beta_1 = (\partial\,\beta/\partial\,r)_{r=r_e}$, ($\alpha_{\parallel}$ and $\alpha_{\perp}$ = polarizability parallel and perpendicular to the line joining the nuclei). Using the older data of Stansbury et al. (*316a*) they estimate that the factor R at $J = 10$ amounts to approximately 25, 24, 12, and 13% for the molecules HCl, HBr, N_2, and O_2 respectively. Thus it seems that with accurate determinations of the intensity ratio of the *O*- and *S*-branch lines having a common *J*-level, it is possible to determine the ratio of the anisotropies $\chi = [\beta(r_e)/\beta_1 \cdot r_e]$, the other constants ($\gamma = 2B_e/\omega_e$) having been determined through the frequency analysis of the spectrum. On the other hand, the intensities of the *Q*-branch lines are modified only by terms second order in γ so that Eqs. (304) and (305) for the intensity, as well as Eq. (295) for the depolarization factor of individual *Q*-branch lines, are correct to first order in γ. (Eq. (15) of James and Klemperer, although written in a more complicated form, is the reciprocal of our Eq. (295 a,b) for the depolarization factor $\rho^Q(J)$). However, the depolarization ratio $\rho^Q(J)$ for the individual Q-branch lines does not offer much help in determining the invariants of the tensor $\partial \boldsymbol{\alpha}/\partial Q_S$. This is so because for large J, $\rho_Q(J)$ tends rapidly toward the small limiting value given by Eq. (298), whereas for low J-values the lines of the Q-branch are too close together or are unresolved to provide good values for $\rho^Q(J)$.

An independent method of determining the ground state polarizability anisotropy of linear and symmetric top molecules has been developed by Scharpen et al. (*316b*). The Stark effect observable in microwave rotational spectra depends upon both the permanent dipole moment (linear field dependence) and the polarizability tensor (quadratic field dependence) of the molecule. Since the contribution due to the polarizability is several orders of magnitude smaller than that due to the dipole moment, exceedingly homogeneous large electric fields are required to render the quadratic field dependence measurable and thus the polarizability anisotropy determinable. Using this technique Scharpen et al. (*316b*) found $\gamma = \alpha_{zz} - \alpha_{xx} = 3.222 \pm 0.046$ Å^3 for N_2O, $\gamma = 4.67 \pm 0.16$ Å^3 for OCS, and $\gamma = 2.7 \pm 0.6$ Å^3 for $CD_3C{\equiv}CH$. For N_2O the value of γ determined from laser light scattering (*285*) is 2.96 Å^3, whereas the older light scattering result (Ref. *277*, p. 353) is 2.79 Å^3. Although the microwave and optical light scattering results are close, the difference between them is most likely due to the fact that the microwave result is a static field value, and that it is measured directly (including the sign of the anisotropy!), whereas the light scattering result is obtained for optical frequencies and represents a population-weighted average over vibrational and rotational states. These facts, however, are believed to cause only minor differences. Most of the difference is probably ascribable to the uncertainty in the value of the average polarizability a that enters into the determination of γ through the depolarization factor, Eq. (292). The microwave technique promises to provide highly accurate values of the anisotropy, these being values for the individual quantum states (i.e. individual vibrational states), rather than averages over an ensemble of states.

C. Line Widths and Line Shifts

We wish to discuss two causes of line width namely the Doppler effect and molecular interactions. It is well known that if a light source moves relative to a stationary observer with a velocity component v_z then the observer will perceive a frequency

$$\nu' = \nu(1+v_z/c)$$

where $\nu = \Delta E/h$ is the eigenfrequency of the radiation emitted by a stationary molecule. The quantity

$$\delta\nu = \nu' - \nu = \nu\frac{v_z}{c} \tag{308}$$

is the Doppler shift of the spectrum line. For a dilute gas in thermal equilibrium at absolute temperature T the fractional number of molecules that have a z-component of velocity in the range between v_z and $v_z + dv_z$ is given by the Maxwell distribution function

$$f(v_z) = \left(\frac{m}{2\pi kT}\right)^{1/2} \exp\left(-\frac{m}{2kT}v_z^{\,2}\right) dv_z \tag{309}$$

Using Eq. (308) to express the distribution function in terms of the frequency ν' we have for the fractional number of molecules that radiate in the frequency range between ν' and $\nu' + d\nu'$

$$f(\nu') = \left(\frac{m}{2\pi kT}\right)^{1/2} \exp\left[-\frac{m}{2kT}\frac{c^2}{\nu^2}(\nu-\nu')^2\right]\frac{c}{\nu}\,d\nu' \tag{310}$$

For the intensity of the observed radiation we thus have (each molecule radiating the same energy $\Delta E = h\nu$ in its own body fixed coordinate system)

$$I(\nu') = I(\nu)\exp\left[-\frac{m}{2kT}\frac{c^2}{\nu^2}(\nu-\nu')^2\right] \tag{311}$$

The intensity is then a Gaussian distribution about the center frequency ν. The full width of the distribution evaluated at half height (i.e. half peak intensity) due to the Doppler effect is then

$$\Delta\nu_{FWHH}^{\mathrm{Do}} = 2\frac{\nu}{c}\left[(2\ln 2)\frac{kT}{m}\right]^{1/2}$$

$$= 2\frac{\nu}{c}(2R\ln 2)^{1/2}\left(\frac{T}{M}\right)^{1/2} \tag{312}$$

where R is the gas constant and M is the molecular weight. This expression is the customary one used in all discussions of Doppler broadening of spectral lines emitted by a gas discharge source as well as for Rayleigh scattering by an isotropically illuminated gas.

For Raman scattering, especially using laser sources with highly unidirectional and monochromatic exciting radiation, Eq. (312) is not suitable. A more detailed calculation which yields an expression for the angular dependence of the Doppler broadening considers the scattering event as an inelastic two body collision process. Let ν_0 be the frequency of the exciting radiation and ν_S be the frequency of the scattered radiation. Further let $\mathbf{v}$ and $\mathbf{v}'$ be the velocity of a molecule of mass m before and after collision. With the x- and y-coordinate axes defining the scattering plane we have the following relations which govern the scattering process:

$$\frac{h\nu_0}{c}+mv_x = \frac{h\nu_S}{c}\cos\theta+mv_x' \tag{313a}$$

$$mv_y = \frac{h\nu_S}{c}\sin\theta+mv_y' \tag{313b}$$

$$mv_z = mv_z' \tag{313c}$$

$$h\nu_0+\tfrac{1}{2}mv^2 = h\nu_S+\Delta E+\tfrac{1}{2}mv'^2 \tag{314}$$

where θ is the scattering angle and ΔE is the internal energy change of the molecule. Solving Eq. (313a,b,c) for v'^2 and substituting the result into Eq. (314) we obtain

$$h\nu_0 = h\nu_S+\Delta E+\frac{h^2}{2mc^2}[\nu_0{}^2+\nu_S{}^2-2\nu_0\nu_S\cos\theta] + \frac{h}{c}[(\nu_0-\nu_S\cos\theta)v_x-\nu_S\sin\theta\, v_y] \tag{315}$$

where the last two terms on the right hand side represent the change in energy due to the recoil and the Doppler effect. We define a frequency $\Delta\nu$

$$\Delta\nu = \Delta\nu^{\mathrm{Rec}}+\Delta\nu^{\mathrm{Do}} \tag{316a}$$

where

$$\Delta\nu^{\mathrm{Rec}} = \frac{h}{2mc^2}[\nu_0{}^2+\nu_S{}^2-2\nu_0\nu_S\cos\theta] \tag{316b}$$

and

$$\Delta\nu^{\mathrm{Do}} = \frac{1}{c}[(\nu_0-\nu_S\cos\theta)v_x-\nu_S\sin\theta\, v_y] \tag{316c}$$

represent the frequency shifts due to recoil and Doppler effect. Since the contribution of $h\Delta\nu$ to the right hand side of Eq. (315) is very small in comparison to the contributions made by $h\nu_S$ and ΔE we have, to a very good approximation, $\nu_S = \nu_0 + \nu_R$ where $\nu_R = \Delta E/h$ is the Raman frequency shift. Computing the RMS average of the shift $\Delta\nu$ we have, first,

$$\overline{(\Delta\nu)^2} = \overline{(\Delta\nu^{\mathrm{Rec}})^2} + \overline{(\Delta\nu^{\mathrm{Do}})^2} \tag{317}$$

where

$$\overline{(\Delta\nu^{\mathrm{Rec}})^2} = \left(\frac{h}{2mc^2}\right)^2 \left[4(\nu_0{}^2 + \nu_0\nu_R)\sin^2\frac{\theta}{2} + \nu_R{}^2\right]^2$$

and (318)

$$\overline{(\Delta\nu^{\mathrm{Do}})^2} = \frac{1}{3}\frac{v_{RMS}^2}{c^2}\left[4(\nu_0{}^2 + \nu_0\nu_R)\sin^2\frac{\theta}{2} + \nu_R{}^2\right]$$

since

$$\overline{v_x{}^2} = \overline{v_y{}^2} = \tfrac{1}{3}v_{RMS}^2 = kT/m \quad \text{and} \quad \nu_S = \nu_0 + \nu_R$$

For the highly unfavorable case of the hydrogen molecule, an exciting wavelength of $\lambda_0 = 5000$ Å, the gas at room temperature (300°K) and with $\nu_R/c = 4161\ \mathrm{cm}^{-1}$ we find that $\overline{(\Delta\nu^{\mathrm{Rec}})^2}/\overline{(\Delta\nu^{\mathrm{Do}})^2} < 1.5 \times 10^{-7}$ hence we may safely ignore the recoil term in Raman scattering in the optical region. The full *RMS* Doppler line width is then (*317*)

$$\Delta\nu_{FW,RMS}^{\mathrm{Do}} = 2[\overline{(\Delta\nu^{\mathrm{Do}})^2}]^{1/2}$$

or

$$\Delta\nu_{FW,RMS}^{\mathrm{Do}} = \frac{2}{c}\left(\frac{kT}{m}\right)^{1/2}\left[4(\nu_0{}^2 + \nu_0\nu_R)\sin^2\frac{\theta}{2} + \nu_R{}^2\right]^{1/2} \tag{319}$$

Experimentally more convenient is the full width at half peak height which is

$$\Delta\nu_{FWHH}^{\mathrm{Do}} = \frac{2}{c}\left(2\ln 2\cdot\frac{kT}{m}\right)^{1/2}\left[4(\nu_0{}^2 + \nu_0\nu_R)\sin^2\frac{\theta}{2} + \nu_R{}^2\right]^{1/2} \tag{320}$$

For Rayleigh scattering $\nu_R = 0$ and we obtain

$$\Delta\nu_{FWHH}^{\mathrm{Do}} = \frac{4\nu_0}{c}\left(2\ln 2\cdot\frac{kT}{m}\right)^{1/2}\sin\frac{\theta}{2} \tag{321}$$

It is clear that for forward scattering ($\theta = 0$) the Doppler line broadening is a minimum. This fact can be turned to good advantage in high resolution studies as has been demonstrated by Lallemand et al. (*318,319*), May et al. (*320*), Murray and Javan (*321*), Cooper et al. (*322,323*), and Clements and Stoicheff (*324*). Figure 33 shows the profile of the $J = 3 \leftarrow J = 1$ pure rotational Raman line of hydrogen gas at 2 atm. pressure for $\theta = 90^\circ$ and $\theta = 2^\circ$ (labeled forward scattering). The residual line width of 0.04 cm^{-1} is the instrumental width composed of the (He-Ne) laser line width and the pass-band width of the Fabry-Perot interferometer used in the study.

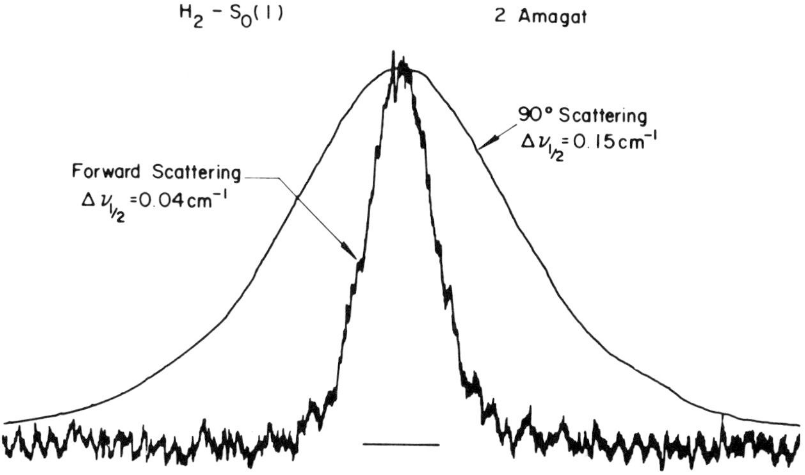

Fig. 33. Profiles of the $J = 3 \leftarrow J = 1$ rotational Raman line of H_2 at 2 atm pressure excited with He-Ne laser radiation (6328 Å) and observed with a pressure scanned Fabry–Perot interferometer. The total instrumental line width is 0.04 cm^{-1} [Ref. (*324*), with permission].

These investigators also were able to partially resolve the Q-branch of the totally symmetric CH stretching vibration in methane ($\nu_R/c = 2917\ cm^{-1}$) and find that the vibration-rotation interaction constant for that state, $B_1 - B_0 = \alpha_1 = -0.0034\ cm^{-1}$.

The foregoing discussion was limited to the scattering of light by an assembly of noninteracting molecules and the results hold therefore only for a dilute gas. Early experiments on the Raman effect in gases were performed with gas pressures up to 100 atm to enhance the intensity of the scattered radiation. It was noted that the pure rotational Raman lines are pressure broadened and ultimately merge into a continuum extending to either side of the Rayleigh line. Insofar as the success of "high resolution" Raman studies depends on having the rotational Raman lines as sharp as possible the pressure broadening effect is very detrimental to molecular structure studies. Such investigations should therefore be conducted with gas pressures which cause a maximum line width equivalent to the limit of resolution imposed by the experimental apparatus and Doppler effect.

Pressure broadening effects are clearly due to the action of intermolecular forces. Since the Raman effect is a second order radiation process, it is to be expected that the broadening mechanism differs in some respects from that which gives rise to the broadening of infrared and microwave absorption lines, since these are produced by a first order radiation process. The study of the pressure broadening of Raman lines is therefore of intrinsic interest since it provides additional data for the understanding of intermolecular forces which could not be obtained by other means. Very striking is the different way in which the density of the gas affects the *Q*-branch lines and the lines in the rotational branches of the totally symmetric vibrations. Whereas the broadening of the *Q*-branch lines is but slight the widths of the rotational lines are very strongly dependent on the gas density. Even in the liquid state the *Q*-branches of O_2 and N_2 are sharp whereas the *O*- and *S*-branches are continuous, even though the molecules undergo practically free rotation (*325*).

In addition to the broadening of the Raman transitions the fluctuations in the gas density at any given pressure also modifies the width of the Rayleigh line. One would expect that for a low pressure gas the Rayleigh line would be simply Doppler broadened in accordance with Eq. (321) and this was shown to be the case for argon and hydrogen at a pressure of 1 atm (*320*). At higher pressures, however, one observes the normal Brillouin scattering (*326,327*) as well as the stimulated Brillouin scattering (*328–330*). The occurrence of a Brillouin effect in gases is to be expected on the basis of a fluid model for the gas. Brillouin scattering will be observed when the mean free path of the molecules of the gas is less than the wave-length of the thermal elastic wave which is appropriate for a given scattering angle (*331*). Pressurization of the gas serves to bring about this condition at a given temperature but of itself is of no importance. Thus, Greytak and Benedek (*332*) observed the normal Brillouin scattering in Ar, Xe, N_2, CO_2, and CH_4 at room temperature and at a pressure of 1 atm. By changing the scattering angle from the forward to the backward direction they were able to map out the change from a hydrodynamic to a kinetic character of the fluctuations that give rise to the spectrum. The smallest Brillouin shift reported by them, observed at a scattering angle of 10.6° for Xenon gas at 25.2°C and a pressure of 795 mmHg is

0.0016 cm^{-1}. The Brillouin scattering effect is also discussed from the view of the kinetic theory of gases (*333*).

Direct evidence of the effects of intermolecular forces is obtained from the line widths. Figure 34 shows the width of the Q(1) vibrational Raman line in hydrogen as a function of the gas density observed in both the forward and backward scattering configurations by Murray and Javan (*321*). (Intermolecular effects are more appropriately described in terms of the density rather than the gas pressure. One Amagat unit of density is the

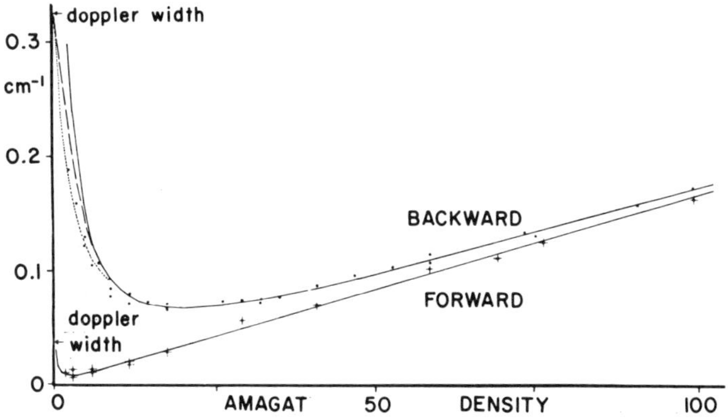

Fig. 34. Line width ($\Delta\nu_{FWHH}$) of the $Q_1(1)$ Raman line of H_2 for forward and backward scattering [Ref. (*321*), with permission].

density of the system at STP.) We note first that with increasing density the Doppler width is reduced so that the line width assumes a minimum value which occurs at different densities for the forward and backward scattering configurations. Thereafter the line width increases linearly with density—the line is then said to be pressure broadened. The same behavior shown in Fig. 34 has also been observed by Cooper et al. (*322,323*) in the S(0) and S(1) lines of pure hydrogen and 1:10 mixtures of hydrogen with the helium and argon, and Lallemand et al. (*318,319*) have studied this behavior using the stimulated Raman effect. The pressure broadening effect has also been studied in O_2, N_2, CO, CO_2 as well as in CH_4. The most recent and detailed results have been reported by Jammu et al. (*110*) who also discuss the results of earlier investigations. The line narrowing and line broadening are described by two different physical mechanisms. If the narrowing and broadening effects are not correlated the line shape can be shown to be Lorentzian the width of which is the sum of a diffusion term and a collision term, namely (*334–336*)

$$\Delta\nu_{1/2} = \frac{k^2 D_0}{\pi\rho} + B\rho \tag{322}$$

where **k** is the difference in wave vectors of the incident and scattered photons, D_0 is the coefficient of self diffusion at 1 Amagat unit of density, ρ is the density and B is the pressure broadening coefficient.

The pressure broadening of the Raman lines of linear molecules has been described mainly by the impact theory of Fiutak and Van Kranendonk (*337*). This is an extension of Anderson's (*338*) theory for absorption spectra according to which the relative translational motion of the molecules is treated by classical mechanics while the rotational motion is described by quantum mechanical perturbation theory. Anderson's theory for absorption spectra has been developed more fully by Tsao and Curnutte (*339*) to include different types of collision interactions for linear as well as for symmetric top molecules. Brannon (*340*) has shown that with very

TABLE 28

Pressure Broadening Coefficients for the Raman Lines of H_2[a]

Line	Theoretical[b]		Experimental	Reference
$S_o(0)$	3.6		2.80 ± 0.05	(*323*)
$S_o(1)$	3.8		3.50 ± 0.05	(*323*)
$S_o(2)$	3.4			
$S_o(3)$	2.6			
$S_o(4)$	1.8			
	isotropic	anisotropic		
$Q_1(0)$	2.2	2.2	2.32 ± 0.04	(*343*)
$Q_1(1)$	0.6	4.0	1.40 ± 0.03	(*343*)
			1.68 ± 0.07	(*321*)
			2.1	(*319*)
$Q_1(2)$	2.6	5.6	2.53 ± 0.03	(*343*)
$Q_1(3)$	3.6	5.2	3.66 ± 0.04	(*343*)
$Q_1(4)$	3.0	4.0		

[a] In 10^{-3} cm^{-1}/amagat. The broadening coefficient is defined as $\Delta\nu_{FWHH}/\rho$ where $\Delta\nu_{FWHH}$ is the full width at half height and ρ is the density.

[b] Computed by Van Kranendonk, Ref. (*341*). (Note that Van Kranendonk reports values for $\Delta\nu_{\frac{1}{2}}/\rho$ where $\Delta\nu_{\frac{1}{2}}$ is the half width.)

simple modifications Tsao and Curnutte's results also account for Raman line broadening and are thus equivalent to the results of Fiutak and Van Kranendonk. The only available numerical computations of Raman line broadening are those performed by Van Kranendonk (*341*) who considers only dipole and quadrupole forces and by Gray and Van Kranendonk (*342*) who also include anisotropic dispersion forces. Table 28 compares the experimental values for the broadening coefficients for H_2 with those computed by Van Kranendonk (*341*) on the basis of quadrupolar anisotropic interaction forces and a hard sphere intermolecular potential for the isotropic part. The agreement is quite good except for the $Q_1(1)$ line. Lallemand and Simova (*319*) have studied the line broadening of the $Q_1(1)$ transition as function of temperature using the stimulated Raman effect. Experiments were also performed with 75%, 48%, and 41% concentration of orthohydrogen. No measurable difference in the broadening coefficient for the $Q_1(1)$ line for these mixtures could be determined contrary to the theoretical expectation. Allin et al. (*343*) suggest that the discrepancy involving the $Q_1(1)$ line is connected with the statistical spread in the vibrational perturbation, an effect which is not accounted for in the theoretical values. The broadening coefficients for the Q-branch transitions are computed separately for the isotropic and anisotropic contributions. The experimental values represent mainly the isotropic parts of the transitions.

Table 29 compares the experimental broadening coefficients for N_2, O_2, CO, and CO_2 with the values computed by Gray and Van Kranendonk (*342*) using electric quadrupolar and anisotropic dispersion forces at room temperature. [There exists no unanimity in the literature in regard to the definition of the broadening coefficient. Jammu et al. (*110*) and Van Kranendonk (*341,342*) define the broadening coefficient as $\Delta\nu_{1/2}/p$ or $\Delta\nu_{1/2}/\rho$ where $\Delta\nu_{1/2}$ is the half width of the line (p = pressure, ρ = density). For consistency we will use $\Delta\nu_{FWHH}/p$ or $\Delta\nu_{FWHH}/\rho$ for the broadening coefficient, where $\Delta\nu_{FWHH} = 2\Delta\nu_{1/2}$ = full width at half height.] In view of the various approximations that enter into the computations the agreement between the magnitudes of the observed and theoretical values is satisfactory. The broadening coefficients exhibit a pronounced J-dependence with the theoretical values decreasing consistently more rapidly with J than the experimental values.

A different approach to the problem of line broadening has been developed by Gordon (*344–348*) by considering the intensity distribution in a vibration-rotation Raman band as a Fourier transform of a correlation function of the molecular rotational coordinates. According to Gordon

TABLE 29

Pressure Broadening Coefficients for the Rotational Raman Lines of N_2, O_2, CO, and CO_2[a]

	N_2		O_2		CO		CO_2	
J	Calc	Obs	Calc	Obs	Calc	Obs	Calc	Obs
0	150				164		352	
1	142		146	124	154			
2	138	104			150	154	338	
3	132	102	136	94	142	148		
4	126	94			134	144	334	268
5	120	96	122	84	126	140		
6	114	94			120	132	324	250
7	110	84	106	80	114	136		
8	106	82			110	128	310	254
9	98	80	92	76	102	122		
10	90	80			92	126	294	236
11	82	76	66	74	84	118		
12	74	74			76	116	276	228
13	68	70	44	70	68	118		
14	60	68					260	224
15	52	66	34	64				
16	46	64					250	216
17			28	60				
18							242	208
19			22	56				
20							236	216
22							230	214
24							226	214
26							222	
28							216	210

[a] In 10^{-3} cm^{-1}/atm. The broadening coefficient is defined as $\Delta\nu_{FWHH}/p$ where $\Delta\nu_{FWHH}$ is the full width at half height. Observed values by Jammu et al. (*110*), as quoted by Gray and Van Kranendonk (*342*). Computed values by Gray and Van Kranendonk (*342*). Values listed are twice those quoted by Gray and Van Kranendonk due to different definition of the broadening coefficient.

(*345*) with increasing gas density the lines in the pure rotational Raman spectrum will suffer both a broadening as well as a displacement. The full line width at half height is given in semi-classical approximation by

$$\begin{aligned} 2\pi\Delta_{FWHH} &= 2n\langle v\rangle\sigma_r \\ &= 2n\langle v \int_0^\infty [1 - P_{el}\cdot\cos 2\,\eta_{\text{Rot}}\cdot\cos^4(\alpha/2)]\cdot 2\pi b\,db\rangle \end{aligned} \quad (323)$$

and the line shift is given by

$$2\pi(\nu-\nu_0) = n\langle v\rangle\sigma_i$$
$$= n\langle v \textstyle\int_0^\infty P_{el}\cdot\sin^2 2\eta_{\mathrm{Rot}}\cdot\cos^4(\alpha/2)\cdot 2\pi b\, db\rangle \qquad (324)$$

where σ_r and σ_i are the real and imaginary parts of the optical cross section, n is the number of molecules per unit volume, v is the relative velocity of the two colliding molecules, P_{el} is the probability that no energy is transferred by a collision (i.e., the probability that the J quantum number is not changed by a collision), η_{Rot} is the rotational phase shift (*346*), α is the angle of reorientation through which the angular momentum of one molecule is rotated by the collision, and b is the impact parameter. The brackets denote a statistical average. The line shift is considered positive away from the Rayleigh line. For the Rayleigh line itself the polarized, isotropic component is not affected by the molecular collisions. The depolarized, anisotropic component exhibits a broadening effect with a line width given by

$$2\pi\Delta\nu_{FWHH} = 2n\langle v\rangle\sigma_r$$
$$= n\langle v \int_0^\infty 6\pi\,(\sin^2\alpha)\, b\, db\rangle \qquad (325)$$

and the line shift is zero.

For the vibration-rotation spectra perturbations of the vibrational motion by collisions become important. These manifest themselves primarily through a vibrational phase shift given by

$$\eta_{\mathrm{vib}} = \hbar^{-1}\int_{-\infty}^{+\infty}(V'-V^0)\,dt \qquad (326)$$

where V' and V^0 are the intermolecular potential energies for the final and initial vibrational states respectively. The width and shift of the lines in the O- and P-branches are then given by Eqs. (323) and (324) with $2\eta_{\mathrm{Rot}}$ replaced by $\eta_{\mathrm{vib}}-2\eta_{\mathrm{Rot}}$ whereas for the R- and S-branch lines $2\eta_{\mathrm{Rot}}$ is replaced by $2\eta_{\mathrm{Rot}}-\eta_{\mathrm{vib}}$. For the individual lines in a resolved Q-branch the line width is determined by the cross section

$$\sigma = \left\langle v\int_0^\infty\left[1-P_{el}\exp(-i\eta_{\mathrm{vib}})\left(\frac{3}{2}\cos^2\alpha-\frac{1}{2}\right)\right]2\pi b\,db\right\rangle \qquad (327)$$

Only one experimental result has been reported on the line width of vibration-rotation lines. According to Bazhulin (*349*) the widths of the O- and S-branch lines of the fundamental vibration-rotation band of oxygen are three times greater than that of the lines in the pure rotation spectrum. Except for hydrogen the individual lines comprising a Q-branch are very closely spaced on account of the smallness of the vibration-rotation interaction. The pressure broadening then causes the lines to overlap and form a continuous band (in N_2 this occurs at $\sim$ 40 atm at room temperature). For unresolved bands the pressure dependence has been studied by Gordon (*346*). A particular result of this work is the prediction that after the lines in a Q-branch have been broadened sufficiently to merge into a continuum the Q-branch does not broaden any further. Instead, it becomes narrower with increasing density. This has indeed been observed to be the case for nitrogen and carbon monoxide (*346a*) and is the explanation for the sharp line like Q-branches of the totally symmetric vibrations for substances in the liquid state of aggregation (*325*). Another approach developed by Gordon to the problem of intermolecular interactions which obviates the detailed calculations that are necessary in computing line widths and shifts is the method of moment analysis of the total spectrum (*350*). This approach supplements the techniques that are based on the impact approximation in that it is capable of describing the intensity distribution in the wings of a band where the impact approximation is apparently inadequate.

Cooper et al. (*351*) investigated the pressure dependence of the width of the depolarized Rayleigh line. For N_2 and CO_2 they find for the broadening coefficient 0.05 and 0.11 cm^{-1}/atm, respectively, which are about one half the values for the broadening coefficients of the rotational Raman lines (Table 29). For H_2 the broadening coefficients is 0.005 cm^{-1}/atm, almost the same as that for the rotation lines (Table 28).

Using Eq. (325) it is thus possible to obtain a cross section for the reorientation collision

$$\sigma_r = \frac{\pi}{\langle v \rangle} \frac{\Delta\nu_{FWHH}}{n} = \frac{\pi k T_0}{\langle v \rangle} \left(\frac{\Delta\nu_{FWHH}}{p} \right) \tag{328}$$

where $(\Delta\nu_{FWHH}/p)$ is the pressure broadening coefficient and where $\langle v \rangle = (8kT_0/\pi\mu)^{1/2}$ is the mean relative velocity of a pair of colliding molecules with reduced mass μ. For CO_2, N_2, and H_2 the cross sections thus deduced are, respectively, 81, 28, and 0.77 Å^2. Corroborative results are obtained from nuclear spin relaxation and from the Senftleben effect (*352*) (influence of a magnetic field on viscosity) in gases since the cross section σ_r enters into the description of both effects. The cross sections obtained from the Senftleben effect (*353*) are 53, 24, and 1.1 Å^2 for CO_2, N_2, and H_2 respectively, which are in reasonable agreement with the results obtained from light scattering. The NMR technique has thus far been applied only to N_2. The reorientation cross section for N_2 determined by Speight and Armstrong (*354*) is 26 Å^2.

The spectrum of the depolarized Rayleigh light scattered by gases has been studied in detail by Hess (*355–358*) from the basis of the kinetic theory of gases. The essential results of this work may be summarized as follows. Eq. (322) is shown to be invalid if the mean free path is greater than the wavelength of light and the diffusion coefficient D_0 that appears in Eq. (322) is not the coefficient of self diffusion, but is rather a "tensor polarization" diffusion coefficient given by $D_T = k_B T_0/m\omega_{TF}$ where ω_{TF} is a relaxation coefficient for the "tensor polarization flux" (k_B = Boltzmann constant, T_0 = absolute temperature, m = molecular mass). In general the line shape function for the depolarized Rayleigh line is not Lorentzian and the line width is then not given by Eq. (322) but by a more cumbersome relationship. This behavior of the depolarized Rayleigh line is also expected to be exhibited by the rotational Raman lines. Hess (*358*) further predicts the existence of damped "tensor polarization waves" in a gas which cause a splitting of the depolarized Rayleigh line into two components shifted by $\pm\omega_{\mathrm{sh}}$ away from ω_0, where ω_{sh} is given by

$$\omega_{\mathrm{sh}}^2 = \omega_{\mathrm{Dop}}^2 - \tfrac{1}{4}(1-\varepsilon)^2\omega_{TF}^2$$

where $\omega_{\mathrm{Dop}} = k^2 k_B T_0/m$, and $\varepsilon = \omega_T/\omega_{TF}$ is the ratio of the relaxation coefficients for the tensor polarization (ω_T) and the tensor polarization flux (ω_{TF}). For most gases of linear molecules except hydrogen and its isotopes $\varepsilon \simeq 1$, so that the splitting then occurs for all pressures and is determined by ω_{Dop} only. This Brillouin effect of the depolarized Rayleigh line in gases is distinct from that observed in liquids (*359*) which is due to shear waves (*360*). If the gas finds itself in a homogeneous magnetic field the depolarized Rayleigh line is split into five components $\omega_0 + m\omega_H$ ($m = 0, \pm 1, \pm 2$) where the characteristic frequency $\omega_H = \gamma H$, where γ is the rotational gyromagnetic ratio and H is the magnetic field. To be sure, the effect is small, fields of the order of 100 kOe being required to fully resolve the splitting. Thus far the only experimental work on the depolarized Rayleigh line in gases is that performed by Cooper et al. (*351*) and their work was limited to the pressure broadening region only. Further work needs to be done on this subject, particularly at low pressures where the diffusion broadening is the predominant effect.

Pressure induced line shifts have been observed in hydrogen (*318,319, 323,361–363*), methane (*361*), and nitrogen (*343*). According to May et al.

(*363*) the frequency shifts of the Q-branch lines in hydrogen can be represented by the relation

$$Q_1(J, \rho) - Q_1(J, O) = a_J\rho + b_J\rho^2$$

where $Q_1(J, O)$ is the Raman frequency of the free molecule, ρ is the relative density (in Amagat units), and a_J and b_J are temperature dependent constants whose average values are of the order -2.5×10^{-3} cm^{-1}/Amagat and $+5.8 \times 10^{-6}$ cm^{-1}/Amagat^2 at $T_0 = 300°$K, respectively, whereas at $T_0 = 85°$K the average values of a_J and b_J are -9.4×10^{-3} cm^{-1}/Amagat and $+5.8 \times 10^{-6}$ cm^{-1}/Amagat^2. The strongly temperature dependent linear coefficient has been shown to be of the form

$$a_J = a_i + a_c(n_J/n)$$

where a_i, a constant for all the Q-lines, is due to the isotropic intermolecular forces and the term $a_c(n_J/n)$, where (n_J/n) is the relative population of the initial J-level, is due to the in-phase coupled oscillations of pairs of molecules. The repulsive overlap and attractive dispersion forces give, respectively, positive and negative contributions to a_i of which the former is strongly temperature dependent whereas the latter is not. The coupling coefficient a_c is, however, determined primarily by the dispersion forces. While the linear coefficient is thus adequately accounted for, the description of the nonlinear coefficient b_J in terms of the intermolecular forces is not well understood at this time.

Similar to the shifts of the Q-branch lines the density dependence of the frequencies of the pure rotational Raman lines of H_2 can be represented by (*323,362*)

$$S_0(J, \rho) - S_0(J, O) = c_J\rho + d_J\rho^2$$

Only the $J = 2 \leftarrow J = 0$ and $J = 3 \leftarrow J = 1$ lines have been studied. According to Cooper et al. (*323*) for pure H_2 the shift is linear with c_0 and c_1 both of the order 10^{-4} cm^{-1}/Amagat whereas for a 1:10 mixture of H_2 in He $c_1 = 10.6 \times 10^{-4}$ and $d_1 = 29 \times 10^{-7}$, and for H_2 in Ar $c_1 = 12.4 \times 10^{-4}$ and $d_1 = 14 \times 10^{-7}$, the units of c_1 and d_1 being cm^{-1}/Amagat and cm^{-1}/Amagat^2, respectively. The shift of the rotational lines is determined, in addition to the isotropic forces, by the anisotropic intermolecular forces; this theory has not yet been sufficiently developed to give an accurate account of the shift.

D. Miscellaneous Topics

There are several other topics which have bearing on the subject of Raman intensities. As mentioned in the beginning of this chapter this discussion of the Raman effect in gases is limited to the nonresonant effect. It is nevertheless of interest to keep in mind that as the exciting frequency approaches an absorption frequency of the molecule profound changes in the rotational fine structure of the Raman bands are to be expected.

The theory of the resonance Raman effect in gases has been briefly described by Placzek (*20*) and has been developed in detail by a number of other authors (*364*) (the polarizability approximation is no longer valid). If the exciting frequency ν_0 lies so close to the exact resonance frequency ν_{res} that the difference between them is comparable to the rotational frequencies of the molecule we speak of the "rotational resonance Raman effect." The theory of this effect has been developed in detail by Morozov (*365*) for the case of diatomic molecules. Significant modifications of the intensity distribution in the vibration-rotation Raman band as well as of the depolarization factor of the Q-branch are demonstrated. For the Rayleigh line the depolarization factor is (*366*)

$$\rho^{\text{Ray}} = \frac{1}{2} \cdot \frac{2J(J+1)+1}{3J(J+1)-1}$$

where J is the total angular momentum of the initial, intermediate (resonant), and final state. For the lines of the vibrational Q-branch ($\Delta J = 0$) with resonant intermediate state $J+1$ we have (*365,367*)

$$\rho^{Q} = \frac{1}{2} \cdot \frac{J(6J+7)}{4J^2+8J+5}$$

whereas if the intermediate state is $J-1$,

$$\rho^{Q} = \frac{1}{2} \cdot \frac{(J+1)(6J-1)}{4J^2+1}$$

(the contribution due to radiation damping is neglected). For large J both expressions for ρ^Q converge toward the value 3/4. The depolarization factor for the O- and S-branch lines is unaffected by resonance; its value is 3/4. The only quantitative experiment on the resonance Raman effect in gases has been performed by Holzer et al. (*368*) who studied the vibrational Raman spectra as well as the transition to the case of resonance fluorescence of Cl_2, Br_2, BrCl, ICl, and IBr by using the various output frequencies of the argon-ion laser.

As pointed out by Placzek (*20*) the depolarization factor in the resonance region is markedly sensitive to the effect of external perturbations. In particular, the effect of external fields (electric, magnetic) should always cause an increase in the value of the depolarization factor. However, if the external field is parallel to the electric vector of the exciting radiation then in first approximation the polarization of the scattered light is not modified. Earlier experiments by Buchheim (*369*) and Douglas (*370*) who measured the depolarization factors of Raman lines, albeit for liquid substances, in the presence of strong fields (up to 70,000 V/cm) were performed far away from resonance and no measurable effect on the depolarization factor, frequency, width, or intensity of the Raman lines could be ascertained. On the other hand, Singh (*371*) notices a red shift of the Rayleigh lines (4358, 5461 Å) and of one Raman line of CCl_4(218 cm^{-1}) when placed in an electric field as well as changes in the intensity of the Rayleigh lines. Experiments on gases using the modern techniques of laser Raman spectroscopy have not yet been performed.

The resonance Raman effect is also expected to enhance possible Jahn-Teller effects in molecules in excited electronic states which are involved in the Raman scattering (*372*). On the other hand a Jahn-Teller effect in ReF_6, OsF_6, and similar highly symmetric systems is expected to distort the otherwise spherical top rotator into a symmetric top rotor. This would consequently allow a pure rotational Raman effect for such molecules even outside the resonance region (*373*).

Finally, the theory of the Raman effect has been attacked anew in a series of papers by Chiu (*374*). Using the modern techniques of the theory of the angular momentum several new details, including a novel odd-parity Raman scattering effect, are developed in these papers.

VIII. CONCLUDING REMARKS

In this chapter I have endeavored to give an exposition of the Raman effect in gases insofar as it is studied with modern high-resolving power spectroscopic instruments. We can distinguish three areas of study of this phenomenon: (1) molecular structure studies, including the determination of the polarizability invariants, (2) the study of intermolecular forces, and 3) the studies of special effects particularly the resonant Raman effect. The order in which these areas are listed is indicative of the relative amount of effort that has been expended thus far on each by the various investigators active in the field of Raman spectroscopy of gases.

That modern high-power lasers have revolutionized the study of the

Raman effect is perhaps a gratuitous statement. And yet the full potential of the laser source in Raman spectroscopy remains to be realized. Primarily this is a problem of instrumental resolving power and of collecting (photographically or photoelectrically) the mass of detailed information available from an intrinsically weak source, the dilute scattering gas. This is of course an old problem to the molecular spectroscopist and is nearly identical to that faced by the astronomer. Although remarkable advances in technique have been made which allow the recording of heretofore unobservable Raman spectra, both as regards resolution (see Figs. 23–27) and intensity, it is hoped that still better techniques will be developed in the near future which will allow the full realization of the potential of the laser source in Raman spectroscopy.

Acknowledgments

This work was supported in part by a grant from the National Science Foundation which is herewith gratefully acknowledged. Thanks are also due to Dr. Joseph J. Barrett for communicating, prior to publication, the details of his interferometric scanning technique for obtaining Raman spectra, to Dr. D. Lepard for providing Fig. 12, to Prof. Joseph Shapiro for helpful discussions, and to the various authors for permission to quote from their publications.

REFERENCES

1. J. C. McLennan and J. H. McLeod, *Trans. Roy. Soc. Can. III*, **23,** 19 (1929); *Nature* **123,** 160 (1929).
2. E. J. Allin, T. Feldman, and H. L. Welsh, *J. Chem. Phys.*, **24,** 1116 (1956); S. S. Bhatnagar, E. J. Allin, and H. L. Welsh, *Can. J. Phys.*, **40,** 9 (1962).
3. R. W. Wood, *Nature* **123,** 166, 279 (1929); *Phys. Rev.*, **33,** 1097 (1929); *Phil. Mag.*, **7,** 1929 (1929).
4. F. Rasetti, *Proc. Natl. Acad. Sci.*, **15,** 234, 515 (1929); *Nuovo Cim.*, **6,** 356 (1929); *Phys. Rev.*, **34,** 367, 548 (1929).
5. S. Bhagavantam, *Nature*, **128,** 70, 188, 272 (1931); *Ind. J. Phys.* **6,** 319, 331. 557 (1931).
6. S. Bhagavantam, *Ind. J. Phys.*, **7,** 632 (1932).
7. F. Rasetti, *Z. Physik*, **61,** 598 (1930).
8. B. Trumpy, *Z. Physik*, **84,** 282 (1933).
9. E. Amaldi, *Z. Physik*, **79,** 492 (1932).
10. S. Bhagavantam, *Phys. Rev.*, **42,** 437 (1932).
11. F. Rasetti, *Nuovo Cim.*, **7,** 261 (1930); *Z. Physik*, **66,** 646 (1930).
12. W. V. Houston and C. M. Lewis, *Phys. Rev.*, **37,** 227 (1931); *Proc. Natl. Acad. Sci.*, **17,** 229 (1931).

13. A. Langseth and J. R. Nielsen, *Phys. Rev.*, **44,** 326, 911 (1933).
14. R. G. Dickinson, R. T. Dillon, and F. Rasetti, *Phys. Rev.*, **34,** 582 (1929).
15. E. Amaldi and G. Placzek, *Naturwiss.*, **20,** 521 (1932); *Z. Physik*, **81,** 259 (1933).
16. C. M. Lewis and W. V. Houston, *Phys. Rev.*, **44,** 903 (1933).
17. S. Bhagavantam, *Nature*, **129,** 830 (1932); **130,** 740 (1932).
18. C. M. Lewis and W. V. Houston, *Phys. Rev.*, **41,** 389 (1932).
19. G. Placzek and E. Teller, *Z. Physik.*, **81,** 209 (1933).
20. G. Placzek, "Rayleigh Streuung und Ramaneffekt," in *Handbuch der Radiologie* (G. Marx, ed.), Akad. Verlagsgesellschaft, Leipzig, 1934, Part 2, Vol. 6, p. 205 [English Transl. by A. Werbin, U.C.R.L. Translation No. 526 (L)].
20a. F. Rasmussen and S. Brodersen, *J. Mol. Spectry.*, **25,** 166 (1968).
21. S. Bhagavantam, *Proc. Ind. Acad. Sci.*, **2A,** 303, 310, 477 (1935).
22. G. K. Teal and G. E. MacWood, *J. Chem. Phys.*, **3,** 760 (1935).
23. J. Cabannes and A. Rousset, *Compt. Rend.* **202,** 1825 (1936); **206,** 85 (1938); *J. Phys. Radium*, **1,** 155, 181, 210 (1940).
24. J. R. Nielsen and N. E. Ward, *J. Chem. Phys.*, **10,** 81 (1942).
25. H. L. Welsh and M. F. Crawford, *Phys. Rev.*, **72,** 524 (1947).
26. H. L. Welsh, M. F. Crawford, T. R. Thomas, and G. R. Love, *Can. J. Phys.*, **30,** 577 (1952).
27. H. L. Welsh, C. Cumming, and E. J. Stansbury, *J. Opt. Soc. Am.*, **41,** 712 (1952).
28. H. L. Welsh, E. J. Stansbury, J. Romanko, and T. Feldman, *J. Opt. Soc. Am.*, **45,** 338 (1955).
29. B. P. Stoicheff, "High Resolution Raman Spectroscopy," in *Advances in Spectroscopy I* (H. W. Thompson, ed.) Wiley-Interscience, New York, 1959, pp. 91–174.
30. B. P. Stoicheff, "Raman Effect," in *Experimental Physics, Molecular Physics* (D. Williams, ed.), Vol. 3, Academic, New York, 1962, pp. 111–155.
31. J. Brandmüller and H. Moser, *Einführung in die Ramanspektroskopie*, Dr. Dietrich Steinkopf Verlag, Darmstadt, 1962.
32. See, for example, H. A. Kramers, *Die Grundlagen der Quantentheorie, Quantentheorie des Elektrons und der Strahlung*, Akad. Verlagsges., Leipzig 1938 (English Transl., *Quantum Mechanics*, Chapt. 8, North-Holland, Amsterdam, 1957); D. I. Blochintsev, *Quantum Mechanics*, Chapt. 15, Reidel, Dodrecht-Holland, 1964; W. Heitler, *The Quantum Theory of Radiation* (2nd Ed.), Chapt. 3, Oxford, 1944; see also Placzek, Ref. 20.
33. See Ref. (*20*), Chap. 14.
34. See, for example, J. Behringer and J. Brandmüller, *Z. Elektrochem*, **60,** 643 (1956); J. Behringer, *Z. Elektrochem.*, **62,** 906 (1958); J. Behringer, "Observed Resonance Raman Spectra" in *Raman Spectroscopy, Theory and Practice* (H. Szymanski, ed.), Plenum, New York, 1967, pp. 168–223; A. C. Albrecht, *J. Chem. Phys.* **34,** 1476 (1961).
35. See the chapter by J. A. Köningstein and O. S. Mortensen in this book.
36. See Ref. (*20*), Chapt. 6 and 21, and Ref. (*19*).
37. See, for example, E. B. Wilson, Jr., J. C. Decius, and P. C. Cross, *Molecular Vibrations*, McGraw-Hill, New York, 1955, Appendix IV.
38. M. Tinkham, *Group Theory and Quantum Mechanics*, McGraw-Hill, New York, 1964, pp. 124–130.
39. A. R. Edmonds, *Angular Momentum in Quantum Mechanics* Princeton University Press, Princeton, N.J., 1957, Chapt. 5.

40. M. E. Rose, *Multipole Fields*, Wiley, New York, 1955, pp. 18–23.
41. S. Bhagavantam and T. Venkatarayudu, *Theory of Groups and its Application to Physical Problems*, 3rd ed., Andhra University Press, Waltair, 1962 pp. 207–215.
42. G. Herzberg, *Molecular Spectra and Molecular Structure, II. Infrared and Raman Spectra of Polyatomic Molecules*, Van Nostrand Co., New York, 1954, Table 55, pp. 252, 253; Ref. (*20*) Tables 4–9.
43. I. M. Mills, *Molec. Physics*, **8,** 363 (1964).
44. E. L. Hill and E. C. Kemble, *Proc. Natl. Acad. Sci.*, **15,** 387 (1929); J. H. Van Vleck, *Proc. Natl. Acad. Sci.*, **15,** 754 (1929).
45. J. D. Louck and W. H. Shaffer, *J. Mol. Spectry.*, **4,** 285 (1960).
46. J. T. Hougen, *J. Chem. Phys.*, **37,** 1433 (1962).
47. E. B. Wilson, Jr., *J. Chem. Phys.*, **3,** 276 (1935).
48. E. B. Wilson, Jr., *J. Chem. Phys.*, **6,** 740 (1938).
49. K. Schäfer, *Z. Physik. Chem.*, **B40,** 357 (1938).
50. H. C. Allen, Jr., and P. C. Cross, *Molecular Vibrotors*, (Wiley, New York, 1963).
51. H. H. Nielsen, *Phys. Rev.*, **66,** 282 (1944).
52. D. H. Rank, G. Skorinko, D. P. Eastman, and T. A. Wiggins, *J. Opt. Soc. Am.*, **50,** 421 (1960).
53. T. A. Wiggins, E. K. Plyler, and E. D. Tidwell, *J. Opt. Soc. Am.*, **51,** 1219 (1961).
54. W. J. Lafferty, A. G. Maki, and E. K. Plyler, *J. Chem. Phys.*, **40,** 224 (1964).
55. J. J. Barrett and A. Weber, *J. Opt. Soc. Am.*, **60,** 70 (1970).
56. Ref. (*37*), pp. 330–332.
57. L. Tisza, *Z. Physik*, **82,** 48 (1933) and Ref. (*56*).
58. J. D. Louck, Ph.D. Thesis, Ohio State University, 1958.
59. K. T. Hecht, *J. Mol. Spectry.*, **5,** 355, 390 (1960).
60. J. Morét-Bailly, Thesis, Faculté des Sciences de Paris, Editions de la Revue d'Optique theoretique et instrumentale Paris, 1961.
61. J. Herranz, *J. Mol. Spectry.*, **6,** 343 (1961).
62. J. Herranz and B. P. Stoicheff, *J. Mol. Spectry.*, **10,** 448 (1963).
63. E. Teller, "Theorie der langwelligen Molekülspektren," in *Hand-und Jahrbuch der Chemischen Physik* (A. Eucken and W. Wolf, eds.), Akad. Verlagsges., Leipzig, 1934, Vol. 9, Part II, p. 43.
64. Brief expositions of the requisite aspects of the theory are found in Refs. (*42*) and (*50*) as well as in M. W. P. Strandberg, *Microwave Spectroscopy*, Methuen, London, 1954 and in C. H. Townes and A. L. Schawlow, *Microwave Spectroscopy*, McGraw-Hill, New York, 1955.
65. S. C. Wang, *Phys. Rev.*, **34,** 243 (1929).
66. B. S. Ray, *Z. Physik*, **78,** 74 (1932).
67. G. W. King, R. M. Hainer, and P. C. Cross, *J. Chem. Phys.*, **11,** 27 (1943).
68. C. Van Winter, *Physica*, **20,** 274 (1954).
69. E. A. Hylleraas, *Z. Physik*, **190,** 226 (1966).
70. D. G. Burkhard and W. E. Brittin, *J. Mol. Spectry.*, **18,** 87 (1965).
71. Ref. (*19*), Sect. 8. See also Herzberg, Ref. (*42*), pp. 59, 60 and 489–491.
72. H. H. Howe, Ph.D. dissertation, George Washington Univ. 1939.
73. E. K. Plyler and E. D. Tidwell, "High Resolution Spectra in the Region from 2 to 6 μ," in *Advances in Molecular Spectroscopy* (A. Mangini, ed.), MacMillan, New York, 1962, pp. 1336–1342.
74. A. G. Maki and T. A. Toth, *J. Mol. Spectry.*, **17,** 136 (1965).

75. J. Pinard, *J. Phys.*, **28,** 136 (1967); Thèse, Paris, 1968, *Ann. Phys.*, **4,** 147 (1969).
76. M. A. Thomas and H. L. Welsh, *Can. J. Phys.*, **38,** 1291 (1960).
77. S. Brodersen and E. H. Richardson, *J. Mol. Spectry.*, **4,** 439 (1960).
77a. H. L. Welsh, G. G. Shepherd, E. H. Richardson, M. A. Thomas, and A. Weber, *Spectrochim. Acta*, **10,** 225 (1958).
78. D. H. Rank, G. D. Saksena, G. Skorinko, D. P. Eastman, T. A. Wiggins, and T. K. McCubbin, Jr., *J. Opt. Soc. Am.*, **49,** 1217 (1959).
79. W. F. Murphy, W. Holzer, and H. J. Bernstein, *Appl. Spectr.*, **23,** 211 (1969) and references cited therein.
80. A. Weber and E. A. McGinnis, *J. Mol. Spectry.*, **4,** 195 (1960).
81. B. P. Stoicheff, *Can. J. Phys.*, **32,** 330 (1954).
82. E. H. Richardson, S. Brodersen, L. Krause, and H. L. Welsh, *J. Mol. Spectry.*, **8,** 406 (1962); E. H. Richardson, Ph.D. thesis, University of Toronto, 1959.
83. A. Weber, S. P. S. Porto, J. J. Barrett, and L. E. Cheesman, *J. Opt. Soc. Am.*, **57,** 19 (1967).
84. S. Brodersen (Aarhuus University, Denmark) private communication.
85. V. I. Tyulin and V. M. Tatevskii, *Optics and Spectry.*, **15,** 18 (1962).
86. I. S. Bowen, *Astrophys J.*, **88,** 113 (1938).
87. K. Tanner and A. Weber, *J. Mol. Spectry.*, **10,** 381 (1963).
88. R. A. Peters, Ph.D. Thesis, Fordham University, 1967.
89. B. J. Monostori and A. Weber, *J. Mol. Spectry.*, **15,** 158 (1965).
90. B. J. Monostori and A. Weber, *J. Mol. Spectry.*, **12,** 129 (1964).
91. K. A. Rooney, W. Zijlstra, and A. Weber, unpublished work.
91a. W. F. Edgell, Ph. A. King, and J. W. Amy, *J. Am. Chem. Soc.*, **39,** 2691 (1957).
91b. A. Danti and R. C. Lord, *Spectrochim. Acta*, **13,** 180 (1958).
92. K. Suryanarayana Rao, B. P. Stoicheff, and R. Turner, *Can. J. Phys.*, **38,** 1516 (1960).
93. B. P. Stoicheff, *Can. J. Phys.*, **40,** 358 (1962).
94. D. W. Lepard, D. E. Shaw, and H. L. Welsh, *Can. J. Phys.*, **44,** 2353 (1966).
95. D. W. Lepard, D. M. C. Sweeney, and H. L. Welsh, *Can. J. Phys.*, **40,** 1567 (1962).
95a. D. Lepard, Ph.D. Thesis, University of Toronto, 1966.
96. D. E. Shaw and H. L. Welsh, *Can. J. Phys.*, **45,** 3823 (1967).
96a. E. Hirota, *J. Chem. Phys.*, **55,** 981 (1971).
97. H. H. Claassen, H. Selig, and J. Shamir, *Appl. Spectry.*, **23,** 8 (1969).
98. E. K. Plyler and H. J. Kostkowski, *J. Opt. Soc. Am.*, **42,** 360 (1952).
99. J. J. Barrett and N. I. Adams, III, *J. Opt. Soc. Am.*, **58,** 311 (1968).
100. J. J. Barrett and J. D. Rigden, Ninth European Congress on Molecular Spectroscopy, Madrid, Spain, Sept. 1967.
101. W. H. Fletcher, J. D. Allen, and W. J. Wiley, *Appl. Optics*, **6,** 1130 (1967).
102. A. Weber and S. P. S. Porto, *J. Opt. Soc. Am.*, **55,** 1033 (1955).
103. F. Stenman, *Comm. Phys-Math. Soc. Sci. Fennica*, **31,** No. 5 (1965).
103a. J. Morét-Bailly and H. Berger, *Compt. Rend.*, **269B,** 416 (1969).
103b. N. H. Rich and H. L. Welsh, *J. Opt. Soc. Am.*, **61,** 977 (1971).
103c. A. Chapput, M. Delhaye and J. Wrobel, *Compt. Rend.* **272B,** 461 (1971).
103d. R. A. Peters, W. J. Walker and A. Weber, (to be published).
104. D. L. Renschler, J. L. Hunt, T. K. McCubbin, Jr., and S. R. Polo, *J. Mol. Spectry.*, **31,** 173 (1969).

105. A. Kastler, *Appl. Optics*, **1**, 17 (1962).
106. A. Weber, unpublished work.
107. J. Schlupf and A. Weber, unpublished work.
108. J. J. Barrett and S. A. Myers, *J. Opt. Soc. Am.*, **61**, 1246 (1971).
109. A. Röseler, *Optik*, **24**, 606 (1966/1967).
110. K. S. Jammu, G. E. St. John, and H. L. Welsh, *Can. J. Phys.*, **44**, 797 (1966).
110a. D. W. Lepard, *Can. J. Phys.*, **48**, 1664 (1970).
111. W. J. Walker and A. Weber, *J. Mol. Spectry.*, **39**, 57 (1971).
111a. M. Hercher, *Appl. Optics* **8**, 1103 (1969).
111b. *Kodak Plates and Films for Science and Industry*, Kodak Publication No. P-19 (Eastman Kodak Co, 1967) p. 12d.
111c. J. Schlupf and A. Weber, to be published.
112. Ref. (*42*), pp. 15–21.
113. G. Herzberg, *Molecular Spectra and Molecular Structure I. Spectra of Diatomic Molecules*, 2nd ed. D. van Nostrand, New York, 1950, pp. 128–141.
114. B. P. Stoicheff, *Can. J. Phys.*, **32**, 630 (1954).
115. D. Andrychuk, *Can. J. Phys.*, **29**, 151 (1951).
116. T. Feldman, G. G. Shepherd, and H. L. Welsh, *Can. J. Phys.*, **34**, 1425 (1956).
117. J. H. Callomon and B. P. Stoicheff, *Can. J. Phys.*, **35**, 373 (1957).
118. L. Krause and H. L. Welsh, *Can. J. Phys.*, **34**, 1431 (1956).
119. C. K. Møller and B. P. Stoicheff, *Can. J. Phys.*, **32**, 635 (1954).
120. See Ref. (*42*), Chapt. 1 and Ref. (*113*), Chapt. 1.
121. Ref. (*113*), pp. 223–224.
122. D. L. Renschler, J. L. Hunt, T. K. McCubbin, Jr., and S. R. Polo, *J. Mol. Spectry.*, **32**, 347 (1969).
123. H. Fast, H. L. Welsh, and D. W. Lepard, *Can. J. Phys.*, **47**, 2879 (1969).
123a. K. C. Shotton and W. J. Jones, *Can. J. Phys.*, **48**, 632 (1970).
124. B. P. Stoicheff, *Can. J. Phys.*, **35**, 730 (1957).
125. T. Yoshino and H. J. Bernstein, *J. Mol. Spectry.*, **2**, 213 (1958).
126. B. P. Stoicheff, *Can. J. Phys.*, **36**, 218 (1958).
127. Ref. (*42*), pp. 215–218.
128. H. W. Schrötter and H. J. Bernstein, *J. Mol. Spectry.*, **12**, 1 (1964).
129. W. J. Jones, B. P. Stoicheff, and J. K. Tyler, *Can. J. Phys.*, **41**, 2098 (1963).
130. C. G. LeFévre and R. J. W. LeFévre, *J. Chem. Soc.*, **1956**, 3549.
131. K. Tanner, Dissertation, Fordham University, 1962.
132. See, for example, the compilation of rotation constants of a large number of molecules obtained from microwave spectra in B. Stark, Molecular Constants from Microwave Spectroscopy, in *Landolt-Börnstein* (editors K. H. Hellwege and A. M. Hellwege) group II, vol. 4, Springer Verlag, Berlin—Heidelberg—New York, 1967.
133. G. W. Chantry, H. A. Gebbie, R. J. L. Popplewell, and H. W. Thompson, *Proc. Roy. Soc.*, **A304**, 45 (1968) and references cited therein.
134. Quoted in Ref. (*135* and *136*).
135. M. R. Aliev, S. I. Subbotin, and V. I. Tyulin, *Optics and Spectry.*, **24**, 47 (1968).
136. V. I. Tyulin and S. I. Subbotin, *Optics and Spectry.*, **26**, 200 (1969).
137. S. I. Subbotin, R. Kh. Safiullin, V. I. Tyulin, and V. M. Tatevskii, *Optics and Spectry.*, **24**, 41 (1968).
138. W. J. Lafferty and E. K. Plyler, *J. Chem. Phys.*, **37**, 2688 (1962).
139. H. C. Allen, Jr. and E. K. Plyler, *J. Chem. Phys.*, **31**, 1062 (1959).

140. B. P. Stoicheff, *Can. J. Phys.*, **33,** 811 (1955).
141. W. J. Jones and B. P. Stoicheff, *Can. J. Phys.*, **42,** 2259 (1964).
141a. T. K. McCubbin, Jr., V. Withstandley, and S. R. Polo, *J. Mol. Spectry.*, **31,** 95 (1969).
142. R. C. Lord and B. P. Stoicheff, *Can. J. Phys.*, **40,** 725 (1962).
143. B. P. Stoicheff, *Can. J. Phys.*, **32,** 339 (1954).
144. A. Langseth and B. P. Stoicheff, *Can. J. Phys.*, **34,** 350 (1956).
144a. J. Schlupf and A. Weber (to be published).
144b. J. Schlupf and A. Weber (to be published).
145. J. E. Lancaster and B. P. Stoicheff, *Can. J. Phys*,. **34,** 1016 (1956).
146. B. J. Monostori, Dissertation, Fordham University, 1964.
146a. B. J. Monostori and A. Weber (to be published).
147. A. Weber, *J. Mol. Spectry.*, **14,** 53 (1964).
148. P. G. Favero and A. Mirri, *Nuovo Cimento*, **30,** 502 (1963).
149. R. Antilla, *Ann. Acad. Sci. Fenn. Ser. A*, VI, Phys, No. 254 (1967).
150. See Herzberg, Ref. (*42*), pp. 342–346.
151. J. Romanko, T. Feldman, and H. L. Welsh, *Can. J. Phys.*, **33,** 588 (1955).
152. S. Brodersen and E. H. Richardson, *J. Mol. Spectry.*, **6,** 265 (1961).
153. P. M. Mathai, G. G. Shepherd, and H. L. Welsh, *Can. J. Phys.*, **34,** 1448 (1956).
154. H. H. Guenthard, R. C. Lord, and T. K. McCubbin, *J. Chem. Phys.*, **25,** 768 (1956).
155. J. Overend and H. W. Thompson, *Trans. Faraday Soc.*, **52,** 1295 (1956).
156. I. M. Mills, W. L. Smith, and J. L. Duncan, *J. Mol. Spectry.*, **16,** 349 (1965).
157. K. N. Rao and E. K. Palik, *J. Mol. Spectry*, **1,** 24 (1957).
158. Ref. (*29*) p. 140.
159. B. Monostori and A. Weber, *J. Chem. Phys.*, **33,** 1867 (1960).
160. C. W. Gullikson, J. R. Nielsen, and A. T. Stair, Jr., *J. Mol. Spectry.*, **1,** 151 (1957).
161. B. P. Stoicheff, C. Cumming, G. E. St. John, and H. L. Welsh, *Phys. Rev.*, **84,** 592 (1951); *J. Chem. Phys.*, **20,** 498 (1952).
162. T. Feldman, J. Romanko, and H. L. Welsh, *Can. J. Phys.*, **33,** 138 (1955).
163. G. G. Shepherd and H. L. Welsh, *J. Mol. Spectry.*, **1,** 277 (1957).
164. R. A. Olafson, M. A. Thomas, and H. L. Welsh, *Can. J. Phys.*, **39,** 419 (1961).
165. For CH_4 see, for example, J. S. Burgess, E. E. Bell, and H. H. Nielsen, *J. Opt. Soc. Am.*, **43,** 1058 (1953).
166. For CD_4 see, for example, H. M. Kaylor and A. H. Nielsen, *J. Chem. Phys.*, **23,** 2139 (1955).
167. J. Herranz, J. Morcillo, and A. Gómez, *J. Mol. Spectry*, **19,** 266 (1966).
168. R. S. McDowell, *J. Mol. Spectry.*, **21,** 280 (1966).
169. J. K. Wilmshurst and H. J. Bernstein, *Can. J. Chem.*, **35,** 226 (1957).
170. H. C. Allen, Jr. and E. K. Plyler, *J. Res. Natl. Bur. Standards*, **63A,** 145 (1959).
170a. F. N. Masri and W. H. Fletcher, *J. Chem. Phys.*, **52,** 5759 (1970).
171. F. J. Nolan, M. Sidran, and J. W. Blaker, *J. Chem. Phys.*, **41,** 588 (1964).
172. H. H. Nielsen, *Revs. Modern Phys.*, **23,** 90 (1951); "The Vibration-Rotation Energies of Molecules and their Spectra in the Infrared," in *Handbuch der Physik*, (S. Flügge, ed.) Springer-Verlag, Berlin, 1959, Vol. 37, Part 1, pp. 173–313.
173. D. Kivelson and E. B. Wilson, Jr., *J. Chem. Phys.*, **20,** 1575 (1952); **21,** 1229 (1953).

174. D. W. Davidson, B. P. Stoicheff, and H. J. Bernstein, *J. Chem. Phys.*, **22,** 289 (1954).
175. D. J. Marais, N. Sheppard, and B. P. Stoicheff, *Tetrahedron Letters*, **17,** 163 (1962).
175a. A. R. H. Cole, G. H. Mohay, and G. A. Osborne, *Spectrochim. Acta*, **23A,** 909 (1967).
176. B. P. Stoicheff, *Can. J. Phys.*, **35,** 837 (1957).
177. Z. B. Gribova, V. I. Tyulin, and V. M. Tatevskii, *Optics and Spectry.*, **15,** 172 (1963).
178. G. O. Sørensen, *J. Mol. Spectry.*, **22,** 325 (1967).
179. S. I. Subbotin, V. I. Tyulin, C. I. Katayev, and V. M. Tatevskii, *Optics and Spectry.*, **19,** 361 (1965).
180. S. S. Butcher and C. C. Costain, *J. Mol. Spectry.*, **15,** 40 (1965).
181. S. S. Butcher, *J. Chem. Phys.*, **42,** 1833 (1965).
182. J. Romanko, T. Feldman, E. J. Stansbury, and A. McKellar, *Can. J. Phys.*, **32,** 735 (1954).
183. J. M. Dowling and B. P. Stoicheff, *Can. J. Phys.*, **37,** 703 (1959).
184. H. C. Allen and E. K. Plyler, *J. Am. Chem. Soc.*, **80,** 2673 (1958).
185. W. L. Smith and I. M. Mills, *J. Chem. Phys.*, **40,** 2095 (1964).
186. K. Kuchitsu, T. Oka, and Y. Morino, *J. Mol. Spectry.*, **15,** 51 (1965).
187. R. Van Riet and M. de Hemptinne, *Bull. Acad. Royale Belg.*, **45,** 381 (1959).
188. B. P. Stoicheff, *J. Chem. Phys.*, **21,** 755 (1953).
189. T. Feldman, J. Romanko, and H. L. Welsh, *Can. J. Phys.*, **34,** 737 (1956).
190. R. L. Arnett and B. L. Crawford, *J. Chem. Phys.*, **18,** 118 (1950); B. L. Crawford, J. E. Lancaster, and R. Inskeep, *J. Chem. Phys.*, **21,** 678 (1953).
191. J. Kraitchman, *Am. J. Phys.*, **21,** 17 (1953).
192. H. Goldstein, *Classical Mechanics*, Addison Wesley, Cambridge, 1950, Chapter 5.
193. C. C. Costain, *J. Chem. Phys.*, **29,** 864 (1958).
194. See J. E. Wollrab, *Rotational Spectra and Molecular Structure*, Academic, New York, 1967, Chapter 4.
195. T. Oka, *J. Phys. Soc. Japan*, **15,** 2274 (1960).
196. T. Oka and Y. Morino, *J. Phys. Soc. Japan*, **16,** 1235 (1961).
197. T. Oka and Y. Morino, *J. Mol. Spectry*, **6,** 472 (1961).
198. Y. Morino, K. Kuchitsu, and T. Oka, *J. Chem. Phys.*, **36,** 1108 (1962).
199. M. Toyama, T. Oka, and Y. Morino, *J. Mol. Spectry.*, **13,** 193 (1964).
200. D. R. Herschbach and V. Laurie, *J. Chem. Phys.*, **37,** 1668 (1962).
201. V. Laurie and D. R. Herschbach, *J. Chem. Phys.*, **37,** 1687 (1962).
202. E. B. Wilson, Jr. and J. B. Howard, *J. Chem. Phys.*, **4,** 260 (1936); Ref. (37) Chapter 11.
203. C. Eckart, *Phys. Rev.*, **47,** 552 (1935); see also S. M. Ferigle and A. Weber, *Am. J. Phys.*, **21,** 102 (1953).
204. L. S. Bartell, *J. Chem. Phys.*, **23,** 1219 (1955).
205. K. Kuchitsu and L. S. Bartell, *J. Chem. Phys.*, **35,** 1945 (1961).
206. L. S. Bartell, K. Kuchitsu, and R. J. DeNeuii, *J. Chem. Phys.*, **35,** 1211 (1961).
207. K. Kuchitsu and L. S. Bartell, *J. Chem. Phys.*, **36,** 2460, 2470 (1962).
208. L. S. Bartell, *J. Chem. Phys.*, **38,** 1827 (1963).
209. L. S. Bartell, *J. Chem. Phys.*, **42,** 1681 (1965).
210. C. Courtoy, *Ann. Soc. Sci. Bruxelles*, **73,** 5 (1959).
211. B. P. Stoicheff, *Tetrahedron Letters*, **17,** 135 (1962).

212. A. Langseth and C. K. Møller, *Acta. Chem. Scand.*, **4,** 725 (1950).
213. D. E. Shaw, D. W. Lepard, and H. L. Welsh, *J. Chem. Phys.*, **42,** 3736 (1965).
214. L. S. Bartell and H. K. Higginbotham, *J. Chem. Phys.*, **42,** 851 (1965).
215. L. S. Bartell, E. A. Roth, C. D. Hollowell, K. Kuchitsu, and J. E. Young, Jr., *J. Chem. Phys.*, **42,** 2683 (1965).
216. K. Kuchitsu, *J. Chem. Phys.*, **44,** 906 (1966).
217. A. Almenningen, O. Bastiansen, and M. Traetteberg, *Acta. Chem. Scand.*, **13,** 1699 (1959).
218. Y. Morino, J. Nakamura, and P. W. Moore, *J. Chem. Phys.*, **36,** 1050 (1962).
219. W. Haugen and M. Traetteberg, *Acta. Chem. Scand.*, **20,** 1726 (1966).
219a. A. Almenningen, O. Bastiansen, and M. Traetteberg, *Acta. Chem. Scand.*, **12,** 1221 (1958).
219b. K. Kuchitsu, T. Fukuyama, and Y. Morino, *J. Mol. Structure*, **1,** 463 (1967–1968).
220. A. Almenningen, O. Bastiansen, and M. Traetteberg, *Acta. Chem. Scand.*, **15,** 1557 (1961).
221. O. Bastiansen, F. N. Frisch, and K. Hedberg, *Acta. Cryst.*, **17,** 538 (1964).
222. A. Almenningen, O. Bastiansen, and P. N. Skancke, *Acta. Chem. Scand.*, **15,** 711 (1961).
223. M. Davis and O. Hassell, *Acta. Chem. Scand.*, **17,** 1181 (1963).
224. N. V. Alekseev and A. I. Kitaigorodskii, *J. Struct. Chem.*, **4,** 145 (1963); *Zh. Strukt. Khim.*, **4,** 163 (1963).
225. W. V. F. Brooks, B. N. Cyvin, S. J. Cyvin, P. C. Kvande, and E. Meisingseth, *Acta. Chem. Scand.*, **17,** 345 (1963).
225a. L. H. Bauer, K. Katada, and K. Kimura. in *Structural Chemistry and Molecular Biology*, (A. Rich and N. Davidson, eds.), W. H. Freeman & Co. S. Francisco and London, 1969; pp. 653–670.
226. H. J. Bernstein, *Spectrochim. Acta.*, **18,** 161 (1962).
227. E. B. Wilson, Jr., *J. Chem. Phys.*, **7,** 1047 (1939); **9,** 76 (1941); see Ref. (*37*) for a detailed exposition of the method and for an extensive bibliography.
228. S. J. Cyvin, *Molecular Vibrations and Mean Square Amplitudes*, Elsevier, Amsterdam, 1968.
228a. J. Brandmüller and H. J. Schrötter, *Z. Phys.*, **149,** 131 (1957).
229. S. R. Polo, *J. Chem. Phys.*, **24,** 1133 (1956).
230. R. J. Malhiot and S. M. Ferigle, *J. Chem. Phys.*, **22,** 717 (1954).
231. R. J. Malhiot and S. M. Ferigle, *J. Chem. Phys.*, **23,** 30 (1955).
232. See Ref. 37, Appendix VI; J. C. Decius, *J. Chem. Phys.*, **16,** 1025 (1948); S. M. Ferigle and A. G. Meister, *J. Chem. Phys.*, **19,** 982 (1951); J. B. Lohman, ONR Technical Report No. 17 (1951), NR-019-102; T. Shimanouchi, *J. Chem. Phys.*, **25,** 660 (1956).
233. See Ref. (*37*), Appendix XII.
234. S. Califano and B. Crawford, Jr., *Z. Electrochem.*, **64,** 571 (1960).
235. S. Califano and J. Heicklen, *Spectrochim. Acta*, **17,** 901 (1961).
236. L. S. Mayants, *Optics and Spectry.*, **16,** 410 (1964).
237. G. B. Shaltuper, *Optics and Spectry.*, **18,** 208 (1965).
238. D. E. Freeman, *J. Mol. Spectry.*, **10,** 75 (1963); **20,** 75, 463 (1966).
239. J. R. Ferraro and J. S. Ziomek, *Introductory Group Theory and its Application to Molecular Structure*, Plenum, New York, 1969.
240. J. H. Meal and S. R. Polo, *J. Chem. Phys.*, **24,** 1119, 1126 (1956).

241. D. R. J. Boyd and H. C. Longuet-Higgins, *Proc. Roy. Soc.*, **A213,** 55 (1952).
242. See Ferigle and Weber, Ref. (*203*). The expression for $B_{pjj'}$ given in this paper should be multiplied by -1.
243. A. M. Walsh, Dissertation, Fordham University, 1965.
244. H. A. Jahn, *Phys. Rev.*, **56,** 680 (1939); W. H. J. Childs and H. A. Jahn, *Proc. Roy. Soc.*, **A169,** 451 (1939).
245. R. C. Lord and R. E. Merrifield, *J. Chem. Phys.*, **20,** 1348 (1952).
246. D. W. Lepard, *Can. J. Phys.*, **44,** 461 (1966).
247. R. S. McDowell, *J. Chem. Phys.*, **41,** 2557 (1964); **43,** 319 (1965).
247a. R. S. McDowell, *J. Chem. Phys.* **46,** 1535 (1967).
248. L. Nemes, *J. Mol. Spectry.*, **28,** 59 (1968); **30,** 123 (1969).
249. J. L. Duncan, *Spectrochim. Acta.*, **20,** 1197 (1964).
250. E. A. Clark, Dissertation, Fordham University, 1966; see also E. A. Clark and A. Weber, *J. Chem. Phys.*, **45,** 1759 (1966).
251. I. M. Mills and J. L. Duncan, *J. Mol. Spectry.*, **9,** 244 (1962).
252. L. Nemes, J. L. Duncan, and I. M. Mills, *Spectrochim. Acta*, **23A,** 1803 (1967).
253. See Herzberg, Ref. (*42*); Table 18, p. 113 and Table 33, p. 139.
254. For a brief review of intensity perturbation produced by Coriolis interaction see I. M. Mills, *Pure and Appl. Chem.*, **11,** 325 (1965).
255. A. Andersen, R. Stølevik, J. Brumvoll, S. J. Cyvin, and G. Hagen, *Acta Chem. Scand.*, **21,** 1759 (1967).
256. J. L. Duncan and G. R. Burns, *J. Mol. Spectry.*, **30,** 253 (1969) and references to the experimental data contained therein.
257. R. C. Lord and I. Nakagawa, *J. Chem. Phys.*, **39,** 2951 (1963).
258. E. B. Wilson, Jr., *J. Chem. Phys.*, **5,** 617 (1937).
259. J. C. Decius, *J. Chem. Phys.*, **38,** 241 (1963).
260. J. K. G. Watson, *J. Chem. Phys.*, **45,** 1360 (1966); **46,** 1935 (1967).
261. J. M. Dowling, *J. Mol. Spectry.*, **6,** 550 (1961); see also Ref. 196.
262. Ref. (*172*) p. 208.
263. Ref. (*172*) p. 249.
264. Ref. (*250*) Appendix V.
265. J. M. Dowling, R. Gold, and A. G. Meister, *J. Mol. Spectry.*, **1,** 265 (1957).
266. M. Petzuch, *Z. Naturforsch.*, **24a,** 637 (1969).
267. D. M. Dennison, *Revs. Modern Phys.*, **12,** 175 (1940); see also G. E. Hanson and D. M. Dennison, *J. Chem. Phys.*, **20,** 313 (1952).
268. O. Redlich, *Z. Physik. Chem.*, **B28,** 371 (1935); see also Herzberg, Ref. (*42*) p. 231.
269. A fourth order theory of vibration rotation spectra has been developed by Goldsmith, Amat, and Nielsen and the centrifugal distortion correction based on the inclusion of terms of the sixth power of the angular momentum operators has been considered in detail by K. T. Chung and P. M. Parker, *J. Chem. Phys.* **43,** 3865 (1965) who also give the references to the Goldsmith-Amat-Nielsen theory.
270. M. R. Aliev and V. T. Aleksanyan, *Optics and Spectry.*, **24,** 241 (1968).
271. P. N. Daykin, S. Sundaram, and F. F. Cleveland, *J. Chem. Phys.*, **37,** 1087 (1962).
272. I. M. Mills, *Spectrochim. Acta.*, **16,** 35 (1960); J. Aldous and I. M. Mills, *Spectrochim. Acta*, **18,** 1073 (1962); **19,** 1567 (1963); Refs. (*249*, *252*, and *256*) for specific discussions of ethane, allene, and cyclopropane calculations.
273. K. Hedberg and M. Iwasaki, *J. Chem. Phys.*, **36,** 589 (1962).
274. M. Iwasaki and K. Hedberg, *J. Chem. Phys.*, **36,** 594 (1962).

275. D. Papousek and J. Pliva, *Spectrochim Acta*, **21,** 1147 (1965).
276. S. Bhagavantam, *Scattering of Light and the Raman Effect*, Chemical Publishing Co., Brooklyn, N.Y., 1942.
277. H. A. Stuart, *Molekülstruktur*, (3rd Edition) Springer Verlag, Berlin—Heidelberg—New York, 1967.
278. I. L. Fabelinskii, *Molecular Scattering of Light*, Plenum, New York, 1968.
278a. For diatomic molecules see Herzberg, Ref. (*113*), p. 133ff. For polyatomic molecules see Herzberg, Ref. (*42*) pp. 16, 22ff.
279. J. Cabannes and Y. Rocard, *J. de Phys.*, **10,** 52 (1929).
280. S. Bhagavantam, *Ind. J. Phys.*, **6,** 331 (1931).
281. M. Born, *Optik*, Springer Verlag, Berlin, 1933, pp. 541–543.
282. See also Ref. (*31*) pp. 18–21; Ref. (*276*) pp. 162–165; Ref. (*278*) pp. 253–255, also, H. A. Stuart, *Die Struktur des Freien Moleküls*, Springer Verlag, Berlin, 1952, pp. 357–361.
283. M. W. Wolkenstein, *Struktur und Physikalische Eigenschaften der Moleküle*, B. G. Teubner Verlagsges., Leipzig, 1960.
284. M. V. Volkenstein, *Configurational Statistics of Polymeric Chains*, Wiley-Interscience, New York, 1963.
285. N. J. Bridge and A. D. Buckingham, *Proc. Roy. Soc.*, **A295,** 334 (1966).
286. R. Rudder and D. R. Bach, *J. Opt. Soc. Am.*, **58,** 1260 (1968).
287. F. T. Gucker, S. Basu, A. A. Pulido, and G. Chiu, *J. Chem. Phys.*, **50,** 2526 (1969).
288. R. L. Rowell, G. M. Aval and J. J. Barrett, *J. Chem. Phys.*, **54,** 1960 (1971).
289. W. Kolos and L. Wolniewicz, *J. Chem. Phys.*, **46,** 1426 (1967).
290. G. A. Victor, J. C. Browne, and A. Dalgarno, *Proc. Phys. Soc.*, **92,** 42 (1967).
290a. G. A. Victor and A. Dalgarno, *J. Chem. Phys.*, **50,** 2535 (1969).
291. A. Dalgarno, T. Degges, and D. A. Williams, *Proc. Phys. Soc.*, **92,** 291 (1967).
292. A. Dalgarno and D. A. Williams, *Mon. Not. Roy. Astron. Soc.*, **124,** 313 (1962).
293. D. M. Golden and B. Crawford, Jr., *J. Chem. Phys.*, **36,** 1654 (1962).
294. Z. Kecki and H. J. Bernstein, *J. Molec. Spectry.*, **15,** 378 (1965).
295. M. Kirn, *Ann. Physik*, **64,** 566 (1921).
296. T. Yoshino and H. J. Bernstein, *J. Molec. Spectry.*, **2,** 213 (1958).
297. See Stuart, Ref. (*277*) Chapter 8; Wolkenstein, Ref. (*283*) pp. 370–374.
298. E. H. Meyer and G. Otterbein, *Physik Z.*, **32,** 290 (1931); G. Sachse, *Physik Z.*, **36,** 357 (1935); S. N. Wang, *J. Chem. Phys.*, **7,** 1012 (1939); K. G. Denbigh, *Trans. Faraday Soc.*, **36,** 936 (1940).
299. K. S. Pitzer, *Adv. Chem. Phys.*, **2,** 59 (1959).
300. R. J. W. LeFévre, *Adv. Phys. Org. Chem.*, **3,** 1 (1965).
301. R. L. Jernigan and P. J. Flory, *J. Chem. Phys.*, **47,** 1999 (1967).
302. R. L. Rowell and R. S. Stein, *J. Chem. Phys.*, **47,** 2985 (1967).
303. M. W. Wolkenstein, *Compt. Rend. Acad. Sci. USSR*, **30,** 784 (1941); **32,** 185 (1941); *Zh. Eksperim. i Teor. Fiz.*, **11,** 642 (1941); **18,** 138 (1948); *J. Phys.* (*USSR*) **5,** 185 (1941).
304. M. W. Wolkenstein and M. A. Eliashevich, *Compt. Rend. Acad. Sci. USSR*, **41,** 366 (1943); **43,** 55 (1944); *Zh. Eksperim. i Teor. Fiz.* **15,** 124 (1945); *J. Phys.* (*USSR*) **9,** 101, 326 (1945); *Acta Physiocochim. USSR*, **20,** 525 (1945).
305. M. W. Wolkenstein, M. A. Eliashevich, and B. I. Stepanov, *Molecular Vibrations*, State Publishers of Technical-Theoretical Literature, Moscow-Leningrad, 1949, vol. 2.

306. D. A. Long, *Proc. Roy. Soc.*, **A217,** 203 (1953).

307. S. M. Ferigle and A. Weber, *Can. J. Phys.*, **32,** 799 (1954).

308. L. M. Sverdlov, *Optics and Spectry.*, **11,** 419 (1961); **15,** 70 (1963).

309. D. A. Long, D. C. Milner, and A. G. Thomas, *Proc. Roy. Soc.*, **A237,** 197 (1956); D. A. Long and D. C. Milner, *Trans. Faraday Soc.*, **54,** 1 (1958); D. A. Long and G. Miller, *Trans. Faraday Soc.*, **54,** 330 (1958); D. A. Long, R. B. Gravenor, and D. C. Milner, *Trans. Faraday Soc.*, **59,** 46 (1963).

310. L. M. Sverdlov and N. I. Prokofeva, *Optics and Spectry.*, **18,** 16 (1965).

311. A. Weber and S. M. Ferigle, *J. Chem. Phys.*, **23,** 2207 (1955).

312. R. H. Krupp, S. M. Ferigle, and A. Weber, *J. Chem. Phys.*, **24,** 355 (1956).

313. See for example the most recent work by V. I. Vakhlyueva, S. M. Kats, and L. M. Sverdlov, *Optics and Spectry.*, **24,** 431 (1968); M. G. Borisov and L. M. Sverdlov, *Optics and Spectry.*, **24,** 37 (1968) and references to earlier papers contained therein.

314. W. Holzer, *Absolute Intensitäten der Ramanlinien halogensubstituierter Methane in der Gasphase*, Dissertation, Munich, 1967.

315. W. Holzer, *J. Mol. Spectry.*, **27,** 522 (1968).

316. T. C. James and W. Klemperer, *J. Chem. Phys.*, **31,** 130 (1959).

316a. E. J. Stansbury, M. F. Crawford and H. L. Welsh, *Can. J. Phys.*, **31,** 954 (1953).

316b. L. H. Scharpen, J. S. Muenter, and V. W. Lawrie, *J. Chem. Phys.*, **53,** 2513 (1670).

317. C. H. Townes in *Advances in Quantum Electronics* (J. R. Singer, ed.) Columbia Univ. Press, New York, 1961, p. 3.

318. P. Lallemand, P. Simova, and G. Bret, *Phys. Rev. Letters,* **17,** 1239 (1966).

319. P. Lallemand and P. Simova, *J. Mol. Spectry.*, **26,** 262 (1968).

320. A. D. May, E. G. Rawson, and H. L. Welsh in *Physics of Quantum Electronics* (P. L. Kelly, E. Lax, and P. E. Tannenwald, eds.) McGraw-Hill, New York, 1966, p. 260.

321. J. R. Murray and A. Javan, *J. Mol. Spectry.*, **29,** 502 (1969).

322. V. G. Cooper, A. D. May, E. H. Hara, and H. F. P. Knaap, *Can. J. Phys.*, **46,** 2019 (1968).

323. V. G. Cooper, A. D. May, and B. K. Gupta, *Can. J. Phys.*, **48,** 725 (1970).

324. W. R. L. Clements and B. P. Stoicheff, *J. Mol. Spectry.*, **33,** 183 (1970).

325. M. F. Crawford, H. L. Welsh, and J. H. Harrold, *Can. J. Phys.*, **30,** 81 (1952).

326. D. P. Eastman, T. A. Wiggins, and D. H. Rank, *Appl. Optics,* **5,** 879 (1966).

327. E. G. Rawson, E. H. Hara, A. D. May, and H. L. Welsh, *J. Opt. Soc. Am.*, **56,** 1403 (1966).

328. E. E. Hagenlocker and R. W. Rado, *Appl. Phys. Letters,* **7,** 236 (1965).

329. D. I. Mash, V. V. Morozov, V. S. Starunov, and I. L. Fabelinskii, *J.E.T.P. Letters,* **2,** 342 (1965).

330. D. H. Rank, T. A. Wiggins, R. V. Wick, and D. P. Eastman *J. Opt. Soc. Am.*, **56,** 174 (1966).

331. For a detailed discussion of the hydrodynamic theory see Fabelinskii, Ref. (*278*), pp. 262–272 as well as R. D. Mountain, *Rev. Modern Phys.*, **38,** 205 (1966); M. Rytov, *Sov. Phys. JETP,* **27,** 147 (1968); B. N. Felderhof, *J. Chem. Phys.*, **44,** 602 (1966).

332. T. J. Greytak and G. B. Benedek, *Phys. Rev. Letters,* **17,** 179 (1966).

333. M. Nelkin and S. Yip, *Phys. Fluids*, **9,** 380 (1966); J. Foch, *Phys. Fluids*, **11,** 2336 (1969); A. Sugawara and S. Yip, *Phys. Fluids*, **10,** 1911 (1967); E. P. Gross in *Lectures in Theoretical Physics* (W. E. Brittin ed.) Gordon and Breach, New York, 1967, Vol. 9c.
334. M. Nelkin and A. Ghatak, *Phys. Rev.*, **135, A***4* (1964).
335. S. G. Rautian and I. I. Sobelman, *Sov. Phys. USPEKHI*, **9,** 701 (1967).
336. J. I. Gersten and H. M. Foley, *J. Opt. Soc. Am.*, **58,** 933 (1968).
337. J. Fiutak and J. Van Kranendonk, *Can. J. Phys.*, **40,** 1085 (1962); **41,** 21 (1963).
338. P. W. Anderson, *Phys. Rev.*, **76,** 647 (1949).
339. P. J. Tsao and B. Curnutte, *J. Quant. Spectrosc. Radiat. Transfer*, **2,** 41 (1962).
340. P. J. Brannon, *J. Quant. Spectrosc. Radiat. Transfer*, **8,** 1615 (1968).
341. J. Van Kranendonk, *Can. J. Phys.*, **41,** 433 (1963).
342. C. G. Gray and J. Van Kranendonk, *Can. J. Phys.*, **44,** 2411 (1966).
343. E. J. Allin, A. D. May, B. P. Stoicheff, J. C. Stryland, and H. L. Welsh, *Appl. Optics*, **6,** 1597 (1967).
344. R. G. Gordon, *J. Chem. Phys.*, **42,** 3658 (1965).
345. R. G. Gordon, *J. Chem. Phys.*, **44,** 3083 (1966).
346. R. G. Gordon, *J. Chem. Phys.*, **45,** 1649 (1966).
346a. A. D. May, J. C. Stryland and G. Varghese, *Can. J. Phys.*, **48,** 2331 (1970).
347. R. G. Gordon, *Adv. Magn. Resonance*, **3,** 1 (1968).
348. R. G. Gordon, W. Klemperer, and J. I. Steinfeld, *Ann. Rev. Phys. Chem.*, **19,** 215 (1968).
349. P. A. Bazhulin, *Sov. Phys. USPEKHI*, **5,** 661 (1963).
350. R. G. Gordon, *J. Chem. Phys.*, **40,** 1973 (1964).
351. V. G. Cooper, A. D. May, E. H. Hara, and H. F. A. Knaap, *Phys. Letters*, **27A,** 52 (1968); *I.E.E.E. J. Quant. Electron.*, **QE-4,** 720 (1968).
352. H. Senftleben, *Phys. Z.*, **31,** 822, 961 (1930).
353. From measurements by J. Korving, H. Hulsman, G. Scoles, H. F. P. Knaap, and J. J. M. Beenakker, *Physica*, **36,** 177 (1967) as quoted by Cooper et al., Ref. 351.
354. P. A. Speight and R. L. Armstrong, *Can. J. Phys.*, **47,** 1475 (1969).
355. S. Hess, *Phys. Letters*, **29A,** 108 (1969).
356. S. Hess, *Z. Naturf.*, **24a,** 1675 (1969).
357. S. Hess, *Z. Naturf.*, **24a,** 1852 (1969).
358. S. Hess, *Z. Naturf.*, **25a,** 350 (1970).
359. V. S. Starunov, E. V. Tiganov, and I. I. Fabelinskii, *J.E.T.P. Letters*, **4,** 176 (1966); A. Szöke, E. Courtens, and A. Ben-Reuven, *Chem. Phys. Letters*, **1,** 87 (1967); G. I. A. Stegeman and B. P. Stoicheff, *Phys. Rev. Letters*, **21,** 202 (1968).
360. V. Volterra, *Phys. Rev.*, **180,** 156 (1969).
361. A. D. May, J. C. Stryland, and H. L. Welsh, *J. Chem. Phys.*, **30,** 1099 (1959).
362. A. D. May, V. Degen, J. C. Stryland, and H. L. Welsh, *Can. J. Phys.*, **39,** 1769 (1961).
363. A. D. May, G. Varghese, J. C. Stryland, and H. L. Welsh, *Can. J. Phys.*, **42,** 1058 (1964).
364. See, for instance, E. M. Verlan, *Optics and Spectry.*, **20,** 557 (1966) and references to earlier papers cited therein.
365. V. A. Morozov, *Optics and Spectry.*, **18,** 111 (1965); **19,** 17 (1965).
366. G. Placzek, *Ref.* (*20*) p. 248.
367. G. Placzek, Ref. (*20*) p. 371.

368. W. Holzer, W. F. Murphy, and H. J. Bernstein, *J. Chem. Phys.*, **52**, 399, 469 (1970).
369. W. Buchheim, *Phys. Z.*, **36,** 694 (1935).
370. A. E. Douglas, *J. Chem. Phys.*, **16,** 849 (1948).
371. L. Singh, *Proc. Phys. Soc.*, **66,** 309 (1953).
372. E. M. Verlan, *Optics and Spectry.*, **24,** 197 (1968); **26,** 491 (1969).
373. I. B. Bersuker, *Optics and Spectry.*, **12,** 294 (1962).
374. Ying-Nan Chiu, *J. Chem. Phys.*, **52,** 3641, 4950 (1970); *J. Opt. Soc. Am.*, **60,** 607 (1970).

CHAPTER 10

Raman Spectra of Molecular Crystals

RODRIGUE SAVOIE

DEPARTMENT OF CHEMISTRY
UNIVERSITÉ LAVAL
QUEBEC, CANADA

I. INTRODUCTION

In contrast with the direct methods frequently used in crystal structure analysis, such as X-ray and neutron diffraction, Raman spectroscopy is primarily concerned with lattice dynamics. But since selection rules for optical activity ultimately depend on molecular and crystal symmetries, this method can be of great help in elucidating crystal structures. Although it cannot in general yield the exact space group and specify the interatomic distances in a given crystal, it can be used with advantage in eliminating certain structures, or deciding between many possible ones. This is especially true in connection with X-ray diffraction studies, because of the very small scattering cross section of hydrogen atoms. It can in all cases, however, be a source of valuable information about intra- and intermolecular forces in crystals and about atomic and molecular motions, properties which are intimately related to such quantities as the specific heat, elasticity, and thermal expansion and conductivity of solids.

The practical use of Raman spectroscopy has long been hampered by the intrinsic weakness of the Raman effect. Fluorescence, either from impurities or the sample itself, and Tyndall scattering were also important limiting factors. However, renewed interest in this technique, as a tool for both qualitative analysis and fundamental research, has been aroused in the last decade through the availability of good-quality photoelectric recording spectrometers. The high light-gathering power and the highly discriminating monochromators of these instruments greatly improved the quality of Raman spectra. The major instrumental innovation, however, has been the introduction of laser sources. These instrumental developments have made of Raman spectroscopy a method of structural analysis which can now be favorably compared to the more widely used technique of infrared absorption. Of course, each of these two methods has its experimental advantages and drawbacks, but both types of spectra should be obtained, whenever possible. This is because selection rules usually predict different infrared and Raman-active components and the combined results will in most cases give a more complete description of a vibrational spectrum. The complementary nature of infrared and Raman spectroscopy is such that a great part of this chapter could also be applied to the infrared. For this reason, we will make frequent use of infrared data to confirm or extend conclusions based on Raman spectra alone.

We will not concern ourselves here with characteristic frequencies, although Raman spectroscopy is likely to develop into a widely used method of qualitative analysis, especially in organic chemistry (*1*,*2*). Solid-state Raman spectra are often called for in connection with this, in most cases because the sample is a solid at room temperature or because of the narrowing of the bands upon solidification. Given the limited scope of this chapter, it seems more appropriate to restrict our discussion to those results which depend specifically upon the solid state of aggregation. Also, it is not our intention to present a complete literature survey of recently published papers on Raman spectra of molecular crystals. Instead, the spectra of small molecules will be analyzed, since they best illustrate the way in which Raman spectroscopy can be used to gain information on the structure and the vibrational energy levels of molecular solids. For the reader interested in this field for analytical purposes only, more general works on vibrational spectra are suggested (e.g., Refs. *3* and *4*). References to Raman spectra of particular compounds may also be found in general reviews on Raman spectroscopy (*5*,*6*).

II. EXPERIMENTAL TECHNIQUES

The experimental techniques used in obtaining Raman spectra of solids vary considerably, depending on the type of excitation used and the temperature to be attained. Although it is expected that laser sources will gradually replace conventional arc sources, the latter will probably be used for some time yet and sampling techniques for conventional Toronto-arc source excitation will also be described. Other sources and sampling techniques have been reviewed by Stoicheff (*7*). Also, given the importance of fundamental studies on simple molecular crystals, whose melting points are generally low, special emphasis will be placed on low temperature methods. Ferraro has contributed a well written chapter on Raman instrumentation and sampling techniques to a recent book on Raman spectroscopy (*8*).

A. Room Temperature Raman Spectra

The study of solid samples at room temperature, using the Toronto-arc source, can be achieved in a number of ways depending on the nature of the material. Polycrystalline and amorphous powders can be conveniently studied in a hollow-cone cell, which facilitates the penetration of the sample by the exciting light and the exit of the Raman radiation (*9–11*). This arrangement yields surprisingly good results and allows scanning to be made quite close to the exciting line. If a very small amount of the sample is available (20 mg or more), better results are obtained by pressing it into a pellet, either in the pure form or diluted in KBr, and placing it in such a way that it is most effectively viewed by the monochromator (*12*). Single crystals can be studied in the same way, the best results being obtained when they are polished to a rod shape with a flat surface filling as much as possible of the entrance aperture of the spectrometer. When a large number of good-quality small single crystals (a few millimeters or more in size) are available, considerable intensity enhancement is possible by immersing them in a liquid with equal, or nearly equal, refractive index (*13*). Finally, it is often possible to obtain large and relatively clear polycrystalline masses of compounds by slow cooling of the melt. This can be done in fairly large cylindrical cells (e.g. 20 mm diam. × 100 mm long) which are well adapted to low temperature studies.

The study of solids using laser excitation has already been discussed (see Chapter 4). Special arrangements for powders have been recently published (*14,15*). Focusing the beam has the advantage of increasing considerably the spectral intensity and is compatible with microsamples (*16*). Some intensity enhancement is also achieved by moistening powder samples with appropriate liquids. Single crystals, even small ones, are ideally suited for Raman work with laser excitation since they allow polarization studies to be made for various crystal orientations. The results so far obtained, mostly with ionic and covalent crystals, are nothing less than spectacular when compared to similar studies done with conventional exciting light sources.

B. Low Temperature Raman Spectra

The most versatile and commonly used arrangement for low temperature studies of solids with Toronto-arc source excitation is the straight Dewar with flat windows at the end (*17,18*). The sample, obtained in most cases as a clear or translucent polycrystalline solid resulting from a slow cooling of the liquid, is contained in a relatively large cylindrical cell which is cooled by a flow of cold nitrogen gas [Fig. 1(a)]. If care is taken to compress the cooling gas before it expands in the Dewar, a temperature as low as that of liquid nitrogen (77°K) can easily be attained (*19*). This type of cryostat has also been used at lower temperatures, using liquid helium as the refrigerant (*20,21*). The same arrangement can be used for temperatures up to a few hundred degrees centigrade by blowing hot air on the sample cell (*21*) or by passing an electric current through a small-diameter resistance wire wrapped around it (*22*). Some L-shaped Dewars have also been built (*23,24*) for use with spectrometers in which the lamp axis is horizontal. A serious drawback in the use of the type of Dewar discussed here is the large amount of sample necessary to obtain high Raman intensity: the sample is further away from the light-collecting optics than normal and much light is lost by reflection on glass surfaces. These difficulties can be partly remedied by using a cell in which the

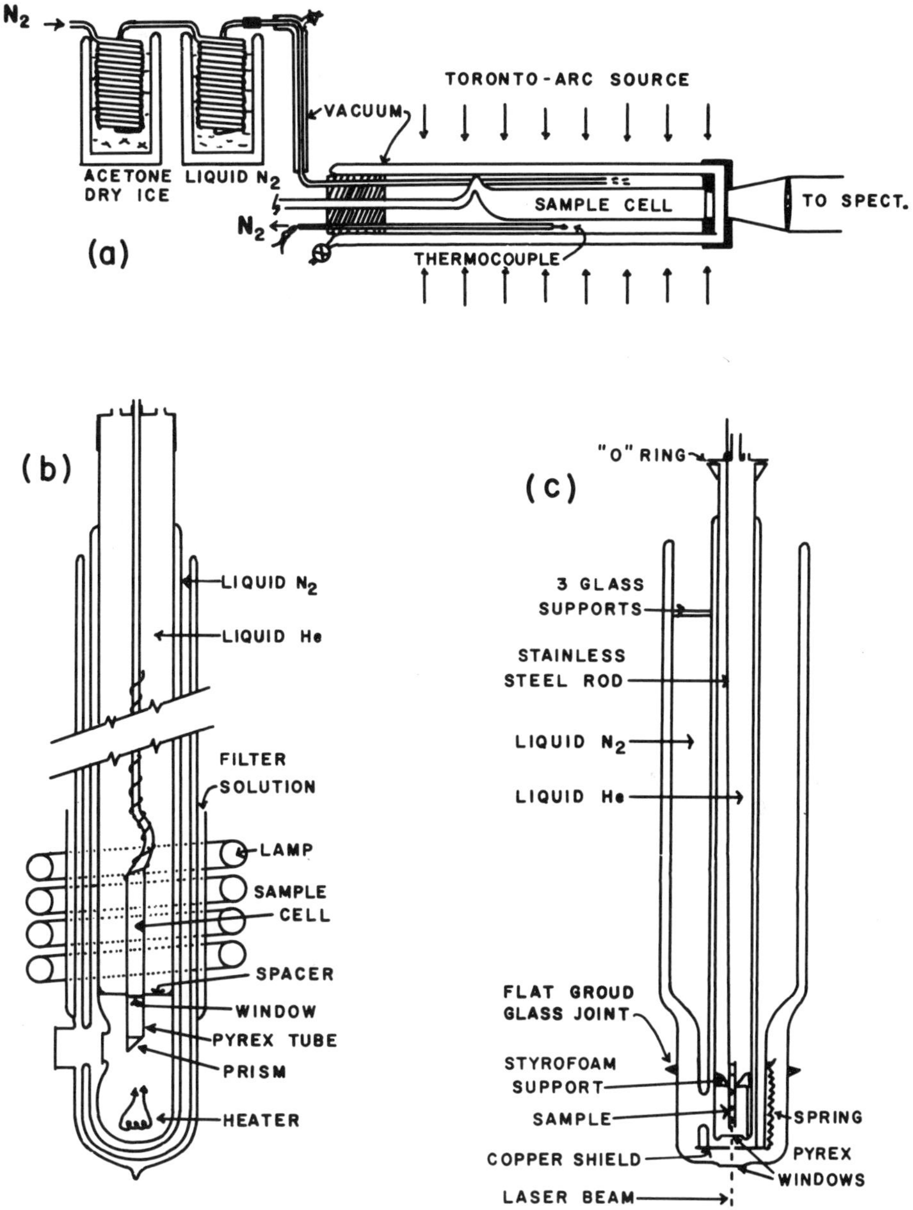

Fig. 1. Cryostats for Raman studies at (a) liquid nitrogen and (b, c) liquid helium temperatures. Courtesy of: (a) *Can. J. Chem.* (Ref. *22*), (b) *Can. J. Phys.* (Ref. *28*), and (c) *J. Chem. Phys.* (Ref. *31*).

window is replaced by a light pipe which transmits the image of the slit to the end of the sample and also serves as a thermal window (*25*).

Raman studies at liquid helium temperature with spectrometers equipped with conventional sources have been few, mostly because of the difficulties involved in the construction of adequate cryostats. The Dewar type cryostat described above can be used with liquid helium (*20,21*), but it seems that the amount of refrigerant needed makes it prohibitively expensive, unless spectra can be recorded very quickly. A very low temperature cryostat for Raman studies was built by Taylor et al. (*26*). The cooling of the sample cell was effected by metal fins in thermal contact with a liquid H_2 pot. Welsh and his group (*27,28*) used a glass cryostat for their studies on solid H_2 [Fig. 1(b)]. They were able to attain temperatures as low as 2°K by pumping on the liquid helium used as refrigerant. Their Dewar, however, is designed for spectrometers where the axis of the Toronto-arc lamp is vertical; modifications to adapt it to horizontal lamps would be almost impossible. A liquid-helium cryostat specifically designed for the Cary 81 spectrometer, but which could very easily be modified for use with vertical lamps, has been used by Savoie and Anderson (*29*) in the study of a number of molecular crystals.

There has been very little work published as yet on low temperature Raman spectra using laser excitation. It is expected however, that experimental procedures will be greatly simplified as a result of this type of excitation, since the laser beam is very narrow and highly collimated. In fact, conventional cryostats, such as those commonly used in infrared experiments, could be used, with minor modifications of their tail section and sample compartment. Such an arrangement, in which gaseous samples were deposited onto a cold copper block, has already been used by Leroi and his group (*30*) and satisfactory spectra were obtained. Gee and Robinson (*31*) recently described a cryostat used for the study of crystalline benzene at liquid helium temperature [Fig. 1(c)]. Russell (*32*) obtained spectra (at 20°K) of single crystals attached to a cold finger in a low temperature cryostat.

III. VIBRATIONS IN SOLIDS

The problem of vibrational spectra of crystals has recently been reviewed by Dows (*33*) and Mitra (*34*). Although not Raman oriented, these works provide a good background in this field. Recent papers by Cowley (*35*) and Loudon (*36*) deal specifically with the Raman scattering from crystals, but the theory is almost completely applied to ionic and covalent solids. Lattice dynamics in general have been extensively discussed (*37,38*). In order to make this chapter readily understandable, even to those who are not familiar with solid-state vibrational spectra, we will base our discussion on very simple models. Experience has shown that this is usually a good approximation with molecular crystals.

A. Effects of Condensation on Spectra

Two more or less drastic changes usually occur in vibrational spectra upon condensation of the samples.

1. Frequency Shifts

These are usually small for molecular crystals with weak intermolecular forces. In general, stretching vibrations are shifted to lower frequencies (red shifts), whereas bending-type motions are weakly displaced to higher frequencies (blue shifts). This arises from a certain electronic redistribution in the condensed phases because of molecular interactions, and also from the close packing of molecules, which hampers atomic displacements.

The frequency shifts accompanying the formation of hydrogen bonds are especially large for the vibrations involving displacements of the shared protons. The O—H stretching vibrations in particular may be shifted to lower frequencies by many hundred cm^{-1} and at the same time display considerable broadening. These shifts have been shown to be related to the strength of the O—H bond and to the O...O and O—H distances of the bonded species (*39*). An extreme case is found in crystalline $HCrO_2$ where the O—H stretching mode occurs at 1700 cm^{-1} (*40*), as compared to about 3500 cm^{-1} expected for the free molecule. The torsional modes are also very sensitive to H-bond formation and usually show appreciable blue shifts. For example, the O—H torsion in $HClO_4$ occurs at 310 cm^{-1} in the gas phase, whereas it is shifted to 480 cm^{-1} in the spectrum of the solid at 77°K (*41*). In this compound, the O—H stretching mode shows a red shift of 300 cm^{-1} upon condensation to the solid, which indicates an average H-bond energy ($\simeq$3 kcal/mole).

Although difficult to evaluate with precision, band intensities usually vary to a certain extent upon condensation, because of molecular interactions (*42*). Bands whose frequencies are strongly affected by hydrogen bonding are likely to show the greatest intensity changes.

2. Changes in Spectral Distribution

Besides bands due to internal vibrations, gas-phase spectra of light molecules are also characterized by low frequency lines corresponding to molecular rotations. These may also occur in combination with internal modes, yielding vibration–rotational bands. The infrared and Raman activity of these modes is of course a function of the molecular geometry. In contrast with the condensed phases, atomic and molecular motions in gases are well described in terms of rotations and internal vibrations.

Upon condensing the gas to a liquid, important changes are seen in the spectra. Since molecular rotations usually become appreciably hindered, the fine structure characteristic of transitions between the various rotational levels in the gas disappear. Internal vibrations yield relatively broad bands as a result of molecular interactions in a highly disordered environment. This disorder also causes the potential hindering molecular rotation to vary considerably from one molecule to the next in the liquid. Consequently, a broad featureless continuum is expected in the low frequency region, except in special cases where relatively stable molecular aggregates exist. For example, Walrafen (*43*) has observed broad bands centred at approximately 60, 160, and 600 cm^{-1} in the Raman spectrum of liquid water. Some molecules on the other hand, still exhibit some rotational behavior in the liquid phase, as evidenced by unresolved rotational wings alongside the fundamentals. This phenomenon is well illustrated in the Raman spectrum of liquid methane (*23*).

Vibrational bands become sharper in the solid phase and are often split into multiplets. This splitting may result from the local anisotropy of the crystalline field in the case of a degenerate vibration, or it may arise from the coupling of identical vibrations of adjacent molecules in the unit cell of the crystal. Both these effects are closely related to the crystal structure and will be discussed in detail. Hindered rotations (librations) and translations cause low frequency bands to appear in spectra. These lattice modes are also important in connection with crystal structures and make a large contribution to the specific heat of solids. Their frequencies vary considerably and depend strongly on the molecular masses and moments of inertia, as well as on the nature of the bonding between the molecules. Strongly hydrogen-bonded molecules with small moments of inertia may display librational modes with frequencies as high as 1000 cm^{-1}, as in the case of crystalline HF (*19*). Weakly bonded solids with molecular weight smaller than 100 usually show lattice modes in the 50–200 cm^{-1} region (*44*). Lattice modes are usually shifted to higher frequencies when the temperature is lowered, as a direct consequence of the lattice contraction and the strengthening of intermolecular bonding.

B. Vibrations of a Linear Diatomic Chain

The problem of determining the normal modes of vibration of even a small crystal with its almost infinite number of atoms, each of these with its three degrees of freedom of motion, may appear to be intractable. However, Raman and infrared spectra of crystals usually contain but a relatively small number of discrete lines. How this simplification occurs is well illustrated by considering the vibrations of a simple linear diatomic chain. The solution to this problem was originally obtained by Born and von Kármán (*45*); see also (*34*,*37*,*38*, and *46*).

The model, illustrated in Fig. 2, consists of equally spaced alternating

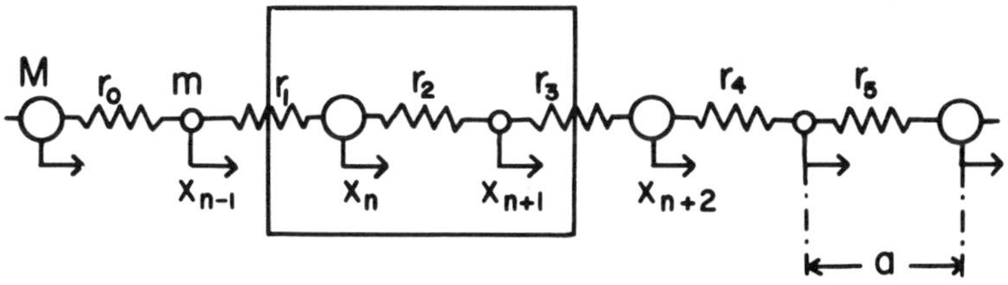

Fig. 2. Linear diatomic chain.

atoms of masses M and m, forming a chain composed of a very large number of unit cells with two particles per cell. For simplicity, only motions along the length of the chain will be considered. The kinetic energy, T, for any unit cell (except those at the end of the chain) containing the two atoms arbitrarily labeled n and $n+1$ is given by:

$$2T = M\dot{x}_n{}^2 + m\dot{x}_{n+1}^2 \tag{1}$$

Assuming nearest-neighbor interactions only, and harmonic contributions only, the potential energy, V (*47*) can be written as:

$$2V = f(\Delta r_1{}^2 + \Delta r_2{}^2 + \Delta r_3{}^2) \tag{2}$$

where f is the force constant and Δr the variation of the distance between two particles at any given time:

$$f = (\partial^2 V/\partial x^2)_0 \tag{3}$$

$$\begin{aligned} \Delta r_1 &= x_n - x_{n-1} \\ \Delta r_2 &= x_{n+1} - x_n \\ \Delta r_3 &= x_{n+2} - x_{n+1} \end{aligned} \tag{4}$$

In terms of the atomic displacements, x, the expression for the potential energy becomes:

$$2V = f(x_{n-1}^2 + 2x_n^2 + 2x_{n+1}^2 + x_{n+2}^2 - 2x_{n-1}x_n - 2x_n x_{n+1} - 2x_{n+1}x_{n+2}) \tag{5}$$

Lagrange's equations of motion can be written in the form:

$$\frac{d}{dt}\frac{\partial T}{\partial \dot{x}_j} + \frac{\partial V}{\partial x_j} = 0 \tag{6}$$

where $j = n$ and $n+1$. Substitution of the expressions for T and V [Eqs. (1 and 5)] in Eq. (6) yields the equations of motion for particles n and $n+1$:

$$\begin{aligned} M\ddot{x}_n &= f(x_{n-1} + x_{n+1} - 2x_n) \\ m\ddot{x}_{n+1} &= f(x_n + x_{n+2} - 2x_{n+1}) \end{aligned} \tag{7}$$

This system of linear and homogeneous equations has an infinite number of solutions. By analogy with motions taking place in an elastic continuum, convenient solutions are:

$$\begin{aligned} x_n &= A_n \exp i\{\omega t + n\mathbf{k}a\} \\ x_{n+1} &= A_{n+1} \exp i\{\omega t + (n+1)\mathbf{k}a\} \end{aligned} \tag{8}$$

where A represents an amplitude, ω an angular frequency, ($= 2\pi\nu$ cycles/sec), and a the nearest-neighbor spacing at equilibrium. The wave vector $\mathbf{k}$ is defined as $2\pi/\lambda$, where λ is the wavelength of the vibrational excitation wave traveling along the chain. With the above substitution, the Eqs. in (7) yield the set of algebraic equations:

$$\begin{aligned} (M\omega^2 - 2f)A_n + (2f\cos \mathbf{k}a)A_{n+1} &= 0 \\ (2f\cos \mathbf{k}a)A_n + (m\omega^2 - 2f)A_{n+1} &= 0 \end{aligned} \tag{9}$$

The solutions for ω are obtained from the secular determinant

$$\begin{vmatrix} M\omega^2 - 2f & 2f\cos \mathbf{k}a \\ 2f\cos \mathbf{k}a & m\omega^2 - 2f \end{vmatrix} = 0 \tag{10}$$

Thus

$$\omega^2 = f/\mu \pm \{f^2/\mu^2 - (4f^2 \sin^2 \mathbf{k}a)/Mm\}^{\frac{1}{2}} \tag{11}$$

where μ is the reduced mass per unit cell ($\mu = Mm/(M+m)$. This function is seen to vary periodically with $\sin^2 \mathbf{k}a$ and all the values of ω^2 are obtained if $\mathbf{k}$ is restricted to the range

$$-\pi/2a \leqq \mathbf{k} \leqq \pi/2a \tag{12}$$

This region is termed the first Brillouin zone (*48*). The relation between the frequency and the wave vector **k**, known as the dispersion relation, is schematically illustrated in Fig. 3. It consists of two branches arising from the positive and negative signs in Eq. (11). One of these branches tends to zero as $\mathbf{k} \rightarrow 0$ and is referred to as the acoustical branch. The

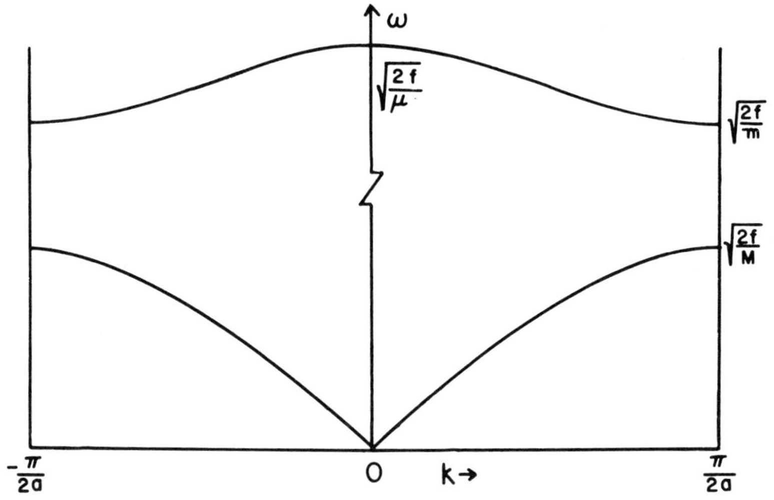

Fig. 3. Dispersion curve for a linear diatomic chain: optical branch (top) and acoustical branch (bottom).

other, known as the optical branch, has a finite value at the center of the zone ($\mathbf{k} = 0$). Making $\mathbf{k} = 0$ in Eq. (11) yield the two frequencies

$$\omega = \begin{cases} 0 & \text{(acoustical)} \\ (2f/\mu)^{\frac{1}{2}} & \text{(optical)} \end{cases} \tag{13}$$

Similarly, at the edge of the Brillouin zone, the frequencies have the values

$$\omega = \begin{cases} (2f/M)^{\frac{1}{2}} & \text{(acoustical)} \\ (2f/m)^{\frac{1}{2}} & \text{(optical)} \end{cases} \tag{14}$$

where $\mathbf{k} = \pm\pi/2a$.

The relative amplitudes of motion of the two particles in the unit cell for any value of **k** can be obtained by substituting in Eq. (9) the values of ω^2 obtained from Eq. (11). For $\mathbf{k} = 0$, it is found that

$$\begin{aligned} A_n &= A_{n+1} \\ MA_n &= -mA_{n+1} \end{aligned} \tag{15}$$

Thus, at the center of the zone, the acoustical mode corresponds to a displacement of the whole chain as a rigid unit, whereas for the optical mode the two particles in every cell move in opposite directions, so as to keep the center of mass of each cell stationary.

The center of the Brillouin zone is of special importance in considering interaction of light with a crystal. Consider, for example, the possible excitation of a given optical mode by infrared absorption, assuming this process to be allowed by symmetry. Of course, conservation of energy then requires that the photon and the vibration have the same frequency. But also, momentum should be conserved in the process. A quantized lattice vibration (phonon) acts for most practical purposes as if it possessed a momentum $\hbar\mathbf{k}$, where $\mathbf{k}$ is in the range of the first Brillouin Zone $-\pi/2a \leqq \mathbf{k} \leqq \pi/2a$. It is thus required that

$$\hbar\mathbf{Q} = \hbar\mathbf{k} \tag{16}$$

where $\mathbf{Q}$ is the wave vector ($= 2\pi/\lambda$) of the absorbed photon. Since the wavelength of infrared (and even visible) light is large compared to the lattice constant, a, $\mathbf{Q}$ is very small (10^3 cm^{-1} as compared to $\mathbf{k} = 10^8$ cm^{-1} at the edge of the zone). Optical transitions will then occur essentially at $\mathbf{k} = 0$. The same applies to Raman scattering processes. In this case, when a phonon is created by the inelastic scattering of a photon whose change in frequency causes its wave vector to change from $\mathbf{Q}$ to $\mathbf{Q}'$, it is required that

$$\hbar Q - \hbar Q' = \hbar k \tag{17}$$

Since Q and Q' are both small, clearly their vector difference is also small. It should be added that more complex processes can also occur. For example, combination processes involving acoustical and optical modes at $\mathbf{k} \neq 0$ can occur in the case of a linear diatomic chain, provided the vibrations in the two branches are characterized by opposite $\mathbf{k}$ values (then $\Sigma\, \hbar\mathbf{k} = 0$). Since the frequency distribution is symmetric about the zone center, the frequency of the overall process can be obtained by adding the individual frequencies of the acoustical and optical modes for the same value of $\mathbf{k}$ in the range $\mathbf{k} = 0$ to $\pi/2a$. Of course, the spectral intensity of such processes is generally much lower than in fundamental transitions. Furthermore, this intensity will not be the same for all values of $\mathbf{k}$, since the density of states is much greater near the center and the edge of the Brillouin zone, at least for the optical branch. Two- (and sometimes three-) phonon processes are of special importance in dealing with ionic and covalent crystals, but they will not be discussed here.

C. Vibrations in Three-dimensional Crystals

Equations of motion for three-dimensional crystals are quite complex. Reasonably good solutions have so far been obtained only for highly symmetrical lattices with a very small number of atoms (or ions) per unit cell (see Refs. *34*,*37*,*38*, and *46* for appropriate references). Quite generally, if a lattice contains N primitive cells, with n particles per cell, the $3nN$ degrees of vibrational freedom are distributed on $3n$ branches, 3 of which are acoustical and the remaining $3n-3$ optical.

As in the case of the linear chain discussed above, the conservation of momentum requires that fundamental optical transitions occur at $\mathbf{k} = 0$. Thus, a maximum of $3n-3$ fundamentals should be observed in vibrational spectra, since the three acoustical branches have vanishing frequencies at the center of the Brillouin zone. These $3n-3$ fundamentals correspond to in-phase motions of equivalent atoms in each primitive cell. The symmetry and optical activity of these vibrations can therefore be predicted from a consideration of the primitive cell only. Also, it is easily seen that in a molecular crystal containing n (nonlinear) molecules per cell and z atoms per molecule, the $3nz$ degrees of freedom of motion will be distributed into $n(3z-6)$ internal virbations, $3(n-1)$ "translational" lattice modes, $3n$ "librational" lattice modes, and 3 acoustical modes with zero limiting frequencies. In other words, each of the internal vibrations of the molecule can give rise to a maximum of n components in the crystal spectrum. If a vibration is degenerate in the free molecule, this degeneracy may be lifted in the solid, which will bring more components into play. The external degrees of freedom, corresponding to hindered motions of essentially rigid molecules, will appear as low frequency vibrations which can be subdivided into librations and translations.

D. Unit-cell Modes

Any crystal structure can be described by one of the 230 space groups (*49*). A space group contains, besides other symmetry operations, the translations ($n_a a$, $n_b b$, and $n_c c$) along the unit-cell axes which generate the whole lattice by taking any unit cell into another. It can be shown that any space group is the product of a translation group (formed of the translation operations) and another group, called the factor (or unit-cell) group. Factor groups are always isomorphous with one of the 32 point groups. (These define the various crystalline classes). Thus, the character table of any factor group is identical to that of the corresponding point group, although the former may contain symmetry operations (such as those induced by glide planes and screw axes) which are not purely point operations.

In the present discussion, the unit cell is taken as the smallest volume of a crystal that will generate the whole lattice by translations along suitably chosen axes. Crystallographers often select unit-cell vectors so as to relate them more conveniently to the symmetry elements of the lattice, although the unit cell thus defined may not be primitive. The number of primitive cells per crystallographers' unit cell can easily be determined for any space group from a consideration of the lattice symmetry or from the number of coordinates of equivalent positions in a cell (*49*).

Since the only modes that may occur as fundamentals in vibrational spectra of crystals are those for which $\mathbf{k} = 0$, only those transitions corresponding to in-phase motions of equivalent atoms and structural groups need to be considered. The unit cell can therefore be treated as a large molecule in itself and the usual group-theoretical procedures (e.g., Refs. *47*, *50*, and *51*) applied to determine the symmetry classification and optical activity of the fundamental modes. This general procedure was first introduced by Bhagavantam and Venkatarayudu (*52*,*53*) and summarized by Mitra (*34*) who slightly modified it for use with linear molecules and ions (*54*).

The procedure consists in obtaining, for all symmetry operations (R) of the point group isomorphous with the factor group, the character $\chi(R)$ of the reducible representations corresponding to the various degrees of freedom of atoms or structural units in the primitive cell. The number of times (n) any particular irreducible representation (Γ_κ) is contained in a reducible representation is given by the simple formula

$$n(\Gamma_\kappa) = (1/h) \sum_R \chi(R)\chi_\kappa(R) \tag{18}$$

where h is the order (the total number of symmetry operations) of the point group, $\chi(R)$ and $\chi_\kappa(R)$ the character of the reducible and irreducible representations respectively for operation (R).

The way in which the characters of a reducible representation are obtained for the various symmetry operations in a group is straightforward. $\chi(R)$ can be expressed as

$$\chi(R) = N(R)C(R) \tag{19}$$

where $N(R)$ is the number of units (atoms, molecules, or ions) remaining invariant when operated on by (R), and $C(R)$ the contribution to character per such unit. When the three degrees of freedom of motion of a unit are considered, these contributions are given by

$$C(R) = \pm 1 + 2\cos(2\pi k/n) \quad (20)$$

where the plus and minus signs stand, respectively, for proper and improper rotations (C_n^k and S_n^k) equivalent to the symmetry operations (R). Values of $C(R)$ obtained from this formula are given in Table 1.

In dealing with the representation for the librational modes of the crystal, the contribution per invariant (polyatomic) unit can be obtained from the transformation matrix of the angular momentum vector. For nonlinear units, this contribution is given by the expression

$$C_L(R) = 1 \pm 2\cos(2\pi k/n) \quad (21)$$

where the plus and minus signs have the same meaning as in Eq. (20). In the case of linear units, Mitra (*53*) has shown that

$$C_L(R) = \pm 2\cos(2\pi k/n) \quad (22)$$

except for rotations C_2 perpendicular to the molecular C_∞ axis and reflections in planes containing the latter, for which $C_L(R) = 0$. Values of $C_L(R)$ for linear and nonlinear units are collected in Table 1.

TABLE 1

Contribution to Character per Invariant Unit

Operation[a] (R)	Contribution $C(R)$	$C_L(R)$ Nonlinear	$C_L(R)$ Linear
$E = C_1^1$	3	3	2
C_2^1 ∥	−1	−1	−2
C_2^1 ⊥	−1	−1	0
C_3^1, C_3^2	0	0	−1
C_4^1, C_4^3	1	1	0
C_6^1, C_6^5	2	2	1
$\sigma = S_1^1$ ∥	1	−1	0
$\sigma = S_1^1$ ⊥	1	−1	−2
$i = S_2^1$	−3	3	2
S_3^1, S_3^5	−2	2	1
S_4^1, S_4^3	−1	1	0
S_6^1, S_6^5	0	0	−1

[a] ∥ and ⊥ refer to orientation with respect to the molecular axis in linear units.

In order to obtain the total representation of the unit cell as a whole, each atom in the unit cell is taken as a unit. The dimension of the reducible representation thus obtained is 3 times the number of atoms per cell, as seen from the product $N(R)C(R)$ for the identity operation (E). The number of times (n_i) each irreducible representation of the point group is contained in the total representation is readily obtained from Eqs. (18–20).

The translatory lattice oscillations (including acoustical modes) are obtained in exactly the same way, except that each structural group is taken as a unit. In molecular crystals, this unit will obviously be a molecule, but the procedure can also be applied to ions in ionic crystals. The acoustical modes are easily characterized, since these translations of the whole unit cell transform in the same way as the Cartesian coordinates x, y, and z. Character tables indicate to which irreducible representation these correspond, but care should be taken to label the crystallographic axes in a way which is consistent with that used in point groups. Acoustical modes can also be characterized directly from the above equations, by taking the whole primitive cell as a unit; then $x(R) = C(R)$.

TABLE 2

Characters of the Various Representations[a]

Representation	Character
All unit-cell modes	$N_a(R)\ C(R)$
Translational modes (including acoustical)	$N_s(R)\ C(R)$
Acoustical modes	$C(R)$
Purely translational modes	$[N_s(R)-1]\ C(R)$
Librational modes	$N_p(R)\ C_L(R)$

[a] $N_a(R)$ = number of atoms unshifted under the symmetry operation R; $N_s(R)$ = number of structural groups (molecules or ions) invariant under R; $N_p(R)$ – number of polyatomic groups (molecules or ions) invariant under R; and $C(R)$ and $C_L(R)$ = contribution to character per invariant unit (see Table 1).

The characters of the reducible representations for the librational modes are obtained from Eq. (19), by making $N(R)$ equal to the number of molecules (or polyatomic ions in ionic crystals) invariant under operations (R). The contributions per invariant unit are obtained from Eqs. (21, 22) or from Table 1.

The characters for the various representations are summarized in Table 2. The procedure is generalized to cover the case of ionic crystals as well. In molecular solids, $N_s = N_p$.

The numbers of (a) total modes (n_i), (b) translational modes (T' acoustical and T optical), and (c) librational modes (R') can readily be obtained from the character of the various representations and the character table of the appropriate point group (Eq. 18). The numbers of internal modes (n_i') of each species are then obtained by subtracting ($T+T'$) and (R') from the total number of modes (n_i). The infrared and Raman activity of the various vibrational species follow the usual rules. The components of the dipole derivative or polarizability tensor transform as the Cartesian coordinates x, y, and z or their products respectively, whose corresponding

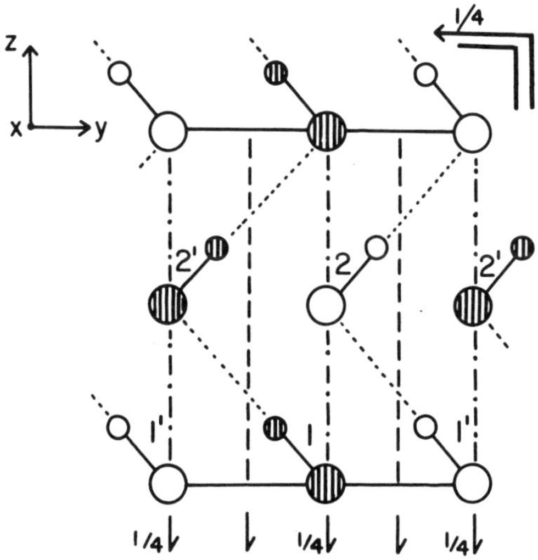

Fig. 4. Crystal structure of HCl in its low temperature phase, after Sándor and Farrow (*56*). Molecules 1 and 2 are located in planes of symmetry at $x = 0$ and $1/2\ a$.

irreducible representations are indicated in standard tables (e.g., *47, 50, 51*). (This is only true if the choice of the crystal axes follow the conventions used in point groups.)

The above procedure will now be illustrated by the determination of the fundamental modes of crystalline HCl in its low temperature modification. Although unable to locate the hydrogen atoms in this crystal, X-ray diffraction studies by Natta (*55*) showed that the unit cell is face-centered orthorhombic. A recent neutron-diffraction investigation by Sándor and Farrow (*56*) indicated that the crystal consists of planar zigzag chains, all oriented in the same way and arranged in parallel layers. The structure, defined by the space group C_{2v}^{12} with four molecules per crystallographic unit cell (two per primitive cell), is illustrated in Fig. 4. The symmetry elements of the space group are included in the figure. The orientations of the three crystal axes have been chosen so as to conform to the standard setting given in the international tables for X-ray crystallography (*49*). This is somewhat arbitrary but, in any case, the orientations of these axes must always be unambiguously specified if any meaning is to be derived from the symmetry classification of the fundamentals. Also, in order to be able to find how x, y, z, and their products transform, directly from the character table of the C_{2v} point group, the z crystallographic axis must be chosen so as to be oriented along the C_2 screw axes of the crystal.

The vibrational analysis for crystalline HCl in the low temperature phase is summarized in Table 3. The choice of the primitive cell is not

TABLE 3

Vibrational Fundamentals of Crystalline HCl in the Low Temperature Phase[a]

$C_{2v}{}^{12}$	E	C_2	σ_{zx}	σ_{yz}	$T+T'$	T'	T	R'	n_i'	n_i	Activity
A_1	1	1	1	1	2	1	1	1	1	4	R IR
A_2	1	1	−1	−1	1	0	1	1	0	2	R —
B_1	1	−1	1	−1	1	1	0	1	0	2	R IR
B_2	1	−1	−1	1	2	1	1	1	1	4	R IR
$N_a(R)$	4	0	0	4							
$N_s(R) = N_p(R)$	2	0	0	2							
$C(R)$	3	−1	1	1							
$C_L(R)$	2	0	−2	0							
$N_a(R)C(R)$	12	0	0	4							
$N_s(R)C(R)$	6	0	0	2							
$N_p(R)C_L(R)$	4	0	0	0							

[a] Vibrational modes are as follows, T = translational (excluding acoustical); T' = acoustical; R' = librational; n_i' = internal; n_i = total.

unique here, but it is obvious that the two molecules per cell should have different orientations, such as molecules (1) and (2) in Fig. 4. It should also be borne in mind in what follows that any translation operations which take a molecule into a similar position in another primitive cell (e.g. (1) → (1′) or (2) → (2′)) are treated as identity operations. Thus, if a symmetry operation takes molecule (1) into (2′), this is equivalent to (1) → (2) since (2′) → (2) can be brought about by a translation operation.

In connection with Table 3, it is easily seen that the identity operation (E) leaves 2 molecules (4 atoms) invariant; thus, $N_s(R) = 2$ and $N_a(R) = 4$ under operation E. It is seen in Fig. 4 that there are two sets of C_2 axes, the first in the $x = 0$ plane and the second in the $x = 1/4$ plane. Both of these are oriented in the z direction, and generate a C_2 rotation followed by a translation of $\frac{1}{2}c$ along the z-axis (where c is the unit-cell dimension along this axis). Both sets of axes take molecule (1) into (2) or (2′), so that no structural unit is invariant under this operation ($N_a(R) = N_s(R) = 0$ under C_2). The same occurs with the σ_{xz} sets of glide planes. The first set at $y = \frac{1}{4}$ involves a reflection through the plane followed by a translation of $\frac{1}{2}c$ along the z-axis. The second (diagonal glide plane) generates a reflection followed by a translation of $\frac{1}{2}a+\frac{1}{2}c$. In the yz dimension, the molecules are located in a plane of symmetry and the corresponding reflection operation leaves the two molecules per primitive cell invariant. There is also a glide plane at $x = \frac{1}{4}$, but the corresponding symmetry operation may be considered as identity since molecule (1) is taken into (1′) and (2) into (2′). Thus, 2 molecules and 4 atoms are invariant under the σ_{yz} operation. The values of $C(R)$ and $C_L(R)$ in Table 3 were taken directly from Table 1, and the various vibrational species were determined from the equations given previously.

This simple analysis on crystalline HCl is still incomplete, since it is also desirable to find which atomic or molecular motions correspond to the various vibrational species. For example, Table 3 predicts two internal modes (A_1 and B_2) for the stretching vibrations of the HCl molecules. From the character table of the C_{2v} point group, it is seen that an A_1 vibration is symmetric with respect to the C_2 operation, while a B_1 vibration is not. It is easy to conclude in this case that the A_1 species correspond to stretching motions where both molecules in each primitive cell simultaneously stretch, since molecule (1) is taken into (2) under the C_2 (screw axis) operation. The B_2 mode then corresponds to one molecule per cell being stretched while the other is compressed.

In more complicated cases, such as those commonly encountered with larger molecules, it may be necessary to obtain the characters of the transformation matrices for each set of internal and external coordinates, in order to facilitate the assignment. This will be illustrated by the determination of the vibrational species corresponding to the translational lattice modes along the z-axis in HCl. The reducible representation can be obtained from the transformation equations relating displacement vectors

$\mathbf{T}_1$ and $\mathbf{T}_2$ on molecules (1) and (2) respectively. For the identity operation,

$$T_1 \overset{E}{\rightarrow} T_1'(= T_1)$$
$$T_2 \overset{E}{\rightarrow} T_2'(= T_2)$$
$$T_1' = 1T_1 + 0T_2$$
$$T_2' = 0T_1 + 1T_2$$

or, in matrix notation,

$$\begin{vmatrix} T_1' \\ T_2' \end{vmatrix} = \begin{vmatrix} 1 & 0 \\ 0 & 1 \end{vmatrix} \begin{vmatrix} T_1 \\ T_2 \end{vmatrix}$$

The character of the representation (the sum of the elements on the diagonal of the transformation matrix) is then equal to 2 for this symmetry operation. The transformation matrices for the other operations are

$$\begin{matrix} C_2 \text{ (screw)} & \sigma_{zx} \text{ (glide)} & \sigma_{yz} \\ \begin{vmatrix} 0 & 1 \\ 1 & 0 \end{vmatrix} & \begin{vmatrix} 0 & 1 \\ 1 & 0 \end{vmatrix} & \begin{vmatrix} 1 & 0 \\ 0 & 1 \end{vmatrix} \end{matrix}$$

The characters of this representation ($\chi(E) = 2$, $\chi(C_2) = 0$, $\chi(\sigma_{zx}) = 0$, $\chi(\sigma_{yz}) = 2$) can be used in Eq. (18) to obtain the irreducible representations

$$\Gamma(T_z) = A_1 + B_2$$

The T_z acoustical mode is identified as an A_1 species from the character table of the C_{2v} point group. The B_2 mode therefore corresponds to the T_z translational lattice mode in which molecules (1) and (2) move one against the other in the z direction. The same procedure can be used to determine the distribution of the vibrational species among the various internal and external degrees of freedom of motion. The molecular and atomic displacements corresponding to the vibrational species obtained for crystalline HCl (Table 3) are schematically illustrated in Fig. 5. As is the case with internal vibrations of free molecules, this description is only approximate, since considerable coupling may occur between vibrational motions of like symmetry, especially in the lattice region where the frequencies are not too different.

A detailed analysis, such as that given above, may get quite cumbersome when applied to more complicated crystals, and simplified procedures will now be discussed. The fundamental theory of vibrations in crystals elaborated by Halford (*57*), Hornig (*58*), and Winston and Halford (*59*), has considerably simplified the analysis of vibrational spectra of solids.

These basic theoretical works have been reviewed many times (*33,34,60*), so that we will rather emphasize the basic ideas behind this theory and its practical aspects.

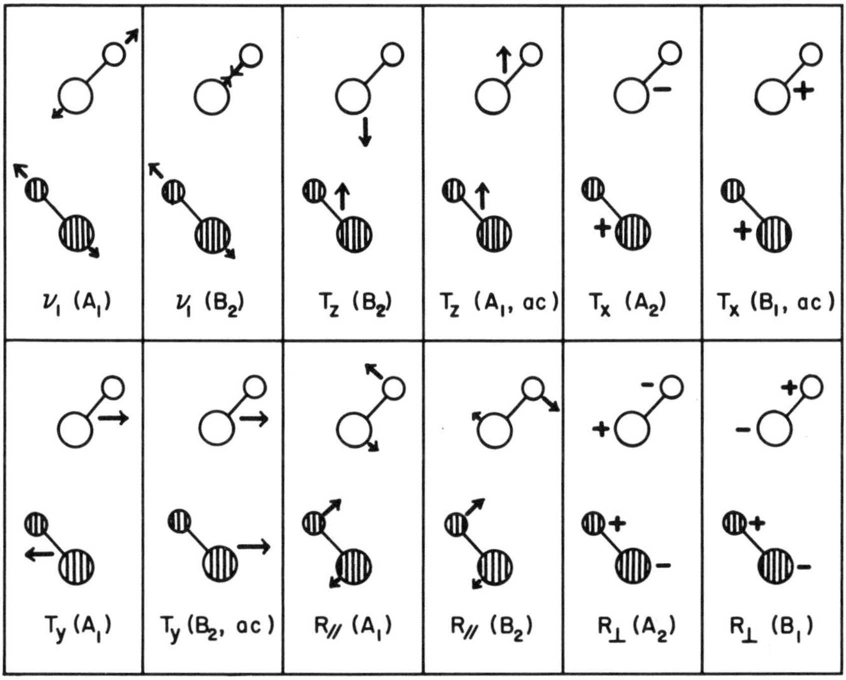

Fig. 5. Schematic description of the vibrational fundamentals of crystalline HCl in its low temperature modification.

E. The Site Approximation

The simplest model of some value for a molecular crystal is the "oriented gas" model (*61*), in which the solid is considered as an assembly of non-interacting molecules rigidly oriented in their equilibrium positions. Such a model predicts that vibrational spectra may be influenced by the orientations of the molecules with respect to the electric-field vector of the incident radiation. It fails however, to account for the splitting of the fundamentals which is often observed in crystal spectra. Also, selection rules for optical activity are sometimes apparently altered in solids, and bands forbidden in the free-molecule approximation are observed to be active. Thus, the assumption of no interaction between molecules in crystals is too drastic in most cases and perturbing effects have to be introduced.

In dealing with real crystals, a first refinement, introduced by Halford (*57*), takes into account the effect of the static crystalline field on molecular vibrations. This process first reveals itself by a more or less important shift of the vibrational energy. The magnitude of the frequency shifts may be very small in crystals containing weakly bound nonpolar molecules, but it may be considerable in other cases. The crystalline field may also cause the removal of the vibrational degeneracy present in the free molecule. Since these effects arise from a static field, it is intuitively expected that the local symmetry at the molecular location in the crystal will be of importance in explaining these phenomena.

Any point in a crystal has a local symmetry about it which can be described by one of the 32 point groups. Most points are of course located on general positions in the unit cell and have the trivial C_1 symmetry. However, some special locations, or sites, may be on one or more symmetry elements, whose corresponding operations leave these points invariant. After Halford (*57*), the point group which describes a local symmetry in a unit cell is called a site group. It must be emphasized that site groups contain the operations induced by all the symmetry elements which leave the site invariant. Any point on a given site in a unit cell is carried into an equivalent point with the same site symmetry by operations which are not purely point operations, and by those induced by symmetry elements which are not coincident with this point. There is, therefore, a definite number of special positions with the same site symmetry in any unit cell. The possible site symmetries and the corresponding equivalent positions for any of the 230 space groups have been conveniently tabulated (*49*).

The effect of the crystalline field on vibrational spectra of crystals can readily be taken into account, at least qualitatively, if one considers that the vibrations in solids are perturbed by the environment. These interactions, and the environment itself, have a certain symmetry which may be lower than that of the free molecule. The vibrations are then better described by the irreducible representations of the site group. The easiest way to proceed, in practice, is to correlate the irreducible representations of the free molecule and those of the site group. This can be achieved by comparing the character tables of the two groups, taking only those symmetry operations which are common to both groups. Correlation tables between the species of the various groups are available for a large number of groups (*47*). Care should be taken in using these since, in some instances, more than one correlation exists between a given pair of groups. In such cases, the situation is defined by specifying the choice of molecular and crystallographic axes. For example, if a molecule of C_{2v} symmetry lies on a site of C_s symmetry in a crystal, a B_1 vibration will be transformed into either an A' or an A'' species, depending on whether the symmetry plane in the crystal coincides with the σ_{zx} or the σ_{yz} molecular plane. It should also be noted that the representations must have the same overall dimensions in the free-molecule and site approximations. For example, a triply degenerate vibration in a tetrahedral molecule ($F_2(T_d)$) is transformed into an A mode if the site has C_1 symmetry ($A(C_1)$). In fact, $F_2(T_d)$ is transformed into $3A(C_1)$; i.e., the degeneracy is removed and 3 components are predicted in the site approximation.

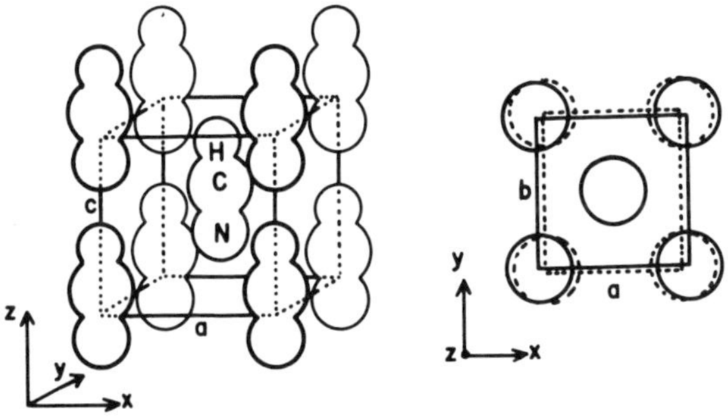

Fig. 6. Crystal structure of HCN. At right, full lines represent the high temperature form and broken lines the low temperature modification. After Dulmage and Lipscomb (*63*); reprinted by courtesy of *Acta Cryst.*, **4** (1951), p. 333.

The effect of the crystalline field on vibrational spectra will now be illustrated in the case of crystalline HCN. This compound has two solid phases, with transition at $-102.8°C$ (*62*). The high-temperature modification (Phase I) has a tetragonal structure described by the space group C_{4v}^9-I4mm (*63*). The two molecules per crystallographic unit cell are located on sites of C_{4v} symmetry. The crystal then consists of linear chains of HCN molecules, all the molecules and the chains being similarly oriented along the crystallographic z-axis. In the low temperature phase (Phase II), the structure is quite similar to that in Phase I, except that the tetragonal structure has become distorted, the unit cell dimensions being different along the x and y axes ($a = 4.13$ Å, $b = 4.85$ Å as compared to $a = b = 4.63$ Å in Phase I). The structure is then orthorhombic and is defined by the space group $C_{2v}^{20}-\text{Imm}$ with the two molecules per cell, located on sites of C_{2v} symmetry. The crystal structures of HCN in its two solid phases are illustrated in Fig. 6.

The fundamental vibrations of the linear HCN molecule (symmetry $C_{\infty v}$) consist of two internal stretching modes (ν_1 and ν_3; A_1 species) and a doubly degenerate bending mode (ν_2; E_1 species). It is seen from the character table of the $C_{\infty v}$ group that these fundamentals should be active in both the infrared and Raman spectra. Upon condensation to the solid in Phase I, the molecules take the effective symmetry of the site (C_{4v}). It is noted that the principal axes of the free-molecule and the crystal coincide in this case. The symmetry operation $C_\infty{}^\varphi$ in the $C_{\infty v}$ group is transformed into C_4 and C_2 in the C_{4v} group, while σ_v is transformed into σ_v and σ_d. It is obvious that A_1 species of the $C_{\infty v}$ group becomes A_1 species in the C_{4v} group, since the characters for these representations are all equal to one in both groups (see Table 4). In order to find the representation $[\Gamma(C_{4v})]$ into which $\nu_2[E_1(C_{\infty v})]$ is transformed in the site

TABLE 4

Comparison between the Character Tables of the $C_{\infty v}$, C_{4v}, and C_{2v} Groups

$C_{\infty v}$	E	$2C_\infty{}^\phi$		$\infty\sigma_v$			
A_1	1	1		1		z	$\alpha_{xx}+\alpha_{yy}$, α_{zz}
A_2	1	1		−1		R_z	
E_1	2	$2\cos\phi$		0		R_{xy}, x, y	$(\alpha_{yz}, \alpha_{zx})$
E_2	2	$2\cos 2\phi$		0			$(\alpha_{xx}-\alpha_{yy}, \alpha_{xy})$
C_{4v}	E	$2C_4$	C_2	$2\sigma_v$	$2\sigma_d$		
A_1	1	1	1	1	1	z	$\alpha_{xx}+\alpha_{yy}$, α_{zz}
A_2	1	1	1	−1	−1	R_z	
B_1	1	−1	1	1	−1		$\alpha_{xx}-\alpha_{yy}$
B_2	1	−1	1	−1	1		α_{xy}
E	2	0	−2	0	0	R_{xy}, x, y	$(\alpha_{yz}, \alpha_{zx})$
C_{2v}	E	—	C_2	$\sigma_v(zx)$	$\sigma_v(yz)$ —		
A_1	1		1	1	1	z	α_{xx}, α_{yy}, α_{zz}
A_2	1		1	−1	−1	R_z	α_{xy}
B_1	1		−1	1	−1	R_y, x	α_{zx}
B_2	1		−1	−1	1	R_x, y	α_{yz}

approximation, the ϕ angle in the $C_{\infty}{}^{\varphi}$ operation of the $C_{\infty v}$ group is made equal to $\pi/2$ and π. Thus, the characters of the $\Gamma(C_{4v})$ representation are: $x(E) = 2$, $x(C_4) = 0$, $x(C_2) = -2$, $x(\sigma_v) = 0$, and $x(\sigma_d) = 0$, which identifies this representation as an E species of the C_{4v} group. The correlation diagram between the free-molecule vibrational species and those of the site is given in Table 5. The correlation with the species of the C_{2v} site in Phase II is also included. It is obtained in the same way as above or, more simply, from the correlation table between the C_{4v} and C_{2v} group (*47*).

TABLE 5

The Site Effect on Crystalline HCN

Site (Phase I)	Free molecule	Site (Phase II)
C_{4v}	$C_{\infty v}$	C_{2v}
A_1 (*R*, *IR*) ——	—— A_1 (ν_1, ν_3) ——	—— A_1 (*R*, *IR*)
E (*R*, *IR*) ——	—— E_1 (R_{xy}, ν_2) ——	—— [B_1 (*R*, *IR*); B_2 (*R*, *IR*)

The effect of the crystalline field on HCN is summarized by the correlation diagram (Table 5). In Phase I, no splitting of the vibrations is predicted, although frequency shifts are expected with respect to the gas phase. It is also seen from the character table of the C_{4v} group that all the vibrational species should be infrared and Raman active. Furthermore, since the bands in both types of spectra arise from identical vibrations, they should have identical frequencies (within experimental error). The infrared spectrum of crystalline HCN in Phase I is not available, but the three fundamentals appear at 3145 cm^{-1} (ν_3), 2098 cm^{-1} (ν_1), and 819 cm^{-1} (ν_2) in the Raman spectrum at -90°C (*64*). Comparison with gas-phase frequencies (*65*) shows that the C—N stretching mode (ν_1) is practically uninfluenced by the state of aggregation. The C—H stretching mode however, is strongly shifted ($\nu_3 = 3311$ cm^{-1} in the gas) because of hydrogen bonding, while the doubly degenerate bending mode ($\nu_2 = 712$ cm^{-1} in the gas) shows an unusual blue shift of more than 100 cm^{-1}. In Phase II, the correlation diagram predicts a splitting of the bending vibration, both components being active in infrared and Raman. The predicted doublet has been observed at 828/838 cm^{-1} in the infrared spectrum at -180°C (*66*) and occurs with identical frequencies in the Raman spectrum at -196°C (*64*).

Correlation diagrams, such as that given in Table 5, can be used to determine the number and symmetry of the lattice modes, as will be discussed in more detail in the next section. In this case, the two degrees of freedom of molecular rotation yield a doubly degenerate $R_{xy}(E_1)$ species in the gas phase. Free rotations cannot be treated as vibrations in a free molecule, but these motions are transformed into lattice modes in the solid and should therefore be taken into account. The site approximation then predicts a libration (E species) to appear in the low frequency region of the Raman and infrared spectra of HCN in Phase I. A relatively sharp peak at 161 cm^{-1} in the Raman spectrum at $-90°C$ (*64*) probably corresponds to this libration. The same appears at 149 cm^{-1} in DCN, which is consistent with the $I^{-\frac{1}{2}}$ frequency dependence of this vibration (I = moment of inertia of the molecule). In Phase II, the librational mode should be split into two components, only one of which has been observed (173 cm^{-1} in HCN and 163 cm^{-1} in DCN) in the Raman spectrum at liquid-nitrogen temperature. This is by no means taken as a failure of the theory. It may be that the splitting is very small in this case, or that one component is much weaker than the other and has not been detected. Far-infrared studies on crystalline HCN and DCN are now in progress (*67*). It should be pointed out that molecular translations could also have been included in the correlation diagram, but they would have yielded the three acoustic modes in the site approximation. This effect therefore, does not (formally at least) lead to the translational lattice modes with nonzero frequencies.

The reason why ν_2 and R_{xy} of crystalline HCN are split in Phase II, but not in Phase I, is obvious. In the high-temperature phase the molecules lie on sites of C_{4v} symmetry, which means that the environment (and consequently the interactions with this environment) is the same along the crystallographic x and y directions. In the low temperature phase, the spacing between the molecules is larger in the y direction than along the x-axis. The potential opposing the bending and librational motions of the molecules is then slightly different in the xz and yz planes and the degeneracy of these modes is removed. It should be pointed out that, although the group-theoretical procedure used above predicts ν_2 and R_{xy} to be split in Phase II, it gives no indication as to the frequency separation between the two components. This could only be obtained from a detailed vibrational analysis, based on a suitable crystal potential. Similarly, the analysis does not predict to which species (B_1 or B_2) each of the two observed components of ν_2 belongs. On physical grounds however, the high-frequency component can be assigned to the B_1 mode since the latter takes place in the *xz* plane, in which the molecules are more closely packed. This assignment could be confirmed by polarization studies on a single crystal, since the B_1 and B_2 species involve changes of different components of the polarizability tensor (α_{zx} and α_{yz} respectively). Also, even if the theory predicts both components of the ν_2 doublet to be infrared and Raman active, it tells nothing about the intensity of each band in the two types of spectra. In order to calculate the intensities in this case, the bond moment derivatives would be required, besides the normal coordinates obtained from a vibrational analysis. It is clear that such calculations are possible for simple molecular crystals only [e.g., see Ref. (*19*)].

F. The Coupling Effect

The inadequacy of the site approximation was quickly pointed out (*68*), following its introduction by Halford. However, it was shown by Hornig (*58*) and Winston and Halford (*59*) that results identical to those obtained by the longer method of Bhagavantam and Venkatarayudu could be achieved through the site approximation, if the coupling between identical vibrations in adjacent molecules was taken into account. In this last refinement, neighboring molecules are considered to exchange energy by resonance between like vibrations. Thus, if a primitive cell contains *N* molecules, each fundamental vibration of these will give rise to *N* components (which may be degenerate). The number of fundamental components observed in crystal spectra then depends on the number of molecules per primitive cell, and also on the site and unit-cell symmetries. In practice, the correlation diagram with the site symmetry is extended to the unit-cell symmetry, in order to take the coupling effect into account. The factor group (unit-cell group) is isomorphous with the corresponding point group, which has to be a super-group of the site group. The dimensions of the representations in the factor group have to be *N* times larger than those in the site group, since each free-molecule fundamental gives rise to *N* components through intermolecular vibrational coupling.

As an illustration of the method, the correlation diagram for crystalline HCl in its low temperature phase is given in Fig. 7. The intramolecular stretching vibration, ν_1, is transformed into an A' species in the site approximation, which means that the motion takes place in the symmetry plane of the site. Since there are two molecules per primitive cell, there will be two stretching modes in the crystal. In the first (A_1 species in the

C_{2v} unit-cell group) the two molecules per cell stretch in phase; in the second (B_2 species), the two stretching motions are exactly out-of-phase. (The molecular vibrations in both of these modes are, however, in phase with the stretching vibrations of corresponding molecules in the other primitive cells.) Infrared and Raman spectra of crystalline HCl and DCl at 70°K (*69*) are reproduced in Fig. 8. The predicted factor-group splitting is clearly observed and the components have coincident

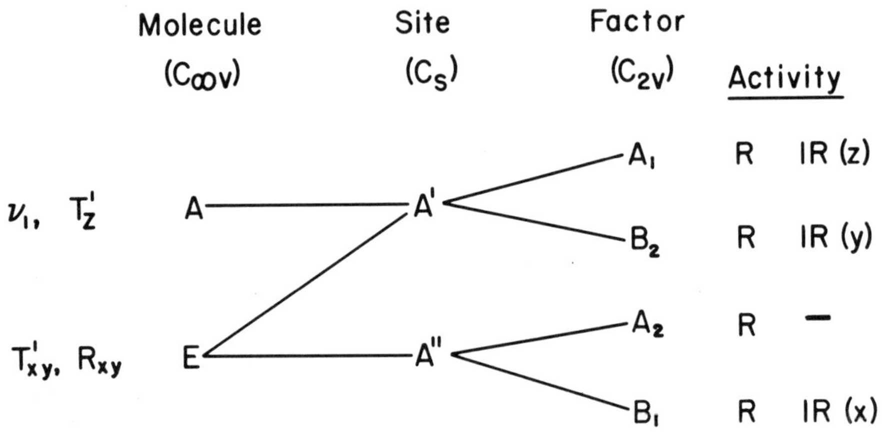

Fig. 7. Correlation diagram for crystalline HCl in its low temperature phase.

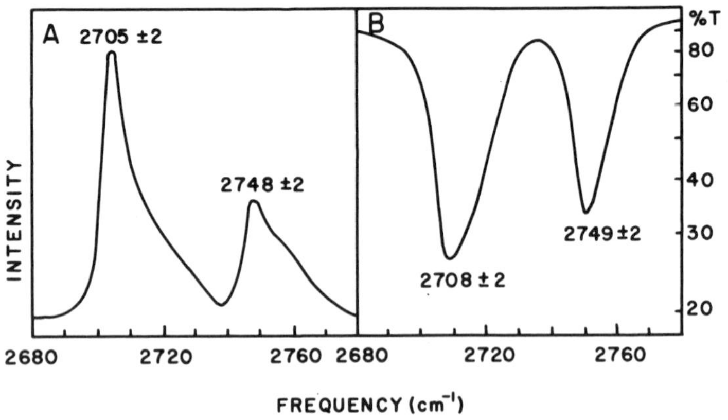

Fig. 8. Raman (*A*) and infrared (*B*) spectra of crystalline HCl in its low temperature phase. After Savoie and Anderson (*69*).

frequencies (within the combined experimental error) in the two types of spectra. It is also seen that all the components are asymmetrical, high-frequency shoulders being clearly observed in the Raman spectra. These complicating features will be discussed later (see Section V).

The correlation diagram (Fig. 7) also includes the external degrees of freedom of motion of the molecules. For example, the doubly degenerate rotation (E_1 species) is split into A' and A'' species in the site approximation, which indicates that the molecular librations are not equivalent in the crystal, one taking place in the plane of symmetry (A' species) and the other perpendicular to it (A'' species). Further splitting is brought about by coupling, so that four librational modes should be observed in the Raman spectrum (three in the infrared). As for the translations (T_z' and T_{xy}' in the free molecule), they are transformed into $2A_1+2B_2+A_2+B_1$ species in the crystal. After the removal of the three acoustic modes (A_1, B_1 and B_2 species), the predicted translational modes have A_1, A_2 and B_2 symmetries. The lattice modes are extremely weak in the Raman spectrum of crystalline HCl, which explains why only four of the seven predicted bands were observed (*70*). The far-infrared spectrum, obtained by Anderson et al. (*71*), shows two sharp peaks at 86 and 109 cm^{-1} which shift very little upon deuteration. These are assigned to the two predicted infrared-active translational modes (A_1 and B_2 species). The librational modes appear at higher frequencies (broad bands at 217 and 296 cm^{-1}) and are markedly shifted upon deuteration.

It should be noted that the method used here to obtain the fundamental modes of crystals yields exactly the same results as the method discussed in Section III, D. The main advantage in using correlation diagrams is that the crystalline field and coupling effects are more easily visualized. Also, it is usually easier to apply and it can save considerable time. It is sometimes claimed that the method of Bhagavantam and Venkatarayudu is more appropriate in the case of complex or ionic crystals, particularly when dealing with lattice modes. The fact is that the theory of Halford and Hornig can easily be applied to crystals containing more than one chemical species. This will be illustrated in the case of crystalline sodium formate, for which an analysis by the method of Bhagavantam and Venkatarayudu has been published (*72*).

An X-ray diffraction study of sodium formate (Na^+ $HCOO^-$) by Zachariasen (*73*) has shown this crystal to be monoclinic (space group C_{2h}^6) with two molecules (four ions) per primitive cell. Both types of ions are located on sites of symmetry C_2. For simplicity, the first setting is chosen for the crystallographic axes (*49*); the *z*-axis is then parallel to the

C_2 axes of the C_{2h}^6 space group. This choice differs from that of Charlton and Harvey (*72*), but it should only affect the labeling of the various vibrational species, and not the overall result. Let us first consider the lattice as being built of formate ions only. The correlation diagram between the free-ion, site, and unit-cell groups (see Table 6) yields all

TABLE 6

Correlation Diagrams for Crystalline Sodium Formate

Mode	$HCOO^-$			Na^+	
	Free ion	Site	Unit cell	Site	Free ion
	C_{2v}	C_2	C_{2h}	C_2	
(T_z, ν_1,ν_2,ν_3)	A_1		A_g		
		A		A	T_z
(R_z)	A_2		A_u		
(T_x, R_y, ν_4, ν_5)	B_1		B_g		
		B		B	T_x, T_y
$T_y, R_x, \nu_6)$	B_2		B_u		

the internal and librational modes of the formate ions. Furthermore, since the other ion (Na^+) is monatomic, these are the only internal and librational modes of the crystal (at $\mathbf{k} = 0$). It is seen from the diagram that all the internal modes of the free formate ion are split into either A_g+A_u or B_g+B_u components in the unit-cell group. The same occurs with the three degrees of rotational freedom. The librational modes will then correspond to $A_g+A_u+2B_g+2B_u$ vibrational species. The exclusion principle can be applied here, since the crystal contains centers of inversion, so that the *g* species will be Raman active only and the *u* species infrared active only. The procedure for obtaining the translational modes is quite simple. The two types of ions are first treated separately, in two different correlation diagrams, which have been combined in Table 6. In the case of the sodium ion, T_z is transformed into an A species of the C_2 site, since this motion is symmetrical with respect to the C_2 operation. The T_x and T_y motions are transformed into B species, being asymmetrical under this operation. The translational motions (in the factor group) obtained from the two diagrams are the following:

$$\begin{aligned} HCOO^-&: A_g+A_u+2B_g+2B_u \\ Na^+&: A_g+A_u+2B_g+2B_u \end{aligned}$$

The translational lattice modes of the crystal are obtained by first adding these and then removing (once) the three acoustic modes (A_u+2B_u species). The translational lattice mode with nonzero frequencies in sodium formate are then $2A_g+A_u+4B_g+2B_u$ species, which is in complete agreement with those obtained by the method of Bhagavantam and Venkatarayudu. The explanation for the above procedure in connection with the translational lattice modes is readily understood by the following example. Let us consider the translational motions along the z crystallographic axis, T_z (T_y in Ref. *72*), only. The correlation diagram for $HCOO^-$

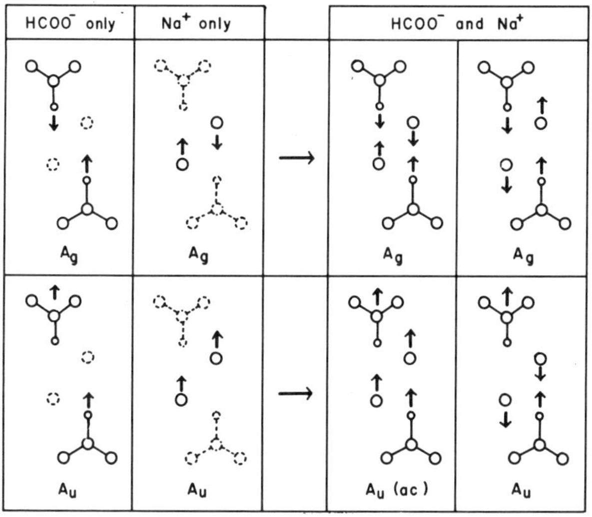

Fig. 9. Coupling of the T_z motions of the Na^+ and $HCOO^-$ ions in crystalline sodium formate.

indicates that the motions will have A_g and A_u symmetries. The two modes are illustrated in Fig. 9. Similarly, by considering the Na^+ ions only, two modes are obtained (A_g and A_u species). However, the translational motions of the two types of ions are not independent in the crystal. For example, the A_u modes of the individual ions can be combined in two different ways. If the motions of the two types of ions in a unit cell are in-phase, the T_z acoustical mode is obtained. If the motions are out-of-phase, that is if the Na^+ lattice moves as a whole against the $HCOO^-$ lattice, the T_z lattice mode of the crystal is obtained. The A_g motions of the Na^+ and $HCOO^-$ ions taken individually can be combined in a similar way, and yield the two $T_z(A_g)$ lattice modes of the crystal. These are illustrated in Fig. 9. An interesting feature about this method is that when the two types of ions (or molecules in a complex molecular crystal) do not have the same site symmetry it may happen that some vibrational specics are shared by one type of ions only. In such a case, the motions involve the latter only, the ions of the other type remaining stationary during the vibration.

IV. POTENTIALS AND FORCE CONSTANTS

Although it is relatively easy to predict the number of optically active vibrations of a solid of known crystal structure, it is more difficult to treat the problem on a quantitative basis. A vibrational analysis of a free molecule is not an easy matter, except in the simplest cases. In crystals, the situation is even more complex since molecular interactions have to be taken into account. Various methods have been used to explain observed vibrational spectra in terms of potentials, force constants, and structural parameters. First, a general crystal potential can be assumed which specifically contains terms for molecular interactions, and the problem solved by methods commonly used in the treatment of free molecules. Second, attempts have been made, with various degrees of success, to explain the frequency shifts and the splitting of bands in solid spectra by adding a small perturbation term to the potential function of the free molecule. Finally, intermolecular potential functions based on various physical properties have been obtained which can be used to predict the lattice mode frequencies in simple molecular crystals.

A. Normal Coordinate Analyses

Wilson's **GF** matrix method, so widely used in normal coordinate treatments of polyatomic molecules (*47,74*), has been shown by Shimanouchi et al. (*75*) to be applicable to the determination of the fundamental modes of crystals (in the $\mathbf{k} = 0$ approximation). The frequencies are obtained as solutions of a secular equation of the type

$$|\mathbf{GF} - \mathbf{E}\omega^2| = 0 \tag{23}$$

In Eq. 23, **G** is the inverse kinetic energy matrix (*47,76*), **F** the potential energy matrix, **E** a unit matrix with the same order as **G** and **F**, and ω

has the same meaning as in Eq. 8 ($\omega = 2\pi\nu$ cycles/sec). The procedure will be illustrated for the linear diatomic chain discussed earlier (this chapter, Section III, B).

Considering the vibrations along the chain only, a $\mathbf{G}''$ matrix of infinite order can be constructed in terms of the internal displacement coordinates Δr (see Fig. 2).

$$
\begin{array}{c|cccccc}
 & \cdots\Delta r_0 & \Delta r_1 & \Delta r_2 & \Delta r_3 & \Delta r_4 & \Delta r_5\cdots \\
\hline
\vdots & & & & & & \\
\Delta r_0 & (\mu_1+\mu_2) & -\mu_2 & 0 & 0 & 0 & 0 \\
\Delta r_1 & -\mu_2 & (\mu_1+\mu_2) & -\mu_1 & 0 & 0 & 0 \\
\Delta r_2 & 0 & -\mu_1 & (\mu_1+\mu_2) & -\mu_2 & 0 & 0 \\
\Delta r_3 & 0 & 0 & -\mu_2 & (\mu_1+\mu_2) & -\mu_1 & 0 \\
\Delta r_4 & 0 & 0 & 0 & -\mu_1 & (\mu_1+\mu_2) & -\mu_2 \\
\Delta r_5 & 0 & 0 & 0 & 0 & -\mu_2 & (\mu_1+\mu_2) \\
\vdots & & & & & &
\end{array}
= \mathbf{G}''
$$

The $\mathbf{G}''$ matrix elements contain only the inverses of the atomic masses: $\mu_1 = 1/M$ and $\mu_2 = 1/m$. Assuming a simple potential of the form

$$2V = f(\ldots \Delta r_1{}^2 + \Delta r_2{}^2 + \Delta r_3{}^2 \ldots)$$

the corresponding $\mathbf{F}''$ matrix only contains the force constant f on the diagonal, all the other elements being equal to zero. It is seen that the $\mathbf{G}''$ and $\mathbf{F}''$ matrices are of infinite order, although they consist of a mere repetition of sub-matrices of finite size. To obtain the $\mathbf{G}$ and $\mathbf{F}$ matrices for the normal modes in the crystal, these submatrices (indicated by dotted rectangles) are summed. That is

$$
\mathbf{G}' = \begin{vmatrix} 0 & -\mu_1 \\ 0 & 0 \end{vmatrix} + \begin{vmatrix} \mu_1+\mu_2 & -\mu_2 \\ -\mu_2 & \mu_1+\mu_2 \end{vmatrix} + \begin{vmatrix} 0 & 0 \\ -\mu_1 & 0 \end{vmatrix}
$$

$$
= \begin{vmatrix} \mu_1+\mu_2 & -(\mu_1+\mu_2) \\ -(\mu_1+\mu_2) & \mu_1+\mu_2 \end{vmatrix}
$$

Similarly

$$
\mathbf{F}' = \begin{vmatrix} f & 0 \\ 0 & f \end{vmatrix}
$$

The solutions are obtained from the secular equation

$$|\mathbf{G}'\mathbf{F}' - \mathbf{E}\omega^2| = \begin{vmatrix} f(\mu_1+\mu_2)-\omega^2 & -f(\mu_1+\mu_2) \\ -f(\mu_1+\mu_2) & f(\mu_1+\mu_2)-\omega^2 \end{vmatrix} = 0$$

Upon expanding the determinant:

$$\omega^4 - 2f(\mu_1+\mu_2)\omega^2 = 0$$

Therefore, $\omega^2 = 0$ and $2f(\mu_1+\mu_2)$. This result is similar to that obtained earlier (Eq. 13).

In more complicated cases, advantage can be taken of the symmetry to diagonalize the secular equation. Symmetry coordinates (S) can be constructed from the internal coordinates (R) in the usual manner (*47,77*):

$$\mathbf{S} = \mathbf{UR} \tag{25}$$

If the symmetry coordinates are properly grouped, the $\mathbf{G}'$ and $\mathbf{F}'$ matrices will be diagonalized by the similarity transformation

$$\mathbf{G} = \mathbf{UG}'\tilde{\mathbf{U}} \quad \text{and} \quad \mathbf{F} = \mathbf{UF}'\tilde{\mathbf{U}} \tag{26}$$

where $\tilde{\mathbf{U}}$ is the transpose of matrix $\mathbf{U}$. The normal frequencies are then obtained from Eq. 23.

This type of normal coordinate treatment has been applied to various molecular crystals (*20,78–81*). In general, simple potential functions are used, in order to minimize the number of force constants. These are then calculated from observed frequencies and used to determine the frequencies of the unobserved normal modes. The solutions thus obtained are possibly not unique and their correctness depends ultimately on how well the true crystal potential function has been approximated. However, the method has the advantage of yielding at least an estimate of the magnitude of the restoring forces between atoms and molecules in crystals and it can explain the general features observed in vibrational spectra. An illustrative example is obtained in crystalline benzene, whose optical frequencies were calculated by Harada and Shimanouchi (*80*). These authors used an intermolecular potential based on short-range hydrogen–hydrogen interactions, with five unknown force constants. These were calculated from the frequencies of five well-assigned Raman frequencies of the crystal. They were then used in conjunction with a suitable intramolecular potential to calculate all of the normal vibrations of the crystal. Although not perfect, the agreement between observed and calculated lattice modes and splittings of the internal vibrations was quite adequate. A similar type of calculation on crystalline thiourea, including a treatment of the Raman and infrared band intensities, was recently reported (*81*).

B. The Vibrational Exciton Approach

Various attempts have been made to explain the splittings and frequency shifts of the vibrational transitions in crystals. The vibrational exciton theory developed for this purpose had its origin in the theory of electronic excitations in crystals put forward by Davydov (*82*), whose name is often associated with correlation field splitting. (To avoid any confusion in the literature, it is suggested that the term "Davydov splitting" be reserved for the splitting of electronic energy levels.) Davydov's theory has been well reviewed by McClure (*83*) and Misra (*84*). The theory of vibrational excitons in crystals has been summarized by Dows (*33*). The formalism of the theory parallels the electronic exciton theory and is simplified by the replacement of electronic wave functions by vibrational wave functions, as discussed by Hexter (*85*). Although a complete treatment would be too lengthy to present here, the main features of this theory will be summarized.

To simplify, let us first consider the case of a diatomic molecule treated as an harmonic oscillator. The vibrational energy levels of the isolated molecule are the eigenvalues of the Schrödinger equation

$$H\psi = E\psi \tag{27}$$

where the vibrational wave functions (ψ) can be expressed in terms of the Hermite functions (*86*). In the ground state

$$\psi = (\gamma/\pi)^{\frac{1}{4}} \exp(-Q^2/2); \quad \gamma = 4\pi^2 \nu/h. \tag{28}$$

In the solid the crystal potential (V) will perturb the energy by a small amount, E', and the Schrödinger equation becomes

$$\{\Sigma\, H + V\}\phi = \{\Sigma\, E + E'\}\phi. \tag{29}$$

The vibrational ground state of the crystal may be taken as the product of all N individual molecules' vibrational eigenfunctions

$$\phi_0 = \psi_1 \psi_2 \psi_3 \ldots \psi_p \ldots \psi_N \tag{30}$$

From first-order perturbation theory,

$$E_o = w_o + 1/2 \sum_l \sum_k \int \psi_l \psi_k V_{lk} \psi_l \psi_k \, d\tau \tag{31}$$

where w_o is the crystal energy in the vibrational ground state ($= \Sigma\, h\nu/2$) and the interactions are expressed as a sum over all pairs of molecules, l and k. The pairwise additivity in intermolecular potentials has recently been studied (*87*). It seems that deviations are small, at least for weakly interacting nonpolar molecules.

Let us now consider the case where molecule p is vibrationally excited in a crystal containing one molecule per cell. We define the function

$$\phi_p = \psi_1\psi_2\psi_3 \cdots \psi_p' \cdots \psi_N \tag{32}$$

where ψ_p' is a first excited harmonic oscillator wave function

$$\psi_p' = 2^{\frac{1}{2}}\pi^{-\frac{1}{4}}\gamma^{\frac{3}{4}}Q \exp(-\gamma Q^2/2) \tag{33}$$

The localized excitation function ϕ_p has a degeneracy (N) equal to the number of molecules in the crystal. Furthermore, it does not represent a true wave function for the crystal since it does not belong to representations of the space group. To remove the degeneracy in Eq. (33), we can take a sum function (in the $\mathbf{k} = 0$ case)

$$\Phi = N^{-\frac{1}{2}}\Sigma\, \phi_p \tag{34}$$

which represents a one-quantum vibrational excitation with the energy spread over the entire crystal. This excited-state function is often called a one-site exciton.

For polyatomic molecules the isolated-molecule vibrational function (ψ) becomes a product of $3n-6$ orthogonal harmonic oscillator functions. The term V_{lk} in Eq. (31) then has to include the interactions between each normal mode of molecule l and each of those of molecule k. It is customary to assume coupling to take place between like normal modes only. This assumption seems experimentally justified and allows the original orthogonality to be retained. The situation is more complex when there is more than one molecule per primitive cell. Usually, in molecular crystals, the molecules occupy a given set of sites, these being related by the operations of the factor group. The one-site excitons (Φ_a) corresponding to a particular vibrational excitation (a) are combined so as to yield representations of the factor group

$$\Phi^\alpha = \Sigma\, U_{\alpha a}\Phi_a \tag{35}$$

where α indicates the representation, and the sum is taken over all of the occupied equivalent sites of the unit cell. The coefficients $U_{\alpha a}$ are those of a unitary matrix which relates the symmetry coordinates and the normal coordinates [see, e.g., Ref. (*47*), pp. 117*ff*]. The concept of "interchange-symmetry" recently introduced by Kopelman (*88*) can be helpful in the classification of the vibrational eigenstates of crystals and other related problems.

The real difficulty in the treatment pursued here lies in the inadequacy of our knowledge of the interaction potential. In Eq. (31) the interactions were expressed as a sum over pairs of molecules

$$V = \tfrac{1}{2}\sum_{l}\sum_{k} V_{lk} \tag{36}$$

Methods for the summations arising from this definition have been published (*89*). As for the interaction terms, V_{lk}, they can be expanded as power series in the normal coordinates (Q)

$$V_{lk} = V_{lk}^{0} + V_{l}{}'Q_{l} + V_{k}{}'Q_{k} + \tfrac{1}{2}(V_{l}{}''Q_{l}{}^{2} + V_{k}{}''Q_{k}{}^{2} + 2V_{lk}''Q_{l}Q_{k}) \tag{37}$$

where V' and V'' are the first and second derivatives of V with respect to the normal coordinates. Interactions in molecular crystals are usually assumed to be mainly of the dipole–dipole type, such that

$$V_{lk} = (\mu_{l}\mu_{k}/R_{lk}^{3})(\cos\theta_{lk} - 3\cos\theta_{l}\cos\theta_{k}) \tag{38}$$

where μ_l is the permanent dipole moment of molecule l, R_{lk} the distance between the centers of gravity of molecules l and k, θ_{lk} the angle between the two dipole moment vectors, and θ_l the angle between the dipole moment vector of molecule l and the vector R_{lk}. Since the interaction potential must explicitly include the functional dependence on the vibrational coordinates, the dipole moments are expanded in series in the normal coordinates

$$\mu = \mu^{0} + \sum_{i}\mu_{i}{}'Q_{i} + \tfrac{1}{2}\sum_{i}\sum_{j}\mu_{ij}''Q_{i}Q_{j} \tag{39}$$

where μ^0 is the permanent dipole moment of the molecule and μ' and μ'' the derivatives.

When the dipole–dipole interactions [Eq. (38)], including the dependence of the dipole moments on the normal coordinates (Eq. 39), are included in a perturbation treatment of the vibrational states of molecular crystals, it turns out that the energy levels are perturbed by two factors [see Ref. (33), p. 677]. The first is of little practical value since it contains second derivatives of the dipole moment, and very little is known of these quantities. The second term, which is solely responsible for factor-group splitting, contains first derivatives of the dipole moment. Since these can be obtained from infrared absolute intensities, it is possible to calculate factor-group splittings and compare the results with those observed experimentally.

The crystal potential based on dipole–dipole interactions has had some success in explaining the splitting of vibrational energy levels in a number of molecular crystals. Fox and Hexter (*90*) give many examples where the calculated and observed splittings are in reasonable agreement. This is usually the case for strong transitions, where it is observed that the splitting is roughly proportional to the dipole derivative and, therefore, to the intensity of the band, as predicted from the theory. In certain crystals, however, as in ethylene (*91*) and the methyl halides (*92*), it is found that weak bands can display important splittings, which points out the inadequacy of the chosen interaction potential in the case of weak transitions.

Calculations based on the dipole–dipole interaction potential have indicated that the magnitude of the splitting and the shape of a band can be very strongly influenced by the shapes and dimensions of the crystallites usually found in solid samples (*89*). These effects are especially important in infrared studies, when the sample is deposited from the vapor onto a cold substrate. X-ray scattering studies of such polycrystalline deposits have indicated particle sizes of 50 to 100 Å, the crystallites usually having preferred orientations (*93*).

The failure of the dipole–dipole interaction potential to explain the magnitude of the splitting of weak bands in a number of crystalline compounds indicates that other interactions are present. In the case of ethylene, Dows (*94*) has had reasonable success with an interaction potential based on hydrogen–hydrogen repulsions. More recently, Walmsley and Pople (*95*) have calculated the lattice modes of carbon dioxide, using an intermolecular force law between pairs of molecules based on a Lennard–Jones 6–12 potential and taking into account electric quadrupole interactions. The frequencies obtained for the translational modes were in close agreement with the observed values. However, the calculated librational frequencies, arising solely from the quadrupole part of the potential, were only about two thirds of the observed values, which shows the approximate nature of the potential function used. Better results were obtained in similar calculations on N_2 and CO (*96*).

To conclude this section, it is seen that although existing theories are still inadequate in a number of cases, the interpretation of coupling constants in terms of specific molecular interactions is now reasonably well established.

V. APPARENT ANOMALIES IN RAMAN SPECTRA

The theory previously discussed (Section III) allows predictions to be made concerning the number of bands that should be present in Raman spectra of crystals of known structures. In practice, however, even if the crystal structure of a given compound is known without any doubt, it is common to find that its Raman spectrum does not quite fit the theoretical predictions. When some of the predicted bands and splittings are not observed, it is usually because they are too weak or because of overlapping. However, more often than not, apparently anomalous features appear in vibrational spectra which are not always easily explained. Also, band shapes may appear distorted, giving the false impression that many components are present where only one is predicted. In such cases, there is always the remote possibility that the known crystal structure is in error. This can be particularly true in the case of X-ray diffraction studies of hydrogenic compounds because of the low scattering cross section of hydrogen atoms. A typical example is that of hydrazine, whose crystal structure obtained from X-ray diffraction studies (*97*) differs slightly from that determined by neutron diffraction (*98*). The far-infrared spectrum (*99*) favors the latter and Raman data suggest that both structures are in error (*100*). However, apparent anomalies in Raman spectra of crystals quite generally arise from other sources which will now be briefly discussed.

A. Anharmonicity Effects

The effects of anharmonicity on vibrational spectra of crystals have been discussed by Hornig (*58*) and by Winston and Halford (*59*). A more extensive study has been published by Walnut (*101*). As in the case of free molecules, the main effect of anharmonicity is to allow combinations and overtones to appear in the spectra. In crystals, combinations of internal and lattice modes can also occur and have effectively been observed on many occasions. Theoretically, the law of conservation of momentum then requires that the two individual excitations have equal but opposite wave vectors, so that such processes can occur at any point in the Brillouin zone. This may allow combinations of internal and acoustical modes to be optically active (*102*) and leads essentially to the removal of all restrictions on overtones and combinations.

Anharmonic coupling between lattice and internal modes may also split degeneracy of a fundamental vibration, even if the equilibrium site symmetry is degenerate (*58*). This is because molecular motions may distort the site symmetry. For example, in a body-centered cubic crystal of T_d symmetry, displacement of a center molecule in the unit cell may lower the site symmetry from T_d to C_{2v} and a splitting of the triply degenerate vibrations may result. In such cases, a degenerate vibrational mode can be split if the square of its symmetry species contains those of translation or rotation (*58*). In the example given above, the E modes will not be split since $E \times E = A_1 + A_2 + E$ and the translations and rotations have F_2 and F_1 symmetries respectively (in the T_d group).

The importance of temperature on the effects discussed here should be emphasized. Anharmonic coupling of lattice and internal modes depends linearly on the lattice vibrational amplitudes. This effect should then be less at low temperature. Similarly, difference bands involving low frequency vibrations should gradually disappear as the temperature is lowered, since their intensities is proportional to the population of excited vibrational states. At high temperature, the effect of anharmonicity becomes more important, as lattice and low frequency internal modes are excited, and a broadening of the lines should result, accompanied by an increase in the intensity of the combination bands. In the harmonic approximation, line intensities should be independent of temperature. Hence, any band whose intensity strongly depends on temperature may arise from anharmonic effects although other factors, such as orientational effects, may be implicated.

B. Disorder and Impurities

The term "disorder," when used to describe the state of a crystal, is not very specific and can be taken to mean a number of things. First, it may be the result of imperfect crystallization, in which case the crystal may exist as an amorphous powder or as an assembly of small crystallites of various sizes and orientations. This is often the case in infrared experiments when samples are deposited from the vapor onto a cold window. The quality of such samples can usually be improved by annealing, although this is not always possible in view of the finite vapor pressure of the sample which can sublime away from the substrate when the temperature is raised. The effect of particle size on factor-group splittings of polycrystalline materials has been mentioned in a previous section (Section IV, B). In such cases, the crystal frequencies may differ from those of a bulk crystal and the $\mathbf{k} = 0$ approximation is no longer applicable. This usually results in a broadening of the lines, since it allows the observation of the equivalent of part of the exciton branch.

Some crystals are inherently disordered or may exist as such over a certain temperature range. In most cases the disorder is orientational in character; i.e., the molecules are arranged on or near regular positions in the solid, but are irregularly oriented. Well-known examples are those of some varieties of ice (*103*) and the high-temperature modifications of HCl (*104*) and CH_4 (*28*). A solid can also be both positionally and orientationally disordered, in which case it is usually referred to as a glass. Vitreous ice, whose far-infrared spectrum has recently been reported (*103*) is a typical example of such. X-ray studies of disordered crystals often yield structures which are (statistically at least) of higher order of symmetry than the corresponding ordered structure. However, if X-ray methods are most sensitive to long-range order, the opposite should be true in vibrational spectra (*105*). It is, therefore, expected that the bands will be considerably broadened because of the disorder in the local environment and this is experimentally observed. Furthermore, even if first and second neighbors only are considered, most sites will have C_1 symmetry, so that all the fundamentals and lattice vibrations should be infrared and Raman active, even if they are not in the free-molecule approximation. A theory for translational lattice vibrations in orientationally disordered crystals has recently been advanced (*106*).

Crystals in which molecular rotation is relatively free can be considered as disordered. Depending upon the height of the barrier hindering rotational motions, combinations of these with internal vibrations may yield well-defined combination bands or unresolved rotational wings on each side of fundamentals. The latter usually occurs with spherical molecules, such as CH_4 (*23*) and CF_4 (*24*), and it is then obvious from the shapes of the bands that the situation is much more complex than in the gas phase. Gordon (*107*) has shown that the Fourier transform of infrared and Raman band shapes reveal the degree of "free" molecular rotation in liquids much more clearly than the band shapes themselves. However, this theory would have to be modified in order to be applicable to solids, since diffusion is then very small as compared to liquids.

A special type of disorder can be introduced in crystals by impurities. These are usually of little importance when Raman (and infrared) spectroscopy is used merely as a tool for qualitative analysis. In fundamental studies on crystals however, the presence of impurities may do more than cause new characteristic bands to appear in spectra. In some cases, very small amounts of an impurity can induce important structural changes in crystals. For example, when HCl containing traces of air is quickly condensed at low temperature, it shows in the infrared a strong band at 2778 cm^{-1} (*69,108*) besides the predicted doublet for the HCl stretching modes (see Fig. 8). When care is taken to purify the sample, this extra band, which has been assigned to a metastable phase of HCl, disappears.

Effects of impurities on crystal spectra are seldom that drastic, but there is no doubt that they are present. Impurities are equivalent to defects in crystals and act as barriers to the propagation of excitons. Hence, they will cause lines to be broadened just as lattice defects and disorder in general. They may also cause forbidden bands to appear and modify considerably the distribution of bands in the lattice region of the spectrum.

Isotopic molecules, commonly present in crystals, may act as impurities to some extent. The dynamics of randomly disordered isotopic binary lattices have recently been studied (*109*). When the concentration of the isotopic impurity can be controlled however, it provides a useful tool for the study of crystal structure and lattice dynamics. For example when deuterium is substituted for hydrogen in a molecule, the fundamental vibrations involving motion of this atom are strongly shifted in frequency. If the concentration of the isotopically substituted molecules is small, these are isolated in the host matrix and the coupling effect is very small, because of the frequency difference between like vibrations of the two types of molecules. This may be used to determine whether the splitting of a degenerate vibrational level in a crystal is a factor-group or site effect. A particularly enlightning spectroscopic study of mixed crystals is that on the hydrogen halides by Hornig and Hiebert (*110*).

C. Piezoelectric Crystals

Anomalies have been observed in the Raman spectra of piezoelectric crystals. The triply degenerate modes of cubic crystals of this type, such as $NaClO_3$, $NaBrO_3$ (*111*), and ZnS (*112*), were observed to be split, although this was not predicted from group theory. Similarly, frequencies of some bands in uniaxial crystals were observed to depend on the orientation of the samples with respect to incident light (*113*). The above anomalies are related to the reflection phenomenon, well known to infrared spectroscopists, and have been explained theoretically (*37,60,111,114–118*).

The complex refractive index in an isotropic medium can be described by

$$\tilde{n}^2 = (n-ix)^2 = n_0{}^2 + \rho/(v_t{}^2 - v^2 + ifv)$$

$$\rho = \left(\frac{n_0{}^2+2}{3}\right)^2 \frac{N}{\pi}\left(\frac{\partial\mu}{\partial Q}\right)^2 \tag{40}$$

where n and ix are the real and imaginary parts of the refractive index, n_0 the normal refractive index at higher frequencies, N the number of oscillators per cm^3, f a damping constant, $\partial\mu/\partial Q$ the dipole derivative, and ν the frequency. An infrared reflection band, with low frequency limit near ν_t, can be described by the reflection coefficient

$$R = \{(n-1)^2 + x^2\}/\{(n+1)^2 + x^2\} \tag{41}$$

The variations of n, x, and R in the vicinity of a band are schematically illustrated in Fig. 10.

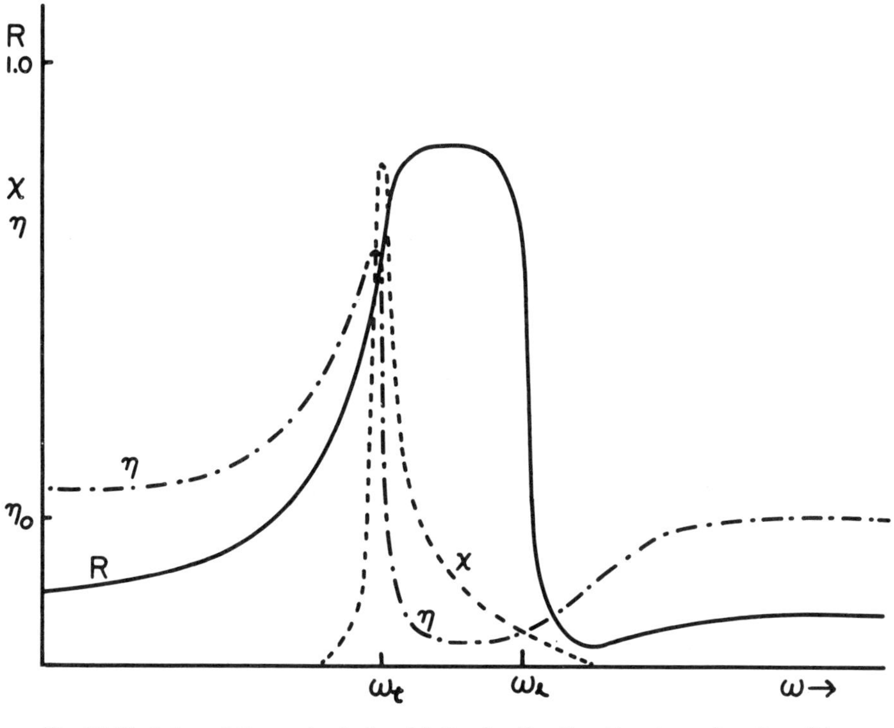

Fig. 10. Variation of R, η, and χ, in the vicinity of a vibrational band, as a function of the circular frequency. After Ketelaar, Haas, and Fahrenfort (*116*); reprinted by courtesy of *Physica*, **20** (1954), p. 1261.

It can be shown that the high-frequency side of the infrared reflection band is approximately limited by the longitudinal frequency, ν_l, which is related to the transverse frequency, ν_t, by the equation

$$\nu_l^2 = \nu_t^2 + \rho/n_0^2 \tag{42}$$

The maximum of absorption in the infrared should coincide with the maximum of x and therefore have a frequency ν_t. In Raman, two peaks should be observed, with frequencies ν_l and ν_t, the former being fixed by the condition $n = x$. The direct observation of the transverse and longitudinal modes in a Raman spectrum provides an easy way to obtain values for $\partial\mu/\partial Q$ (Eqs. 40 and 42). It should be noted however that Eq. (42) has been derived for cubic crystals, with symmetry not lower than T_d, and that it is open to theoretical question since it neglects neighboring band interactions in the frequency dependence of the refractive index (*119*). Longitudinal frequencies can also be obtained from infrared studies (*119–123*). For example, the constants ρ, f, and ν_t can be adjusted so as to obtain the best fit for the infrared reflection band. The value of ν_l is then obtained by plotting the curves for n and x as a function of ν and finding the frequency for which $n = x$. It should be noted that the longitudinal modes will appear in Raman spectra only if $\partial\mu/\partial Q \neq 0$ (Eq. 42). The particular mode involved should then be infrared-active. This is only possible in noncentrosymmetric crystals (piezoelectric crystals).

In uniaxial crystals, the frequency of the extraordinary ray varies with the angle (ϕ) between the wave vector of the exciton and the crystal axis according to the equation

$$\nu_\phi^2 = \nu_t^2 + (\rho/n_0^2)\sin^2\phi \tag{43}$$

The ordinary ray on the other hand behaves as in cubic crystals. It is, therefore, possible for a Raman band to be shifted in frequency (between ν_t and ν_l), depending on the orientation of the crystal with respect to the exciting light.

The above effects have very often been overlooked in Raman studies of molecular crystals, possibly because it is felt that the values of $\partial\mu/\partial Q$ in molecular crystals are much smaller than in ionic crystals (e.g., the absorption coefficient is smaller in molecular crystals). This is not always the case, however, and the above effects may well be responsible for the appearance of shoulders or well-resolved peaks on the high-frequency side of the Raman bands of a number of molecular crystals, as in SO_2 (*124*), HCl (*69*), and HCN (*64*). This explanation is partly confirmed by the fact that such complicating features have been observed in crystalline ICN (*64*), which has a noncentrosymmetric structure, but were not present in the Raman spectra of ClCN and BrCN (*64*), which consist of antiparallel chains, and are consequently not piezoelectric.

VI. ILLUSTRATIVE EXAMPLE

As an example of the application of Raman (and infrared) spectroscopy to crystal structure analysis, we will consider the case of solid CF_4 in its Phase II, stable below 76.2°K (*125*). Although carbon tetrafluoride has been known for a long time, it has somehow escaped the attention of the crystallographers and the structures of its two solid phases are still unknown. According to NMR studies (*126*) some molecular rotation persists in the solid down to about 55°K, although this rotation is probably restricted to motions about the C_2 molecular axes. Part of the infrared spectrum of Phase II has been studied in the past (*127,128*), but we will limit ourselves to the findings of Fournier et al. (*24*).

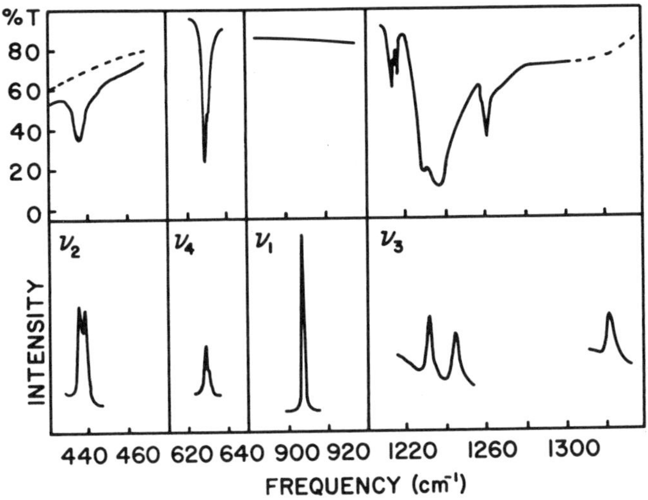

Fig. 11. Infrared (top) and Raman (bottom) spectra of crystalline CF_4 in Phase II. Courtesy of *J. Chem. Phys.* (Ref. *24*).

The free CF_4 molecule has tetrahedral (T_d) symmetry and thus yields four normal modes: $\nu_1(A_1)$, $\nu_2(E)$, $\nu_3(F_2)$, and $\nu_4(F_2)$. The Raman and infrared spectra of the solid at 70°K are reproduced in Fig. 11. It is clear from the sharpness of the bands that the structure is well ordered and that the rotational motions detected by n.m.r. take place on a time scale which is long compared to that of the vibrational transitions. Furthermore, the splitting of many of the fundamentals indicates that there is more than one molecule per cell or that the site symmetry is lower than T_d (or both).

Some of the secondary features in the infrared spectrum can easily be assigned, such as $\nu_3(^{13}CF_4)$ appearing as a weak triplet at ca. 1215 cm^{-1} and $2\nu_4$ at 1261 cm^{-1}. As for the weak peak at 1321 cm^{-1} in the Raman spectrum, it could possibly arise from an impurity, although attempts to identify it by mass spectrometry or by other bands in the spectrum have failed. It could also be a combination of ν_3 and a lattice mode, although the band seems quite sharp and strong for such a transition. Given the large frequency difference with ν_3 ($\simeq 100$ cm^{-1}), it seems unrealistic to assign it to a component of the latter, arising from a factor-group or site splitting. Noting that it approximately corresponds in frequency to the limit of the strong reflection band observed on the high-frequency side of ν_3 in the infrared spectrum, it is tentatively assigned to the longitudinal mode associated with ν_3. The value of $\partial\mu/\partial Q$ thus calculated from Eqs. (40, 42) is roughly 210 $cm^{3/2}$-sec^{-1}, which is comparable to the values obtained for such ionic crystals as $NaNO_3$ and calcite (*114*). The large value of the calculated dipole derivative for ν_3 of CF_4 is consistent with the very strong absorption coefficient in this region. The sample for the infrared study was only a few microns thick. In the Raman spectrum ν_3 is rather weak. (Instrument variables were adjusted so as to give reasonable intensities; in fact, ν_1 is much stronger than the other three fundamentals.)

We will now proceed to find a crystal structure than can explain observed band splittings in the vibrational spectra of CF_4 Phase II. Starting first with the Raman data, we look among the 230 space groups for those in which an appropriate combination of site and factor groups leads to two active components for all the Raman fundamentals, except for ν_1 which appears as a singlet in the spectrum. The elimination is facilitated by the fact that the site group has to be a subgroup of the free-molecule point group and the factor group has to be a supergroup of the site group. (Any group is also considered as being a subgroup or supergroup of itself.) This procedure leaves only four possible combinations which are schematically illustrated in Fig. 12. The numbers on the left-hand side indicate the number of space groups which contain the appropriate site in each set.

We can now use the infrared data to restrict further the number of possible structures. The fact that ν_1 is inactive in the infrared is of no help since it should be so in the four possible sets. The infrared activity of ν_2 however allows the two first combinations to be eliminated. The site symmetry is, therefore, S_4 and the crystal class either S_4 or C_{4h}. A choice between these two sets should be possible by comparing the frequencies of the infrared and Raman F_2 doublets (v_3 and v_4): the frequencies should coincide in the S_4 class, but not in the C_{4h} class. The infrared and Raman v_4 doublets have identical frequencies, within experimental error, but this is not taken to be significant since the splitting is very small (2 cm^{-1}) and the band is little shifted upon condensation. In the v_3 region however, the doublet at 1230/1244 cm^{-1} in the Raman spectrum differ somewhat from that in the infrared at 1229/1237 cm^{-1}. If this is taken to be meaningful, the doublets are not frequency coincident and the crystal class is C_{4h}, with five possible space groups, C_{4h}^{2-6}. Since these structures are

	Site	Factor	A_1	E	F_2
(9)	D_{2d}	D_{4h}	I	I I	I I
(4)	D_{2d}	D_{2d}	I	I I	I I
(5)	S_4	C_{4h}	I	I I	I I
(2)	S_4	S_4	I	I I	I I

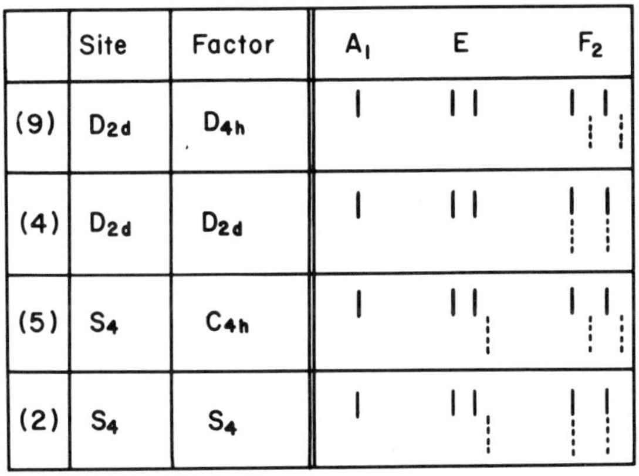

Fig. 12. Possible site and factor-group symmetries for crystalline CF$_4$ in Phase II. Full lines represent Raman components and broken lines infrared components.

centrosymmetric, our above interpretation of the 1321 cm^{-1} Raman peak has to be reexamined. It is also possible that the infrared and Raman v_3 doublets are in fact coincident, since the infrared frequencies are expected to be slightly shifted because of the reflection phenomenon. In this case the crystal space group would be either S_4^1 or S_4^2. It should be possible (in principle at least) to distinguish between the two possible crystal classes from the number of lattice modes in the Raman spectrum. Four such modes are predicted to be active if the class is C_{4h}, whereas only two should be observed if the class is S_4. Unfortunately, these modes, which are expected to be very weak and have very low frequencies (< 100 cm^{-1}), have not been detected in the Raman study. The fact that $v_3(^{13}CF_4)$ appears as a triplet in the infrared spectrum is not of much help either. The two stronger components are probably equivalent to the doublet observed for $v_3(^{12}CF_4)$, the splitting being less (3.4 cm^{-1} as compared to

8 cm^{-1}) because vibrational coupling with neighboring $^{12}CF_4$ molecules is negligible. The weaker peak of the triplet may arise from $^{13}CF_4$–$^{13}CF_4$ pairs.

The possible structures obtained above for carbon tetrafluoride in its Phase II may well be found erroneous once the structure is established by more direct means, e.g., X-ray diffraction.* In fact, any analysis of this type is based on the assumptions that (1) all the components of the various fundamentals have been observed in both types of spectra and, (2) that all the observed splittings are caused by site and coupling effects only. These basic assumptions strongly limit the usefulness of Raman and infrared spectroscopy in the determination of crystal structures. However, it is still true that vibrational spectra can yield important information on possible crystal structures and the various interactions taking place in solids.

VII. CONCLUSION

There is no doubt that the possibilities offered by the technique of Raman spectroscopy will considerably increase in the coming years. For example, the study of chemical species isolated in solid matrices is not yet possible by Raman spectroscopy because of the intensity problem. The use of powerful lasers as exciting sources may well solve this difficulty and work along that line is now in progress in many laboratories. The use of laser sources should also stimulate polarization studies which greatly facilitates band assignments. The accumulation of experimental results should lead to a better understanding of the various effects involved and help develop the theory, upon which the interpretation of experimental data is finally based.

REFERENCES

1. R. N. Jones and J. B. DiGiorgio, in *Standard Methods of Chemical Analysis* (F. J. Welcher, ed.), Part A, Chap. IV, Vol. III, Van Nostrand, Princeton, N.J., 1966.
2. R. N. Jones, J. B. DiGiorgio, J. J. Elliot, and G. A. A. Nonnenmacher, *J. Org. Chem.*, **30,** 1822 (1965).

* A recent X-ray investigation of solid CF_4 indicates that the structure of Phase II is not too different from that deduced here (S. C. Greer and L. Meyer, *J. Chem. Phys.*, **51,** 4583 (1970).

3. G. Herzberg, *Infrared and Raman Spectra of Polyatomic Molecules*, Van Nostrand, New York, 1945.
4. N. B. Colthup, L. H. Doly, and S. E. Wiberley, *Introduction to Infrared and Raman Spectroscopy*, Academic, New York, 1964.
5. R. N. Jones and M. K. Jones, *Anal. Chem.*, **38,** 393R (1966).
6. A. C. Jones and D. D. Tunnicliff, *Anal. Chem.*, **34,** 261R (1962).
7. B. P. Stoicheff, in *Methods of Experimental Physics* (D. Williams, ed.), Sec. 2.3, Vol. 3, Academic, New York, 1962.
8. *Raman Spectroscopy* (H. A. Szymanski, ed.), Plenum, New York, 1967.
9. A. Simon, H. Kriegsmann, and E. Stiger, *Z. Physik. Chem. (Leipsig)*, **205,** 181 (1956).
10. A. V. Bobrov and Kh. E. Sterin, *Opt. i Spektroskopiya*, **17,** 532 (1964) (in Russian); *Opt. Spectry. (USSR)*, **17,** 287 (1964) (English transl.).
11. R. H. Busey and O. L. Keller, Jr., *J. Chem. Phys.*, **41,** 215 (1964).
12. D. C. Nelson and W. N. Mitchell, *Anal. Chem.*, **36,** 555 (1964).
13. R. Savoie and J. Tremblay, *J. Opt. Soc. Am.*, **57,** 329 (1967).
14. B. Schrader and G. Bergmann, *Z. Anal. Chem.*, **225,** 230 (1967).
15. B. Schrader and W. Meier, *Z. Naturforsch.*, **21***a*, 480 (1966).
16. G. B. Benedek and K. Fritsch, *Phys. Rev.*, **149,** 647 (1966).
17. G. B. B. M. Sutherland, *Proc. Roy. Soc. (London)*, **A141,** 535 (1933).
18. J. R. Ferraro, J. S. Ziomek, and K. Puckett, *Rev. Sci. Instr.*, **35,** 754 (1964).
19. J. S. Kittelberger and D. F. Hornig, *J. Chem. Phys.*, **46,** 3099 (1967).
20. M. Ito and T. Shigeoka, *J. Chem. Phys.*, **44,** 1001 (1966).
21. C. H. Perry, J. H. Fertel, and T. F. McNeilly, *J. Chem. Phys.*, **47,** 1619 (1967).
22. R. Savoie and M. Pézolet, *Can. J. Chem.*, **45,** 1677 (1967).
23. M. F. Crawford, H. L. Welsh, and J. J. Harrold, *Can. J. Phys.*, **30,** 81 (1952).
24. R. P. Fournier, R. Savoie, F. Bessette, and A. Cabana, *J. Chem. Phys.*, **49,** 1159 (1968).
25. N. C. Craig and J. Overend, *Spectrochim. Acta*, **20,** 1561 (1964).
26. W. J. Taylor, L. Smith, and H. L. Johnston, *J. Opt. Soc. Am.*, **41,** 91 (1951).
27. E. J. Allin, T. Feldman, and H. L. Welsh, *J. Chem. Phys.*, **24,** 1116 (1956).
28. S. S. Bhatnagar, E. J. Allin, and H. L. Welsh, *Can. J. Chem.*, **40,** 9 (1962).
29. R. Savoie and A. Anderson, *J. Opt. Soc. Am.*, **55,** 133 (1965).
30. J. E. Cahill, K. L. Treuil, R. E. Miller, and G. E. Leroi, *J. Chem. Phys.*, **47,** 3678 (1967).
31. A. R. Gee and G. W. Robinson, *J. Chem. Phys.*, **46,** 4847 (1967).
32. J. P. Russell, *J. Phys. (Paris)*, **26,** 620 (1965).
33. D. A. Dows, in *Physics and Chemistry of the Organic Solid State* (D. Fox, M. M. Labes, and A. Weissberger, eds.), Vol. 1, Chap. 11, Wiley-Interscience, New York, 1963.
34. S. S. Mitra, *Solid State Phys.*, **13,** 1 (1962).
35. R. A. Cowley, *Proc. Phys. Soc. (London)*, **84,** 281 (1964).
36. R. Loudon, *Advanc. Phys.*, **13,** 423 (1964).
37. M. Born and K. Huang, *Dynamical Theory of Crystal Lattices*, 2nd ed., Oxford Univ. Press, London, 1956.
38. A. A. Maradudin, E. W. Montroll, and G. H. Weiss, *Solid State Phys.*, **3,** 1 (1963).
39. E. R. Lippincott and R. Schroeder, *J. Chem. Phys.*, **23,** 1099 (1955).
40. J. J. Rush and J. R. Ferraro, *J. Chem. Phys.*, **44,** 2496 (1966).

41. P. A. Giguère and R. Savoie, *Can. J. Chem.*, **40,** 495 (1962).
42. H. W. Schrötter and H. J. Bernstein, *J. Mol. Spectry*, **12,** 1 (1964).
43. G. E. Walrafen, *J. Chem. Phys.*, **44,** 1546 (1966).
44. A. Anderson and H. A. Gebbie, *Spectrochim. Acta*, **21,** 883 (1965).
45. M. Born and Th. von Kármán, *Phys. Zeit.*, **13,** 297 (1912).
46. J. De Launay, *Solid State Phys.*, **2,** 220 (1956).
47. E. B. Wilson, Jr., J. C. Decius, and P. C. Cross, *Molecular Vibrations*, McGraw Hill, New York, 1955.
48. L. Brillouin, *Wave Propagation in Periodic Structures*, McGraw Hill, New York, 1946.
49. N. F. M. Henry and K. Lonsdale (eds.), *International Tables for X-ray Crystallography*, Vol. 1, Kynoch Press, Birmingham, England, 1952.
50. F. A. Cotton, *Chemical Applications of Group Theory*, Interscience Publishers, New York, 1963.
51. R. M. Hochstrasser, *Molecular Aspects of Symmetry*, Benjamin, New York, 1966.
52. S. Bhagavantam and T. Venkatarayudu, *Proc. Indian Acad. Sci.*, **A9,** 224 (1939); S. Bhagavantam, *Proc. Indian Acad. Sci.*, **A13,** 543 (1941).
53. S. Bhagavantam and T. Venkatarayudu, *Theory of Groups and its Applications to Physical Problems*, Andhra Univ., Waltair, 1951.
54. S. S. Mitra, *Z. Krist.*, **116,** 149 (1961).
55. G. Natta, *Gazz. Chim. Ital.*, **63,** 425 (1933).
56. E. Sándor and R. F. C. Farrow, *Nature*, **171,** 171 (1967).
57. R. S. Halford, *J. Chem. Phys.*, **14,** 8 (1946).
58. D. F. Hornig, *J. Chem. Phys.*, **16,** 1063 (1948).
59. H. Winston and R. S. Halford, *J. Chem. Phys.*, **17,** 607 (1949).
60. W. Vedder and D. F. Hornig, *Advan. Spectry*, **2,** 189 (1961).
61. G. C. Pimentel, *J. Chem. Phys.*, **19,** 1536 (1951).
62. W. F. Giauque and R. A. Ruehrwein, *J. Am. Chem. Soc.*, **61,** 2626 (1939).
63. W. J. Dulmage and W. N. Lipscomb, *Acta Cryst.*, **4,** 330 (1951).
64. M. Pézolet and R. Savoie, *Can. J. Chem.*, **47,** 3041 (1969).
65. D. H. Rank, G. Skorinko, D. P. Eastman, and T. A. Wiggins, *J. Opt. Soc. Am.*, **50,** 421 (1960).
66. R. R. Hoffman and D. F. Hornig, *J. Chem. Phys.*, **17,** 1163 (1949).
67. F. G. Baglin, private communication.
68. L. Couture, *J. Chem. Phys.*, **15,** 153 (1947); *Ann. Phys. (Paris)*, **2,** 5 (1947).
69. R. Savoie and A. Anderson, *J. Chem. Phys.*, **44,** 548 (1966).
70. M. Ito, M. Suzuki, and T. Yokoyama, Technical Report **A–330,** Institute for Solid State Physics, University of Tokyo, Tokyo, Japan (1968).
71. A. Anderson, S. H. Walmsley, and H. A. Gebbie, *Phil. Mag.*, **7,** 1243 (1962). A. Anderson and H. A. Gebbie, *Mol. Physics*, **7,** 401 (1964).
72. T. L. Charlton and K. B. Harvey, *Can. J. Chem.*, **44,** 2717 (1966).
73. W. H. Zachariasen, *J. Am. Chem. Soc.*, **62,** 1011 (1940).
74. E. B. Wilson, Jr., *J. Chem. Phys.*, **7,** 1047 (1939); *ibid*, **9,** 76 (1941).
75. T. Shimanouchi, M. Tsuboi, and T. Miyazawa, *J. Chem. Phys.*, **35,** 1597 (1961).
76. J. C. Decius, *J. Chem. Phys.*, **16,** 1025 (1948).
77. K. Nakamoto, *Infrared Spectra of Inorganic and Coordination Compounds*, Wiley, New York, 1963, p. 45.
78. T. Shimanouchi and I. Harada, *J. Chem. Phys.*, **41,** 2651 (1964).

79. M. Tasumi and T. Shimanouchi, *J. Chem. Phys.*, **43,** 1245 (1965).
80. I. Harada and T. Shimanouchi, *J. Chem. Phys.*, **44,** 2016 (1966).
81. H. Takahashi, B. Schrader, W. Meier, and K. Gottlieb, *J. Chem. Phys.*, **47,** 3842 (1967).
82. A. S. Davydov, *J. Expl. Theoret. Phys.* (*USSR*), **18,** 210 (1948).
83. D. S. McClure, *Solid State Phys.*, **8,** 1 (1959).
84. T. N. Misra, *Rev. Pure Appl. Chem.*, **15,** 39 (1965).
85. R. M. Hexter, *J. Chem. Phys.*, **33,** 1833 (1960).
86. L. Pauling and E. B. Wilson, Jr., *Introduction to Quantum Mechanics*, McGraw Hill, New York, 1935.
87. D. R. Williams, L. J. Schaad, and J. N. Murrell, *J. Chem. Phys.*, **47,** 4916 (1967).
88. R. Kopelman, *J. Chem. Phys.*, **47,** 2631 (1967).
89. R. M. Hexter, *J. Chem. Phys.*, **37,** 1347 (1962).
90. D. Fox and R. M. Hexter, *J. Chem. Phys.*, **41,** 1125 (1964).
91. S. Zwerdling and R. S. Halford, *J. Chem. Phys.*, **23,** 2215 (1956).
92. D. A. Dows, *J. Chem. Phys.*, **33,** 1743 (1960).
93. H. S. Peiser, in *Formation and Trapping of Free Radicals* (A. M. Bass and H. P. Broida, eds.), Chap. 9, Academic, New York, 1960.
94. D. A. Dows, *J. Chem. Phys.*, **36,** 2836 (1962).
95. S. H. Walmsley and J. A. Pople, *Mol. Phys.*, **8,** 345 (1964).
96. A. Ron and O. Schnepp, *J. Chem. Phys.*, **46,** 3991 (1967).
97. R. L. Collin and W. N. Lipscomb, *Acta Cryst.*, **4,** 10 (1951).
98. W. R. Busy, M. Zocchi, and H. A. Levy, *Program of the Annual Meeting of the American Crystallographic Association*, Paper N–3, 1961.
99. F. G. Baglin, S. F. Bush, and J. R. Durig, *J. Chem. Phys.*, **47,** 2104 (1967).
100. M. Guay and R. Savoie, *Can. J. Chem.*, **47,** 201 (1969).
101. T. H. Walnut, *J. Chem. Phys.*, **20,** 58 (1952).
102. S. S. Mitra, *J. Chem. Phys.*, **39,** 3031 (1963).
103. J. E. Bertie and E. Whalley, *J. Chem. Phys.*, **46,** 1271 (1967).
104. G. L. Hiebert and D. F. Hornig, *J. Chem. Phys.*, **27,** 1216 (1957).
105. D. F. Hornig, *J. Chem. Phys.*, **17,** 1346 (1949).
106. E. Whalley and J. E. Bertie, *J. Chem. Phys.*, **46,** 1264 (1967).
107. R. G. Gordon, *J. Chem. Phys.*, **43,** 1307 (1965).
108. L. C. Brunel and M. Peyron, *J. Chim. Phys.* (*Paris*), **63,** 181 (1966).
109. D. N. Payton, III, and W. N. Visscher, *Phys. Rev.*, **154,** 802 (1967).
110. D. F. Hornig and G. L. Hiebert, *J. Chem. Phys.*, **27,** 752 (1957).
111. L. Couture-Mathieu, J. P. Mathieu, and H. Poulet, *Compt. Rend.* (*Paris*), **234,** 1761 (1952).
112. L. Couture-Mathieu and J. P. Mathieu, *Compt. Rend.* (*Paris*), **236,** 371 (1953).
113. H. Poulet and J. P. Mathieu, *J. Phys. Radium*, **17,** 472 (1956).
114. C. Haas and D. F. Hornig, *J. Chem. Phys.*, **26,** 707 (1957).
115. C. Haas and J. A. A. Ketelaar, *Phys. Rev.*, **103,** 564 (1956); *Physica*, **22,** 1286 (1956).
116. J. A. A. Ketelaar, C. Haas, and J. Fahrenfort, *Physica*, **20,** 1259 (1954).
117. J. C. Slater, *Rev. Mod. Phys.*, **30,** 197 (1958).
118. H. Poulet, *Ann. Phys.* (*Paris*), **10,** 908 (1955).
119. G. Andermann and D. A. Dows, *J. Phys. Chem. Solids*, **28,** 1307 (1967).
120. S. Maeda and P. N. Schatz, *J. Chem. Phys.*, **35,** 1617 (1961).
121. J. L. Hollenberg and D. A. Dows, *Spectrochim. Acta*, **16,** 1155 (1960).

122. D. W. Berreman, *Phys. Rev.*, **130,** 2193 (1963).
123. L. Merten, *Z. Naturforsch.*, **A22,** 359 (1967).
124. A. Anderson and R. Savoie, *Can. J. Chem.*, **43,** 2271 (1965).
125. A. Eucken and E. Schröder, *Z. Physik. Chem.*, **B41,** 307 (1938).
126. J. G. Aston, Q. R. Stottlemeyer, and G. R. Murray, *J. Am. Chem. Soc.*, **82,** 1281 (1960).
127. S. Abramowitz and J. J. Comeford, *Spectrochim. Acta*, **21,** 1479 (1965).
128. R. G. Steinhardt, Jr., W. Neilsen, H. W. Morgan, and P. Staats, *J. Chim. Phys. (Paris)*, **63,** 176 (1966); also, 9th European Congress on Molecular Spectroscopy, Abstracts of Papers, p. 234, 1967.

CHAPTER 11

Raman Spectra of Ionic, Covalent, and Metallic Crystals

G. R. WILKINSON

DEPARTMENT OF PHYSICS
KING'S COLLEGE
UNIVERSITY OF LONDON, U.K.

I. INTRODUCTION

A very large number of inorganic compounds were investigated by Raman spectroscopy long before the advent of the laser (*1,2*). However, most of these compounds were studied in solution, and very few detailed polarization studies were made on single crystals. The data obtained were frequently either incomplete or erroneous, and the conclusions that could be drawn about the vibrational symmetry were doubtful due to the lack of good polarization data. The subject has been completely revolutionized by the continuous wave laser whose narrow beam of collimated, polarized, and almost monochromatic radiation is ideal for exciting the Raman spectra of small single crystals. The value of the measurement of the anisotropy of Raman scattering from crystals as a method of assigning vibrations was recognized soon after the discovery of the effect; some excellent pioneering work was carried out on crystals, notably by Indian (*8*) and French workers (*18*). However, it is only since the laser has been used as a source that the observations can be made routinely. The collimation is much more important than the power of the laser beam since the power is frequently less than could be obtained from a good Toronto arc which did so much to keep interest alive in Raman spectroscopy during the 1950's and early 1960's.

Interest in the vibrational spectra of crystals seems equally divided between the solution of structural problems and those problems involving crystal dynamics. The initial aim in either field is a complete evaluation of the $\mathbf{k} = 0$ vibrational spectrum using both Raman and infrared spectroscopy. Once this is achieved the interatomic force field can be computed, and hence, our knowledge of chemical bonding in the condensed phase is furthered. Once the vibrational dispersion curves are known, it is only a short step to obtain the density of vibrational states, the complete set of thermodynamic functions for the crystal then can be calculated. A study of the anharmonicity of vibrations in crystals is intimately connected with such problems as thermal conductivity and expansion. Observations on the changes in spectra and on approaching phase transitions promise to further our understanding of why they occur; already a number of "soft" modes of vibration whose frequencies depend upon temperature have been found.

From a structural point of view, lack of good Raman data has in the past hindered the use of vibrational spectroscopy as a means of determining the arrangement of atoms in a crystal. Now with more complete spectra and good polarization information we can have very much greater confidence in deciding between possible alternative structures. The routine recording of Raman spectra could become as popular as the recording of infrared spectra and would further the vibrational "fingerprint" method of chemical analysis. Its more widespread use in mineralogy as a method of characterizing different minerals is worthy of encouragement.

In this chapter we confine our attention predominantly to the vibrational Raman spectra of simple ionic and covalent ionic crystals due to one-phonon processes. The definition of simple is arbitrary; however, it will be obvious that the examples discussed here are probably of greater physical interest than of chemical structural interest. The restriction of discussion to only one-phonon processes eliminates a wide range of interesting phenomena in inorganic crystals which can be studied by Raman spectroscopy, such as studies on the electronic Raman effect; however, most of these are adequately dealt with elsewhere. We further restrict our attention to the scattering from optical modes. Brillouin scattering which involves acoustic phonons is covered in Chapter 6. Because of its low intensity, multiphonon scattering is given little attention, even though in some cases it gives rise to spectra that are as intense as the one-phonon spectra. Raman scattering from metals, polaritons, and magnons is dealt with very briefly, as is the hyper-Raman effect.

Many different types of scattering mechanisms due to vibrational modes have already been observed in inorganic crystals and we now list some of the phenomena before considering some specific examples of recent Raman work.

A. Vibrational Raman Effect in Molecules and Molecular Ions

Most Raman studies made before the advent of the laser were directed towards an understanding of the internal modes of vibration of molecules and molecular ions. Provided the point group of the molecule is known, group theoretical methods can be used to predict which modes are Raman active. Many of the early studies established the shape of simple molecules (*19*). Now a knowledge of the vibration of molecular ions is a very important first step in the interpretation of the Raman spectrum of a crystal containing such ions.

B. Raman Scattering by Phonons—Selection Rules

As we are primarily concerned with the scattering of radiation by phonons we need only mention that the Raman effect involving vibrational modes in solids arises from the creation of phonons in Stokes scattering and the destruction of phonons in anti-Stokes scattering. Usually one-phonon processes dominate the spectrum which is comparatively simple as only phonons whose wave vector is zero are involved. In two-phonon processes all values of the wave vector contribute to the spectrum.

In noncrystalline solids the restriction of scattering to $\mathbf{k} = 0$ is relaxed and consequently very much wider Raman bands are observed in those solids compared with those in single crystals.

Raman and infrared studies on crystals are complementary; however, beyond recording the infrared selection rules, little space can be given here to corresponding infrared studies or techniques. Reference (*3*) contains an extensive bibliography on infrared studies of crystals.

II. THEORY OF VIBRATIONAL SPECTRA OF SOLIDS

Only a brief outline of the theory of lattice dynamics (*6*) and of scattering mechanisms will be given in this chapter.

A. Vibrations of Molecular Ions

To a first approximation the frequencies of vibration of molecular ions differ very little from one environment to another, and hence, the internal modes may be readily identified. This fact has made feasible the widespread use of infrared and Raman spectroscopy in analytical studies. However, in many investigations it is the effect of the crystal field on the vibrational energy levels that is of prime interest.

The vibration of polyatomic ions has been treated at length in the standard texts on infrared and Raman spectra (*19,4,5*) of polyatomic molecules, so all that is necessary to recall here are the symmetries of various molecular ions and their Raman activity and frequencies.

For an ion containing p atoms there will be $3p-6$ normal modes of vibration or $3p-5$ if the ion is linear. Using standard group theoretical methods the symmetries and the infrared and Raman activities have been classified. The results are given in Fig. 1 for molecular ions of many different symmetries, together with typical examples frequently met with in ionic crystals.

B. Vibrations of a Crystal Lattice

Only a brief outline of the essentials necessary for the understanding of the Raman spectra of crystalline solids will be presented here. A full account together with a discussion of the Raman spectra of solids is given in the standard text on lattice dynamics by Born and Huang (*6*) and by Cowley in Chapter 3.

It is instructive to start with the simple example of the linear diatomic chain, as the solutions of this problem assist in the understanding of the main features of the vibrations of a three dimensional crystal. If the masses of the two types of atoms are M and m and β is the force constant between them, the relationship between the vibrational frequency and the wave vector $\mathbf{k} = 2\pi/\lambda$, where λ is the wavelength of the vibrational wave, is given by:

$$\nu^2 = \frac{\beta}{4\pi^2}\left\{\left(\frac{1}{M}+\frac{1}{m}\right) \pm \left[\left(\frac{1}{m}+\frac{1}{M}\right)^2 - \frac{4\sin^2 \mathbf{k}x}{mM}\right]^2\right\}$$

ν is plotted as a function of the wave vector $\mathbf{k} = 2\pi/\lambda$ in Fig. 2. The root which is proportional to $\mathbf{k}$ at $\mathbf{k} = 0$ represents the acoustic wave, while the branch for which $\nu = (1/2\pi)(2\beta[1/m+1/M]^{1/2}$ at $\mathbf{k} = 0$ is the optical branch. In the latter the different ions move in opposite directions; consequently, if M and m carry different charges, the vibration may lead to a considerable dipole moment which will couple with the electric vector of the electromagnetic wave.

The form of the dispersion curves for a polar cubic diatomic lattice is also shown in Fig. 2. The displacement of the atoms may be parallel or perpendicular to the direction of propagation of the wave. They are either transverse optic (TO) and acoustic (TA), or longitudinal optic (LO) and

Species	Point group	Reduced representation	Examples
A—A	$D_{\infty h}$	Σ^+(R)	O_2^-, S_2^-, Se_2^-, C_2^-
A—B	$C_{\infty v}$	Σ^+(R, IR)	OH^-, CN^-,
A—B—A	$D_{\infty h}$	Σ_g^+(R) + Σ_u^+(IR) + Π_u(IR)	FHF^-, $ClHCl^-$, $BrHBr^-$, N_3^-
A—B—C	$C_{\infty v}$	$2\Sigma^+$(R, IR) + Π(R, IR)	NCO^-, NCS^-
B / \\ A A	C_{2v}	$2A_1$(R, IR) + B_2(R, IR)	NO_2^-, ClO_2^-
B / \\ A C	C_s	$2A'$(R, IR) + A''(R, IR)	(HOD)
A | B / \\ A A	D_{3h}	A_1'(R) + $2E'$(R, IR) + A_2''(IR)	CO_3^{2-}, NO_3^-

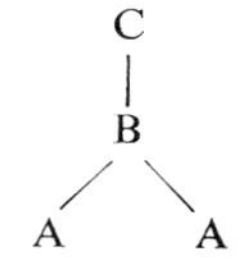	C_{2v}	$3A_1(R, IR) + 2B_2(R, IR) + B_1(R_d IR)$	$HCOO^-$
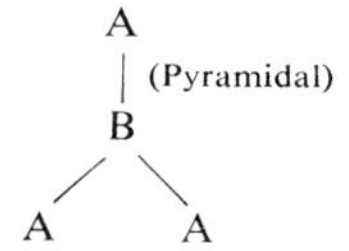	C_{3v}	$2A_1(R, IR) + 2E(R, IR)$	ClO_3^-, BrO_3^-, IO_3^-, PO_3^-
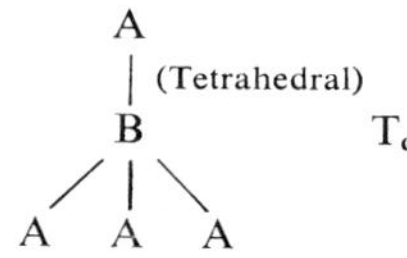	T_d	$A_1(R) + E(R) + 2F_2(R, IR)$	ClO_4^-, BF_4^-, SO_4^{2-}, WO_4^{2-}, MO_4^{2-}, $ZnCl_4^{2-}$, PO_4^{3-}, VO_4^{3-}, AsO_4^{3-}, SiO_4^{4-}
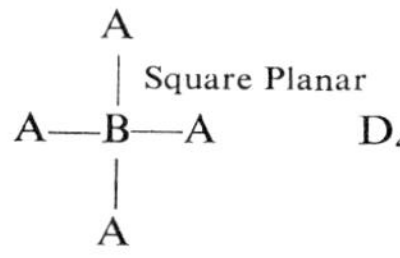	D_{4h}	$A_{1g}(R) + A_{2u}(IR) + B_{1g}(R) + B_{2g}(R) + B_{2u}(\text{Inactive}) + 2E_u(IR)$	$PdCl_4^{2-}$, $PtCl_4^{2-}$, $CuCl_4^{2-}$
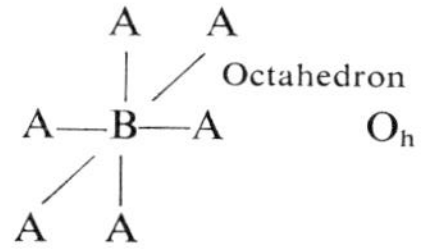	O_h	$A_{1g}(R) + E_g(R) + 2F_{1u}(IR) + F_{2g}(R) + F_{2u}$ (Inactive)	$SnCl_6^{2-}$, $PtCl_6^{2-}$, $PdCl_6^{2-}$, SiF_6^{2-}

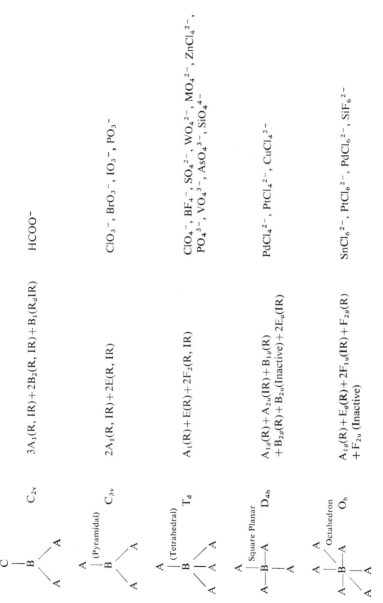

Fig. 1. Symmetry point group and spectroscopic selection rules for some simple molecular ions.

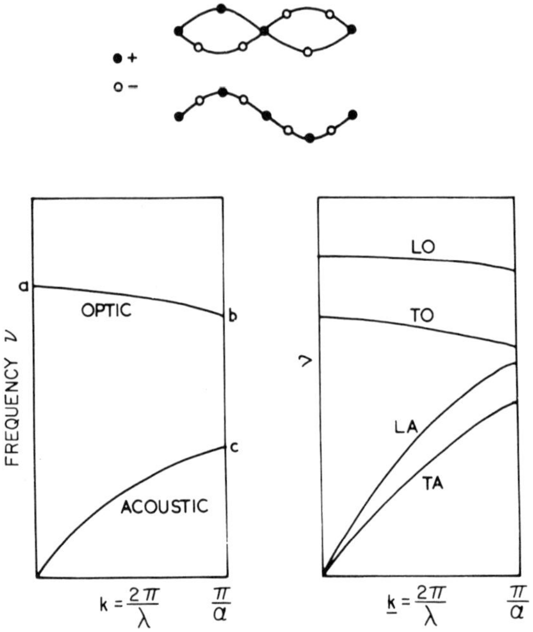

Fig. 2. (a) Linear diatomic chain and (b) cubic diatomic lattice. The dispersion curves ν $v.$ $k = 2\pi/\lambda$ for a linear diatomic chain and a cubic diatomic lattice. The frequency is $\nu = (1/2\pi)(2\beta[1/m+1/M])^{\frac{1}{2}}$ at a and $\nu = (1/2\pi)(2\beta/m)^{\frac{1}{2}}$ at b and $\nu = (1/2\pi)(2\beta/M)^{\frac{1}{2}}$ at c, where β is the force constant and m and M are the atomic masses assuming $M > m$. LO and TO stand for the longitudinal and transverse optic branches. At the top the diagrams illustrate the difference between optical and acoustic vibrations: in the first case a dipole moment is generated, while in the second there is no net charge displacement. [From Ref. (*20*)].

acoustic TA. The separation between the TO and LO branches depends upon the magnitude of the dipole moment created by the vibrational mode.

In the three-dimensional case the potential energy of the crystal may be expressed in terms of the displacement of the atoms $U_x(l, \kappa)$ and $U_y(l'\kappa')$ as

$$\phi_2 = \sum_{l\kappa\alpha} \sum_{l'\kappa'\alpha'} \phi_{xy}(l, \kappa, l'\kappa')U_x(l, \kappa)U_y(l'\kappa')$$

κ identifies the atom in the lth unit cell.

$$\mathbf{r}(l, \kappa) = \mathbf{r}(l)+\mathbf{r}(\kappa)$$

If there are n atoms in the unit cell and N cells, the number of independent coordinates is $3nN$. The equation of motion is

$$m_\kappa\left(\frac{\partial^2}{\partial t^2} U_x(l, \kappa)\right) = - \sum_{l'\kappa' y} \phi_{xy}(l\kappa, l'\kappa')U_y(l'\kappa')$$

while the displacements can be expressed in terms of the normal coordinates $Q(\kappa)$ and polarization vectors $\mathbf{e}(\kappa, k)$

$$U_x(l, \kappa) = \frac{1}{\sqrt{Nm_\kappa}} \Sigma\, e_x(\kappa\mathbf{k})Q(\mathbf{k}))\exp i\mathbf{k}\cdot\mathbf{r}(l\kappa)$$

$$= U_x(\kappa, \mathbf{k}) \exp i(\mathbf{k}\cdot\mathbf{r}(l, \kappa) - \omega(\mathbf{k})t)$$

The equation of motion then becomes

$$\omega^2(\mathbf{k})m_\kappa U_x(\kappa\mathbf{k}) = \sum_{\kappa' y} M_{xy}(\kappa\mathbf{k})U_y(\kappa'\mathbf{k})$$

where

$$M_{xy}(\kappa\kappa'\mathbf{k}) = \sum_{l'} \phi_{xy}(l\kappa, l'\kappa')\exp i\mathbf{k}[\mathbf{r}(l'\kappa') - \mathbf{r}(l, \kappa)] \tag{1}$$

and using matrix notation

$$\omega^2 mU = MU$$

For each value of $\mathbf{k}$ there are $3n$ values of ω^2, and hence, the branches are given by solutions of the secular determinant

$$| M - m\omega^2 | = 0$$

$\omega^2(k)$ are the eigenvectors of the matrix whose elements have the values $M_{xy}(\kappa\kappa' k)/\sqrt{m_\kappa m_{\kappa'}}$.

The wave amplitude is given by $U(\kappa\mathbf{k})$ and the energy by $E = \hbar\omega(\mathbf{k})[n(\mathbf{k}) + \frac{1}{2}]$.

There are three acoustic branches and $3n-6$ optical branches to the phonon dispersion curves. Consequently, for a diatomic lattice such as that for zinc blende there are three acoustic branches and three optical branches. In each case one branch corresponds to a longitudinal wave and the other two to transverse waves.

If the form of the branches can be determined experimentally, the problem of the solution of Eq. (1) consists in finding force constants $-\phi_{xy}(l\kappa, l'\kappa')$ which are consistent with the experimental results for all values of $\mathbf{k}$.

Considerable simplification in the discussion of the modes of vibration of complex crystals can be made by confining discussion to the $\mathbf{k} = 0$ modes which are the important vibrations from the point of view of onc-phonon Raman spectroscopy. The $\mathbf{k} = 0$ modes correspond to a very long wavelength compared with the dimension of the unit cell, and hence, their corresponding atoms in every unit cell throughout the crystal move in phase. The problem reduces to that of considering just the motion in one unit cell. If there are n atoms in the unit cell, there willl be $3n-3$ branches to the phonon dispersion curves. The symmetry classification of these Brillouin zone center modes can be readily accomplished by taking into account the factor group of the crystal. The factor group represents the group formed by the symmetry elements contained in the primitive unit cell. A further simplication that can be made with many molecular ions is to distinguish between internal and external modes of vibration. The external modes can be further subdivided into translatory and rotatory types. The latter are frequently referred to as librational modes.

Two different methods are available for classifying the symmetry of various modes of vibration of the atoms in the unit cell and their Raman activity. The first, which was originally due to Bhagavantam and Venkatarayudu (*8*), treats the atoms in the unit cell as a "molecule" and then uses the standard group theoretical methods to classify the normal modes of vibration and the nature of their Raman spectrum.

The second, which is particularly useful in discussing the vibration of molecular ions in crystals, is the site group method due to Halford (*9,7*). Starting with the normal modes of vibration of the ion in free space it considers the effect of a crystal field of a given symmetry. An example is shown in Fig. 46, p. 944. The quantitative verification of crystal field theory is hindered in molecular ion crystals by the fact that it is almost impossible to observe the "free" ion value.

Hornig (*10*) has shown the equivalence of the two methods and has given expressions for the complete harmonic potential energy of a crystal in the form

$$V = V_L + \Sigma(V_j^0 + V_j') + \sum_j \sum_k (V_{jk} + V_{lj})$$

where V_L is the lattice potential, V_j^0 is the energy of the free molecular ion expressed in terms of its internal coordinates, V_j' is the perturbation due to the crystal field, V_{jk} is the interaction energy between the displacement coordinates of the jth and kth molecular ions, and V_{lj} is the interaction energy between the "internal" and lattice vibrations.

In the oriented gas model, only the first and second terms are taken into account. The perturbation term V_j' is mainly responsible for the difference found between the gaseous and solid states for molecules and for the lifting of vibrational degeneracies. This is known as the static-field effect. The term V_{jk} describes the dynamic-crystal effect arising from inter-ion interactions.

TABLE 1

Site Symmetries

Space group	Wyckoff	C_{2h} E	C_2	Monoclinic i	σ_h
12	1*a*	1	1	1	1
	1*b*	1	1	1	1
	1*c*	1	1	1	1
	1*d*	1	1	1	1
	2*e*	1	0	1	0
	2*f*	1	0	1	0
	2*g*	1	1	0	0
	2*h*	1	1	0	0
	2*i*	1	0	0	1
	4*j*	1	0	0	0

Using the Bhagavantam and Venkatarayudu (*8*) method, Adams and Newton (*11,12*) have given tables which considerably simplify the problem of classifying the $\mathbf{k} = 0$ vibrations of a crystal. They have shown how the tables can be used to determine the factor group representation of any of the 230 space groups, if a description of the structure in terms of the Wykoff notation is available. Table 1 gives an example of a site group table. The first column indicates the space group number, the second has letters denoting each different site in the Wykoff notation together with the number of positions of this type of site in the primitive cell. The following columns show which elements of the factor group are elements of the site group.

Tables which have been derived by Adams and Newton using this type of data have been derived by forming a representation for each site and calculating the number of irreducible representations using the appropriate character table. A factor group analysis is made by reading off appropriate rows from Table 2. The acoustic and optical mode symmetries are obtained

TABLE 2

Unit Cell Modes

Space group	Wyckoff	C_{2h}		Monoclinic	
		A_g	B_g	A_u	B_u
12	1*a*	0	0	1	2
	1*b*	0	0	1	2
	1*c*	0	0	1	2
	1*d*	0	0	1	2
	2*e*	0	0	3	3
	2*f*	0	0	3	3
	2*g*	1	2	1	2
	2*h*	1	2	1	2
	2*i*	2	1	1	2
	4*j*	3	3	3	3

from the character table. In the case of molecular or molecular ionic crystals, the internal and external modes may be distinguished. The number of translatory modes and acoustic modes $T+T_A$ is obtained by summing the rows in Table 2 which correspond to sites of the centers of mass of molecular and atomic ions. The rotatory modes R can be distinguished by summing the rows in Table 3 or 4 corresponding to sites of molecular ions.

TABLE 3

Rotatory Modes

Space group	Wyckoff	C_{2h}		Monoclinic	
		A_g	B_g	A_u	B_u
12	1*a*	1	2	0	0
	1*b*	1	2	0	0
	1*c*	1	2	0	0
	1*d*	1	2	0	0
	2*e*	3	3	0	0
	2*f*	3	3	0	0
	2*g*	1	2	1	2
	2*h*	1	2	1	2
	2*i*	1	2	2	1
	4*j*	3	3	3	3

TABLE 4

Rotation about Z

Space group	Wyckoff	C_{2h} A_g	B_g	Monoclinic A_u	B_u
12	1*a*	1	0	0	0
	1*b*	1	0	0	0
	1*c*	1	0	0	0
	1*d*	1	0	0	0
	2*e*	1	1	0	0
	2*f*	1	1	0	0
	2*g*	1	0	1	0
	2*h*	1	0	1	0
	2*i*	1	0	0	1
	4*j*	1	1	1	1

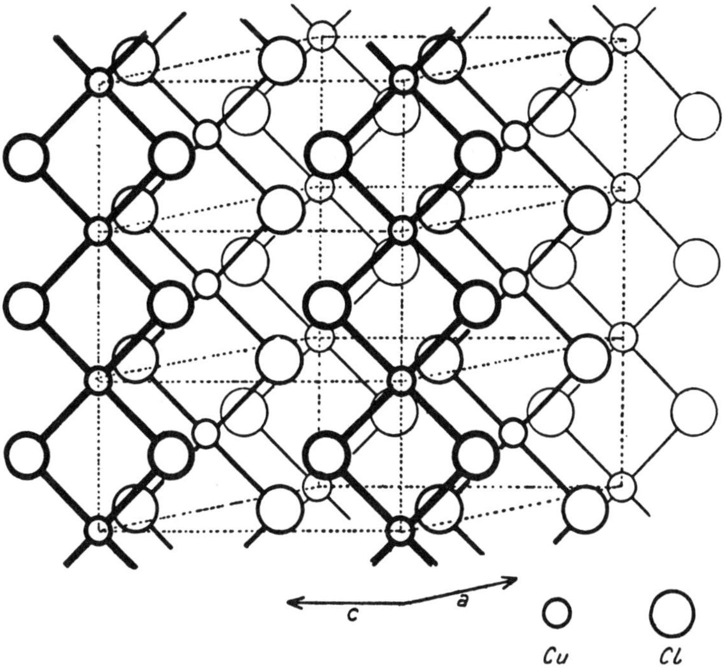

Fig. 3. Monoclinic unit cell of copper (II) chloride.

As an example of the use of the Adams–Newton (*12*) method the symmetry of the $\mathbf{k} = 0$ vibrations in copper (II) chloride will be derived. Figure 3 shows the monoclinic unit cell which has the symmetry of space group C_{2h}^3 (A2*m*) No. 12.

There are two copper atoms on sites *b* and four chlorine atoms on sites *i*. Table 5 shows the analysis for the primitive unit cell which contains a single formula unit. Hence, the $k = 0$ modes of vibration have the following symmetry and spectroscopic activity.

$$\Gamma = 2A_g(R) + B_g(R) + A_u(IR, \|c) + 2B_u(IR, \perp c)$$

TABLE 5

Copper Chloride

C_{2h}	A_g	B_g	A_u	B_u
Cu (1*b*)	0	0	1	2
Cl (2*i*)	2	1	1	2
N (total)	2	1	2	4
$T+T_A$	0	0	1	2
T_A	0	0	1	2
T	0	0	0	0
R	1	0	0	0
N_i internal	1	1	1	2

In these and in all classifications of normal modes of vibration given below the three acoustic modes have been subtracted.

There are nine branches to the phonon dispersion curves, three of which are acoustic and six optical; of the latter three are Raman active and are denoted by (*R*). (Do not confuse this usage with *R* as used to specify a rotatory motion of a molecular ion.) Three modes of vibration are infrared active with atomic displacements parallel or perpendicular to the crystal *C* axis.

C. Raman Selection Rules

The selection rules for Raman scattering from crystals are comparatively simple. It is necessary to consider the following:

a. Conservation of energy

b. Conservation of momentum or wave vector **k**

c. The magnitude of the polarizability derivative component.

For Raman scattering involving one phonon of energy E_p we must have either

$$E_i = E_p + E_s \qquad \text{or} \qquad E_i = -E_p + E_s$$

where E_i and E_s are the energies of the incident and scattered photons. The former gives rise to the Stokes, and the latter, the anti-Stokes lines corresponding to the generation or destruction of phonons. Conservation of wave vector leads to $\mathbf{k}_i = \mathbf{k}_p + \mathbf{k}_s$, and hence, as the wavelength of the scattered radiation differs little from that of the exciting radiation, then effectively $\mathbf{k}_p = 2\pi/\lambda$, the wave vector of the phonon, is zero. Consequently, only long wavelength phonons are involved in one-phonon Raman processes. Hence, we have only to deal with vibrations in which corresponding atoms in unit cells throughout the crystal move in phase. In multiphonon processes all values of $\mathbf{k}$ may be involved.

The intensity of Raman scattering can be derived from a consideration of the matrix elements.

$$[\alpha_{ij}^{v'v''}] = \int \psi_v \alpha_{ij} \alpha_{v'} d\tau = \alpha_{ij}^0 \int \psi_{v'} \psi_{v''}\, d\tau + \sum \frac{\partial \alpha_{ij}}{\partial \varphi} \int \psi_{v'} \varphi \psi_{v''}\, d\tau + \sum \frac{\partial^2 \alpha_{ij}}{\partial \varphi_i \partial \varphi_j} \int \psi_{v'} \varphi_i \varphi_j \psi_v\, d\tau$$

As $\int \psi_{v'} \psi_{v''}\, d\tau$ is zero the intensity of the first order, i.e., one-phonon scattering depends upon $| \partial \alpha_{ij}/\partial \varphi | [\int \psi_{v'} \varphi_i \psi_{v''}\, d\tau]^2$. As in the case of isolated molecules the activity requires the evaluation of $\int \psi_{v'} \varphi_i \psi_{v''}\, d\tau$. In general, numerical solutions are not possible; however, using symmetry considerations the Raman active modes can be identified if the crystal structure is known. The intensity of Raman scattering depends upon $| \partial \alpha_{ij}/\partial \varphi |^2$ which we will frequently abbreviate as $| \alpha'_{ij} |^2$ when it is clear which normal mode is involved. It is important to recognize that α_{ij} is not a constant, but depends upon the frequency of the radiation used for the excitation of Raman scattering; α'_{ij} usually increases as the laser frequency approaches that required for an electronic transition. Hence, there is no unique Raman spectrum in the way that an infrared or ultraviolet absorption spectrum exists, and consequently, the wavelength used for excitation must always be specified.

It is useful to remember that as polarizability has the dimensions of a volume $\sim 10^{-24}$ cm^3 then the polarizability derivative $(\partial \alpha_{ij}/\partial \varphi)$ has the dimensions of an area. A typical value is that of 1 Å^2 for $\partial \alpha_{ij}/\partial \varphi$ for the C—C bond. The vibration of a molecule in free space or in a liquid is not the same as in a crystal; however, it is probably true that the coefficients of the polarizability tensor are less dependent on environment than the dipole derivative factors that control the infrared absorption. Hester (*13*) has given a recent discussion of the problem of Raman intensities in molecules.

D. Long Wavelength Phonons in Crystals

Raman and infrared spectroscopy are principally concerned with the study of long wavelength phonons whose wave vector **k** is effectively zero, corresponding to phonon wavelengths of several thousand atomic spacings. Consequently, the approximation that has been made in deriving the selection rules that corresponding atoms in each unit cell move in phase is satisfactory. In this section we consider the relationship between the direction of propagation of the phonon and its frequency at $\mathbf{k} = 0$. The frequency is determined both by short-range forces and also by electric fields generated during the vibration.

In many crystals, study by Raman scattering and infrared spectroscopy gives complementary information about the normal modes of vibration, because if there is a center of symmetry, modes that are infrared active will not be Raman active and vice versa. However, if there is no center of inversion, i.e., the crystal is piezoelectric, certain modes can be both infrared and Raman active. In such cases the electric field **E** associated with the vibration is given by an Eq. of the form

$$\mathbf{E} = \frac{-4\pi[\mathbf{k}(\mathbf{kP}) - (\omega^2\mathbf{P}/c^2)]}{k^2 - (\omega^2/c^2)}$$

where **P** is the polarization (6). This field leads to the difference between the transverse and longitudinal optic frequencies and to the possibility that the phonon frequency will depend upon direction.

1. Cubic Crystals

The $\mathbf{k} = 0$ mode frequencies are independent of direction in cubic crystals. Born and Huang (*6*) have given a thorough discussion of the long wavelength optic vibrations in polar crystals. In piezoelectric crystals both longitudinal and transverse optical phonons can be Raman active at $\mathbf{k} = 0$. We will denote these frequencies by ν_{LO} and ν_{TO}.

The longitudinal phonon produces the macroscopic electric field **E** which increases the force constant and consequently increases its frequency above that of the transverse phonon. The relationship between the two frequencies was given by Lyddane, Sachs and Teller (*20a*):

$$\frac{\nu_{LO}}{\nu_{TO}} = \left(\frac{\varepsilon_0}{\varepsilon_\infty}\right)^{1/2}$$

where ε_0 and ε_∞ are the static and high frequency dielectric constants. In many simple cubic crystals such as zinc blende a very large field is produced by the *LO* phonon, and hence, the difference in frequency is large. The theory has been extended by Cochran and Cowley (*21*) to take into account several infrared active modes ν^i which give

$$\prod_{i=1}^{n} \left(\frac{\nu_{LO}^i}{\nu_{TO}^i}\right)^2 = \frac{\varepsilon_0}{\varepsilon_\infty}$$

In general, ν_{LO} and ν_{TO} can be measured with greater precision by Raman spectroscopy than by infrared spectroscopy.

2. Uniaxial Crystals

In uniaxial crystals it is necessary to compare the long-range electrostatic forces produced by the longitudinal phonon which produces the *LO–TO* splitting with the difference in short-range interaction forces which result from crystal anisotropy (*14*).

The notation's || and ⊥ are used to designate phonons which are polarized parallel and perpendicular to the crystal optic axis. Pure longitudinal and pure transverse phonons of well-defined symmetry character are observed in Raman scattering when the phonon propagation axis coincides with a principal axis. The table below lists which phonons may be observed for each Cartesian propagation direction and for each of the polarizations.

Phonon propagation direction	Phonon polarization		
	$x(E_1)$	$y(E_1)$	$z(A_1)$
x	$LO^\perp$	$TO^\perp$	$TO^\parallel$
y	$TO^\perp$	$LO^\perp$	$TO^\parallel$
z	$TO^\perp$	$TO^\perp$	$LO^\parallel$

Complete separation may be made between parallel and perpendicular phonons and separate Lyddane-Sachs-Teller relationships may be given for displacements parallel and perpendicular to the optic axis. In cases when the phonon propagation direction is not along one of the axes, it is essential to consider the relative effects of long-range electrostatic and short-range forces. Loudon (14) has divided uniaxial crystals into two categories, as shown in Fig. 4.

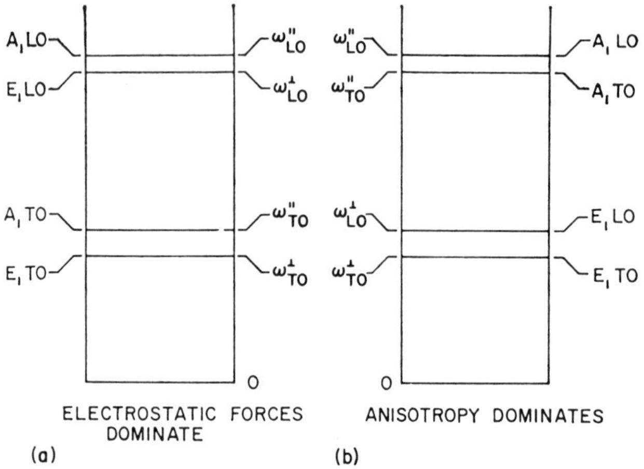

Fig. 4. Schematic energy-level diagrams for the two limiting cases: (a) the electrostatic forces predominate over the anisotropy in the interatomic forces; (b) anisotropy forces predominate over electrostatic forces. The levels are appropriate for that region of the phonon dispersion curve near the zone center but out of the polariton region (i.e., $k \simeq 10^5\ \text{cm}^{-1}$). The relative values of the frequencies reflect a negative uniaxial crystal. (After *14*).

Case I. Electrostatic forces produced by the *LO* phonon are greater than those due to anisotropy of the short-range forces. Considering wurtzite as a specific example the *LO–TO* splitting must be greater than the A_1–E_1 splitting,

i.e., $|\nu^{\parallel}_{LO}-\nu^{\parallel}_{TO}|$ and $|\nu^{\perp}_{LO}-\nu^{\perp}_{TO}| \gg |\nu^{\parallel}_{LO}-\nu^{\perp}_{LO}|$ and $|\nu^{\parallel}_{TO}-\nu^{\parallel}_{TO}|$

Figure 5 shows the E_1, *LO*, and *TO* Raman lines observed in different orientations; there is no change in frequency. With *XZ* scattering, only the *LO* component will be seen when the phonon is propagating in the *X* direction, and only the *TO* for propagation along the *Y* axis. At an angle θ both can be observed. For a phonon propagating in a direction between the *X* and *Z* axes a mixing of A_1 and E_1 modes may occur, and the frequencies of the *LO* and *TO* phonons now depend upon the angle of observation.

$$\nu^2_{LO} = (\nu^{A_1}_{LO})^2 \cos^2\theta + (\nu^{E_1}_{LO})^2 \sin^2\theta$$
$$\nu^2_{TO} = (\nu^{E_1}_{TO})^2 \cos^2\theta + (\nu^{A_1}_{TO})^2 \sin^2\theta$$

Case II. When short-range forces dominate over the long-range forces $|\nu_{LO}^{\parallel}-\nu_{LO}^{\perp}|$ and $|\nu_{TO}^{\parallel}-\nu_{TO}^{\perp}| \gg \nu_{LO}^{\parallel}-\nu_{TO}^{\parallel}$ and $\nu_{LO}^{\perp}-\nu_{TO}^{\perp}$. Figure 6 shows this situation for different propagation and scattering configurations. When E_1 phonons are observed through the XZ polarizability tensor component, they are polarized in the X direction; only the LO phonon is observed. In the direction $\mathbf{k}_2$ a pure mode no longer exists and the frequency is located between the pure longitudinal and pure transverse E_1 frequencies.

$$\nu^2 = (\nu_{TO}^{E_1})^2 \cos^2\theta + (\nu_{LO}^{E_1})^2 \sin^2\theta$$

In the Y direction the phonon is purely transverse. An A_1 phonon propagating in the XZ plane may undergo a shift from LO to TO in character, and in this case for the intermediate direction k_2

$$\nu^2 = (\nu_{TO}^{A_1})^2 \sin^2\theta + (\nu_{LO}^{A_1})^2 \cos^2\theta$$

For a phonon propagating in the z direction only, ν_{LO} will be seen in the A_1 spectrum.

3. Biaxial Crystals

The theory has been extended to orthorhombic crystals by Krauzman (*16*) who has shown that the components of the macroscopic field within the crystal are given by the following equations:

$$\left[\frac{\omega^2}{c^2k^2}\varepsilon_x - s_y^2 - s_z^2\right]E_x + s_x s_y E_y + s_x s_z E_z = 0$$

$$s_y s_x E_x + \left[\frac{\omega^2}{c^2k^2}\varepsilon_y - s_x{}^2 - s_y{}^2\right]E_g + s_y s_z E_z = 0$$

$$s_z s_x E_x + s_z s_y E_y + \left[\frac{\omega^2}{c^2k^2}\varepsilon_z - s_x{}^2 - s_y{}^2\right]E_z = 0$$

where s_i are the components of a unit vector. The calculation of the phonon wave vectors is possible if ε_α, the dielectric parameters, are known as a function of frequency ($\alpha = x, y, z$); neglecting damping

$$\varepsilon_\alpha = (\varepsilon_\alpha)_O + \sum_{i=1}^{n/3} a_\alpha^{TO}[(\omega_{0\alpha}^{TO})^2 - \omega^2]^{-1}$$

$\omega_{0\alpha}^{TO}$ are the transverse optic frequencies.

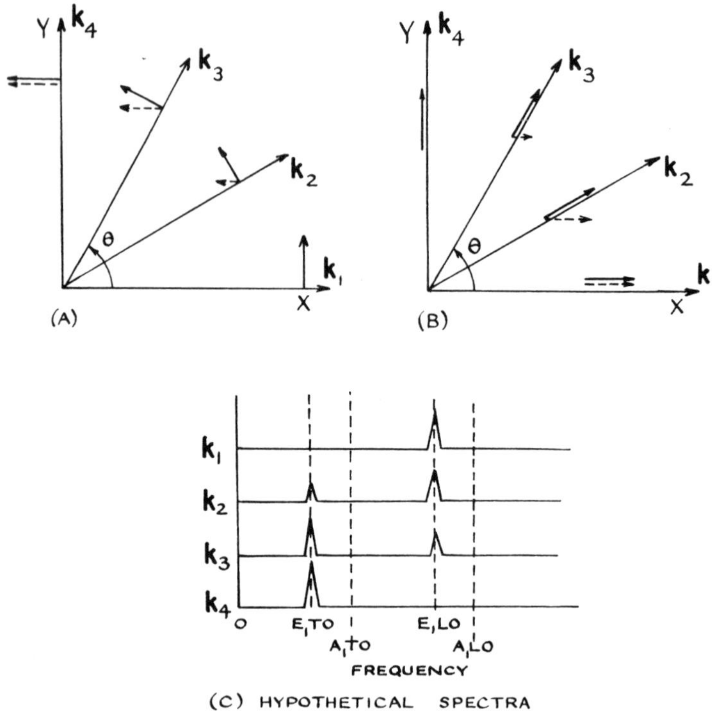

Fig. 5. E_1 phonon propagation in the *xy* plane when electrostatic forces dominate over anisotropy. (A) A transverse phonon is illustrated by the solid-line polarization vectors. The dashed lines correspond to the *xz* component (polarization in the *x* direction) of the polarizability tensor. (B) The longitudinal phonon is presented, and again the dashed line represents the *xz* component of the Raman tensor. (C) Hypothetical spectra of the *xz* tensor component are drawn for each of the propagation directions shown in (A) and (B). The lower diagrams show phonon propagation in the *xz* plane when electrostatic forces dominate over anisotropy. In the propagation directions $\mathbf{k}_1$ through $\mathbf{k}_4$, the solid vector represents the phonon polarization and the dashed vector the A_1 component of the phonon. (A) shows the transverse phonon and (B) the longitudinal. Hypothetical spectra are shown in (C).

Case A. When $s_\alpha = 0$ the values

$$E_\beta = E_{\beta'} = 0 \neq E_\alpha \qquad (\alpha \neq \beta \neq \beta' \neq \alpha = x, y, z)$$

are solutions of the equation with the condition that

$$\varepsilon_\alpha = \frac{k^2 c^2}{\omega^2}$$

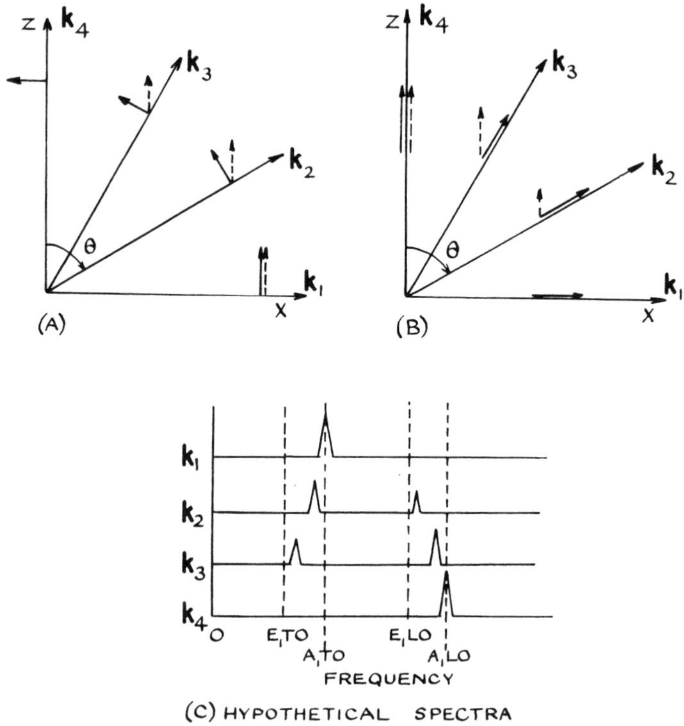

Fig. 5 (cont.)

The transverse optic frequencies $(\omega_{TO}^{i})_{\alpha}$ are independent of **k** if **k** remains in the plane normal to α.

Case B. When $s_{\beta} = s_{\beta'} = 0 \neq s_{\alpha}$ $(\alpha \neq \beta \neq \beta' \neq \alpha = x, y, z)$, one of the solutions is $E_{\beta} = E_{\beta'} = 0 \neq E_{\alpha}$ with the condition that $\varepsilon_{\alpha} = 0$; **E** is parallel to **s**; **D** = 0; and $\mathbf{P} = -\varepsilon_{v}\mathbf{E}$. As ε_{α} at the longitudinal optic frequency is zero, then

$$\varepsilon_{\alpha}^{\infty} = \sum_{i=1}^{n/3} a_{\alpha}^{i}[(\omega_{LO}^{i})_{\alpha}^{2} - (\omega_{TO}^{i})_{\alpha}^{2}]^{-1}$$

This equation can be written in the form

$$\varepsilon_{\alpha}^{\infty}[I] = [A][a] \tag{2}$$

where $[I]$ and $[a]$ are matrices with one column and $n/3$ lines; $[A]$ is a square matrix with elements

$$A_{ji} = [(\omega_{LO}^{j})_{\alpha}^{2} - (\omega_{TO}^{i})_{\alpha}^{2}]^{-1}$$

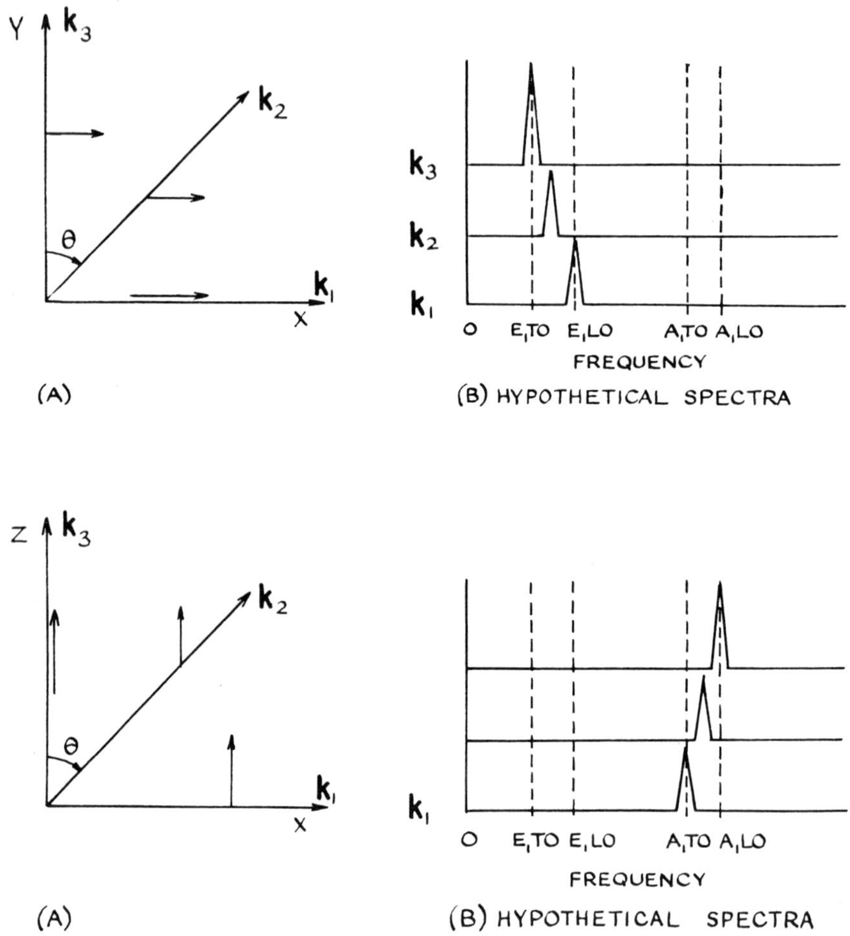

Fig. 6. E_1 phonon propagating in the *xy* plane when anisotropy dominates over electrostatic forces: (A) shows the phonon propagation ($\mathbf{k}_1 - \mathbf{k}_3$) and polarization directions. The corresponding hypothetical spectra are shown in (B). The lower diagrams show the A_1 phonon propagating in the *xz* plane when anisotropy dominates over electrostatic forces. The phonon propagations ($\mathbf{k}_1$, $\mathbf{k}_2$, $\mathbf{k}_3$) and polarization directions are shown in (A) and hypothetical spectra are presented in (B).

where $j, i = 1, 2 \ldots \frac{n}{2}$.

Let $[b] = (\varepsilon_\alpha^\infty)^{-1}[a]$; hence, $[b] = [A]^{-1}[I]$ and

$$\varepsilon_\alpha(\nu) = \varepsilon_\alpha^\infty\{1 + \sum_{i=1}^{n/3} b_\alpha^i[(\omega_{TO}^i)_\alpha^2 - \omega^2]^{-1}$$

The expressions for ε_α where $\alpha = x, y, z$ are inserted in Eq. (2). The determinant Eq. (2) is a sum of fractions that can be reduced to the same denominator. The numerator is a polynomial of degree $(n+3)$ in ω^2 whose roots are given by an ordinator. The results can be used to interpret experimental results in the case when **k** remains in the plane defined by $\mathbf{k}_\alpha = 0$.

E. Raman Intensities

1. Centrosymmetric Crystals

The intensity of Raman radiation scattered by a crystal depends upon the direction of observation and excitation relative to the principal axes of the crystal. The anisotropy of the Raman radiation can be used to deduce the symmetry of the lattice vibration responsible for the scattering.

Vibration of a given symmetry gives rise to a derived polarizability tensor which relates the magnitude of the components of the polarization P to the strength of the exciting electric field components. They have been worked out using standard group theoretical methods and are shown in Table 6 [from Ref. (*14*)]. The irreducible representations of the Raman active lattice vibrations are shown for each crystal class. Where an x, y, or z appears in brackets after an irreducible representation this indicates that the vibration is also infrared active, and it is the direction of polarization that is shown.

The components a, b, c, d, e, etc., are used to denote $\alpha_{\rho\sigma\mu}$, i.e., $\partial\alpha_{\rho\sigma}/\partial r_\mu$, ρ and σ have the values x, y, and z that coincide with the principal axes x_1, x_2, and x_3 which have been defined for all the crystal classes. In general, the Raman tensor is symmetric. It is important to note that $\alpha_{\rho\sigma}$ is not a constant but that it depends upon the frequency of the exciting radiation and may display a resonant character in the vicinity of electronic transitions. In crystalline systems it also depends upon pressure and temperature.

TABLE 6

Raman-Active Vibrational Symmetries and Raman Tensors for the Crystal Symmetry Classes (*14*)

System	Class		Raman tensors			
Monoclinic			$\begin{bmatrix} a & & d \\ & b & \\ d & & c \end{bmatrix}$	$\begin{bmatrix} & e & \\ e & & f \\ & f & \end{bmatrix}$		
	2	C_2	A(y)	B(x, z)		
	m	C_s	A′(x, z)	A″(y)		
	2/m	C_{2h}	A_g	B_g		
Orthorhombic			$\begin{bmatrix} a & & \\ & b & \\ & & c \end{bmatrix}$	$\begin{bmatrix} & d & \\ d & & \\ & & \end{bmatrix}$	$\begin{bmatrix} & & e \\ & & \\ e & & \end{bmatrix}$	$\begin{bmatrix} & & \\ & & f \\ & f & \end{bmatrix}$
	222	D_2	A	$B_1(z)$	$B_2(y)$	$B_3(x)$
	mm2	C_{2v}	$A_1(z)$	A_2	$B_1(x)$	$B_2(y)$
	mmm	D_{2h}	A_g	B_{1g}	B_{2g}	B_{3g}
Trigonal			$\begin{bmatrix} a & & \\ & a & \\ & & b \end{bmatrix}$	$\begin{bmatrix} c & d & e \\ d & -c & f \\ e & f & \end{bmatrix}$	$\begin{bmatrix} d & -c & -f \\ -c & -d & e \\ -f & e & \end{bmatrix}$	
	3	C_3	A(z)	E(x)	E(y)	
	$\bar{3}$	C_{3i}	A_g	E_g	E_g	

			$\begin{bmatrix} a & & \\ & a & \\ & & b \end{bmatrix}$	$\begin{bmatrix} c & & \\ & -c & d \\ & d & \end{bmatrix}$	$\begin{bmatrix} & -c & -d \\ -c & & \\ -d & & \end{bmatrix}$		
	32	D_3	A_1	$E(x)$	$E(y)$		
	3m	C_{3v}	$A_1(z)$	$E(y)$	$E(-x)$		
	$\bar{3}$m	D_{3d}	A_{1g}	E_g	E_g		
Tetragonal			$\begin{bmatrix} a & & \\ & a & \\ & & b \end{bmatrix}$	$\begin{bmatrix} c & d & \\ d & -c & \\ & & \end{bmatrix}$	$\begin{bmatrix} & & e \\ & & f \\ e & f & \end{bmatrix}$	$\begin{bmatrix} & & -f \\ & & e \\ -f & e & \end{bmatrix}$	
	4	C_4	$A(z)$	B	$E(x)$	$E(y)$	
	$\bar{4}$	S_4	A	$B(z)$	$E(x)$	$E(-y)$	
	4/m	C_{4h}	A_g	B_g	E_g	E_g	
			$\begin{bmatrix} a & & \\ & a & \\ & & b \end{bmatrix}$	$\begin{bmatrix} c & & \\ & -c & \\ & & \end{bmatrix}$	$\begin{bmatrix} & d & \\ d & & \\ & & \end{bmatrix}$	$\begin{bmatrix} & & e \\ & & \\ e & & \end{bmatrix}$	$\begin{bmatrix} & & \\ & & e \\ & e & \end{bmatrix}$
	4mm	C_{4v}	$A_1(z)$	B_1	B_2	$E(x)$	$E(y)$
	422	D_4	A_1	B_1	B_2	$E(-y)$	$E(x)$
	$\bar{4}$2m	D_{2d}	A_1	B_1	$B_2(z)$	$E(y)$	$E(x)$
	4/mmm	D_{4h}	A_{1g}	B_{1g}	B_{2g}	E_g	E_g

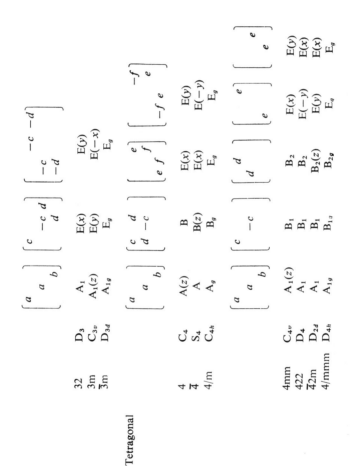

TABLE 6 *continued*

System	Class		Raman tensors					
Hexagonal			$\begin{bmatrix} a & & \\ & a & \\ & & b \end{bmatrix}$	$\begin{bmatrix} & & c \\ & & d \\ c & d & \end{bmatrix}$	$\begin{bmatrix} & & -d \\ & & c \\ -d & c & \end{bmatrix}$	$\begin{bmatrix} e & f & \\ f & -e & \\ & & \end{bmatrix}$	$\begin{bmatrix} f & -e & \\ -e & -f & \\ & & \end{bmatrix}$	
	6	C_6	A(*z*)	$E_1(x)$	$E_1(y)$	E_2	E_2	
	$\bar{6}$	C_{3h}	A′	E″	E″	E′(*x*)	E′(*y*)	
	6/m	C_{6h}	A_g	E_{1g}	E_{1g}	E_{2g}	E_{2g}	
			$\begin{bmatrix} a & & \\ & a & \\ & & b \end{bmatrix}$	$\begin{bmatrix} & & \\ & & c \\ & c & \end{bmatrix}$	$\begin{bmatrix} & & -c \\ & & \\ -c & & \end{bmatrix}$	$\begin{bmatrix} & d & \\ d & & \\ & & \end{bmatrix}$	$\begin{bmatrix} d & & \\ & -d & \\ & & \end{bmatrix}$	
	622	D_6	A_1	$E_1(x)$	$E_1(y)$	E_2	E_2	
	6mm	C_{6v}	$A_1(z)$	$E_1(y)$	$E_1(-x)$	E_2	E_2	
	$\bar{6}$m2	D_{3h}	$A_1{}'$	E″	E″	E′(*x*)	E′(*y*)	
	6/mmm	D_{6h}	A_{1g}	E_{1g}	E_{1g}	E_{2g}	E_{2g}	
Cubic			$\begin{bmatrix} a & & \\ & a & \\ & & a \end{bmatrix}$	$\begin{bmatrix} b & & \\ & b & \\ & & -2b \end{bmatrix}$	$\begin{bmatrix} \sqrt{3}b & & \\ & \sqrt{3}b & \\ & & O \end{bmatrix}$	$\begin{bmatrix} & & \\ & & d \\ & d & \end{bmatrix}$	$\begin{bmatrix} & & d \\ & & \\ d & & \end{bmatrix}$	$\begin{bmatrix} & d & \\ d & & \\ & & \end{bmatrix}$
	23	T	A	E	E	F(*x*)	F(*y*)	F(*z*)
	m3	T_h	A_g	E_g	E_g	F_g	F_g	F_g
	432	O	A_1	E	E	F_2	F_2	F_2
	$\bar{4}$3m	T_d	A_1	E	E	$F_2(x)$	$F_2(y)$	$F_2(z)$
	m3m	O_h	A_{1g}	E_g	E_g	F_{2g}	F_g	F_{2g}

The scattered Raman intensity may be calculated using the table. If the incident and scattered photons have polarizations in the directions of unit vectors $\mathbf{e}_i$ and $\mathbf{e}_s$, respectively, then

$$S = A\Big[\sum_{\rho\sigma = x,y,z} \mathbf{e}_i^{\ \sigma} \alpha_{\sigma\rho} \mathbf{e}_s^{\ \rho}\Big]^2$$

where $\mathbf{e}_i^{\ \sigma}$ and $\mathbf{e}_s^{\ \rho}$ are the components of unit vectors along the principal axes, σ and ρ, and A is a constant of proportionality.

The efficiency of the Raman scattering has the form

$$\frac{S(ijk)}{l d\Omega} = \left\{\frac{4\pi^3 h(\nu_0 - \nu_p)^4 (n+1)}{\nu_p c}\right\}(\alpha_{ijk})^2$$

where ν_0 and ν_p are the wavenumbers of the exciting radiation and of the phonon, respectively; n is the Bose factor $1/[\exp(h\nu/kT) - 1]$; $d\Omega$ is the solid angle of collection, and l is the length of the scatterer. It will be convenient to use $\sigma_p{}'$ for the term in braces.

2. Piezoelectric Crystals

The selection rules derived by the methods described above break down in cases where the crystal has no center of symmetry, and more Raman lines are observed than could be accounted for in theory. Their origin is now well understood, and they arise from $\mathbf{k} = 0$ longitudinal optic modes. The shift in frequency of the longitudinal optic mode from its associated transverse optic mode depends upon the magnitude of the electric field generated by the *LO* mode which is related to the intensity of the associated infrared absorption band.

a. *Cubic Crystals*

Triply degenerate infrared and Raman active modes in a cubic crystal split into two vibrations, one which is transversely, and the other longitudinally polarized. The equation above for the scattering efficiency can be generalized by introducing a unit vector ξ in the direction of mechanical polarization of the phonon. Then

$$S = A\Big[\sum_{\rho,\sigma\tau = x,y,z} \mathbf{e}_i^{\sigma} \alpha_{\sigma\rho}^{\tau} \xi^{\tau} \mathbf{e}_s^{\ \rho}\Big]^2 .$$

τ is given in the brackets in Table 6 after the appropriate irreducible representation symbols. It is essential to sum the contributions of the three tensors for a phonon of given polarization before squaring the equation.

The constant of proportionality in the intensity equation is not the same for scattering from *LO* as for *TO* modes of vibration. This is essentially due to the fact that the electric field accompanying a polar lattice vibration must be taken into account together with the appropriate electro-optic constant. The local field E_{local} and the macroscopic field E_{mac} are related by the equation

$$E_{\text{local}} = E_{\text{mac}} + \frac{4\pi}{3} P$$

where P is the polarization. For a *TO* phonon $E_{\text{mac}} = 0$ while for the *LO* phonon

$$E_{\text{mac}} = -\left(\frac{4\pi M}{V}\right)^{1/2} \omega_{LO} \left(\frac{1}{\varepsilon_\infty} - \frac{1}{\varepsilon_0}\right) r$$

where V is the crystal volume, M the reduced mass, ε_∞ and ε_0 are the optical and static dielectric constants.

$$\langle r^2 \rangle = (v + \tfrac{1}{2})\hbar/2M\omega$$

where v is the vibrational quantum number.

Some confusion has been caused regarding the use of macroscopic or microscopic electric fields for computing the electro-optic contribution to the intensity of the longitudinal optic modes. Johnston (*15*) who has recently given an excellent discussion of the problem considers that the macroscopic field should always be used irrespective of whether the material is an insulator or a semiconductor. He has also drawn attention to the fact that the "electro-optic coefficient" is not a constant and that early papers on the subject only took into account the electronic contribution to the coefficient and did not make allowance for the lattice contribution, which is as important as the varying macroscopic crystal field and has the frequency of the longitudinal optic mode. He has pointed out that the electro-optic contribution is related quantitatively to d(SHG), the second harmonic generation coefficient, and has given relations between it and the electro-optic coefficient r. Accurate values of $|r|$ and $|d|$ and the sign of r/d may be determined from Raman scattering by measuring the intensities of scattering from the *LO* and *TO* modes.

Johnston (*15*) gives for the scattering efficiency of the longitudinal optic mode

$$\frac{S_{ij,m}}{l\,d\Omega} = \sigma'_m \left[\sum_{n=1}^{3N} \alpha_{ijn} U_{nm} - \sum_{\gamma\beta} 16 (e_\infty^{-1})^{\gamma\beta} \sum_{n=1}^{3N} Z_n^\beta U_{nm} \, d_{\gamma ij} \right]^2$$

U is a unitary matrix, Z is an effective transverse charge parameter matrix, and $d_{\gamma ij}$, the electro-optic coefficient. The equation has been shown to be valid for $LiNbO_3$.

b. *Uniaxial Crystals*

A polar uniaxial crystal having two atoms in the unit cell may have three infrared active lattice vibration branches; two of the branches are degenerate for propagation parallel to the C axis; one of these and the remaining branch have a frequency which depends on the direction of propagation of the phonon.

The scattering efficiency can be written (*14*)

$$S \propto \{ \sum_{\rho\sigma\tau = xyz} \mathbf{e}_i^{\sigma} \alpha_{\sigma\rho}^{\tau} (\alpha \xi^{\tau} + \beta \mathbf{k}^{\tau}) \mathbf{e}_s^{\rho} \}^2$$

β is proportional to the electric field strength E. The lattice displacement $\mathbf{r}$ (parallel to ξ) controls the deformation potential scattering. In general, $\mathbf{r}$ is not parallel to the electric field $\mathbf{E}$ (parallel to $\mathbf{k}$) which controls the polar scattering.

F. Effects of Temperature

Raman intensities, linewidths, and frequencies all depend upon temperature. As the temperature is increased the linewidths increase, and there is, in general, a shift to lower frequency. The form of the equation for the scattering efficiency is

$$S(\nu) = S \frac{\Gamma}{(\nu_i - \nu_s - \nu_0 - \Delta)^2 + \Gamma^2}$$

Usually the shift Δ and the halfwidth Γ, which depend upon anharmonic forces, involve very complicated expressions that can be evaluated only numerically and for very simple lattices, such as for diamond.

The temperature dependence and wave vector selection rules for one- and two-phonon scattering are as follows:

	Process	Wave vector	Temperature dependence	
One-phonon	$E_i = E_1 + E_s$	$\mathbf{k}_i = \mathbf{k}_p + \mathbf{k}_s$	$(1+n_1)$	Stokes
	$E_i = -E_1 + E_s$	$\mathbf{k}_i = \mathbf{k}_p + \mathbf{k}_s$	n_1	Anti-Stokes
Two-phonon summation	$E_i = E_1 + E_2 + E_s$	$\mathbf{k}_i = \mathbf{k}_1 + \mathbf{k}_2 + \mathbf{k}_s$	$(1+n_1)(1+n_2)$	Stokes
	$E_i = -E_1 - E_3 + E_s$	$\mathbf{k}_i = -\mathbf{k}_1 - \mathbf{k}_2 + \mathbf{k}_s$	$n_1\ n_2$	Anti-Stokes
Two-phonon difference	$E_i = E_1 - E_2 + E_s$	$\mathbf{k}_i = \mathbf{k}_1 - \mathbf{k}_2 + \mathbf{k}_s$	$(1+n_1)n_2$	Stokes
	$E_i = E_1 + E_2 + E_s$	$\mathbf{k}_i = -\mathbf{k}_1 + \mathbf{k}_2 + \mathbf{k}_s$	$n_1(1+n_2)$	Anti-Stokes

where E_i, E_s = the energy of the exciting and scattered energy

E_1, E_2 = energy of phonons

$\mathbf{k}_i, \mathbf{k}_s$ = wave vectors of photons

$\mathbf{k}_1, \mathbf{k}_2$ = wave vectors of phonons

$$n_1 = \frac{1}{\exp(E/kT)-1}$$

For each of the processes above, the ratio of the intensities is $I(\text{Anti-Stokes})/I(\text{Stokes}) = \exp[-(h\nu/kT)]$ where ν is the frequency of the Raman band. Hence, this ratio cannot be used to distinguish between the different processes. The actual intensity must be observed at different temperatures. A one-phonon process may be distinguished from a two-phonon process as the temperature dependence for the first is $(1+n)$ and for the second $(1+n)^2$.

III. EXPERIMENTAL

In this section we confine our attention to factors which are relevant to a study of the Raman spectra of crystals. (Many of them are discussed in Ref. (*17*) which also gives descriptions of spectrometers that are currently available. Instruments and general techniques are also described by Hathaway in Volume 1, Chapter 4 of this book.)

Nearly all the recent work on the Raman spectra of crystals has been carried out using either the 6328 Å line from a He/Ne laser or the 5145 Å and 4880 Å lines from an argon ion laser. Several lines from the krypton ion laser are also useful. An ideal Raman spectrometer for work on inorganic crystals would incorporate both lasers. In general, the argon ion laser gives a higher intensity beam than the He/Ne; however, the red source enables many colored crystals to be examined, as absorption by most visibly absorbing compounds is less in the red than the green or blue regions. It is possible with many crystals to obtain good Raman spectra as close as 15 cm^{-1} to the exciting line. The output from these gas lasers is plane polarized, and hence, a half wave plate is usually necessary to rotate the plane of polarization through 90°. A piece of polaroid is adequate as an analyzer. However, in view of grating polarization it is essential that a polarization scrambler be placed in the path of the Raman radiation between the analyzer and the monochromator.

It is very important to recognize that if quantitative measurements are to be made of the components of the polarizability tensor, then single crystals of good optical quality are required. In nearly all cases the effort required to grow suitable crystals, to identify the crystal axes, and to cut and polish the surfaces far exceeds that needed to record the spectra. Time spent on good sample preparation is invariably rewarded in terms of the greater reliability of the results and their interpretation.

Crystal growth usually requires considerable trial and error before suitable samples are obtained. Identification of the crystal faces can frequently be carried out by optical inspection, including a measurement of the angles between well developed faces using a goniometer. Confirmation can be obtained by using X-ray diffraction. The method of cutting and polishing depends to a considerable extent on the hardness of the crystal.

It is helpful if the sample is mounted in a crystal goniometer in the laser beam so that the scattering angle can be accurately set and measured. Suitable goniometers for this purpose are available commercially. In general, right angle scattering is the most satisfactory method for obtaining information on the components of the polarizability tensor. The most suitable arrangement is one in which the sample is illuminated from below and the Raman radiation observed horizontally. Back scattering is usually more appropriate if the sample is an intense absorber or if the crystal surfaces are very poor. Some commercial spectrometers are equipped with a hemispherical lens for the efficient collection of the Raman radiation. Good optical contact between the sample and the lens can be achieved with a film of paraffin oil. The measurement of the components of the polarizability tensor presents little difficulty with crystals having an orthorhombic or higher symmetry. Monoclinic and especially triclinic crystals present much greater difficulty and call for a very careful consideration of the principal optic axes of the crystal and the directions of the exciting radiation and of the Raman emission and its polarization.

For the observation of Raman spectra in crystals at room temperature due to one-phonon excitation a monochromator with a resolution of about 1 cm^{-1} is required if a good approximation to the true band contour is to be recorded. To record Raman spectra due to two-phonon processes it is possible and usually necessary to use a much greater slit width of ~ 5 cm^{-1}; however, in such cases important experimental information in the location of critical points in the combined density of vibrational states may be lost. The selection of the angle of the cone of collection calls for some discussion. Maximum signal-noise will be achieved if the scattered

Raman radiation is collected over a large solid angle. On the other hand, great precision in the measurement of the components of the polarizability tensor requires that the scattered radiation be collected from a small solid angle, e.g., a cone of less than 10°. Clearly a compromise must be made in practice, and if a wide angle collector is used so as to gain a high signal-noise then a diaphram must be incorporated to increase the precision of polarization measurements when these are required. If quantitative data on the intensity of Raman bands are required, then it is necessary to make corrections for a number of instrumental factors. These include the variation of detector sensitivity with frequency, polarization that is produced within the monochromator, and the change in monochromator dispersion if the geometrical slit width is kept constant. A careful check on the constancy of the laser output during the recording of a spectrum is required. Frequently, it is desirable to compare the intensity of a Raman band with a secondary standard; one cm cubes of calcite and α-quartz are suitable for this purpose because of their good quality and ready availability and the fact that they give rise to Raman bands which occur in the spectral region most frequently required. Comparison can be made with other secondary standards in the liquid phase, such as carbon tetrachloride and benzene. These materials also provide secondary frequency standards. A list of frequency standards has been given by Loader, (*233*).

Often only very small single crystals are available, and hence, micro-sampling techniques must be used. It is useful in such cases to incorporate a collecting lens of high aperture. Improvement in the signal can frequently be achieved by placing a concave mirror close to the sample so that the exciting laser beam passes twice through the sample; similarly, a concave lens can be located so as to increase the angle of collection by reflecting light back through the crystal into the collecting optics. When an intense laser beam is focused onto a sample which absorbs appreciably at the exciting frequency, then sample heating can be appreciable; hence, in such cases good thermal contact must be made between the crystal and the sample mount. If forced-air cooling is used, secure mounting is required to prevent vibration of the sample, which can introduce "noise" in the spectrum.

When large crystals of very good optical quality can be obtained, it is sometimes advantageous to cause the laser beam to travel many times through the sample so as to increase the signal-noise. This can be achieved by cutting a slightly wedge-shaped block and aluminizing the top and bottom faces, leaving a clear portion for the laser beam to enter. The beam multipasses the sample perpendicular to the axis of observation. The choice of laser source for the study of the Raman spectrum of a specific sample must be carefully considered. It is important to emphasize that there is no unique Raman spectrum in the same way as there is for an absorption spectrum but that it depends upon the frequency of the exciting line. Consequently, the use of different sources can give a wider range of information than if single frequency excitation is used. In general, the higher the frequency of the laser source the greater will be the intensity of the Raman scattering. This is due to first, the fourth power dependence on frequency of excitation and, second, to the resonant character of polarizability. However, if the exciting photon energy is close to the crystal band gap, then absorption occurs in both the exciting radiation and the scattered Raman radiation. Clearly, there is for every Raman band an excitation frequency for which the observed scattering with a given geometry will be a maximum.

Fluorescence and phosphorescence can in some cases obscure the Raman spectrum and make recording difficult. When this occurs, it is desirable to select an exciting frequency that minimizes the fluorescence. It is important to recognize that the emitted fluorescence is anisotropic and is frequently polarized so that in some directions the Raman spectrum can be recorded with very little interference.

Measurement of Raman spectra of crystals at variable temperatures no longer presents difficulties since the introduction of the laser, as it is simple to construct cryostats with a window to allow the exciting beam to enter and a side window for the Raman radiation to be observed following 90° scattering. As well, high temperature measurements can be made in thermostated enclosures with a similar optical arrangement.

Cells to permit studies of the effects of high pressures on the Raman spectrum have been described in the literature (*220*). Measurements may be carried out either by applying a hydrostatic pressure or a uniaxial stress.

The electric field induced Raman effect can be studied in crystals by applying an ac field of about 10 kV/cm to the sample (*107*). As the scattered intensity depends upon the square of the applied electric field the signal is modulated at twice its frequency. A detection system can be used which records only the changes in the spectrum when the field is applied.

On first investigation it might be considered possible and desirable to construct a completely automatic recording Raman spectrometer which would set and reset the sample orientation and record the polarized spectrum in a way that is both graphically and digitally ready for computer processing. Unfortunately, the sample problem is much more difficult than is encountered in an X-ray diffractometer, and even if perfect optical samples cut as spheres were available, considerable difficulty would be experienced because of birefringence in crystals of low symmetry.

A. Determination of the Components of the Raman Polarizability Tensor

All the components of the derived polarizability tensor may be obtained by observing the Raman scattering from a crystal oriented in different directions. The polarization M is related to the electric field of the exciting radiation by

$$M_\rho = \sum_{\sigma = x,y,z} \alpha_{\rho\sigma} E_\sigma$$

where ρ and σ can take the values x, y, and z.

The Raman tensor has the form

$$\begin{bmatrix} \alpha_{xx} & \alpha_{xy} & \alpha_{xz} \\ \alpha_{yx} & \alpha_{yy} & \alpha_{yz} \\ \alpha_{zx} & \alpha_{zy} & \alpha_{zz} \end{bmatrix}$$

The quantity actually determined is the intensity of scattering which is proportional to $| \alpha_{\rho\sigma} |^2$, and consequently, the sign cannot be determined directly. Before discussing the determination of the magnitude of the elements it will be appropriate to deal with the Porto notation (*238*).

Porto Notation

This method of designating the crystal and polarization directions is widely used by Raman spectroscopists;

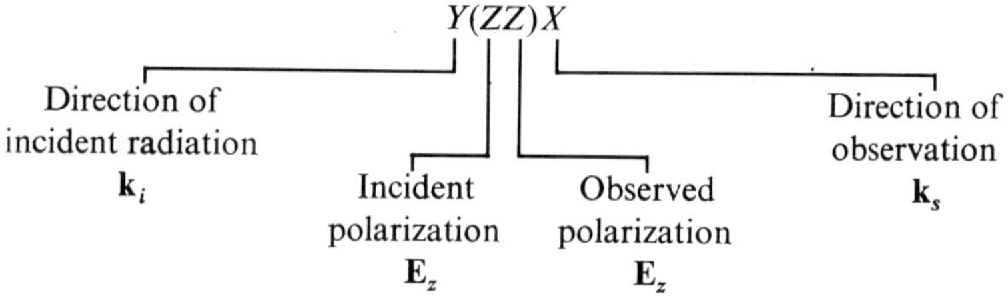

The letters in parentheses give the components of the derived polarizability tensor that are measured by the observation, e.g., in the case shown α'_{zz}

Notation	Geometry
$X(ZY)\bar{X}$	Back scattering
$\bar{X}(ZY)\bar{X}$	Near forward scattering
$X(X'X')Y$	Crystal rotated about the Z axis by 45°
$X(X''Y'')Y$	Crystal rotated about the Z axis by a specified angle

Consider right angle scattering from an orthorhombic crystal. A matchbox will prove a useful aid for visualizing the six possible crystal orientations. For each crystal orientation it is best to fix the analyzer in the scattered beam in front of the monochromator and to record spectra with the polarization of the laser beam parallel and perpendicular to the analyzer polarization. A half wave plate can be used to rotate the plane of polarization of the laser beam. Thus, twelve observations are taken, and all nine components of the Raman tensor are determined with a double check on the diagonal components. Usually the scattering tensor is symmetric, i.e., $\alpha_{\rho\sigma} = \alpha_{\sigma\rho}$, and hence, two observations will have been made on each component. The intensities can be compared with a secondary intensity standard such as the 992 cm^{-1} line of benzene for which Nilsen (*38*) has quoted a value of the scattering cross section of 3.8×10^{-29} cm^2/molecule. In carrying out this measurement it is important that the collecting angle is not altered appreciably on replacing the crystal by the liquid cell.

For 90° and 180° scattering the possible geometries are given in the following table together with the component of the derived polarizability tensor. (Geometaries for 90° scattering are illustrated in Figs. 7 and 8.)

90° scattering		Back scattering	
Geometry	Raman tensor component observed	Geometry	Raman tensor component observed
$Y(ZZ)X$	α_{ZZ}	$X(YY)\bar{X}$	α_{YY}
$Y(XZ)X$	α_{XZ}	$X(ZY)\bar{X}$	α_{ZY}
$Z(YY)X$	α_{YY}	$X(ZZ)\bar{X}$	α_{ZZ}
$Z(XY)X$	α_{XY}	$X(YZ)\bar{X}$	α_{YZ}
$Z(XX)Y$	α_{XX}	$Y(XZ)\bar{Y}$	α_{XZ}
$Z(YX)Y$	α_{YX}	$Y(ZZ)\bar{Y}$	α_{ZZ}
$X(YZ)Y$	α_{YZ}	$Y(ZX)\bar{Y}$	α_{ZX}
$X(ZZ)Y$	α_{ZZ}	$Y(XX)\bar{Y}$	α_{XX}
$X(YY)Z$	α_{YY}	$Z(XY)\bar{Z}$	α_{XY}
$X(ZY)Z$	α_{ZY}	$Z(YX)\bar{Z}$	α_{YX}
$Y(XX)Z$	α_{XX}	$Z(YY)\bar{Z}$	α_{YY}
$Y(ZX)Z$	α_{ZX}	$Z(XX)\bar{Z}$	α_{XX}

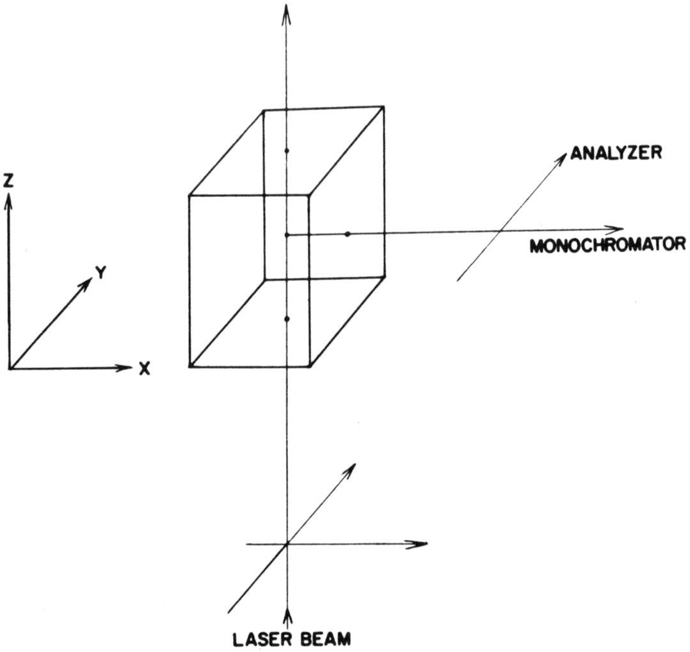

Fig. 7. The 90° Raman scattering from a crystal. The plane of polarization of the laser beam may be rotated through 90° using a half-wave plate. The direction of the analyzer is usually fixed. X, Y, and Z are in general the principal axes of the crystal a, b, and c.

B. Transformation of Axes

It is sometimes convenient to consider the effect of using different sets of reference axes for the polarizability tensor, e.g., to transfer from molecular ion coordinates x, y, z to crystal axis coordinates X, Y, Z; or from indicatrix axes to crystal coordinates. If α^X is the polarizability tensor or derived polarizability tensor referring to crystallographic axes and α^x the tensor referring to the molecular symmetry axes, then

$$P^X = \alpha^X \mathbf{E}^X$$

where $\mathbf{E}$ is the electric vector of the incident radiation and P the polarization referring to the crystallographic axes. Then we have

$$\mathbf{E}^x = T\mathbf{E}^X$$

$$P^x = TP^X$$

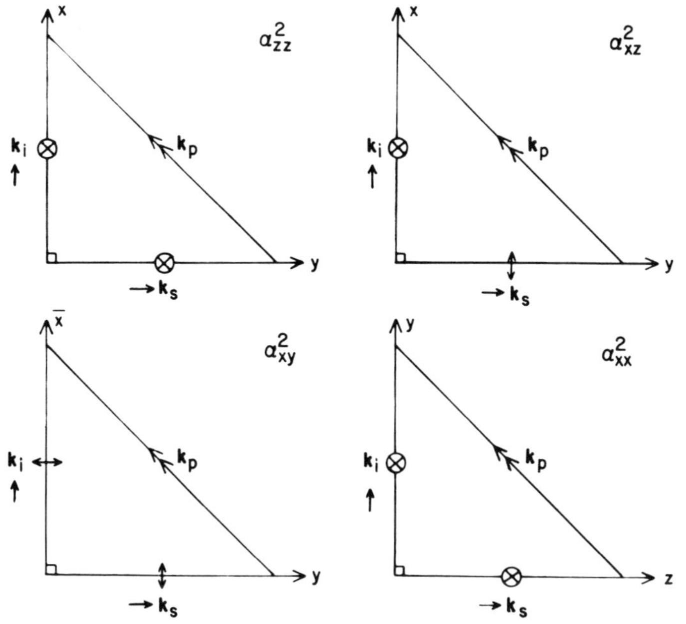

Fig. 8. The direction of propagation and polarization of the incident and scattered photons, and the phonon directions and polarizations; $\alpha_{ij}{}^2$ gives the square of the component of the Raman tensor that is measured.

where P^x and $\mathbf{E}^x$ are referring to the molecular axis and T is the relevant transformation matrix

$$\begin{aligned} P^x &= TP^X \\ &= \alpha^x \mathbf{E}^x \\ &= \alpha^x T\mathbf{E}^X \\ T^{-1}TP^X &= T^{-1}\alpha^x T\mathbf{E}^X \\ P^X &= T^{-1}\alpha^x T\mathbf{E}^X \\ &= \alpha^X \mathbf{E}^X \\ \alpha^X &= T^{-1}\alpha^x T \end{aligned}$$

IV. EXPERIMENTAL RAMAN STUDIES OF CRYSTALS OF DIFFERENT SYMMETRY

The Raman spectra of a wide range of crystals of different symmetry and with many varying types of interatomic bonding have already been studied. Here we discuss some of the results that have been obtained in the last decade on the Raman spectra of ionic, covalent, and a few metallic crystals. In such a rapidly moving field of research no claim to completeness is possible or intended. The examples selected do, however, illustrate the type of information that can be obtained with laser Raman spectroscopy. The substances studied have been classified from the point of view of systematic crystal chemistry (*22, 23*), so emphasizing the relationship which exists between the structure and spectroscopic selection rules. As infrared studies are usually a complementary method of obtaining $k = 0$ phonon frequencies, the *IR* selection rules are also listed as well as the Raman activity.

We start by discussing the Raman spectra of some of the elements, including those in the form of linear covalent chain structures such as selenium, or layerlike two-dimensional structures such as graphite, or as three-dimensional giant molecules such as diamond. The Raman spectra of a few elemental metal crystals are also discussed. We then consider some simple ionic or ionic-covalent structures with composition A_xB_y or $A_xB_yC_z$. Some simple crystals in which molecular ions can be recognized are dealt with and emphasis is placed on the information that can be obtained by Raman spectroscopy on the rotatory and translatory motion of these ions.

A. Elemental Crystals

1. Non-Metals

a. *Diamond, Silicon, Germanium*

These elemental crystals belong to space group 0_h^7 and have two atoms in the primitive unit cell.

$$\Gamma = F_{2g}(R)$$

Thus, there should be a single triply degenerate Raman mode. The form of the derived polarizibility tensor is

$$F_{2g}(x) \quad \begin{bmatrix} 0 & 0 & 0 \\ 0 & 0 & d \\ 0 & d & 0 \end{bmatrix} \qquad F_{2g}(y) \quad \begin{bmatrix} 0 & 0 & d \\ 0 & 0 & 0 \\ d & 0 & 0 \end{bmatrix} \qquad F_{2g}(z) \quad \begin{bmatrix} 0 & d & 0 \\ d & 0 & 0 \\ 0 & 0 & 0 \end{bmatrix}$$

The observed spectrum (*24,25*) for this Raman-active line in diamond occurs at 1333 cm^{-1} and is shown in Fig. 9 for different polarization

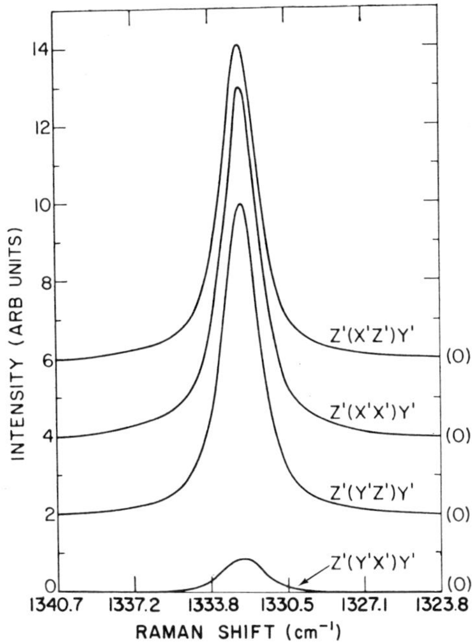

Fig. 9. Polarization features of the first-order Raman line of diamond exhibiting the tensor components $\alpha_{x'z'}$, $\alpha_{x'x'}$, $\alpha_{y'z'}$, and $\alpha_{y'x'}$; X', Y', and Z' are along [110], [110], and [001] respectively. The spectra have been displaced vertically with respect to one another for clarity. The relative intensity scales, the zeros of which are indicated at the right of the figure, are identical for the four spectra displayed. These spectra were excited with the 6328 Å radiation of a He/Ne laser and recorded at 300°K (*24*).

directions. In this experimental work it is convenient to take X' and Y' axes making 45° with X and Y, i.e., to rotate the crystal through 45° about the z axis. The tensors referring to these axes have the form

$$\frac{1}{\sqrt{2}}\begin{bmatrix} 0 & 0 & d \\ 0 & 0 & d \\ d & d & 0 \end{bmatrix} \qquad \frac{1}{\sqrt{2}}\begin{bmatrix} 0 & 0 & d \\ 0 & 0 & -d \\ d & -d & 0 \end{bmatrix} \qquad \begin{bmatrix} d & 0 & 0 \\ 0 & -d & 0 \\ 0 & 0 & 0 \end{bmatrix}$$

The observed spectra are in excellent agreement with theory. Below room temperature neither the frequency nor the linewidth ($\sim 1.6\ \text{cm}^{-1}$) vary much with temperature. The linear pressure dependence (*26*) of this line is shown in Fig. 13. The change in bulk modulus with pressure can

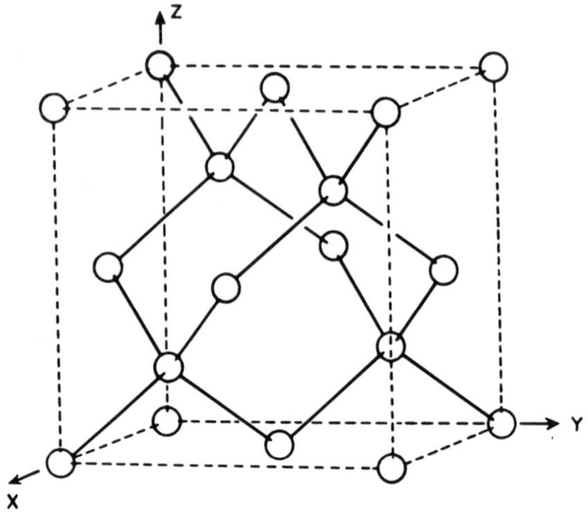

Crystal Structure of Diamond

be determined from this data, $dv/dP = 2.77$ compared with 4.16 and 4.35 for silicon and germanium, respectively.

The effect of an electric field on the Raman scattering by this line has been observed (*27*). The presence of an external electric field removes the

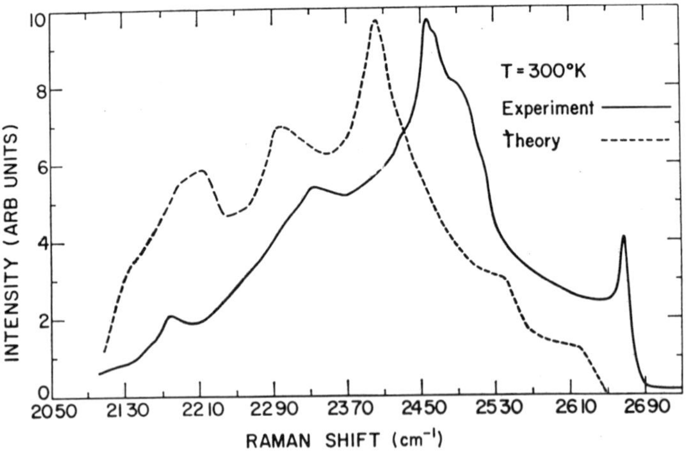

Fig. 10. Comparison of the theoretical calculation of Dolling and Cowley and the experimental results for the room temperature second-order Raman scattering in diamond for Y′(Z′Z′)X′. The strongest peak in their calculation has been normalized to the strongest peak in the experimental spectrum (*24*).

center of symmetry due to the changing electric charge distribution of the atoms by inducing a relative displacement of the sub-lattices. This leads to components of the polarizability tensor changing in magnitude—some that were previously zero become finite. The increase in intensity is bound to depend upon the square of the applied electric field.

The two-phonon (second order) Raman scattering which is comparatively strong in diamond was for a long time the subject of considerable controversy between Raman himself and Born. Figure 10 shows the observed spectrum (*24*) together with the theoretical spectrum calculated from the dispersion curves of diamond that have been determined by neutron scattering. The $k = 0$ frequencies at room temperature are

C	Si	Ge
1332.5 cm^{-1}	520.2 cm^{-1}	300.7 cm^{-1}

Until the advent of lasers it was not possible to obtain the Raman spectrum of silicon or germanium (*28*). However, the single $k = 0$ optical phonon frequencies have now been found for both silicon and germanium and the temperature dependence (*29*) of the frequencies and halfwidths have been studied. The variation of the halfwidth, which is an inverse measure of the phonon lifetime, has been explained in silicon on the assumption that this optical phonon decays into two acoustical phonons of half the frequency.

The intensity of Raman scattering in silicon is much increased due to resonance enhancement (*30*) when observations are made with the NdYAG laser whose beam has a photon energy of 1.165 eV. This is close to the indirect energy gap of silicon which varies from 1.166 eV at 0°K to 1.145 eV at 220°K. The Raman intensity increases markedly as the temperature decreases.

By applying a uniaxial stress to silicon (*31*) the $k = 0$ triply degenerate F_{2g} mode is split, and consequently, the Raman peak exhibits splitting and shifts which are a linear function of the applied stress, as shown in Fig. 11. The directions referred to are 111 (Z''), $11\bar{2}$ (X'') and $1\bar{1}0$($\bar{Y}$).

b. *Selenium*

Trigonal selenium is made up of parallel helical covalently bonded chains arranged at the corners and center of a hexagon. The direction of the chain axis is the c axis. The symmetry is D_3 and there are three atoms in the unit cell, and consequently, there are nine branches to the phonon dispersion curves.

$$\Gamma = A_2(IR, \|^l) + 2E(IR, \perp, R) + A_1\ (R)$$

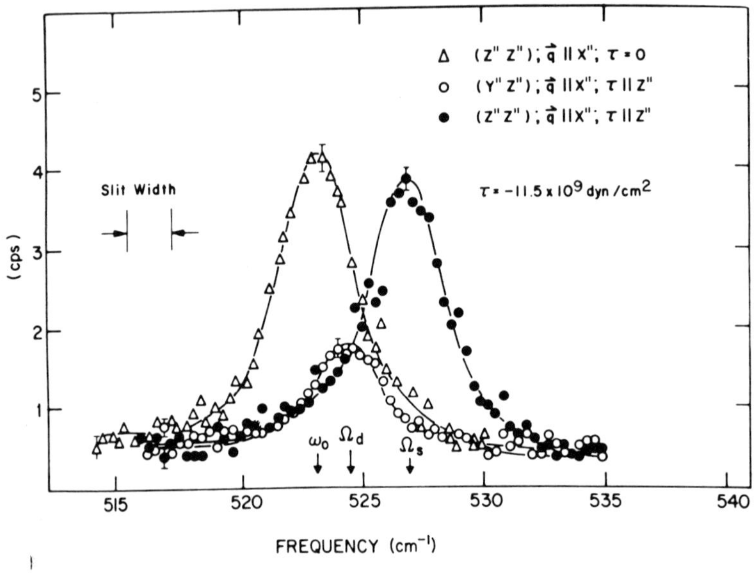

Fig. 11. The first order Raman spectrum of Si at 300°K with a uniaxial stress of 11.5×10^9 dyn/cm^2 applied along the [111] direction. The entries in the parentheses, i.e., $(z''z'')$ and $(y''z'')$, designate the polarization direction of the incident and scattered radiation. In each case the direction of the incident and scattered radiation is along x'' and $-x''$, respectively (31).

As there is no center of inversion the *E* type *LO* phonons should be Raman active. Raman measurements (*32, 33*) on selenium have been made using different sources including a Nd^{3+} YAG laser. The sample was oriented so that the light was always propagated perpendicular to the *c* axis to prevent optical rotation.

c. *Graphite*

Before the advent of the laser it would have appeared impossible to obtain the Raman spectrum of a material like graphite. However, using an argon ion laser good spectra have now been obtained. There are four atoms in the primitive unit cell, and consequently, twelve branches to the

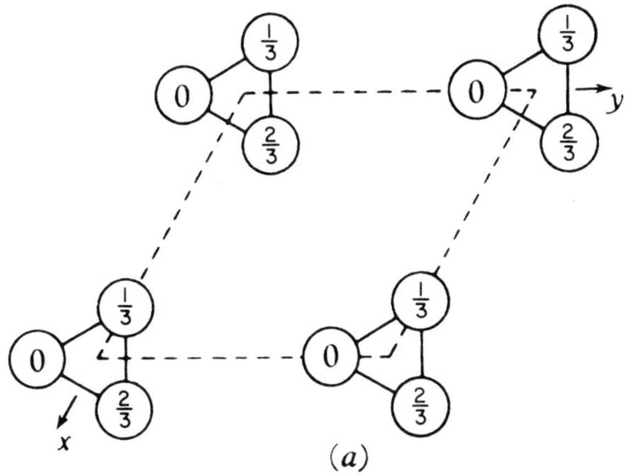

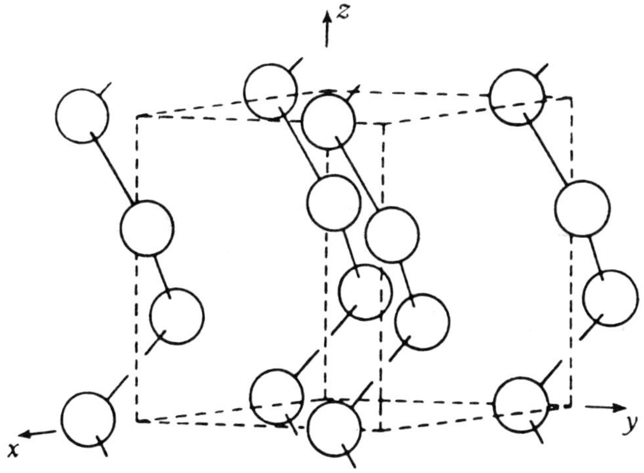

Crystal Structure of Selenium

phonon dispersion curves. The unit cell has a symmetry consistent with the space group D_{6h}^4.

$$\Gamma = 2B_{2g} + 2E_{2g}(R) + A_{2u}(IR, ||^l) + E_{1u}(IR, \perp)$$

The two E_g modes which are Raman active involve the motion of atoms in the plane of the carbon atoms. The two different E_g modes involve atoms in adjacent layers moving either in phase or antiphase. The difference in frequency is expected to be small, and the strong Raman band (*34*) observed experimentally at 1575 cm^{-1} is probably due to both modes. A

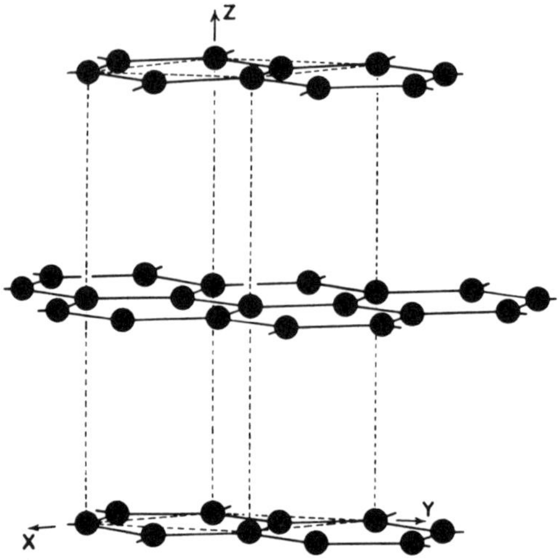

Crystal Structure of Graphite

weaker band at 1355 cm^{-1} has been attributed to an A_{1g} mode which is Raman active in finite crystals.

2. Metals

Only a few years ago most physicists predicted that it would never be possible to observe Raman scattering from phonons in metals. The laser has made it possible, although the depth of penetration is only a few hundred angstroms. This is large enough compared with interatomic spacings to ensure that long wavelength phonons, i.e., $\mathbf{k} \approx 0$ are observed. Experimentally, the techniques that have brought success include making the polished sample to be one of the mirrors inside the laser cavity and using several monochromators in tandem.

The vast majority of elemental metals, e.g., those of cubic close-packed or body-centered cubic structures, contain only one atom per unit cell, and consequently, there are only acoustical branches to the phonon dispersion curves.

a. *Hexagonal Close-Packed (Zn, Mg, and Be)*

There are two atoms in the unit cell which belongs to space group D_{6h}^4. There are three optical branches to the phonon dispersion curves.

$$\Gamma = A_{1u}(F)+E_{2g}(R)$$

Thus, there should be one Raman active mode for which the form of the derived polarizability tensor is

$$E_g$$

$$\begin{bmatrix} d & 0 & 0 \\ 0 & -d & 0 \\ 0 & 0 & 0 \end{bmatrix}$$

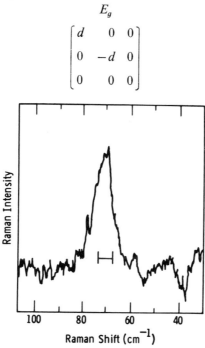

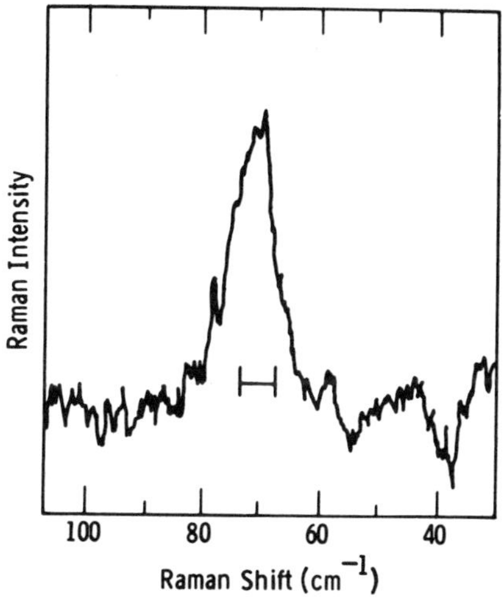

Fig. 12. The observed Raman line for a Zinc single crystal at 300°K. The horizontal line segment indicates the instrumental resolution (35).

Using a single crystal of beryllium, Porto (*35*) has observed a Raman line at 463 cm^{-1} and has shown that $\alpha_{xx} \gg \alpha_{zz}$ and $\alpha_{zx} \approx 0$ as predicted by theory. Raman peaks of similar origin have been observed in zinc and magnesium at 70 cm^{-1} and 120 cm^{-1}, respectively. The Zn spectrum (*35*) is shown in Fig. 12.

The scattering intensity of these metals is about one tenth that of germanium (4880 Å excitation).

b. *Rhombohedral* (*Bi*)

Bismuth forms crystals with a rhombohedral unit cell containing two atoms of space group D_{3d}^5

$$\Gamma = A_g(R) + E_g(R)$$

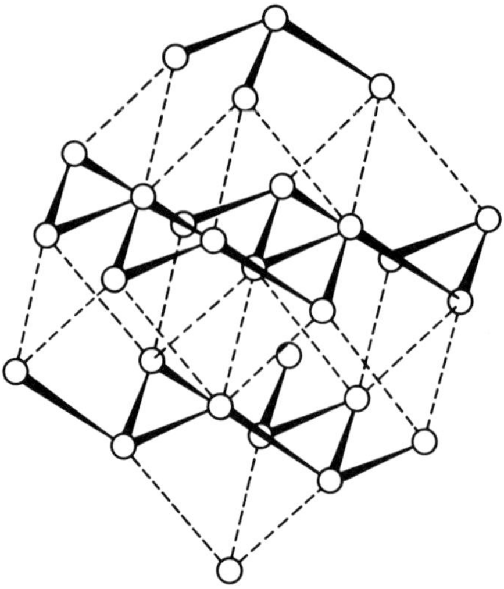

Crystal Structure of Bismuth

In this case, both $k = 0$ optic modes are Raman active (*36*) and occur at 90 cm^{-1} and 60 cm^{-1}.

c. *AuAl$_2$*

$AuAl_2$ has the fluorite structure whose space group is 0_h^5. The F_{2g} mode is Raman active (*36*) and is found at 266 cm^{-1}. The Raman linewidths observed in metals appear to be about an order of magnitude greater than those found in most covalent or ionic crystals, indicating that the phonon lifetime is shorter in metals.

B. Type AX

1. ZINC BLENDE (ZnS)

Many diatomic compounds crystallize with this structure. The space group of the cubic unit cell is $T_d{}^2(F\bar{4}3m)$ and contains four formula units. However, the primitive unit cell contains only one, and consequently, there are three optical branches to the phonon dispersion curves.

$$\Gamma = F_2(IR, R)$$

As there is no center of inversion in the unit cell both the $k = 0$ longitudinal and transverse optic modes are Raman active (*37–45*). The values of derived polarizability tensors for different normal modes of vibration are found in Table 6 where the normal coordinates are taken to be along the base vectors of the cubic unit cell. It is better to transform (*38*) the tensors so that one of the normal coordinates q_{LO} is parallel to the wave vector of the phonon, and the other two, q_{TO_1} and q_{TO_2}, are perpendicular to this wave vector. These tensors are then transformed into the laboratory coordinate system. Poulet's intensity matrices (*221*), which result from squaring the tensor elements and combining the results for the degenerate transverse optic modes, have the following form.

For (100) direction parallel to X, Y, Z:

$$\theta_{LO}(100) \quad \begin{bmatrix} 0 & \frac{1}{2} & 0 \\ \frac{1}{2} & 0 & \frac{1}{2} \\ 0 & \frac{1}{2} & 0 \end{bmatrix} \qquad \theta_{TO}(100) \quad \begin{bmatrix} 0 & \frac{1}{2} & 1 \\ \frac{1}{2} & 0 & \frac{1}{2} \\ 1 & \frac{1}{2} & 0 \end{bmatrix}$$

For a crystal oriented so that a (100) direction is along Y and two (110) directions are along X and Z the intensity matrices are

$$\theta_{LO}(110) \quad \begin{bmatrix} 0 & \frac{1}{2} & 0 \\ \frac{1}{2} & 0 & \frac{1}{2} \\ 0 & \frac{1}{2} & 0 \end{bmatrix} \qquad \theta_{TO}(110) \quad \begin{bmatrix} 1 & \frac{1}{2} & 0 \\ \frac{1}{2} & 0 & \frac{1}{2} \\ 0 & \frac{1}{2} & 1 \end{bmatrix}$$

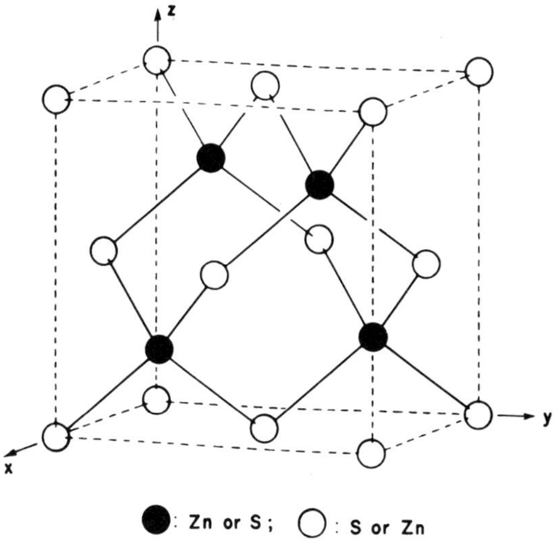

Crystal Structure of Zinc Sulphide

In nonpolar crystals such as diamond the intensity matrix is just the sum of θ_{LO} and θ_{TO} in agreement with the expressions already given. With the (110) orientation the *LO* mode should appear in *XY* and *YZ* polarizations but not in *YY* or *XZ*. Similarly, the *TO* mode should not appear in

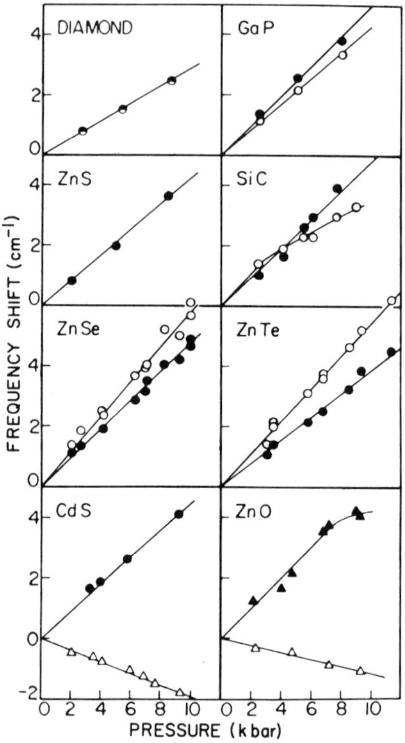

Fig. 13. Frequency shift as a function of pressure for $k \approx 0$ phonons: (◓) triply-degenerate optic mode; (○) LO mode; (◯) TO mode; (▲) high frequency E_2 mode; and (△) low frequency E_2 mode. [The frequencies (in cm^{-1}) at 1-atm pressure are—diamond: 1332; GaP: LO = 402, TO = 364; ZnS: LO = 351; SiC: LO = 971, TO = 795; ZnSe: LO = 252, TO = 206; ZnTe: LO = 206, TO = 179; CdS: LO = 305, E_2 = 42; ZnO: E_2 = 438, 99] (*26*).

the *XY* polarization. In some cases it is difficult to distinguish these one-phonon peaks from two-phonon spectra. Comparison with results on the dielectric parameters ε' and ε'' obtained from a Kramers-Kronig analysis of the infrared reflection spectrum can be valuable; ν_{LO} is found from the frequency at which $\varepsilon' = 0$, and ν_{TO} from the maximum value of ε''.

The accurate values of ν_{LO} and ν_{TO} derived from a Raman study provide a sensitive test of the Lyddane-Sachs-Teller relationship (*20a*):

$$\frac{\nu_{LO}}{\nu_{TO}} = \left(\frac{\varepsilon_0}{\varepsilon_\infty}\right)^{1/2}$$

where ε_O and ε_∞ are the limiting low and high frequency limits of the dielectric constant on the low and high frequency side of the resonance, respectively.

Expressions for the relative intensity of the Raman *LO* and *TO* peaks have already been given. The experimental evidence for the ratio S_{LO}/S_{TO} seems to confirm Loudon's assumption that the macroscopic electric field should be used in most crystals of the zinc blende structure rather than the local field.

If the relative intensity of the two peaks is measured and also the absolute intensity of one of them, the linear electro-optic constant Z_{41} may be estimated. In ZnS the *LO* peak is 9.2 times more intense than the *TO* peak when excited with 4880 Å radiation. The 992 cm^{-1} Raman line of benzene is 9.4 times more intense than the *LO* line. The $d\nu/dp$ for both the *LO* and *TO* frequencies $k = 0$ are very similar in several crystals with the zinc blende structure (*26*) (see Fig. 13). The transverse and longitudinal optic frequencies for several crystals with the zinc blende structure which have been measured by Raman spectroscopy are presented in Table 7.

TABLE 7

Zinc Blende

Crystal	Transverse optic (cm^{-1})	Longitudinal optic (cm^{-1})
SiC (*65*)	796	972
ZnS (*38*)	274	349
ZnSe (*40*)	206	252
ZnTe (*40*)	179	206
CdTe (*68a*)	140	171
BP (*62*)	829	829
AlP (*64*)	440	501
GaP (*60*)	367	403
GaAs (*60*)	268.6	292
InP (*61*)	303.7	345
InSb (*40*)	179	200
AlSb (*60*)	319	340
CuCl (*68*)	172	210 (40°K)

Many of the crystals of the class so far investigated show a rich two-phonon Raman spectrum (*38*). The agreement between theory and experimental results is quite good when reliable phonon dispersion curves are available.

2. WURTZITE (CdS)

Many II—VI compounds such as ZnO, CdS, and CdSe have this structure. Wurtzite belongs to the space group $C_{6v}^4(P6_3mc)$ with two formula units in the primitive unit cell. All the atoms occupy sites of

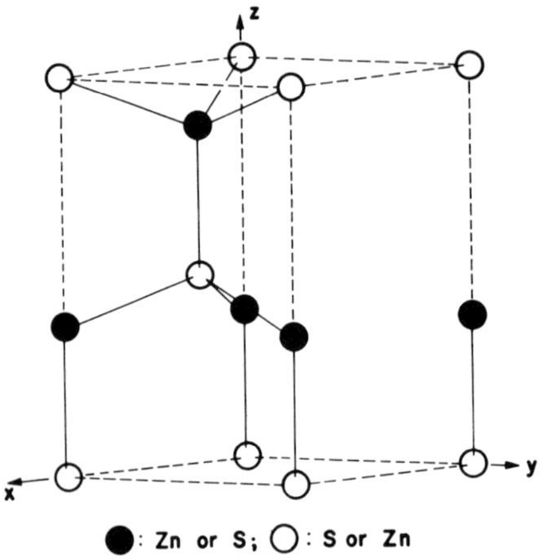

symmetry C_{3V}. The structure can be considered as a slightly distorted zinc blende, one in which the change in the nearest neighbor distance is small; consequently, the anisotropy is not very large. There are nine optical branches to the phonon dispersion curves.

$$\Gamma = A_1\,(IR\|{}'R) + 2B_1 + E_1(IR \perp R) + 2E_2(R)$$

The two E_2 modes are Raman active. The A_1 and E_1 are both infrared and Raman active, and consequently, both longitudinal as well as transverse optic modes can be observed by Raman spectroscopy (*46–64*). The forms of the derived polarizability tensor are as follows:

$$A_1\ \begin{bmatrix} a & 0 & 0 \\ 0 & a & 0 \\ 0 & 0 & b \end{bmatrix} \qquad E_1(x)\ \begin{bmatrix} 0 & 0 & c \\ 0 & 0 & 0 \\ 0 & c & 0 \end{bmatrix} \qquad E_1(y)\ \begin{bmatrix} 0 & 0 & 0 \\ 0 & 0 & c \\ 0 & c & 0 \end{bmatrix} \qquad E_2\ \begin{bmatrix} d & d & 0 \\ d & -d & 0 \\ 0 & 0 & 0 \end{bmatrix}$$

In all wurtzite type crystals studied so far, electrostatic forces dominate over the anisotropy of the short-range forces. Hence, the difference between the *LO* and *TO* frequencies ($k = 0$) is much greater than between the *A* and *E* frequencies ($k = 0$). The experimental arrangements required to observe the phonons of different symmetry (*51*) are shown in Fig. 14.

TABLE 8

Wurtzite Type

Crystal	A_1		E_1		E_2	
	LO	TO	LO	TO	1	2
BeO (*54, 57*)	1085	678	1095	722	684	340
ZnO (*57*)	574	—	583	—	—	—
ZnS (*57*)	352	274	352	274	55	—
CdS (*57*)	305	234	307	243	43	256
CdSe (*163*)	214	171	214	—	—	—
AlN (*62*)	910	—	910	667	—	655
GaN (*63*)	—	533	—	559	145	568

In the case of *X*(*YY*)*Z* and *X*(*ZX*)*Z* orientations in which phonons propagate at 45° to both the *X* and *Z* axes, the scattering from pure *LO* and pure *TO* phonons is equally mixed in character, and consequently, there is no distinction between A_1 and E_1 modes. The *LO* modes of E_1 type can be observed by back scattering, whereas A_1 type *LO* modes can be observed in forward scattering. It is essential to ensure that θ does not exceed about 160° or polaritons will be observed.

The Raman results obtained in a wide range of wurtzite type structures are collected together in Table 8.

The relative intensities of the *LO* and *TO* modes depend as before on the magnitude of the terms for the electro-optic coefficient, and this fact has been used by Arguello (*57*) to calculate these coefficients for CdS, BeO, and ZnS [see, however, Ref. (*15*)]. Many of the *LO* peaks of wurtzite materials show a strong resonance Raman effect.

3. Silicon Carbide Polytypes

Many different polytypes of SiC are known. Some have the zinc blende structure (cubic), others have a wurtzite-like structure ($P6_3mc$) (hexagonal),

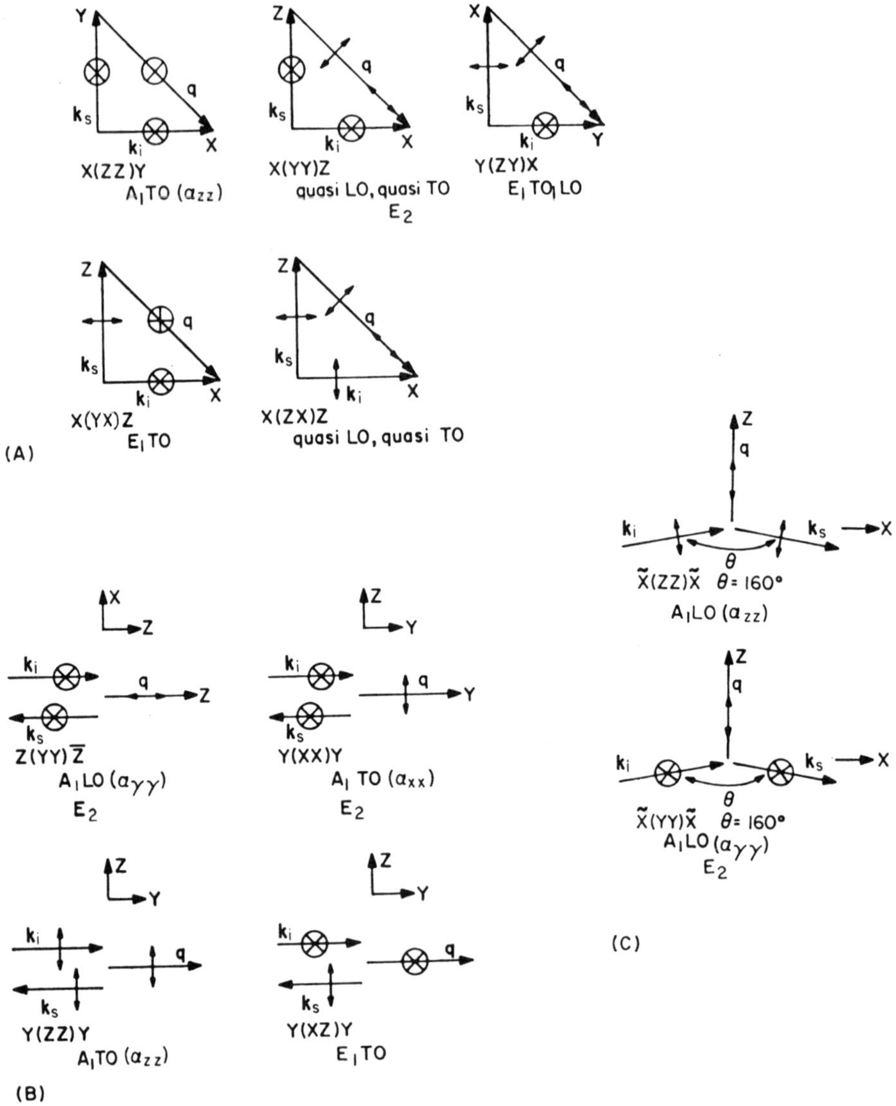

Fig. 14. Scattering diagrams for a variety of orientations when electrostatic forces dominate over anisotropy in a C_{6V} crystal. The directions of the incident and scattered photons are indicated by k_i and k_s, respectively, and the phonon by q. The polarization directions are indicated by small arrows or by circled crosses, the latter indicating a direction perpendicular to the plane of the paper. The predicted phonons are listed below each diagram. Right angle, backward, and forward scattering are illustrated in (A), (B), and (C), respectively. It should be pointed out that the notations used to describe the forward scattering in (C) do not specify the propagation direction. This must be separately indicated, but here the geometry has been selected always to scatter from phonons propagating in the Z direction (*51*).

and some are rhombohedral ($R3m$). Those known as $3C$, $4H$, $6H$, $15R$, and $21R$ have been investigated by Raman spectroscopy (*65,66*). In this notation NH or NR is the number of atomic layers in the stacking unit. The Raman active modes and large zone values of $x = q/q_{max}$ are shown below.

Designation	Atoms in unit cell	Raman active modes	Accessible values of x
$3C$	2	F_1	0
$4H$	8	$3A_1, 3E_1, 4E_2$	0, 0.5, 1
$6H$	12	$5A_1, 5E_1, 6E_2$	0, 0.33, 0.67, 1
$15R$	10	$9A_1, 9E$	0, 0.4, 0.8
$21R$	14	$13A_1, 13E$	0, 0.29, 0.57, 0.86

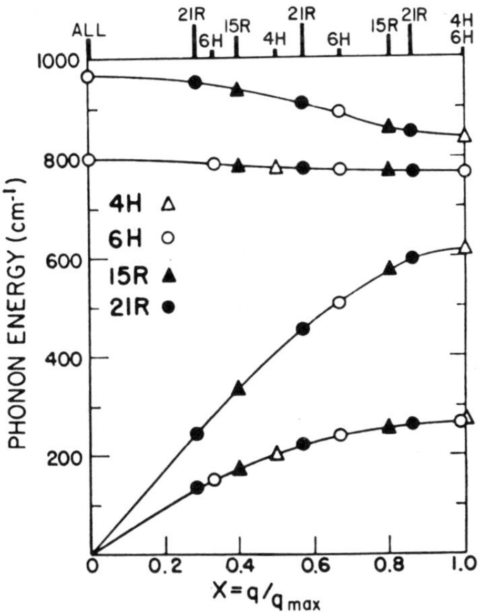

Fig. 15. Combined dispersion curves for SiC using data from four polytypes. For each polytype, the Raman accessible values of $x = q/q_{max}$ are marked at the top of the figure (*66*).

The Raman active phonons have representations A_1, E_1, or E_2 in hexagonal polytypes, or A_1 or E in rhombohedral. The combined experimental data are shown plotted in such a way as to map the joint dispersion curves (*66*) in Fig. 15. These results verify the existence of a common phonon spectrum for all SiC polytypes in the axial direction. Longitudinal and transverse acoustic velocities that are obtained from the slopes of the curves at the origin are in good agreement with directly observed values.

4. Sodium Chloride and Cesium Chloride (NaCl and CsCl)

The alkali halides and many other diatomic ionic crystals have this structure with space groups O_h^1 for the NaCl and CsCl type. There is one formula unit in the cubic unit cell and, hence, three optical branches to the phonon dispersion curves.

$$\Gamma = F_{1u}(IR)$$

There is, therefore, no one-phonon Raman spectrum. The two-phonon or second order spectra of the alkali halides and alkaline earth oxides have been extensively studied (*157*). Interpretation is greatly assisted if the phonon dispersion curves are known, and consequently, comparisons with calculated spectra can be made. The curves are broad since transitions are not restricted to $k = 0$ but may occur anywhere in the Brillouin zone and may involve acoustical as well as optical phonons. Appreciable contributions to the scattering come from regions of the Brillouin zone where there is a high density of vibrational states per unit wave vector interval. Usually, these are where the dispersion curves are nearly flat. A more complete understanding of the spectra can be obtained if critical point analysis is used. Critical points are points in the phonon dispersion curves where every component of $\nabla_k(\nu)$ is either zero or changes sign discontinuously. They occur at minima(m), maxima(M), or saddle points (S_1 and S_2) and usually occur at points of high symmetry in the Brillouin zone, referred to as Γ, X, L, W, and K. This is discussed by Cowley in Chap. 3.

Figure 16 shows the Raman spectrum (*67*) of NaF due to two-phonon processes. The observed spectrum reflects closely the form of the two-phonon density of vibrational states. These polarization studies confirm that the diagonal terms of the polarizability tensor are generally greater than the off-diagonal terms for the various combined modes. This fact is consistent with the assumption that there is a central dependence of the polarizability tensor on the configuration of the first neighbor. Figure 17 compares the Raman spectra (*68*) of KCl and NaCl. The frequency scales are displaced by about 55 cm^{-1}.

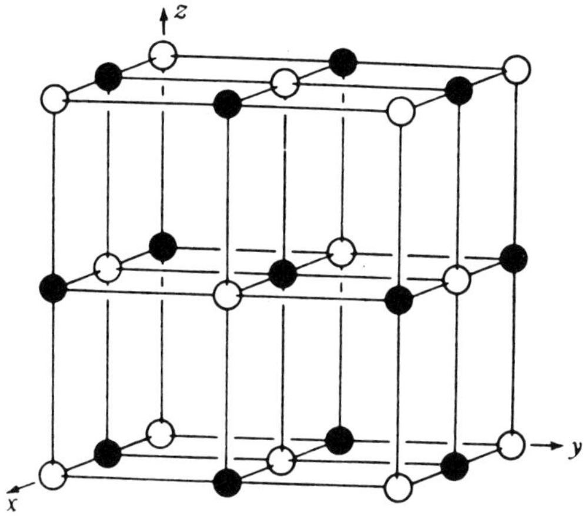

●: Na or Cl; ○: Cl or Na

Crystal Structure of Sodium Chloride

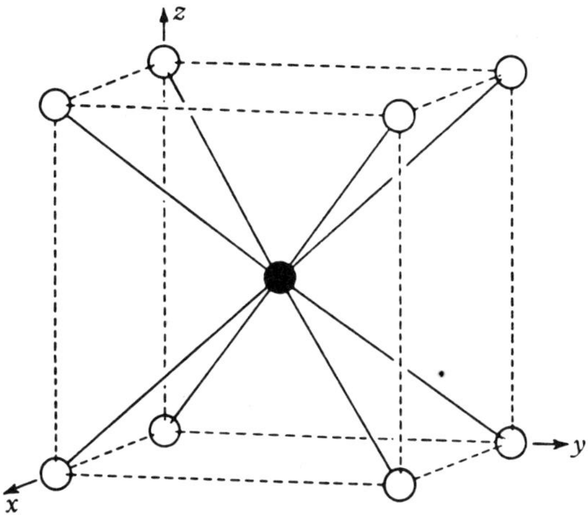

●: Cs or Cl; ○: Cl or Cs

Crystal Structure of Caesium Chloride

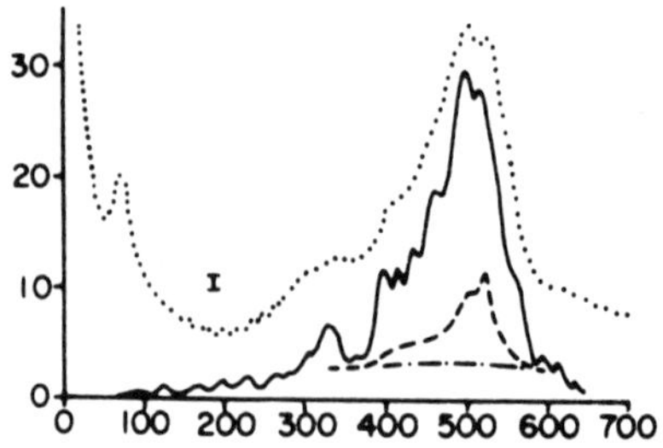

Fig. 16. The two phonon Raman spectrum of sodium fluoride measured at 300°K. (···) unpolarized spectrum; (– – –) Γ_{12} spectrum; (– · – ·) $\Gamma_{25'}$ spectrum; and (———) calculated spectrum *(67)*.

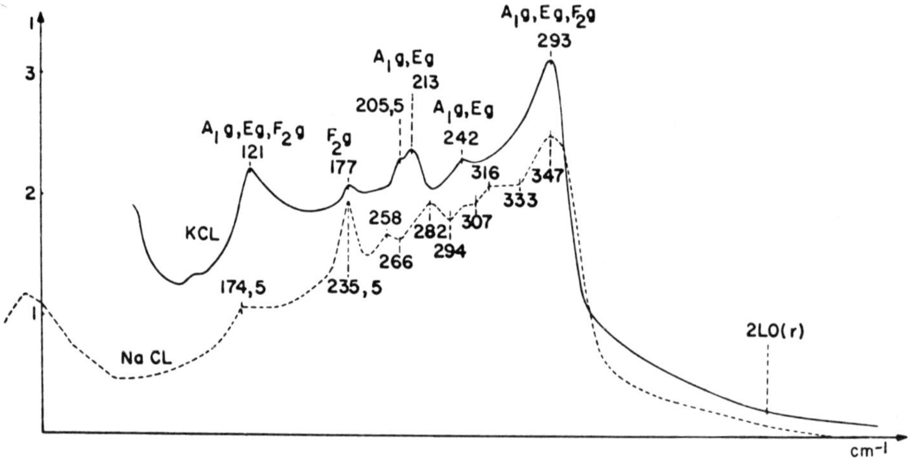

Fig. 17. Comparison of the two-phonon Raman spectra of potassium chloride and sodium chloride; the latter has been shifted to the left by 55 cm^{-1} *(68)*.

5. Germanium Telluride (GeTe)

At high temperature GeTe crystallizes in a β form which has the sodium chloride structure. However, at 670°K a phase change occurs resulting in a low temperature α-phase with the nickel sulfide structure whose space group is C_{3v}^5 and which contains one formula unit:

$$\Gamma = A_1(IR, ||^l, R) + E(IR, \perp, R)$$

Hence, in the α-phase both modes are Raman and infrared active, while in the β-phase the single F_{1u} mode is only infrared active *(69)*. For the

A modes, only the diagonal components of the Raman scattering tensor are finite, but for the B modes both diagonal and off-diagonal components can be observed. Consequently, the A mode is readily distinguished from the B mode. The $\beta \rightarrow \alpha$ transformation involves a static deformation of the NaCl(β) structure along its (111) direction which in the NiS(α) structure becomes the 001 axis. This static deformation corresponds to

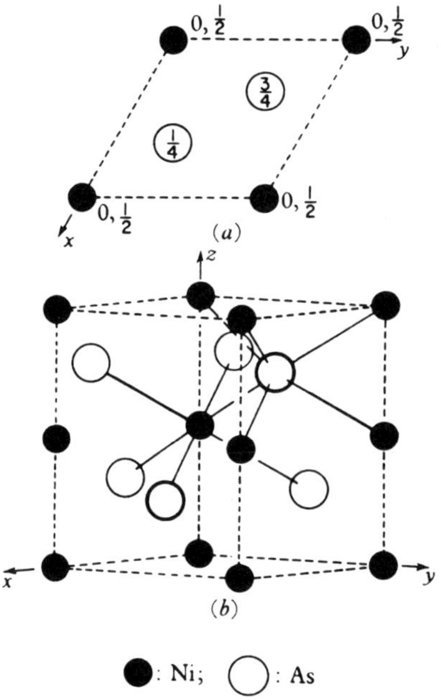

Crystal Structure of Germanium Telluride

dynamical atomic motions described by the eigenvector of the A_1 mode which occurs at low temperature at 140 cm^{-1}. This mode is presumably responsible for the phase transition. The Raman linewidth increases very steeply on approaching the transition temperature. Steigmeier and Harbeke (*69*) conclude that α-GeTe is a displacive type ferroelectric in which the behavior of the phonon modes is modified by perfect screening of the electric field by the conduction electrons.

6. Thallium Iodide (ThI)

At standard temperature and pressure ThI has an orthorhombic structure with four formula units in the D_{2h}^{17} unit cell. Twenty-four branches to the phonon dispersion curves are expected. However, at about 170°C or at a pressure of approximately 5 kbar at room temperature it undergoes a phase transition to a CsCl structure for which

$$\Gamma = F_{1u}(IR)$$

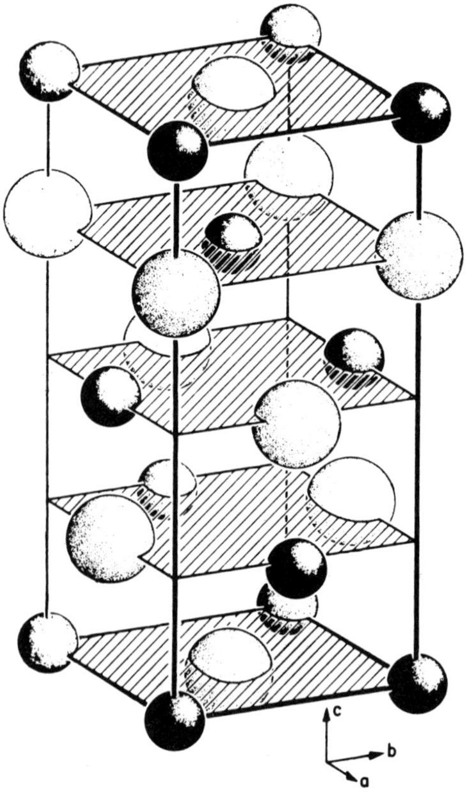

Crystal Structure of Thallium Iodide

and there should be no one-phonon Raman spectrum. Figure 18 shows the Raman peak height (*70*) versus pressure for the 22.5 cm^{-1}(○) and the 29 cm^{-1} band(△). Increasing pressure is represented by open symbols, whereas decreasing pressure is shown by closed symbols. Due to hysteresis the ortho → cubic transition occurs at 4.5 kbar and the cubic → ortho transition at 1.1 kbar. The average Grüneisen γ, calculated from the frequency shifts with pressure, is 3.0 which is close to the value of 3.27 for the macroscopic γ.

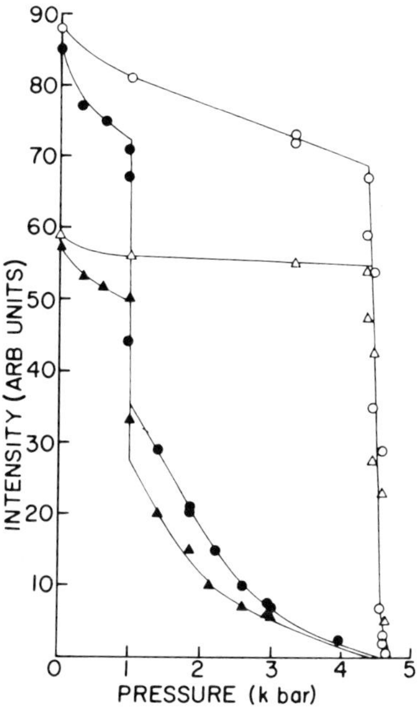

Fig. 18. Raman peak height versus pressure for thallium iodide. Increasing pressure is represented by open symbols, whereas decreasing pressure by closed symbols. ○ = 22.5 cm^{-1} and △ = 29 cm^{-1}.

7. Cinnibar, Mercuric Sulfide (HgS)

This form of mercuric sulfide has three formula units in a hexagonal unit cell of symmetry $D_{3h}^4(P\bar{6}\ 2C)$. Its lattice can be considered as a hexagonal distortion of the NaCl type lattice with close packed helical HgS chains along the C axis. There are fifteen optical branches to the phonon dispersion curves.

$$\Gamma = 2A' \mid (R) + 3A_2''(IR, ||^l) + 5E'(IR, \perp, R)$$

Thus, the A and E modes are Raman active. The E modes are also infrared active, and hence, both LO and TO modes are expected to be active in Raman scattering. Experimentally, a marked complementarity between Raman and infrared intensity is observed. The Raman spectra (*71*) are dominated by the A lines, and the relative magnitudes of the transverse and longitudinal components of the E doublets indicate that the atomic-displacement contribution to the polarizability modulation exceeds the electro-optic contribution.

The measurement of the components of the polarizability tensor is complicated first by the fact that the red He/Ne laser line is very close to the absorption edge of HgS, and second, by its very high optical rotatory power which is one of the greatest known.

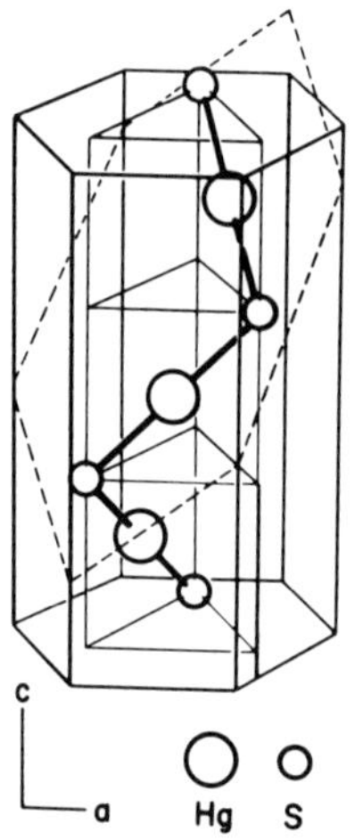

Crystal Structure of Mercuric Sulphide

Poulet and Mathieu (*72*) have calculated the force constants for HgS and find $k = 1.55$, $k_\alpha = 0.06$, and $k_\beta = 0.03$ millidyne/Å where k, k_α, and k_β are respectively the force constants for the Hg-S displacement, and SHgS and HgSHg deformations.

C. Type AX_2

1. Fluorite (CaF_2)

The fluorite structure has a single formula unit in the cubic unit cell. Each metal ion is surrounded by eight anions and each anion by four metal ions at the corners of a tetrahedron. There are nine branches to the phonon dispersion curves. LO_2 and TO_2, which are longitudinal and transverse modes, respectively, are degenerate at $k = 0$. This is the observed frequency in the one-phonon Raman spectrum (*73, 74*):

$$\Gamma = F_{1u}(IR) + F_{2g}(R)$$

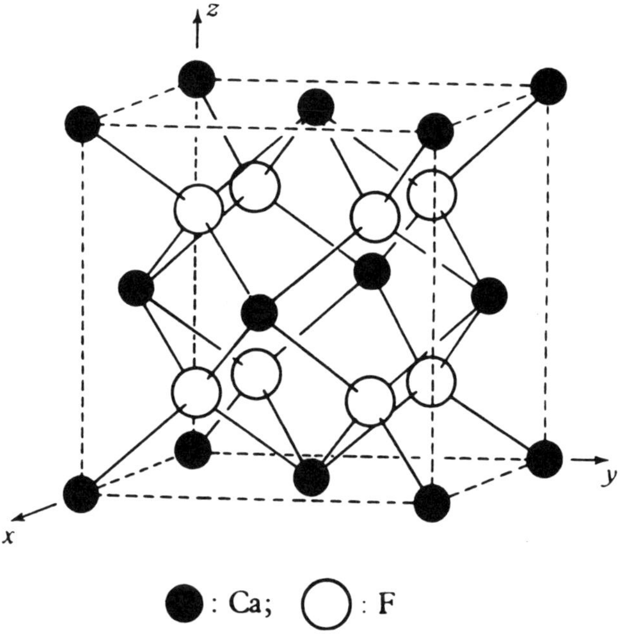

Crystal Structure of Calcium Fluoride

The transverse optic frequencies for several crystals of this type are listed in Table 9.

TABLE 9

Fluorite type

Crystal	Raman Frequency
CaF_2	322 cm^{-1}
SrF_2	285.5
BaF_2	241
CdF_2	317
PbF_2	256
$SrCl_2$	184
UO_2	445
Antifluorite type	
Mg_2Si	258.5
Mg_2Ge	255
Mg_2Sn	221
Mg_2Pb	214

2. Cuprous Oxide (Cu_2O)

Cuprous Oxide has a simple cubic structure with two formula units in a O_h^4 unit cell. There are eighteen branches to the phonon dispersion curves:

$$\Gamma = F_{1g}(R)+A_{2u}+E_u+F_{1u}+2F_{2u}(IR)$$

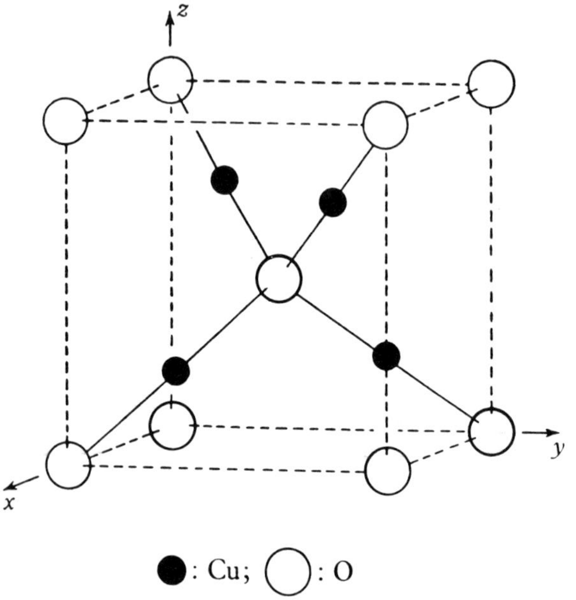

Crystal Structure of Cuprous Oxide

Hence, only one Raman active fundamental of symmetry F_{1g} is expected. A Raman line (*75,76*) which corresponds to this symmetry is found at 220 cm^{-1}. A broad band extending from 360 cm^{-1} to 500 cm^{-1} involves two-phonon processes.

The frequency 220 cm^{-1} is close to the 208 cm^{-1} difference between the two absorption edges which occur in the red region of the visible spectrum.

3. α-Quartz (SiO_2)

The α-quartz structure has three formula units in a hexagonal unit cell belonging to space group D_3. Hence, there should be twenty four optical branches to the phonon dispersion curves:

$$\Gamma = 4A(R)+4B(IR, ||^l)+8E(IR, \perp)$$

As there is no center of inversion, longitudinal optic as well as transverse optic modes can be observed in the Raman spectra of the E type modes of vibration.

Quartz has probably been the subject of more Raman studies than any other inorganic crystal (*78–83*); however, only recently has a satisfactory analysis of the spectra been given by Scott and Porto (*78*) who have correctly identified the Raman active longitudinal optic modes which had previously been assigned by many workers to multiphonon processes (see Fig. 19). They also showed that the frequency splittings between the *LO* and *TO* vibrations due to long-range electrostatic forces are in some cases much greater for quartz than the frequency shifts due to the anisotropy of the short-range interatomic forces.

The Raman polarizability tensor for the A modes of vibration has only diagonal elements; however, for the E modes both diagonal and off-diagonal elements occur.

1. $X(ZZ)Y$ gives A_1 phonons polarized in the z direction ($\nu^{\perp}$)
2. $X(ZX)Y$ gives E phonons (both $\nu_{LO}{}^{\perp}$ and $\nu_{TO}{}^{\perp}$)
3. $X(ZX)Z$ gives E phonons $\begin{cases} \nu_{LO} = [\frac{1}{2}(\nu_{LO}{}^{\perp})^2 + \frac{1}{2}(\nu_{LO}{}^{\|})^2]^{\frac{1}{2}} \\ \nu_{TO} = [\frac{1}{2}(\nu_{TO}{}^{\perp})^2 + \frac{1}{2}(\nu_{TO}{}^{\|})^2]^{\frac{1}{2}} \end{cases}$
4. $X(YX)Y$ gives E phonons (both $\nu_{LO}{}^{\perp}$ and $\nu_{TO}{}^{\perp}$)
5. $X(YY)Z$ gives both A_1 and E phonons $\begin{cases} \text{For } A_1, \nu = [\frac{1}{2}(\nu^{\|})^2 + \frac{1}{2}(\nu^{\perp})^2]^{\frac{1}{2}} \\ \text{For } E, \ \nu = [\frac{1}{2}(\nu_{LO}{}^{\perp})^2 + \frac{1}{2}(\nu_{LO}{}^{\|})^2]^{\frac{1}{2}} \end{cases}$
6. $Z'(X'Z')X'$ gives both A_1 and E phonons
7. $X'(X'Z')Z'$ gives both A_1 and E phonons

It will be noted that for scattering in case 7, where the crystal is cut at 45°, the E-type longitudinal optic vibrations will be eliminated, since E phonons do not have polarization in the Z direction.

For the very intensely infrared absorbing mode at 1072 cm^{-1}, $\nu_{LO}-\nu_{TO}$ is more than twenty times as large as $\nu^{\|}-\nu^{\perp}$, and consequently, we have the good approximation that

$$\nu_{LO}^2 = (\nu_{LO}^{\|} \cos\theta)^2 + (\nu_{LO}^{\perp} \sin\theta)^2$$

$$\nu_{TO}^2 = (\nu_{TO}^{\|} \sin\theta)^2 + (\nu_{TO}^{\perp} \cos\theta)^2$$

Here, θ is the angle between the c axis and the direction of phonon propagation, $\|$ denotes phonon propagation in the z direction, and $\perp$ denotes phonon propagation in the xy-plane.

Masso et al. (*79*) have carried out measurements on the width and intensities of all the Raman active lines in α-quartz and have determined the

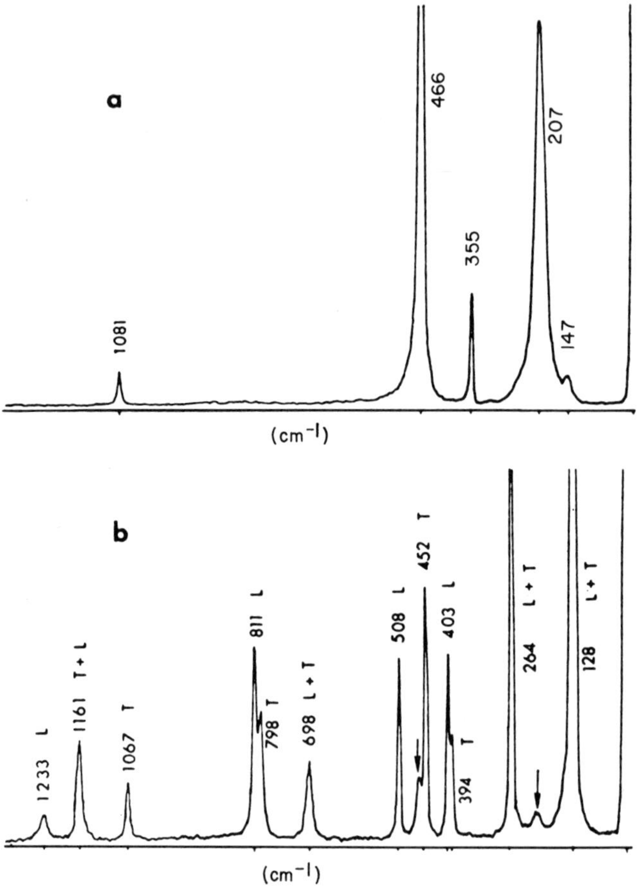

Fig. 19. Room-temperature Raman spectra of α-quartz with measured values of frequencies in cm^{-1}, and Scott and Porto's (Ref. *78*) polarization assignments (L = longitudinal, T = transverse). (a) The x(zz)y spectrum showing the A_1 modes. (b) The x(yx+yz)y spectrum showing the E modes. The arrows indicate intense A_1 modes being transmitted due to imperfect alignment.

relative values of the Raman tensor elements for the various modes of vibration. They have attempted to verify the equation for the scattered Raman intensity for the *E*-type vibrations.

$$s = [\sum_{\rho,\sigma,\tau=x,y,z} \mathbf{e}^i_\sigma \alpha^\tau_{\sigma\rho}(A\xi^\tau + B\mathbf{k}^\tau)\mathbf{e}^s_\rho]^2$$

where A is a scattering coefficient related to the lattice deformation and B gives the contribution due to the electro-optic effect associated with the E vibration. The ratio of the scattered intensity for a purely longitudinal vibration to that of a purely transverse vibration ($B = 0$) is

$$\eta = \frac{(A+B)^2}{A^2}$$

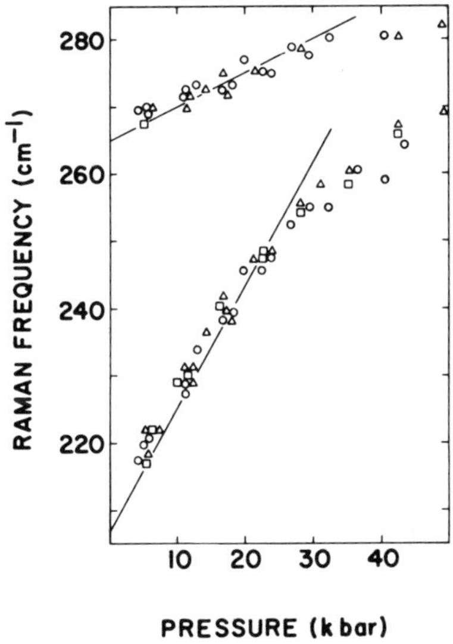

Fig. 20. A plot of the frequencies of the 207-cm^{-1} line (open points) and 265-cm^{-1} line (closed points) of the Raman spectrum of α-quartz vs pressure. For each point the orientation of the optic axis of the sample along the direction of compression, laser excitation, or observation of the scattered light is indicated by circles, triangles, or squares, respectively. The uncertainties of the frequency of each point are 2 cm^{-1} for the 207-cm^{-1} line and 4 cm^{-1} for the 265-cm^{-1} line. At pressures above 30 kbar, the 265-cm^{-1} line often cannot be resolved from the 207-cm^{-1} line (*81*).

Values of η for several different modes were calculated and were found to be approximately unity.

The halfwidths of all the Raman active lines were found to be less than 8 cm^{-1} with the exception of the 207 cm^{-1} band which is 20 cm^{-1} wide.

Pine and Tannewald (*80*) have carried out very accurate measurements on the temperature dependence of the Raman linewidth and shifts of the 128 and 466 cm^{-1} modes between 5° and 300°K. They have interpreted their data in terms of three-phonon interaction using the dispersion curves for α-quartz.

Raman studies have been made on the pressure dependence (*81*) of the spectrum of α-quartz, and the results for two of the modes are shown in Fig. 20. The pressure dependence $d\nu/dP$ for several frequencies is summarized below:

128 cm^{-1}	207 cm^{-1}	265 cm^{-1}	464 cm^{-1}	697 cm^{-1}	795 cm^{-1}	807 cm^{-1}
0.6 cm^{-1} $kbar^{-1}$	1.8	0.5	0.9	0.8	0.8	0.8

These frequencies, which are also the ones that show a strong temperature dependence, increase with pressure. The frequencies of the other Raman active lines except those at 145, 450, and 509 cm^{-1}, which are too weak to be measured, are almost independent of pressure. Scott (*84*) has observed the frequency and intensity dependence of polarization spectra in forward scattering experiments, and he obtains good agreement with theory. The polarization associated with the *E*-type 1072-cm^{-1} phonon is observed to range in frequency from 1072 to 822 cm^{-1} as the scattering angle is changed.

TABLE 10

Zone-Center Phonon Frequencies (cm^{-1})

Osc. strength	GeO_2 (trigonal) $\varepsilon_0 = 7.11$	α-Quartz SiO_2: $\varepsilon_0 = 4.32$	Osc. strength
0.01	121 *E*(TO+LO)	128 *E*(TO+LO)	0.001
0.01	166 *E*(TO+LO)	265 *E*(TO+LO)	0.05
	212 A_1	207 A_1	
	261 A_1	356 A_1	
3.32	326 *E*(TO)	450 *E*(TO)	0.82
	372 *E*(LO)	401 *E*(LO)	
0.47	385 *E*(TO)	394 *E*(TO)	0.33
	440 A_1	464 A_1	
	~456 *E*(LO)	509 *E*(LO)	
0.10	492 *E*(TO)	697 *E*(TO)	0.02
	512 *E*(LO)	697 *E*(LO)	
0.08	583 *E*(TO)	795 *E*(TO)	0.11
	595 *E*(LO)	807 *E*(LO)	
0.57	857 *E*(TO)	1072 *E*(TO)	0.67
	880 A_1	1085 A_1	
	919 *E*(LO)	1163 *E*(LO)	
0.01	961 *E*(TO)	1163 *E*(TO)	0.01
	972 *E*(LO)	1235 *E*(LO)	

Germanium dioxide has three stable forms, one of which is the same as α-quartz. The observed zone-center Raman frequencies (*84*) are compared with the corresponding ones of quartz in Table 10.

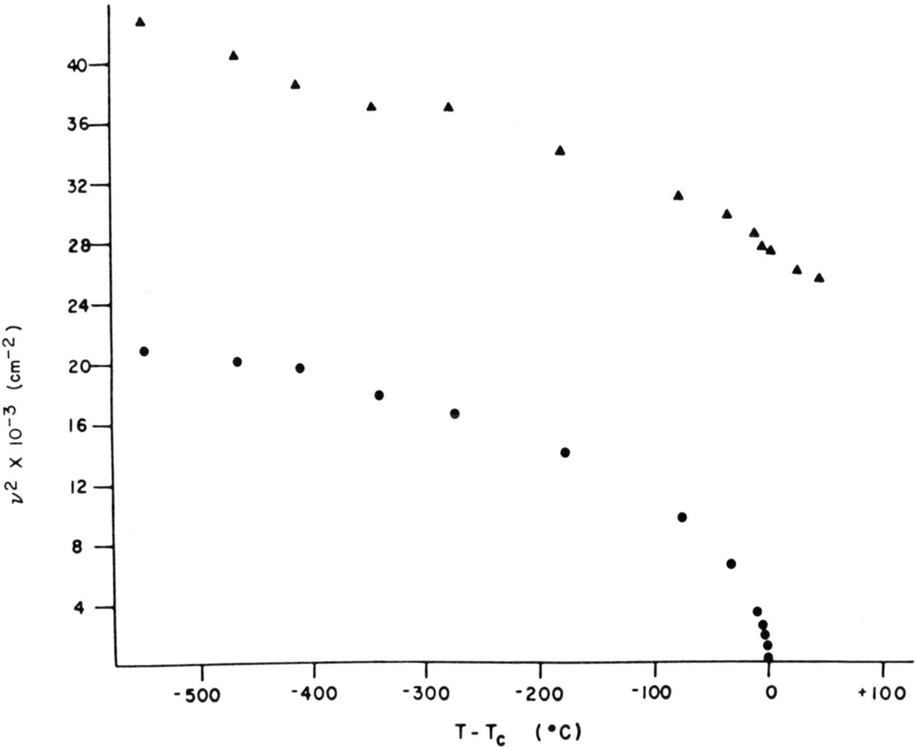

Fig. 21. Symbols show the square of the frequency of 147-cm^{-1} and 207-cm^{-1} lines as a function of temperature, ν^2 vs $T - T_C$. (▲) 207-cm^{-1} mode (room temp freq); (●) 147-cm^{-1} mode (room temp freq) (*77*).

Quartz undergoes a phase transition from the α-phase to a high temperature β-phase with symmetry D_6 at 573°C (846°K). For β-quartz

$$\Gamma = A_1(R) + 2B_1 + 2A_2(IR, ||^l) + 3B_2 + 4E_1(IR, \perp) + 4E_2(R)$$

The change in the Raman spectrum through the transition has been studied by Cummins (*77*) and Scott (*83*). Scott interprets the 207-cm^{-1} mode as being a soft mode which decreases in frequency as the temperature increases. The feature in the spectrum at 147 cm^{-1} is interpreted as involving the excitation of two zone-edge acoustic phonons. As the crystal is heated the soft optic phonon traverses the two-phonon continuum and the optic mode couples anharmonically to part of the acoustic continuum leading to a type of Fermi resonance.

Figure 21 shows (*77*) the plot of ν^2 versus $T-T_c$ for the 147-cm^{-1} and 207-cm^{-1} modes. The temperature dependence of the former is given by $\nu^2 \approx |T-T_c|^{\gamma}$ where $0.4 \leqq \gamma \leqq 0.5$.

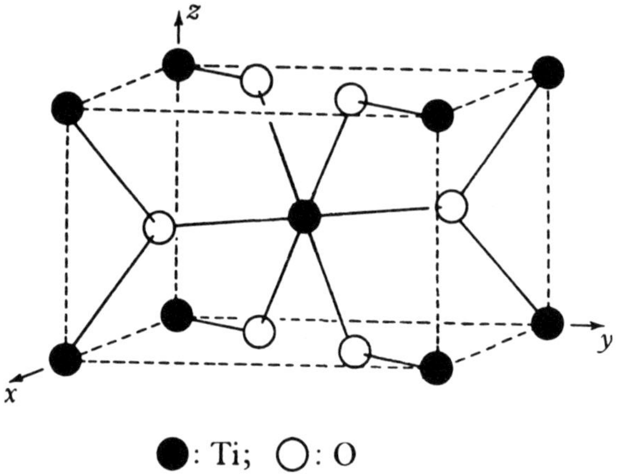

Crystal Structure of Rutile

4. Rutile Type (TiO_2)

The tetragonal unit cell, which belongs to the D_{4h}^{14} space group, contains two formula units. Typical examples, which have been studied by Raman spectroscopy, include MgF_2, MnF_2, ZnF_2, FeF_2, TiO_2, and SnO_2. The cations are located at sites with D_{2h} symmetry and the anions occupy sites with C_{2v} symmetry. The metal ions are surrounded by six fluoride or oxygen ions at the corners of a slightly distorted octahedron, while the three metal ions coordinating each anion lie in a plane at the corners of a nearly equilateral triangle. Eighteen branches are predicted for the phonon dispersion curves. Three of these are acoustic and fifteen, optical. The symmetries of the $\mathbf{k} = 0$ optical modes together with their infrared and Raman activity can be represented by

$$\Gamma = A_{1g}(R)+A_{2g}(F)+A_{2u}(IR, ||^{l})+B_{1g}(R)+B_{2g}(R) +2B_{1u}(F)+E_g(R)+3E_u(IR, \perp)$$

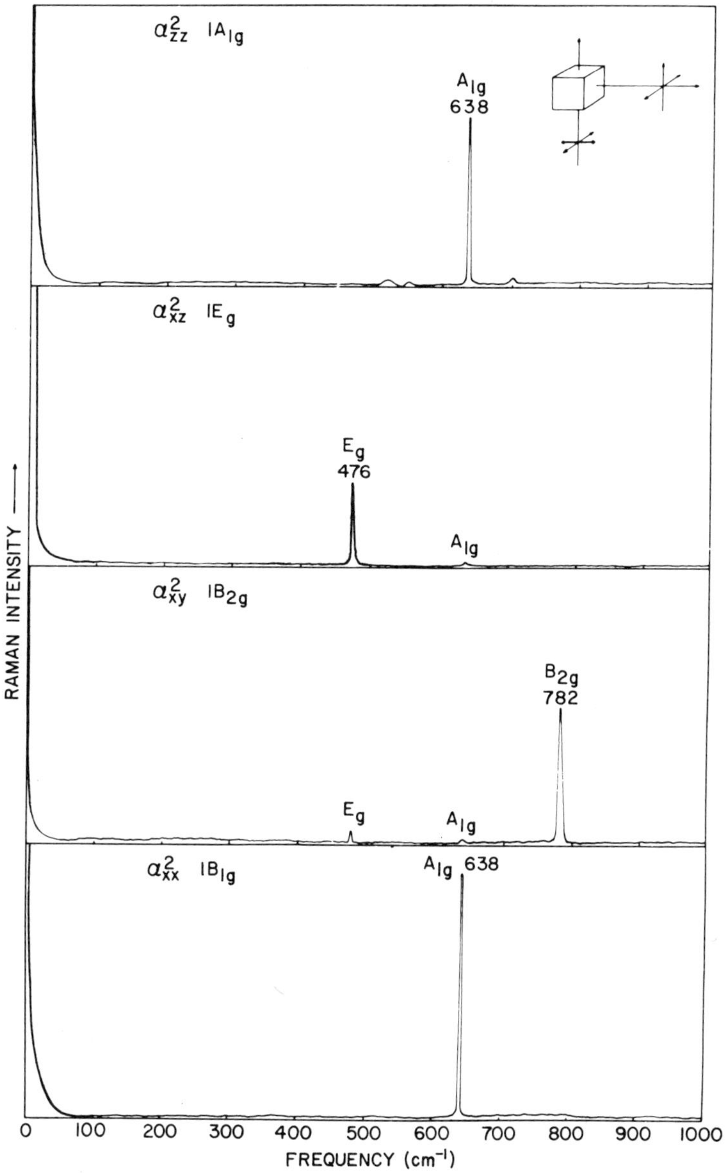

Fig. 22. Raman spectrum of tin oxide, SnO_2 (100°K; 5145 Å excitation) *(87)*.

Each of these crystals exhibits strong lines of A_{1g} and E_g symmetries and a sharp low frequency line of B_{1g} symmetry (*85–87*). Figure 22 shows the polarized Raman spectra for SnO_2, and Table 11 lists the frequencies of zone-center phonons for crystals of the rutile type which have so far been investigated.

TABLE 11

Rutile Type

Crystal	B_{1g}	E_g	A_{1g}	B_{2g}
MgF_2 (*85*)	92	295	410	515
MnF_2 (*85*)	61	247	341	476
FeF_2 (*85*)	73	257	340	496
CoF_2 (*86*)	68	246	366	494
ZnF_2 (*86*)	70	253	350	522
TiO_2 (*85*)	143	447	612	826
GeO_2 (*84*)	170	680	702	870
SnO_2 (*87*)	—	476	638	782

5. ANATASE (TiO_2)

Titanium dioxide may also crystallize into a further structure which may be classified under D_{4h}^{19}

$$\Gamma = A_{1g}(R)+A_{2u}(IR, ||^{l})+2B_{1g}(R)+B_{2u}(F)+3E_g(R)+2E_u(IR, \perp)$$

Hence, six Raman active modes are expected, and all of these have been observed (*88*). A sharp and very intense band at 144 cm^{-1} involves a similar movement in the bridge from TiO_6 octahedra of anatase to that

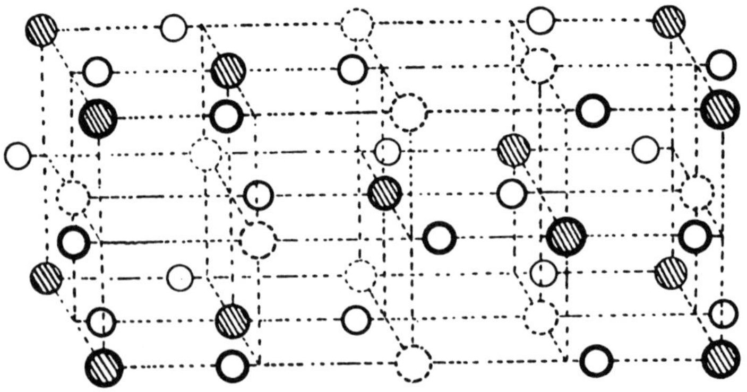

Crystal Structure of Anatase

for the B_{1g} fundamental of rutile. Raman spectroscopy can be used to determine the approximate anatase content of impure rutile.

6. Cadmium Chloride ($CdCl_2$)

The $CdCl_2$ type of structure is trigonal with space group D_{3d}^5, and the unit cell contains a single formula unit. The structure is made up of layers

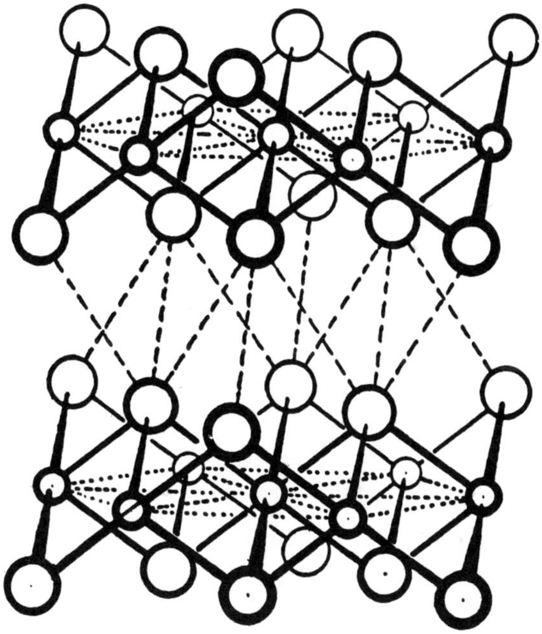

Crystal Structure of Cadmium Chloride

of chloride ions, which are very nearly cubic close-packed, with cadmium ions sandwiched between alternate chloride layers arranged perpendicular to the C axis of the crystal. Each cation is located at the center of an octahedron consisting of six anions and which is compressed along the C direction. The unit cell possesses a center of inversion, and hence, the Raman active modes are infrared inactive.

$$\Gamma = A_{1g}(R) + E_g(R) + A_{2u}(IR, ||^l) + E_u(IR, \perp)$$

So far, only the E_g Raman active mode (*89*) has been experimentally observed. Its frequency is 232 cm^{-1}.*

* The A_{1g} and E_g moles occur at 244 cm^{-1} and 157 cm^{-1} in $MgCl_2$ which has the same structure as $CdCl_2$.

7. Mercuric Iodide (HgI_2)

This compound is of interest on account of the phase change from a red form to a yellow form that occurs at 399°K on increasing the temperature, or at 13 kbar on increasing the pressure. It has a layer type of structure with each mercury atom coordinated by four iodine neighbors arranged at the corners of a regular tetrahedron, and each of these halogen atoms

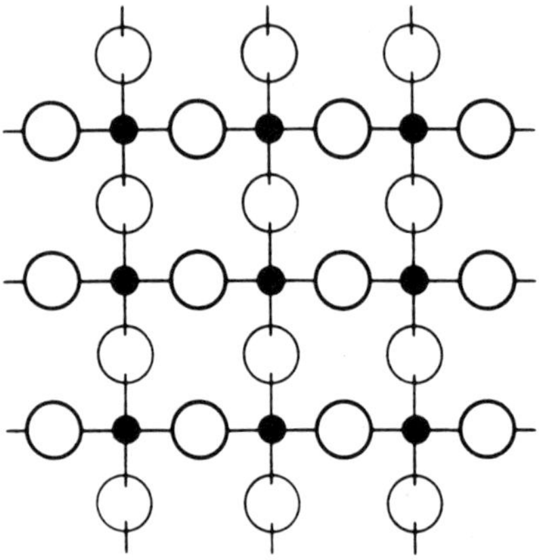

●: Hg; ○: I

Crystal Structure of Mercuric Iodide

is bound to two mercury neighbors to give a sheetlike structure. The crystal as a whole is made up of a superposition of such sheets. In the melt and vapor, HgI_2 molecules occur.

For the red form of the crystal

$$\Gamma = A_{1g}(R)+B_{1g}(R)+B_{2g}(R)+3E_g(R)+A_{2u}(IR, ||^l)+B_{1u}(F)+2E_u(IR, \perp)$$

Mercuric iodide is a very intense Raman scatterer when excited with a He/Ne laser (*90*, *114*) and it is possible to record the spectrum using a spectral slitwidth of 0.25 cm^{-1} and to observe the 17.5 cm^{-1} band. The observation of lines as close as this to the exciting line is possible in comparatively few crystals. A very marked change occurs in the Raman spectrum when the crystal is completely converted to the yellow form which is best considered as a crystal containing HgI_2 molecules. In the red form, four Raman bands are predicted; however, only three strong bands are observed at 17.5, 29, and 114 cm^{-1} (*216*). The weaker bands have been interpreted as being due to two-phonon processes (see Fig. 23).

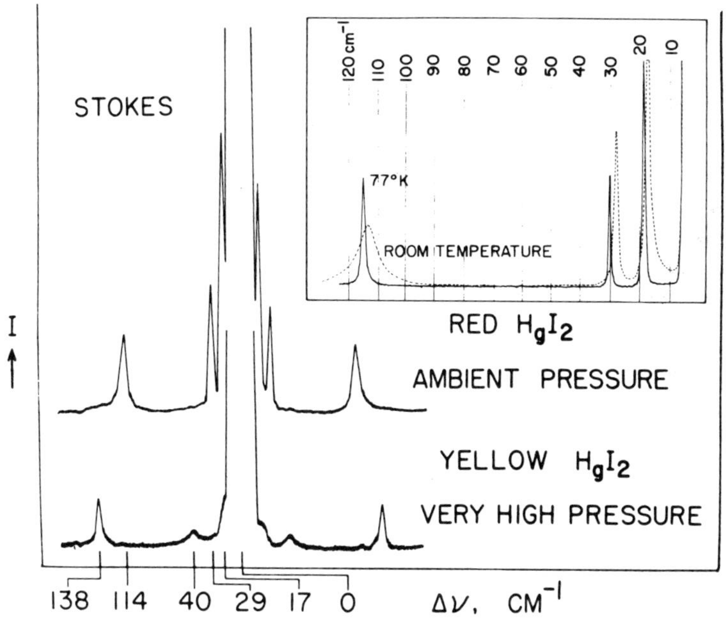

Fig. 23. Raman spectra of HgI_2 in a diamond high-pressure cell in the two phases *(90)*.

8. Molybdenum Disulphide MoS_2

MoS_2 has a layer structure consisting of a sheet of molybdenum atoms sandwiched between two sheets of sulphur atoms. Alternate layers which are identical are held together by very weak van der Waals forces which account for the easy cleavages along the basal plane. MoS_2 belongs to space group D_{6h} ($P6_3/mmc$) and has two formula units in a hexagonal unit cell. The Mo atoms are situated in sites of symmetry D_{3h} whilst the S atoms are located in C_{3v} sites.

$$\Gamma = A_{1g}(R) + A_{2u}(IR, \|^{l}, c) + B_{1u} + 2B_{2g} + E_{1g}(R)$$
$$+ E_{1u}(IR\perp) + E_{2u} + 2E_{2g}(R)$$

Three of the four Raman active modes have been observed using the back-scattering technique. The unobserved vibration certainly has a very low frequency as it involves the relative motion of the layers.

The E_{1u} and E_{2g} modes are expected to be nearly degenerate and it is experimentally observed that their frequencies are the same within the limits of accuracy of measurement. The near degeneracy of the inactive

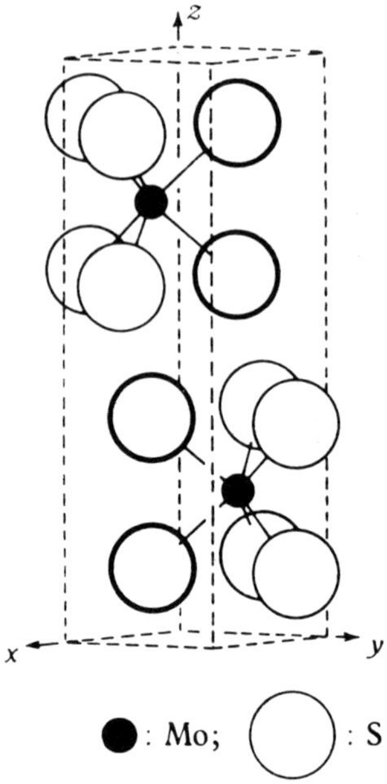

Crystal Structure of Molybdenum Disulphide

E_{2u} mode and Raman active E_{1g} mode should also be noted. Verble and Wieting (*239*) have pointed out that a similar mode degeneracy is likely to be characteristic of all layer compounds with more than one layer in the primitive unit cell.

D. Type AXY

1. Antimony Sulfo-Iodide (SbSI)

This ferroelectric material has an orthorhombic structure with space group D_{2h}^{16}(Pnam). Below the transition temperature at 288°K the space group changes to C_{2v}^{9}(Pna2_1). In both phases there are four formula units in the unit cell. The Raman (*91, 217*) and infrared spectra have been interpreted using a simplified structure having only two SbSI units. The change is then from $C_{2h}^{2}(P2_1/m) \rightarrow C_2^2(P2_1)$, and as there are six atoms in each unit cell there are fifteen optical branches to the phonon dispersion curves. For C_{2h}^{2}, the Raman active modes are, for $\Gamma = 6A_g+3B_g$ and for C_2, $\Gamma = 8A+7B$.

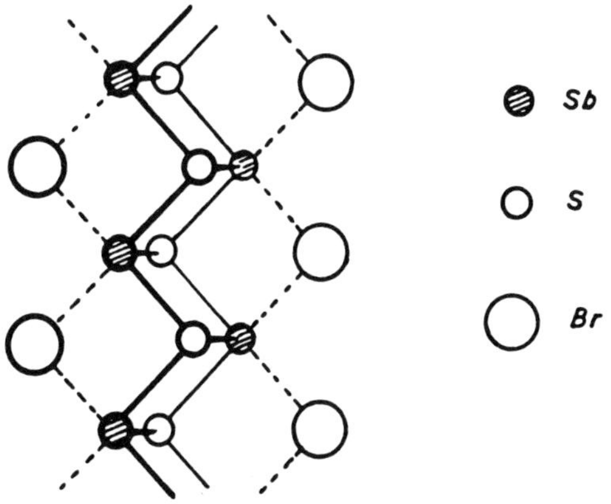

Crystal Structure of Antimony Sulfo-Iodide

Both forms of the Raman tensors are such that A-type modes may be readily distinguished from B-type.

$$A_g, A \qquad \begin{bmatrix} a & d & 0 \\ d & b & 0 \\ 0 & 0 & c \end{bmatrix} \qquad\qquad B_g, B \qquad \begin{bmatrix} 0 & 0 & e \\ 0 & 0 & f \\ e & f & 0 \end{bmatrix}$$

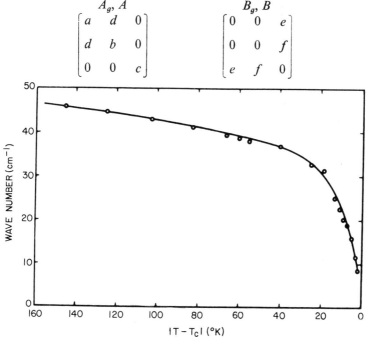

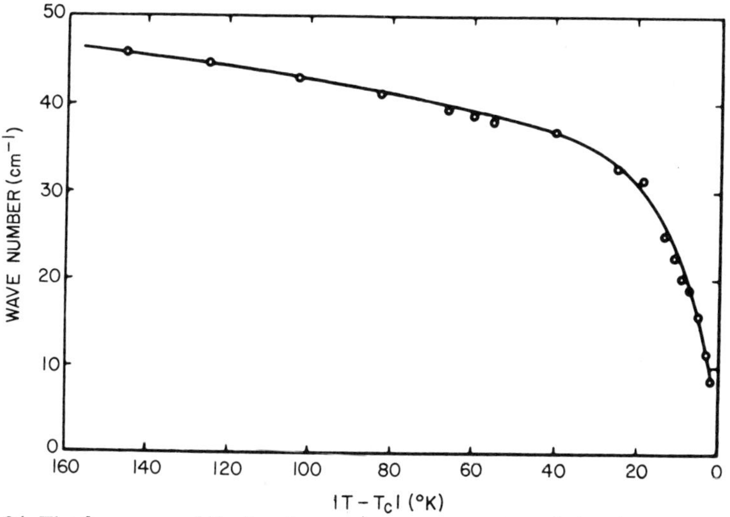

Fig. 24. The frequency of the low frequency transverse; A mode in SbSI plotted as a function of $T_C - T$ in the ferroelectric phase (*91*).

Perry has observed $6A_g$ and $2B_g$ in the paraelectric phase at 300°K and has found a marked change in intensity on cooling as the optical absorption edge (Energy gap = 1.95 eV at 300°K) increases above the exciting laser energy of 1.96 eV. Although the majority of Raman lines are relatively independent of temperature, the band which occurs at 50 cm^{-1} at 100°K moves to a lower frequency as T approaches T_c from below. This is shown in Fig. 24. The softening of this mode completely determines the temperature dependence of the static dielectric constant ε_0' along the c axis in the ferroelectric phase. This mode of vibration can be associated with the soft mode present in the paraelectric phase which has been observed as a peak in ε'' at ~0.5 cm^{-1} at 308°K.

These results confirm that antimony sulfo-iodide is a displacive ferroelectric similar to the peroskovites.

2. Barium Chlorofluoride and Strontium Chlorofluoride (BaClF and SrClF)

Barium chlorofluoride and strontium chlorofluoride have a tetragonal unit cell containing two formula units and having symmetry $D_{4h}^7(P4\ mmm)$. There should be fifteen optical branches to the phonon dispersion curves:

$$\Gamma = 2A_{1g}(R)+B_{1g}(R)+3E_g(R)+2A_{2u}(IR, ||^l c)+2E_u(IR, \perp c)$$

The division of the modes into pairs of even or odd parity, e.g., $E_g - E_u$, $A_{1g} - A_{2u}$, $B_{1g} - A_{2u}$, can be considered as arising from the in-phase and out-of-phase motion of triatomic BaClF groups. The Raman frequencies have been interpreted by Scott (*92*) who has suggested that "internal" Ba-Cl stretching vibrations and "external" vibrations in which BaCl groups move as rigid units occur in these materials. Lithium hydroxide (LiOH) has the same symmetry and the same number of atoms in the unit cell and, consequently, the same selection rules.

E. Type AX_3

1. Lanthanum Trifluoride *etc.*

Several of the rare earth fluorides including LaF_3, CeF_3, PrF_3, and NdF_3 have been studied by Raman spectroscopy, and on the basis of the polarization and intensities, their structures would appear to be the same. The unit cell of $D_{3d}^4(P\bar{3}c1)$ symmetry probably contains six formula units for which the Raman active species are

$$\Gamma = 5A_{1g}(R)+12E_g(R)+6A_{2u}(IR, ||^l)+||E_u(IR, \perp)$$

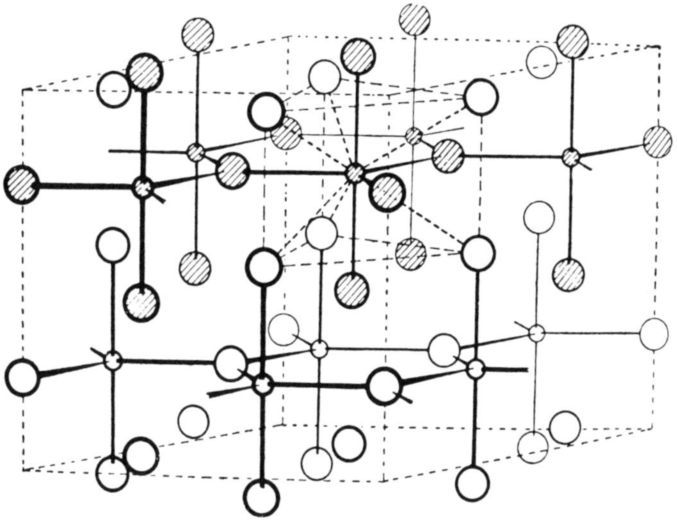

Crystal Structure of Lanthanum Trifluoride

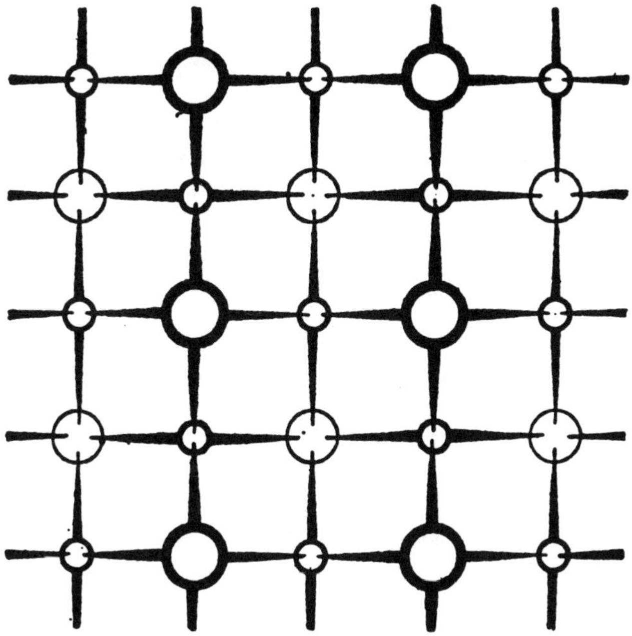

All five A_{1g} and twelve E_g modes have been observed (*95*). In general, the frequencies of the Raman active modes increase from La to Nd, which is to be expected in view of the lanthanide contraction, i.e., the effective ionic radius decreases with increasing atomic number.

2. Lanthanum Trichloride and Lanthanum Tribromide ($LaCl_3$ and $LaBr_3$)

Lanthanum trichloride crystallizes in a hexagonal dipyramidal type of unit cell of space group C_{6h}^2 which contains two formula units. The La^{3+} ions occupy sites of symmetry C_{3h} and the Cl^- sites of symmetry C_s.

$$\Gamma = 2A_g(R)+2B_g(F)+3E_{2g}(R)+2E_{1u}(IR, \perp)+A_u(IR, \perp)$$
$$+2B_u(F)+E_{1g}(R)+E_{2u}(F)$$

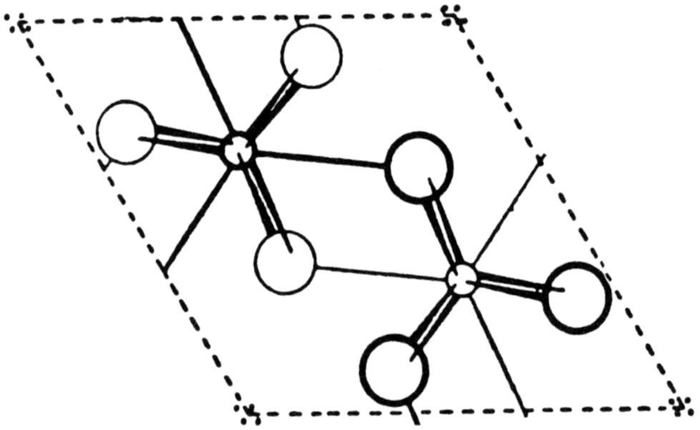

Crystal Structure of Lanthanum Trichloride

Raman spectra have been reported for $LaCl_3$ (*93*), $LaBr_3$ (*94*), and $PrCl_3$ (*223*) which have the same structure; A_g, E_{1g}, and E_{2g} modes are Raman active. The polarizability tensor for the A_g modes has only diagonal elements, that for E_{1g} has only off-diagonal elements, and that for E_{2g} has both. In principle the various modes can be readily differentiated. However, in practice, depolarization due to convergence or to multiple twinning makes this difficult. Figure 25 shows the Raman spectra for $LaBr_3$ at 77°K in which six lines have been identified; three are E_{2g}, two are A_g, and one is E_{1g}. Two of the lines which belong to different symmetry species were found to be separated by only 1.6 cm^{-1}. It was found that the lines could not be resolved at temperatures above 180°K. This clearly shows the importance of recording Raman spectra at low temperatures under high resolution if different components are to be distinguished.

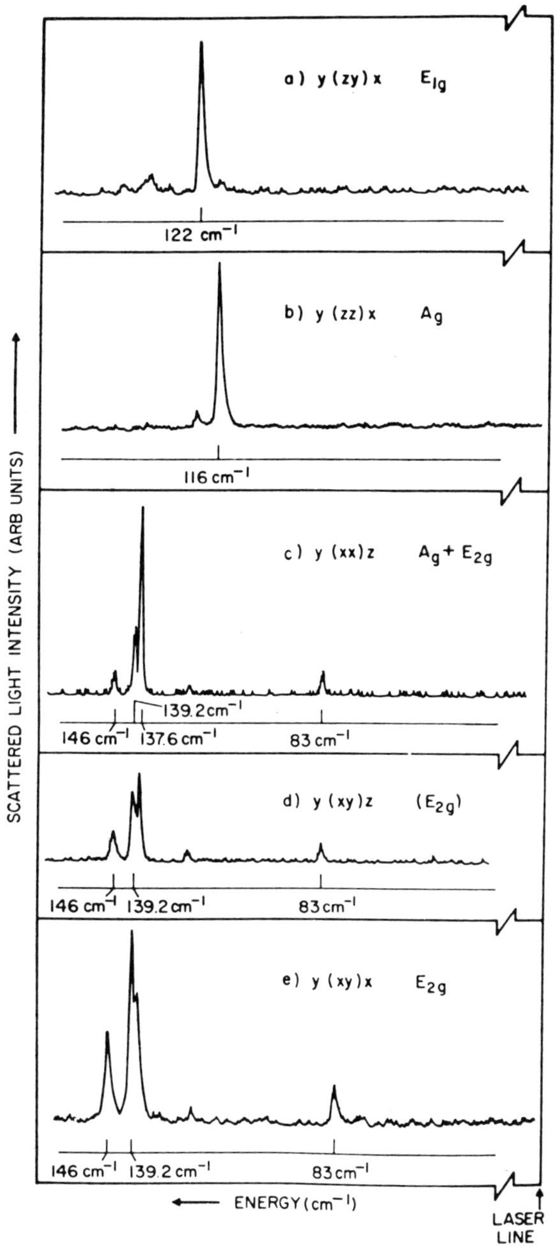

Fig. 25. The Raman spectrum of $LaBr_3$ at 77°K in various polarizations. The irreducible representations of the point group C_{6h} of $LaBr_3$ to which the various Raman tensor components belong are indicated. (a) y(zy)x polarization; (b) y(zz)x; (c) y(xx)z; (d) y(xy)z; the line at 137.6 cm^{-1} arises from depolarization about the optic-axis direction; (e) y(xy)x *(94)*.

F. Type A_2X_2

Mercurous chloride, as well as Hg_2Br_2 and Hg_2I_2, has many of the characteristics of molecular crystals with two molecules in the tetragonal unit cell whose space group is D_{4h}^{17}(I4 *mmm*). The linear molecules are oriented parallel to the crystal *c* axis.

$$\Gamma_{\text{int}} = 4A_{1g}(R) + 2E_{1g}(R) + 2A_{2u}(IR, ||^l) + 2E_{1u}(IR, \perp)$$

$$\Gamma_{\text{rot}} = E_{1g}(R) + A_{2u}(IR, ||^l) + 2E_{1u}(IR, \perp)$$

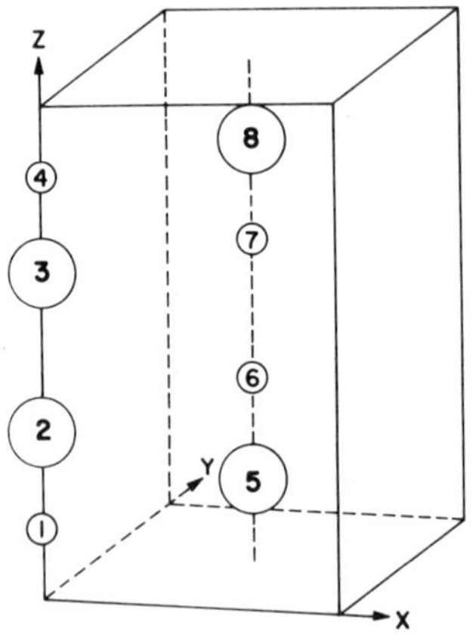

Crystal Structure of Mercurous Chloride

The rotatory mode is observed at 42 cm^{-1}. No splitting of bands due to the internal modes of vibration of the molecules has been observed (*96,88*).

G. Type AXY_2

1. Chalcopyrite ($ZnSiP_2$)

$ZnSiP_2$ crystallizes with the chalcopyrite structure whose space group is $D_{2d}^{12}(I\bar{4}2d)$. The primitive unit cell contains two formula units. Each Zn and Si are tetrahedrally coordinated by four P atoms, and each P atom is tetrahedrally coordinated by two Zn and two Si atoms. If the distinction between Zn and Si is ignored, the structure is seen to be identical with that of zinc blende.

$$\Gamma = A_1(R) + 2A_2(F) + 3B_1(R) + 3B_2(IR, ||^l, R) + 6E(IR, \perp, R)$$

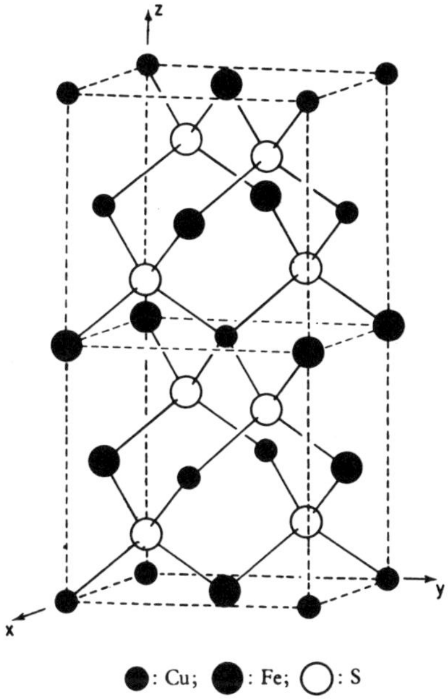

Crystal Structure of Chalcopyrite

Thus, all the $k = 0$ vibrational modes should be Raman active with the exception of the A_2 type. The B_2 and E modes are also infrared active, and it should be possible to observe both longitudinal as well as transverse modes if their oscillator strengths are sufficiently large. The selection rules for each scattering geometry are as follows:

Geometry	Allowed symmetry type
$X(YY)Z$	A_1+B_1
$X(YX)Z$	$B_2(L)+B_2(T)$
$X(ZY)Z$	$E_x(L)+E_x(T)$
$X(ZX)Z$	$E_y(T)$
$X(YZ)Y$	B_2
$X(YZ)Y$	$E_x(L)+E_x(T)$
$X(ZZ)Y$	A_1
$X(ZX)Y$	$E_x(L)+E_y(T)$

Fourteen of the seventeen zone-center optical phonons have been observed by Raman scattering (*97*) and assigned, although for several of the bands the $LO-TO$ splitting was not sufficiently great to be observed.

2. α-$NaFeO_2$

A number of ABX_2 compounds have the α-$NaFeO_2$ layer type structure; A is an alkali metal ion, B = Cr, In, Er, Ho, Y, Yb, and X = O or S (sulfur). They crystallize in the space group D_{3d}^5. The primitive rhombohedral unit cell contains one ABX_2 unit. The ions are arranged in layers perpendicular to the optic axis. The anions form a cubic closely packed

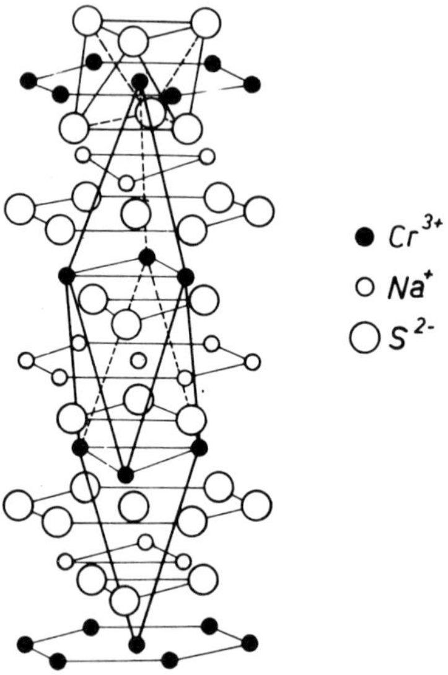

structure while the cations in this packing occupy the octahedral interstices in alternating layers. Twelve branches are expected in the phonon dispersion curves.

$$\Gamma = A_{1g}(R) + 3A_{2u}(IR, ||^l) + E_g(R) + 3E_u(IR)$$

For α_{zz} only the A_{1g} modes should appear, but in α_{xy}, α_{xz}, or α_{yz} only E_g should be active. The Raman spectra of all the 12 compounds listed above have been observed (*98*) and used to calculate the principal force constants, which were found to depend linearly on the shortest distance between the anion layers.

H. Type A_2X_3

1. Corundum (Al_2O_3)

The rhombohedral unit cell contains two formula units and belongs to the space group D_{3d}^6. There are, consequently, twenty seven optical branches to the phonon dispersion curves. The aluminum ions are octahedrally coordinated with two layers of oxygen ions. The site symmetry for the Al^{3+} ions is C_3, whereas the O atoms are on sites having C_2 symmetry. The irreducible representations for the optically active modes are

$$\Gamma = 2A_{1g}(R)+2A_{1u}(F)+3A_{2g}(F)+2A_{2u}(IR, ||^{l})+5E_g(R)+4E_u(IR, \perp)$$

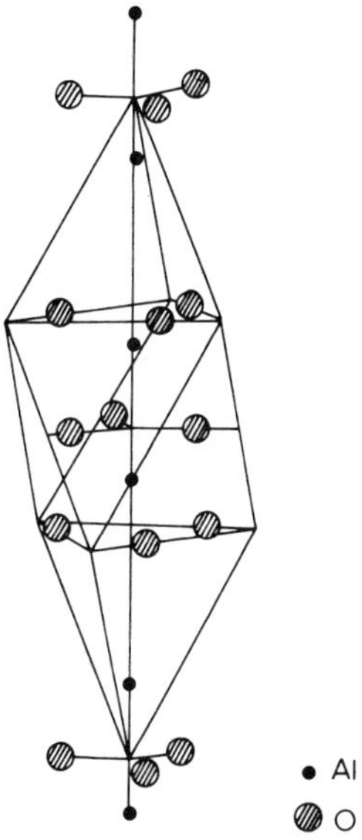

Crystal Structure of Corundum

As there is a center of symmetry in the unit cell all the Raman active modes are forbidden in the infrared, and vice versa.

Corundum is a comparatively weak Raman scatterer (estimated by Krishnan to be one thousandth as great as that for diamond); however, the use of an argon ion laser has permitted the polarized spectrum to be obtained with good signal-to-noise ratio and the symmetries assigned as either A_{1g} or E_g. The A_{1g} modes show bands when $X(ZZ)Y$ observations are recorded while none appear when $Z(XY)X$ are recorded (*99*). The E_g modes appear in the latter but not in the former. The following qualitative prediction can be made after considering the various normal modes: (a) One of the two A_{1g} transitions will have $\alpha_{zz} \gg \alpha_{xx}+\alpha_{yy}$, while for the other A_{1g}, $\alpha_{xx} \gg \alpha_{zz}$; and (b) three of the allowed E_g might be considered to have more internal vibration character, and for such modes $\alpha_{xy} > \alpha_{xz}$ is expected, while the other two E_g modes correspond to external vibrations, and as such the α_{xz} would be expected to be more intense than α_{xy}. All these predictions are confirmed experimentally.

The Raman spectra of Cr_2O_3 and Fe_2O_3, which have the same structure as Al_2O_3, have also been observed (*100*), and results for the three crystals are summarized in Table 12.

TABLE 12

The Raman Active Frequencies (cm^{-1}) for Corundum Type Crystals

Crystal	A_{1g}	E_g	E_g	E_g	E_g	A_{1g}	E_g
Al_2O_3 (*99*)	418	378	432	451	578	645	751
Cr_2O_3 (*100*)	303	—	351	397	530	551	609
Fe_2O_3 (*100*)	226	245	293	298	413	500	612

2. Y_2O_3, Er_2O_3, AND Yb_2O_3

These rare earth oxides have cubic structure (D_{3d}^3, $C\bar{3}m$). The elementary unit cell contains 16 formula units. The 32 rare earth cations are distributed among two different sites; 24 occupy sites with C_2 symmetry and eight ions have the site symmetry C_3.

$$\Gamma = 6A_g + 6E_g + 30F_g + 7A_u + 7E_u + 36F_u$$

Because the physical elementary region is half the size of the unit cell, the number of optical phonon branches is half this number. It is experimentally observed (*101*) that there is a broad gap in frequencies between 200 and 310 cm^{-1} which suggests that the high frequency bands may be assigned to inner vibrations of the REO_6 octahedron. On correlating the vibrational levels of an octahedron in a site of symmetry S_6, the crystal Raman spectrum should consist of $2A_g$, $2E_g$, and $6F_g$ transitions. Observed are $1A_g$, $2E_g$, $5F_g$, and one unassigned. The scattering tensors for the different symmetry types of the group T were transformed from the coordinate system of the cubic crystal ξ, η, ξ whose [111] direction coincides with the direction of the incident laser radiation to the system of experimental observation in which z is the incident laser beam direction and y, the direction of observation. If α, β, γ are the angles which bring the two systems into coincidence, the transformation leads to $R(\alpha, \beta, \gamma)a_i R^{-1}(\gamma, \beta, \alpha)$ for the components of the scattering tensor in the xyz system.

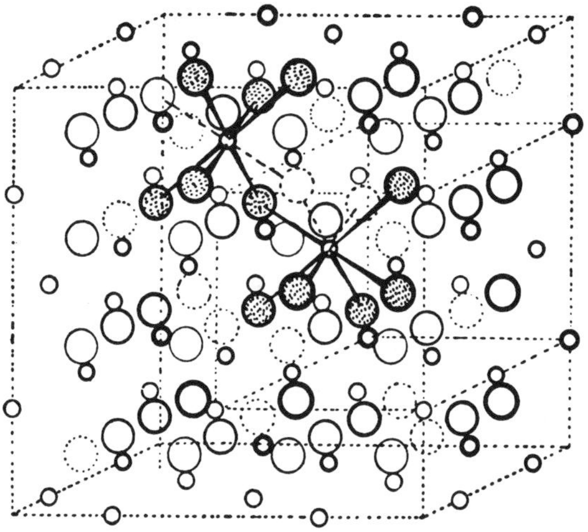

Crystal Structure of Y_2O_3

3. Opiment (As_2S_3)

Arsenic trisulphide crystallizes with four formula units in a monoclinic unit cell of C_{2h} symmetry. As_2S_3 layers occur parallel to the (010) plane and are held together by Van der Waals forces. Covalent bonding occurs between the atoms within the layers. Each arsenic atom has three sulphur neighbours while each sulphur atom is bonded to two arsenic atoms. Spiral chains of As_2S_3 can be distinguished running parallel to the c axis.

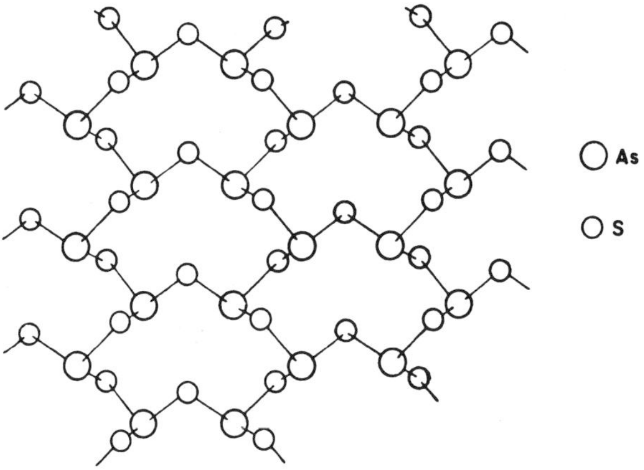

Crystal Structure of Opiment

The unit cell in one layer contains one As_2S_3 unit and belongs to the C_s point group.

$$\Gamma = 5A'(IR\|, R) + 4A''(IR\perp, R)$$

Hence all the modes are both infra-red and Raman active. The Raman spectrum has been reported by Forneris (*240*).

I. Type AXY_3

1. Perovskite

Materials of this type have been the subject of very extensive Raman and infrared studies due to the fact that many of them are ferroelectric (*102–107*). The ferroelectric transition frequently involves a $\mathbf{k} = 0$ optic mode of low frequency which is temperature dependent and which may become zero. Such a mode is usually referred to as being "soft."

There is usually one formula unit in the unit cell which can take several different forms in different materials and at different temperatures. For the cubic form of symmetry O_h^1:

$$\Gamma = 3F_{1u}(IR) + 1F_{2u}(IR)$$

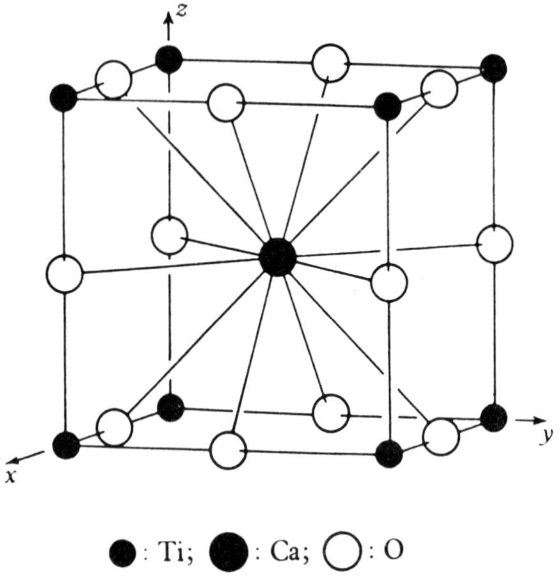

Crystal Structure of Perovskite

Consequently, there is no one-phonon Raman spectrum in this phase. For the tetragonal form of symmetry C_{4v},

$$\Gamma = 3A_1(IR, ||^l R) + B_1(R) + 4E(IR, \perp R)$$

Thus, all the modes in this phase are Raman active, and as the crystal in this phase is piezoelectric the *LO* as well as the *TO* modes are Raman active for the A_1 and *E* type vibrations. There are also orthorhombic and rhombohedral phases.

We will deal with only three examples here which illustrate the type of Raman observations that have been made on perovskites.

a. *Potassium Niobate* ($KNbO_3$)

All these phases occur in potassium niobate, and the dramatic changes (*105*) in spectrum that occur at the phase transitions are shown in Fig. 26.

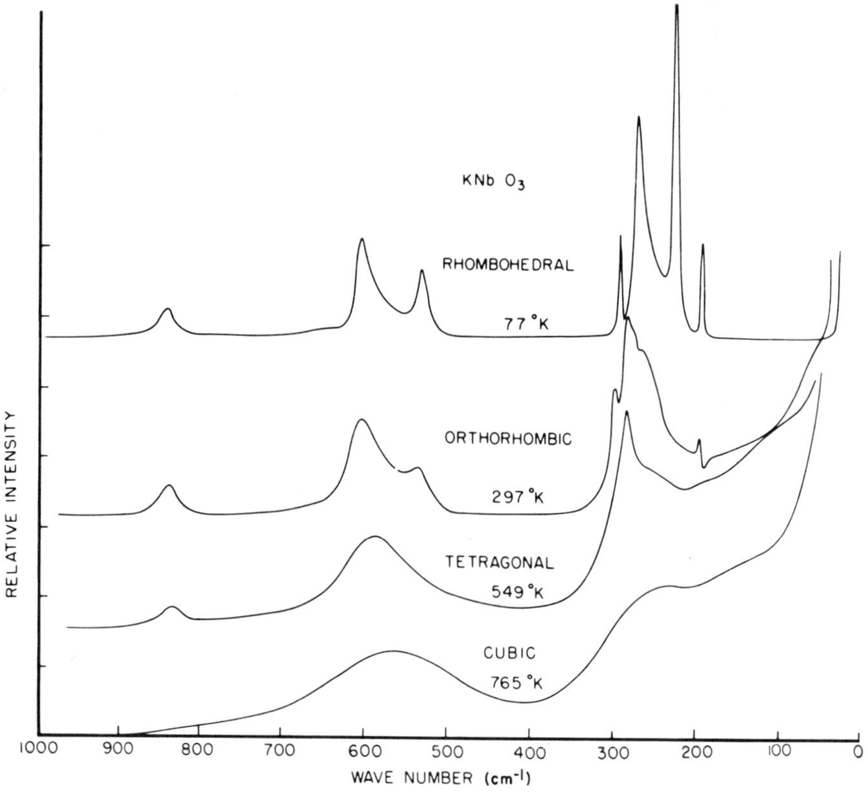

Fig. 26. Raman spectra of $KNbO_3$ in four phases.

TABLE 13

Comparison of Phonons in Perovskites Undergoing $O_h \rightarrow D_{4h}$ Distortions

Cubic O_h		Tetragonal D_{4h}				Trigonal D_{3d}	
I	II	III	IV	V	VI	VII	VIII
$A_{2u}(\Gamma_2')$	$\sim$800 cm^{-1}	A_{2g}	silent	—	—	A_{2g}	silent
$F_{2g}(\Gamma_{25}')$	$\sim$500 cm^{-1}	E_u	*IR*	—	—	E_u	*IR*
		A_{1u}	silent	—	—	A_{1u}	silent
$F_{1u}(\Gamma_{15})$	$\sim$400 cm^{-1}	E_g	xz, yz	—	—	E_g	xx, −yy, xz, yz, xy
		B_{1g}	xx, −yy	460 cm^{-1}	D	A_{1g}	xx, yy, zz
$E_u(\Gamma_{12}')$	200–300 cm^{-1}	B_{2g}	xy	235 cm^{-1}	N, D (?)	E_g	xx, −yy, xz, yz, xy
		A_{2g}	silent	—	—		
$F_{1u}(\Gamma_{15})$	$\sim$110 cm^{-1}	E_g	xx, yz	143 cm^{-1}	N, D	E_g	xx, −yy, xz, yz, xy
		B_{1g}	xx, −yy	—	—	A_{1g}	xx, yy, zz
$F_{2u}(\Gamma_{25})$	soft	E_g	xz, yz	15 cm^{-1} "A"	N	E_g	xx, −yy, xz, yz, xy
		A_{1g}	xx, yy, zz	48 cm^{-1} "D"	D	A_{1g}	xx, yy, zz

I Zone-corner phonon characters $(\frac{1}{2}, \frac{1}{2}\ \frac{1}{2})$ (π/a).
II Zone-corner phonon frequency, estimated by Cowley.
III Zone-centre symmetries below 110°K.
IV Predicted Raman tensor elements.
V Observed Raman frequencies.
VI Observed Raman symmetries (D = diagonal, N = nondiagonal).
VII, VIII Symmetry and selection rules of modes when the $O_h \rightarrow D_{3d}$ transition occurs, as in $LaAlO_3$.

b. *Strontium Titanate* ($SrTiO_3$)

The cubic tetragonal transition in strontium titanate has been studied by many different techniques including Raman scattering. In the cubic phase there is no one-phonon Raman spectrum. However, below 110°K the unit cell has two formula units in a tetragonal unit cell of space group D_{4h}^{18},

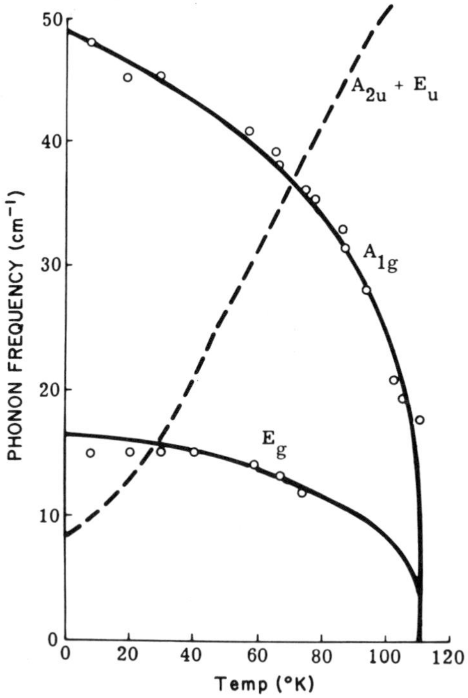

Fig. 27. Temperature dependence of the soft-phonon modes in the tetragonal phase of strontium titanate with zero applied field (*106*).

and hence, there should be twenty seven optical branches to the phonon dispersion curves. The fifteen external modes are as follows:

$$\Gamma_{ext} = A_{1g}(R)+2A_{2g}(F)+E_u(IR,\ \perp)+A_{1u}+3E_g(R)+2B_{1g}(R)+B_{2g}(R)$$

In this phase five sharp Raman lines occur at 15 cm^{-1}, 48 cm^{-1}, 146 cm^{-1}, 235 cm^{-1}, and 460 cm^{-1} (at 15°K).

Table 13 compares the Raman tensor components that are predicted with the experimental results of Worlock, Scott and Fleury (*106*). Because of domain structure the tetragonal axis of the crystal has no unique

MODE	POLARI-ZATION	REPRESEN-TATION		SPLITTING	RAMAN TENSOR
TYPE		O_h	C_{4v}		
IR TO	001		A_1	EXTERNAL FIELD	$\alpha_{XX} = \alpha_{YY}, \alpha_{ZZ}$
IR TO	110	F_{1u}	E	INTERNAL FIELD	α_{XZ}, α_{YZ}
LO	$\bar{1}$10		E		α_{XZ}, α_{YZ}
SILENT	001		B_1	EXTERNAL FIELD	$\alpha_{XX} = -\alpha_{YY}$
SILENT	110	F_{2u}	E		α_{XZ}, α_{YZ}
SILENT	$\bar{1}$10				

Y 010
X 100
Z 001

PHONON
PROPAGATES $\bar{1}$10
ELECTRODE
FIELD DIRECTION 001

SCATTERED LIGHT
INCIDENT LIGHT

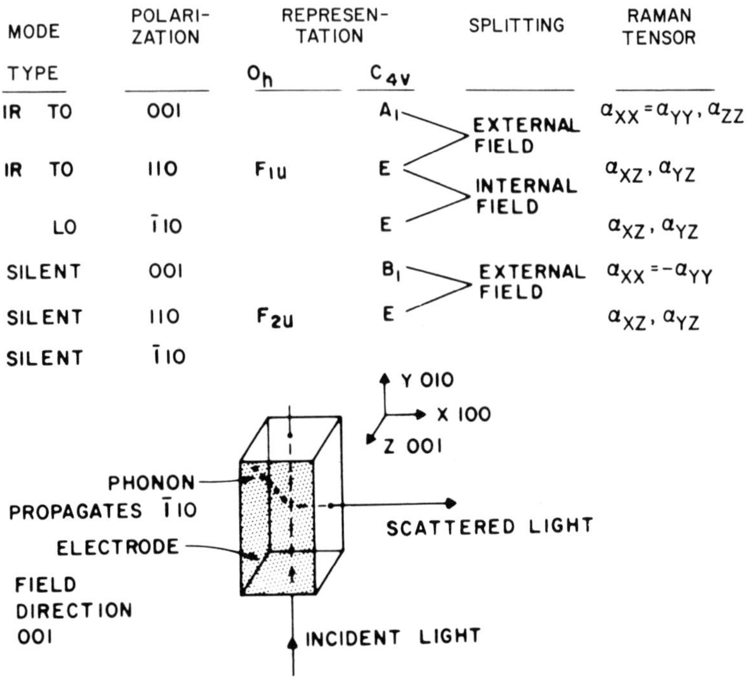

Fig. 28. (a) Symmetries and splittings of various phonon modes in the cubic perovskites. Experimental arrangement as shown forces the A symmetry modes to be transverse. (b) Raman spectra of $KTaO_3$ at 80°K. (1) Intrinsic second order spectrum taken with no applied electric field. The horizontal arrow indicates the frequency range. (2) Electric field induced scattering for the A symmetry low frequency TO mode. E_A was 10,000 V/cm at 210 Hz. Detection at 420 Hz. Intensity units on scale 2 are 1/10 as large as those on scale 1 (*107*).

direction, and it is possible to distinguish only between diagonal and off-diagonal elements in the Raman tensor. Figure 27 shows A_{1g} and E_g modes which decrease in frequency as the temperature approaches the transition point. The solid lines represent curves of the form $v = $ constant $(T_0 - T)^n$ where T_0 is 100°K and n is approximately one third.

c. *Electric Field Induced Scattering in Potassium Tantalate* $(KTaO_3)$

The $KTaO_3$ crystallizes in the cubic perovskite structure, and consequently, there is no one-phonon spectrum. If an electric field is applied, the symmetry of the crystal is reduced to C_{4v}, and hence, some of the

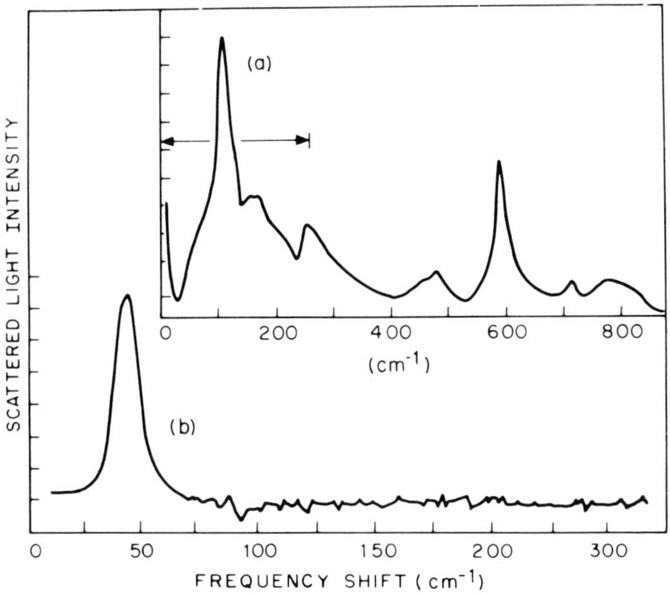

Fig. 28 (cont.)

previously forbidden Raman active modes can be observed *(107)* (see Fig. 28a).

It is assumed that the induced polarizability α_{zz} is proportional to the applied electric field E_A where

$$\alpha_{zz} = \lambda E_A$$

and hence, the induced electric moment responsible for the light scattering is

$$M_z \propto \alpha_{zz} E_z = \lambda E_A E_z$$

where E_z is the magnitude of the optical electric field. The frequency dependence of these parameters is

ν_P for the phonon

ν_O for the laser beam

ν_A for the applied electric field

all of which are sinusoidal. Thus, the dipole moment is expected to have four frequencies

$$\nu_O \pm \nu_P \pm \nu_A$$

The doublets $\nu_O+\nu_P\pm\nu_A$ split by $2\nu_A$ are too close to be seen optically, but their effect can be observed as a beat in the photomultiplier current $I \propto E_A{}^2 \sin 2\pi(2\nu_O t)$. Thus, if a phase sensitive detector is tuned to a frequency $2\nu_O$, only the one-phonon scattering will be observed. This is shown in Fig. 28b where the induced Raman line at 47 cm^{-1} can be clearly distinguished from the second order two-phonon spectrum.

2. Lithium Niobate ($LiNbO_3$)

Lithium niobate is ferroelectric at room temperature. The primitive unit cell contains two formula units, and consequently, there should be thirty branches to the phonon dispersion curves. The crystal space group is $C_{3v}^6(R3c)$.

$$\Gamma = 4A_1(IR||^l c, R)+5A_2(F)+9E(IR\perp c, R)$$

As there is no center of inversion, the A_1 and E modes are both infrared and Raman active, and consequently, the Raman spectra (*108–112*) may be expected to give both LO and TO mode frequencies. Above the Curie temperature $T_c = 1190°C$, the Nb ions become centers of inversion and the Li ions become coplanar with triangles of O ions. The space group is probably $D_{3d}^6(R\bar{3}c)$ where

$$\Gamma = A_{1g}(R)+3A_{2g}(F)+4E_g(R)+2A_{1u}+3A_{2u}(IR, ||^l)+5E_u(IR\perp)$$

Thus, the number of Raman active modes should be 5 above the transition temperature and 13 below. Due to the LO–TO splitting, 26 bands should be observed in the latter case. Barker (*108*) has found and identified 15 of these. From a measurement of the relative intensities of the lines, nonlinear and electro-optic coefficients have been measured. The dependence of the Raman line strength R for different polarizations is given by

$$R = [\varepsilon_i{}^x\varepsilon_s{}^x(c\xi^y+a\xi^z)+\varepsilon_i{}^y\varepsilon_s{}^y(-c\xi^y+a\xi^z)+\varepsilon_i{}^z\varepsilon_s{}^z b\xi^z$$
$$+(\varepsilon_i{}^y\varepsilon_s{}^z+\varepsilon_i{}^z\varepsilon_s{}^y)\, d\xi^y+(\varepsilon_i{}^z\varepsilon_s{}^x+\varepsilon_i{}^x\varepsilon_s{}^z)\, d\xi^x+(\varepsilon_i{}^x\varepsilon_s{}^y+\varepsilon_i{}^y\varepsilon_s{}^x)c\xi^x]^2$$

In this expression ε_1 and ε_2 are the polarization vectors of the incident and scattered light, ξ is the phonon polarization, and a, b, c, and d are the Raman tensor coefficients for a given line. The scattering in $LiNbO_3$ from purely TO modes is much more intense than the scattering by purely LO modes, and consequently, not all the latter could be experimentally detected. Barker has assigned the lowest frequency A_1 transverse mode at 248 cm^{-1}, as the soft mode principally involved in the ferroelectric transition.

3. $LaAlO_3$, $PrAlO_3$, AND $NdAlO_3$

There are two formula units in the unit cell which has space group $D_{3d}^6(R\bar{3}c)$. There are twenty-seven optical branches to the phonon dispersion curves.

$$\Gamma = A_{1u}+3A_{2g}(R)+A_{1g}(R)+4A_{2u}(IR, ||^l)+4E_g(R)+5E_u(IR, \perp)$$

The Al ions are at C_{3i} sites, La ions at D_3, and oxide ions at C_2 sites. The Raman spectrum has been reported by Scott (*113*) who has found that there are soft A_{1g} and E_g modes which are presumably involved in the $D_{3d} \rightarrow O_h$ transition. On plotting the square of the A_{1g} or E_g frequency against temperature, straight lines are obtained which approximately obey a Curie law $\nu^2 \propto (T-T_c)$; however, the values of T_c which are extrapolated from these curves do not appear to be very accurate.

J. Molecular Ionic Crystals

1. TYPE *A* (*XY*)

a. *Lithium Hydroxide and Sodium Hydroxide* (*LiOH and NaOH*)

The Raman spectra of LiOH and NaOH have been studied by Krishnamurti (*224*). Lithium hydroxide crystallizes in a tetragonal unit cell of space group $D_{4h}^7(P4/nmm)$ containing two formula units. The

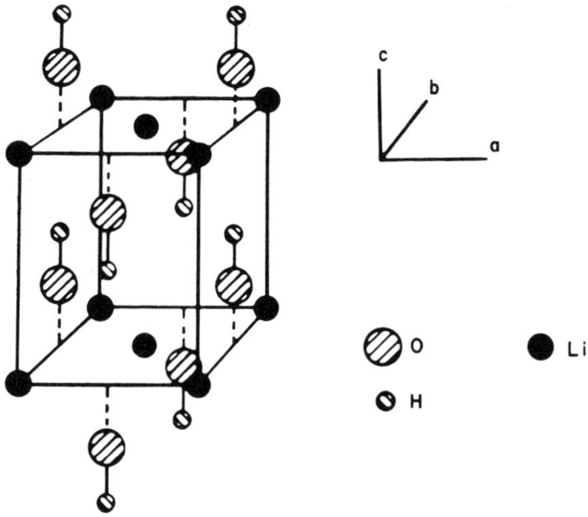

Crystal Structure of Lithium Hydroxide

OH^- ions are located at sites of symmetry C_{4v}. There are fifteen optical branches to the phonon dispersion curves.

$$\Gamma = 2A_{1g}(R)+B_{1g}(R)+2A_{2u}(IR)+3E_g(R)+2E_u(IR, \perp)$$

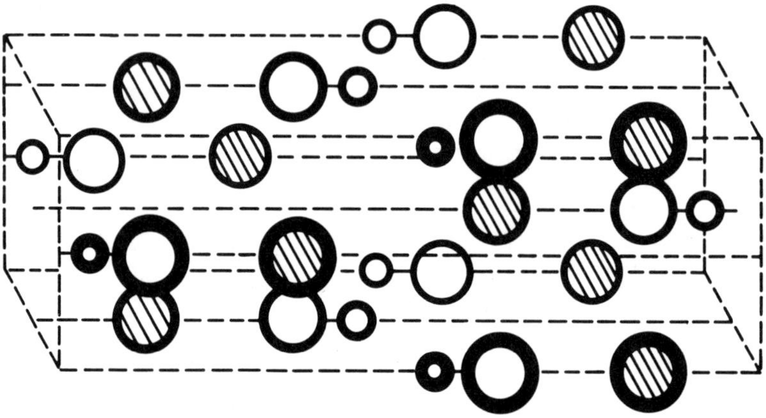

Crystal Structure of Magnesium Hydroxide

2. TYPE $A(XY)_2$

a. *Magnesium Hydroxide and Calcium Hydroxide* [$Mg(OH)_2$ *and* $Ca(OH)_2$]

Magnesium hydroxide belongs to the space group $D_{3d}^3(P\bar{3}m)$ and has one formula unit in the tetragonal unit cell

$$\Gamma_{int} = A_{1g}(R)+A_{2u}(IR, ||^l)$$

$$\Gamma_{trans} = A_{1g}(R)+E_g(R)+A_{2u}(IR, ||^l)+E_u(IR, \perp)$$

$$\Gamma_{rot} = E_g(R)+E_u(IR, \perp)$$

Only A_{1g} modes are observed when the α_{zz} polarizability tensor element is examined. The E_g modes can be seen in α_{xz} and α_{xy} spectra.

Crystal	Translatory A_g	Rotatory E_g	OH internal
$Ca(OH)_2$	359 cm^{-1}	256 cm^{-1}	3620 cm^{-1}
$Ca(OD)_2$	351	185	2672
$Mg(OH)_2$	445	280	3652
$Mg(OD)_2$	—	—	2696

In both $Mg(OH)_2$ and $Ca(OH)_2$ broad peaks are observed (*115*)—in the first at 725 cm^{-1} and in the second at 680 cm^{-1}, which have the character of E_g modes. However, these are probably not fundamentals but result from two-phonon processes.

3. Type $A(XY_2)$

a. *Potassium Bifluoride* (KHF_2)

Potassium bifluoride has a tetragonal unit cell of space group D_{4h}^{18} (*I*4/*mcm*) which contains two formula units, and hence, there are twenty one optical branches to the phonon dispersion curves.

$$\Gamma_{\text{int}} = A_{1g}(R)+B_{2g}(R)+A_{2u}(\text{I}R, \|^{l})+B_{1u}+2E_u(IR, \perp)$$

$$\Gamma_{\text{trans}} = A_{2g}+E_g(R)+A_{2u}+B_{1u}+2E_u(IR, \perp)$$

$$\Gamma_{\text{rot}} = A_{2g}+B_{1g}(R)+E_g(R)$$

A small contraction in the hydrogen bond length on deuteration has been confirmed through a frequency shift of the symmetric stretching mode, F-H-F in the Raman spectrum (*115*).

4. Type $A(XYZ)$

a. *Potassium Thiocyanate* (*KNCS*)

The Raman spectrum of KNCS has been studied by Dao and Wilkinson (*225*). The crystal structure of KNCS is orthorhombic and the D_{2h} unit cell contains four formula units. The potassium ions are located on the twofold axis. The linear NCS ions are arranged in planes perpendicular to the *b* axis and are oriented so that ions are almost at right angles to one another. The unit cell has dimensions a = 6.66 Å, b = 6.635 Å, and c = 7.58 Å, and hence, the crystal is almost uniaxial. The activities of the normal modes of vibration are as follows:

$$\Gamma_{\text{int}} = 3A_g(R)+1A_u(F)+3B_{1g}(R)+1B_{1u}(IR)+1B_{2g}(R)$$
$$+3B_{2u}(IR)+1B_{3g}(R)+3B_{3u}(IR)$$

$$\Gamma_{\text{rot}} = 1A_g(R)+1A_u(F)+1B_{1g}(R)+1B_{1u}(IR)+1B_{2g}(R)$$
$$+1B_{2u}(IR)+1B_{3g}(R)+1B_{3u}(IR)$$

$$\Gamma_{\text{trans}} = 4A_g(R)+2A_u(F)+4B_{1g}(R)+1B_{1u}(IR)$$
$$+2B_{2g}(R)+3B_{2u}(IR)+2B_{3g}(R)+3B_{3u}(IR)$$

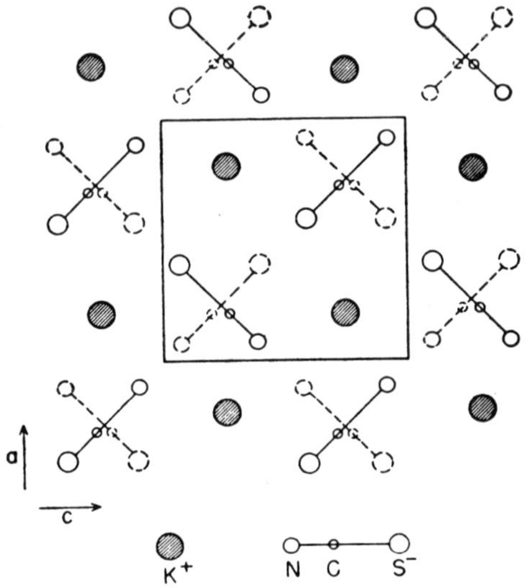

Crystal Structure of Potassium Thiocyanate

5. Type $A(X_3)_2$

a. *Barium Azide* $[Ba(N_3)_2]$

Barium azide is monoclinic with two formula units in the unit cell which belongs to space group $C_{2h}^2(P2_1/m)$.

$$\Gamma = 14A_g(R)+7B_g(R)+6A_u(IR)+12B_u(IR)$$

There are two different types of azide ion. Azide I ions, which are symmetric, are oriented parallel to the crystal *a* axis; and the azide II ions, which are not symmetric, have N_1-N_2 and N_2-N_3 distances of 1.177 and 1.158 Å, respectively, and lie parallel to the *C* axis. The A_g modes

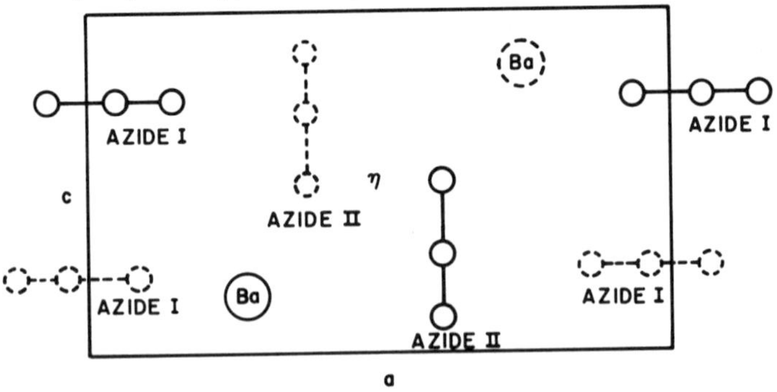

Crystal Structure of Barium Azide

lead (*116*) to finite values of α_{xx}, α_{yy}, α_{zz}, and α_{xy}; B_g modes lead to α_{xz} and α_{yz}.

6. Type $A(XY_2)$

a. *Sodium Nitrite* ($NaNO_2$)

At room temperature the sodium nitrite unit cell is orthorhombic with space group $C_{2v}^{20}(Imm)$, as shown in Fig. 29.

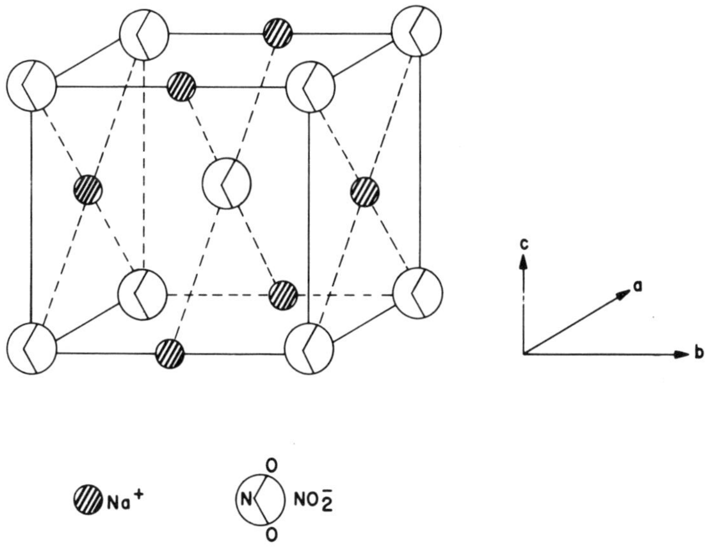

Fig. 29. Structure of $NaNO_2$ in its ferroelectric phase.

The primitive cell contains a single formula unit, and hence, there are nine optical branches to the phonon dispersion curves at $\mathbf{k} = 0$:

$$\Gamma_{\text{int}} = 2A_1(IR||^l b, R) + B(IR||^l c, R)$$

$$\Gamma_{\text{ext}} = A(IR||^l b, R) + A_2(R) + 2B_1(IR||^l c, R) + 2B_2(IR||^l a, R)$$

All the modes are Raman active and are readily distinguished, as shown in Fig. 30. Because A_1, B_1, and B_2 modes are infrared active, longitudinal optic modes are observed as well as transverse optic modes. With the exception of the A_1 translatory mode, all the expected Raman active lines have been observed and identified (*117–122*). The frequencies of all the

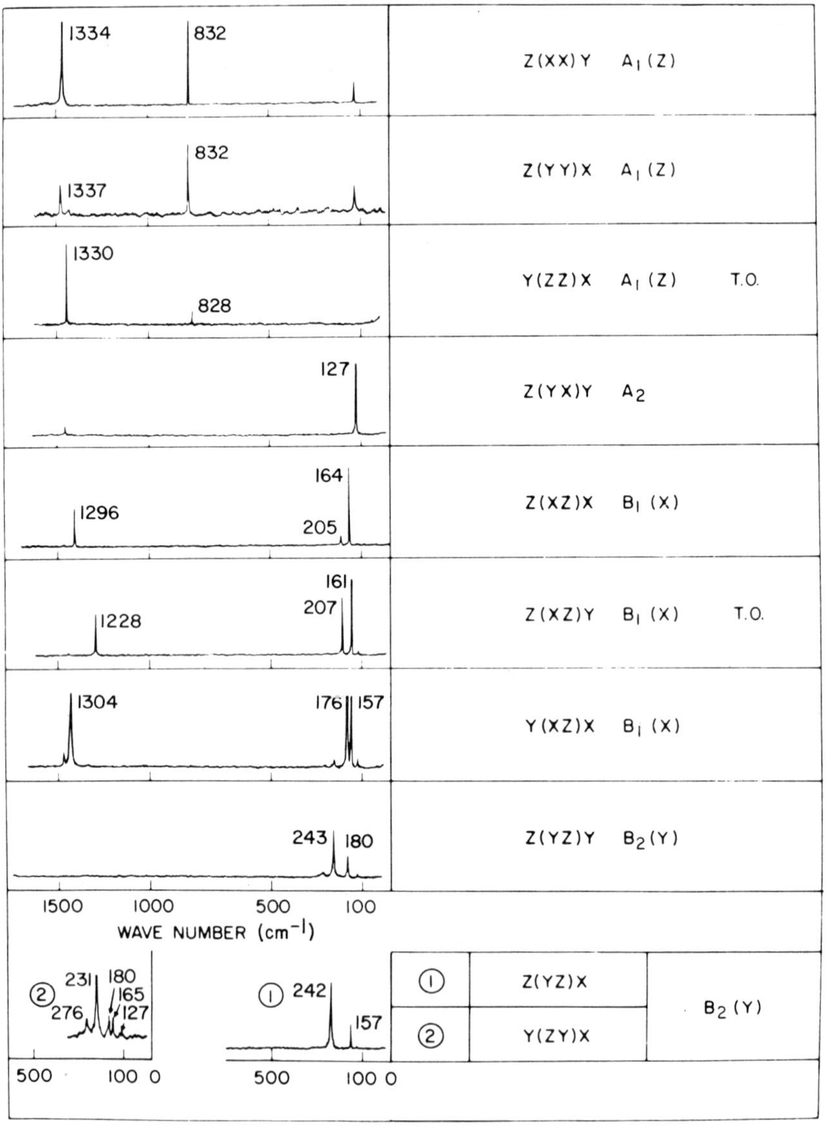

Fig. 30. The Raman spectra of sodium nitrite for different orientations showing the identification of the various lines to normal modes of vibration (*122*).

B-type modes depend upon the orientation of the phonon propagation vector with respect to the crystallographic axes. The largest shift occurs for the asymmetric stretching vibration whose vibrational frequency varies from 1226 to 1360 cm^{-1}. The observed frequency can be represented to a first approximation by

$$\nu = \nu_{TO} + (\nu_{LO} - \nu_{TO}) \cos^2 \theta$$

where θ is the angle between the phonon propagation and polarization directions. Figure 31 shows this variation in frequency of the internal B_1 mode for phonon wave vectors inclined at an angle of 40.7° with the crystallographic z axis, i.e., the b axis. This angle was selected rather than 45° because the crystal is biaxial, and hence, $|\mathbf{k}_i| \neq |\mathbf{k}_s|$. The angle θ between the phonon wave vector $\mathbf{k}$ and the phonon polarization angle can easily be expressed (*122*) in terms of the angle α to give

$$\nu = \nu_{TO} + (\nu_{LO} - \nu_{TO}) 0.42 \sin^2 \alpha$$

The LO frequency for this mode obtained from infrared reflection studies is 1362 cm^{-1} and from $Y'(X'Z)X'$ Raman observation is 1360 cm^{-1}. Hence

$$\nu = 1226 + 55 \sin^2 \alpha$$

As can be seen from Fig. 31 this approximation is not particularly good.

The measured Raman halfwidths for these lines vary from 12 cm^{-1} for the TO mode to 2.9 cm^{-1} for the LO mode indicating that the latter has a longer lifetime than the former.

Asawa (*122*) poses the question why only the asymmetric vibrations show a large frequency shift with orientation. The answer is that these are usually the most intense infrared transitions, and consequently, the differences between ν_{LO} and ν_{TO} are large.

Sodium nitrite undergoes a phase transition at 163°C (436°K), and the symmetry of the unit cell becomes $D_{2h}^{25}(Immm)$ for which

$$\Gamma_{\text{int}} = A_g(R) + B_{1u}(IR||^l b) + B_{2u}(IR||^l a) + B_{3u}(IR||^l c)$$

$$\Gamma_{\text{trans}} = B_{1u}(IR||^l b) + B_{2u}(IR||^l a) + B_{3u}(IR||^l c).$$

$$\Gamma_{\text{rot}} = B_{1g}(R) + B_{2g}(R)$$

As the crystal now has a center of inversion, the various modes of vibration are infrared or Raman active, but not both. The change in the Raman spectrum through the transition has been recorded as the temperature is changed. Two B_1 type bands, which occur at 155 cm^{-1} and

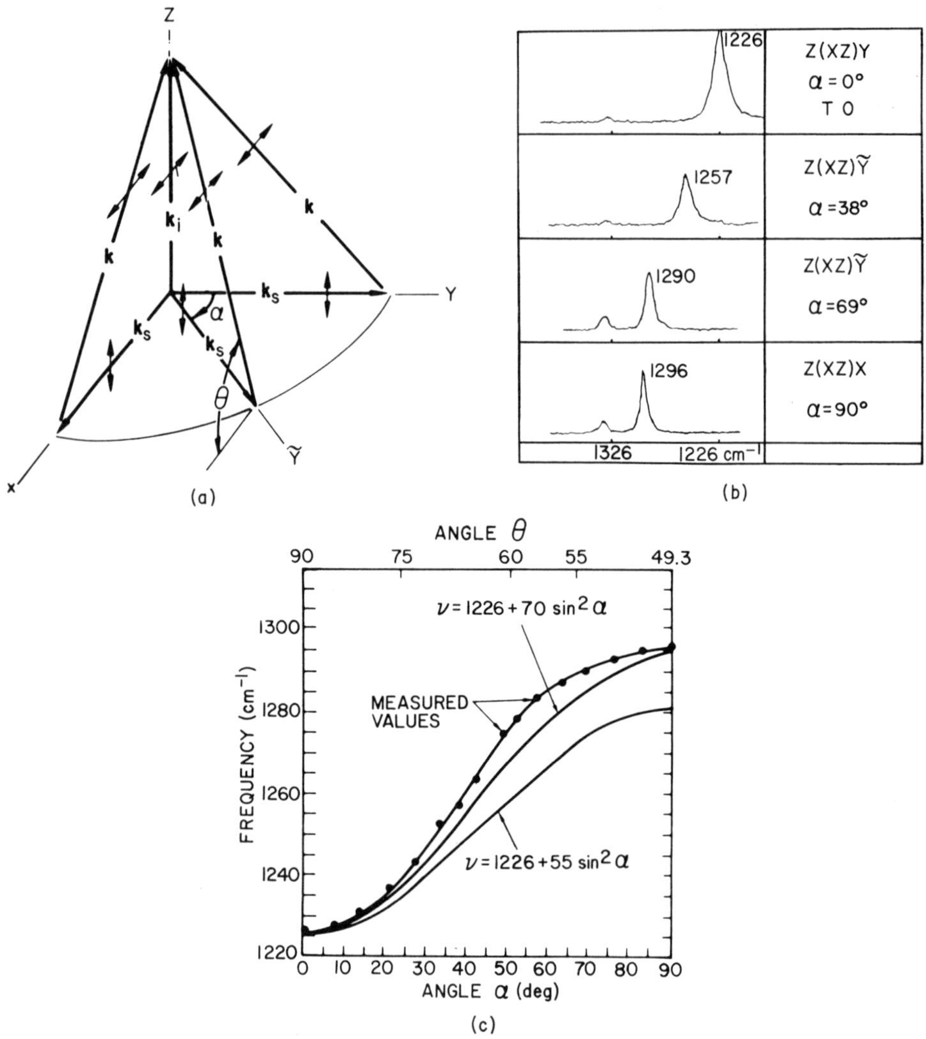

Fig. 31. (a) Polarization and orientation of the photon and phonon propagation wave vectors with respect to the crystal axes. $\mathbf{k}_i$: incident photon; $\mathbf{k}_s$: scattered photon; $\mathbf{k}$: optical phonon. α is the angle between the y axis and $\mathbf{k}_s$. The B_1 (x) phonon is polarized along x. When the $\mathbf{k}_s$ direction is along y, a pure transverse wave is excited, whereas when the $\mathbf{k}_s$ direction is along x, a mixed transverse longitudinal wave occurs. θ is the angle between the phonon propagation direction and the phonon polarization direction. (b) Spectra of the phonon frequency shifts with propagation direction change. The $B_1(x)$ mode, the asymmetric internal vibration of the NO_2^- molecule near 1250 cm^{-1}, exhibited a large frequency shift with changing phonon propagation direction. The mode is observed with the $z(xz)\tilde{y}$ scattering, where $\tilde{y}$ lies in the xy plane. The $B_1(x)$ mode frequency change as the propagation direction is rotated about the z axis by the angle α from the zy plane is shown for $\alpha = 0°$, 38°, 69°, and 90°. The weak line near 1330 cm^{-1} is a depolarized $A_1(z)$ component. (c) Frequency of the $B_1(x)$ mode as a function of the angle α and θ for the geometry of (a). The two simplified theoretical curves discussed in the text are shown (*137*).

162 cm^{-1} at room temperature, decrease in frequency as the crystal is heated and, at the transition temperature, fall markedly in frequency to 124 cm^{-1} where only a single frequency is observed. The other modes of vibration show little change in frequency. If in the low temperature phase there are B_1 and B_2 modes at the transition, we have

$$B_1 \rightarrow B_{2g} \quad \text{and} \quad B_2 \rightarrow B_{2u}$$

Only the first will then be Raman active. These are translatory modes parallel to the c (162 cm^{-1}) and b (155 cm^{-1}) axes. An inspection of experimental X-ray measurements on the variation of the cell dimension through the transition shows that c and a undergo marked changes at the phase change.

7. Type $A(XY_3)$

a. *Calcite* [$CaCO_3$, $LiNO_3$, $NaNO_3$, *and* KNO_3 *(Phase I)*]

The calcite structure belongs to the space group D_{3d}^6 with the cations occupying S_6 and the anions, D_3 sites. The latter are oriented with the molecular ion planes perpendicular to the crystal c axis. There are two

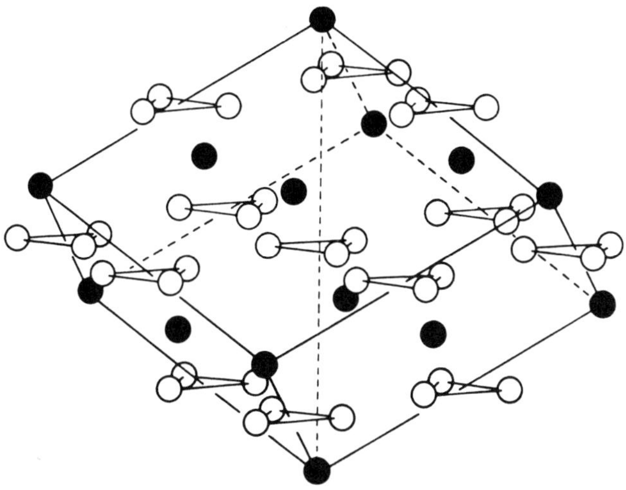

●: Ca; ○: O

Crystal Structure of Calcite

formula units in the unit cell, and consequently, twenty-seven optical branches are expected to the phonon dispersion curves.

$$\Gamma = A_{1g}(R)+2A_{1u}(F)+3A_{2g}(F)+3A_{2u}(IR, ||^{l})+4E_g(R)+5E_u(IR, \perp)$$

The Raman spectrum is dominated by the A_{1g} symmetric stretching mode of the anion. The E_g asymmetric stretching and bending modes give rise

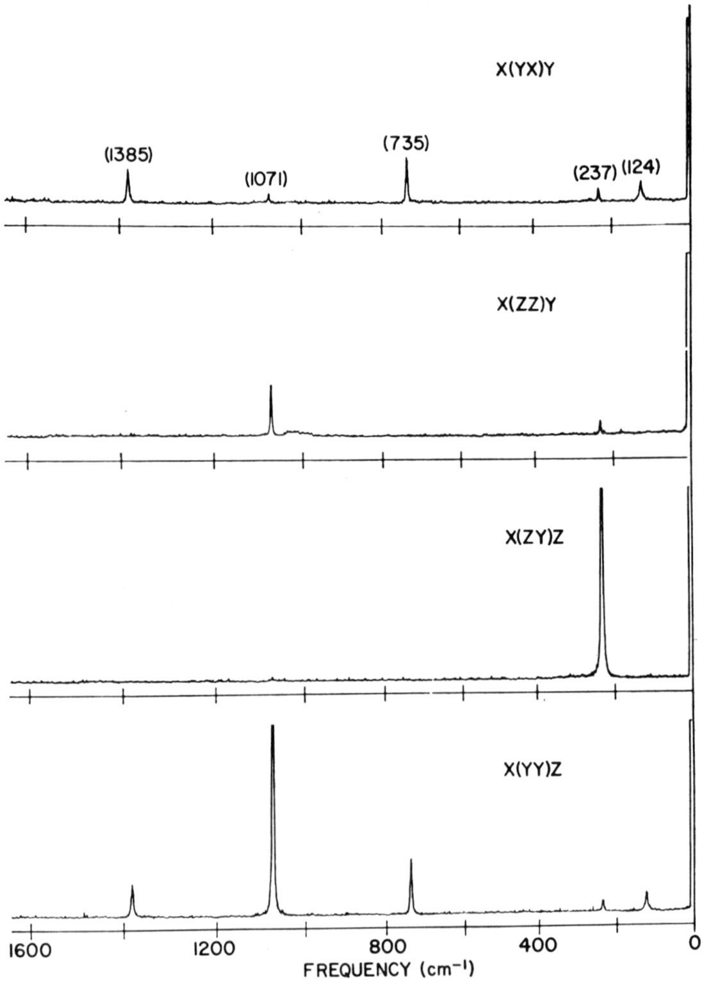

Fig. 32. Raman spectra of $LiNO_3$ in the four unique polarization orientations (*124*).

to much weaker Raman lines. Two Raman active external modes of vibration of E_g-type symmetry occur. The higher frequency mode is rotatory, while the lower frequency one is translatory in origin. Polarized Raman studies have been reported for $CaCO_3$ (*123*), $LiNO_3$ (*124*), $NaNO_3$ (*126*), and KNO_3 (phase I) (*130*).

By using a $Na^{15}NO_3$ crystal Leroi et al. (*126*) have confirmed that the lower frequency external mode is of translatory origin by observing a downward shift of 0.8 cm^{-1} for this band in the isotopically enriched sample. This observation was made at 35°K, and it was also observed that both external mode frequencies increased by about 15 cm^{-1} at this temperature. The halfwidths of 10 cm^{-1}(T) and 18 cm^{-1}(R) narrowed considerably on cooling to 2 cm^{-1} and 3.5 cm^{-1}, respectively. The Raman spectra for $LiNO_3$ are shown in Fig. 32 for the four unique polarization orientations. The Raman scattering is strong enough to permit the identification of isotopically substituted ^{18}O and ^{15}N in natural abundance at 1050 and 1354 cm^{-1}, respectively, shifted by 21 cm^{-1} and 30 cm^{-1} from the normal species. The overtones $2\nu_1$, $2\nu_2$, $2\nu_4$ and combination tone $\nu_3+\nu_4$ were also observed; however, despite a careful search no combinations between nitrate ion internal modes and external modes could be found. Potassium nitrate has been studied in the calcite phase by both Balkanski (*130*) and by Nakagawa (*127*). The former workers report a value of 1428 cm^{-1}, but this would appear to be $2\nu_2$ since they observed ν_2 at 714 cm^{-1}. The correct value for ν_3 at 160°C would appear to be 1390 cm^{-1}.

There is little variation in the frequency of ν_1, ν_3, and ν_4 on changing the cation from Li to Na to K. However, the rotatory and translatory modes show more marked shifts.

	Rotatory (cm^{-1})	Translatory (cm^{-1})
$LiNO_3$	237	124
$NaNO_3$	185	98
KNO_3 (160°C)	120	81

These modes of vibration do not involve the cation, and consequently, the shifts must be due to a change in the distance between the nitrate ions. Nakagawa (*127*) has shown that the two Raman active frequencies are governed almost exclusively by the force constant $f(0 \ldots 0)$. The principal interaction force constant $f(M^+ \ldots 0)$ is 0.12 millidyn/Å in both Li and $NaNO_3$ and has a value of 0.095 millidyn/Å in KNO_3. These values are very similar to the force constant $f(M^+ \ldots Cl^-)$ in the alkali halides.

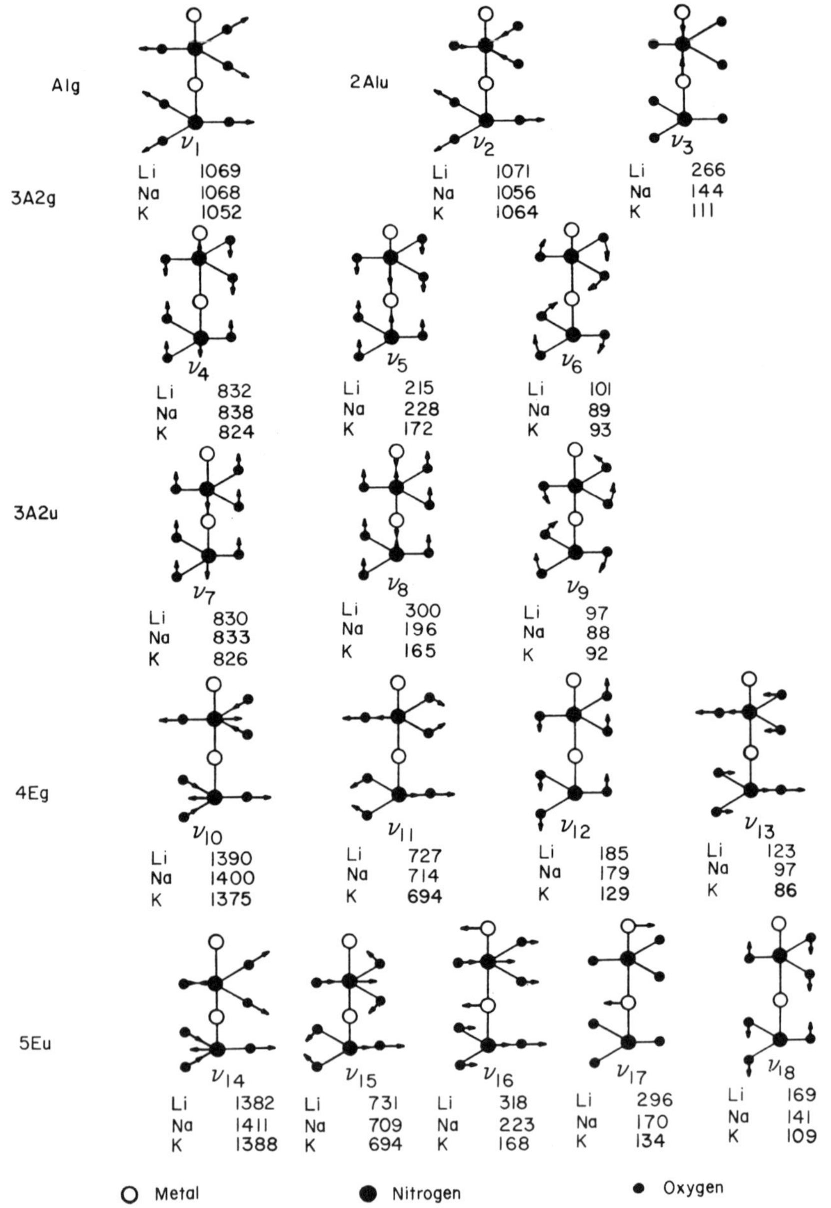

Fig. 33. The vibrational modes of the alkali metal nitrates. All listed frequencies in cm^{-1} are calculated values. For the degenerate species (E_g and E_u), only one component of a degenerate pair is drawn for each mode (*127*).

The vibrational modes of the alkali metal nitrates together with Nakagawa's calculated frequencies are shown in Fig. 33. He has used 11 force constants to calculate 18 frequencies of which 11 have been observed.

In calcite the α_{zx} component for the 283 cm^{-1} band is greater than for the 156 cm^{-1} band; the halfwidth of the former is also greater than for the latter. Comparing these observations with $NaNO_3$ it would appear that the higher frequency mode is rotatory and the lower frequency mode is translatory. Measurements (*125*) on the temperature behavior of the A_{1g} CO_3 symmetric stretching mode at 1086 cm^{-1} show that it has a halfwidth of about 1.1 cm^{-1} at 300°K and is much narrower, $\sim$0.4 cm^{-1}, at liquid helium temperature. The frequency is very insensitive to the application of pressure to the crystal or to other changes in environment, e.g., in aragonite the frequency is 1087 cm^{-1}.

b. *Aragonite* [$CaCO_3$ *and* KNO_3 *(Phase II)*]

Aragonite is another form of $CaCO_3$ with four formula units in the orthorhombic unit cell of space group $D_{2h}^{16}(Pnma)$. There are fifty seven optical branches to the phonon dispersion curves. While the symmetry of the anion in calcite is D_3, it is C_6 in aragonite.

$$\begin{aligned}
\Gamma_{\text{int}} &= 4A_{1g}(R)+2A_{2g}(R)+4B_{1g}(R)+2B_{2g}(R)+2A_{1u}(F)\\
&\quad +4A_{2u}(IR)+2B_{1u}(IR)+4B_{2u}(IR)\\
\Gamma_{\text{rot}} &= A_{1g}(R)+2A_{2g}(R)+B_{1g}(R)+2B_{2g}(R)+2A_{1u}(F)\\
&\quad +A_{2u}(IR)+2B_{1u}(IR)+B_{2u}(IR)\\
\Gamma_{\text{trans}} &= 4A_{1g}(R)+2A_{2g}(R)+4B_{1g}(R)+2B_{2g}(R)+2A_{1u}+3A_{2u}(IR)\\
&\quad +B_{1u}(IR)+3B_{2u}(IR)
\end{aligned}$$

Some studies have been carried out on aragonite itself (*128*). However, the crystal potassium nitrate is more interesting, since it can be obtained at atmospheric pressure in three different crystallographic phases by varying the temperature. In phase II the structure is of the aragonite type. This form is stable from room temperature to about 130°C. Above this temperature, phase I exists which has the calcite structure.

In the temperature range 125–105°C a ferroelectric phase III is obtained by cooling, and this phase has C_{3v}^5 symmetry with one formula unit in the unit cell for which

$$\begin{aligned}
\Gamma_{\text{int}} &= 2A_1(IR, ||^l, R)+2E(IR, \perp, R)\\
\Gamma_{\text{trans}} &= A_1(IR, ||^l, R)+E(IR, \perp, R)\\
\Gamma_{\text{rot}} &= A_2(F)+E(IR, R)
\end{aligned}$$

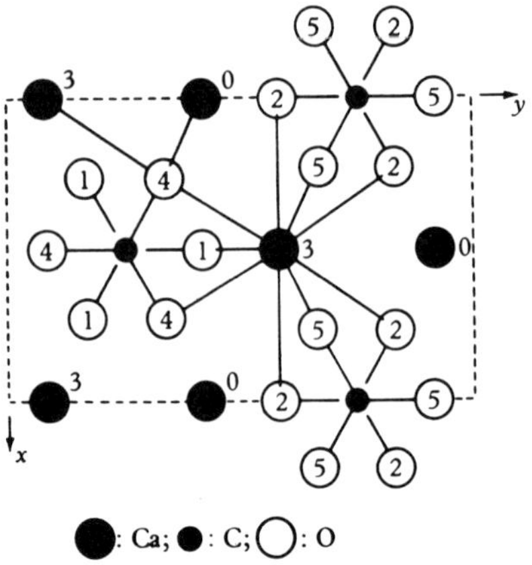

Crystal Structure of Aragonite

Balkanski (*130*) and Krishnan (*131*) have shown from studies of the Raman spectra of the various structures, that a close correspondence exists between the normal modes of the different phases. All the predicted covalent and rotational modes were found, and the agreement between group theory predictions and experimental results is almost perfect.

c. *Sodium Chlorate* (*NaClO*$_3$)

In both sodium chlorate and sodium bromate there are four formula units in the cubic unit cell which belongs to the space group $T^4(P2, 3)$. The internal modes of the molecular ions may be treated separately.

$$\Gamma_{\text{int}} = 2A(R)+2E(R)+6F(IR, R)$$
$$\Gamma_{\text{ext}} = 3A(R)+3E(R)+8F(IR, R)$$

$NaClO_3$ is one of the few examples where all the optical modes in a crystal ion can be observed by Raman spectroscopy (*133*). Further, as there is no center of inversion both the *TO* and *LO* mode frequencies can be obtained. The correlation diagram for the internal modes together with the observed frequencies are shown in Fig. 34; ν_1 and ν_3 are the symmetric and asymmetric stretching modes of the chlorate ions, and ν_2 and ν_4 are the corresponding bending modes. The low frequency vibrational levels are shown in Fig. 35. These are separated into three groups. The two lowest frequency groups of levels involve translatory motion, while the high frequency levels are due to rotatory motion of the chlorate ions.

The static dielectric constant ε_0' has a temperature dependence that is typical of a ferroelectric material with a transition temperature of 593°K.

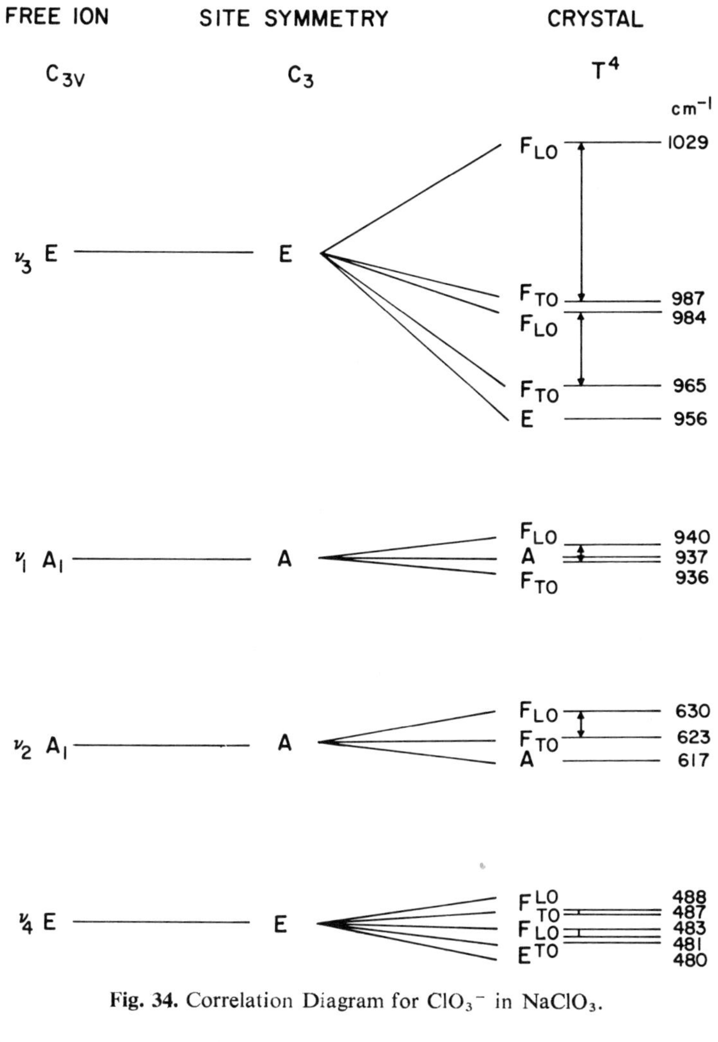

Fig. 34. Correlation Diagram for ClO_3^- in $NaClO_3$.

The Raman lines show little variation in frequency with temperature except for the 200 cm^{-1} mode (at 100°K) which shifts to lower frequency and broadens as the temperature is increased. The shift between 83°K and 483°K is 45 cm^{-1}. This increase only qualitatively explains the temperature dependence of the dielectric constant ε_0'.

The Raman tensors for both the A and E modes have only diagonal components. These can be separated by rotating the crystal through 45°

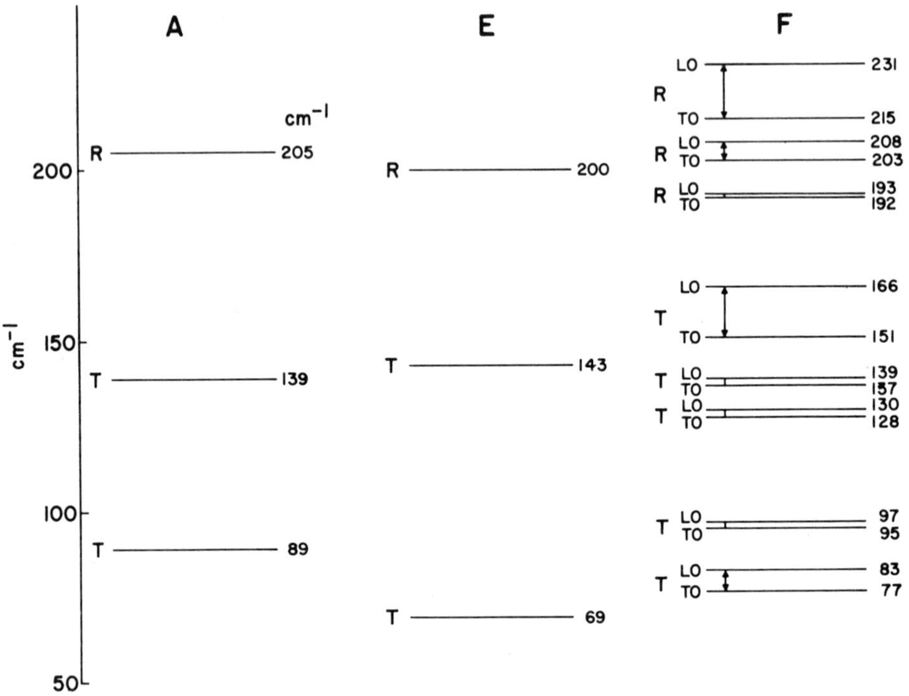

Fig. 35. $NaClO_3$ low frequency vibrational levels (100°K).

when the A tensor is unchanged, but the E tensor acquires off-diagonal components: $Z(XX)Y$ gives A and E components, $Z(Y'X')Y'$ gives E modes. The F_{TO} values are obtained from $Z(YZ)Y$ and F_{LO} values by back scattering from $Z(YX)\bar{Z}$. The primed coordinates are those resulting from a 45° rotation of the crystal about the z axis.

$NaClO_3$ is optically active with α equal to about $4°mm^{-1}$; consequently, care is required to ensure that both the incident and scattered light travel only a short distance through the crystal $RbClO_3$ has been studied by Hwang (*218*).

d. *Lithium Iodate* ($LiIO_3$)

Lithium iodate belongs to the $C_6^6(P63)$ space group, and there are two formula units to the unit cell.

$$\Gamma = 4A(IR, ||^{l}R)+5B+4E(_1(IR\perp, R)+5E_2(R)$$

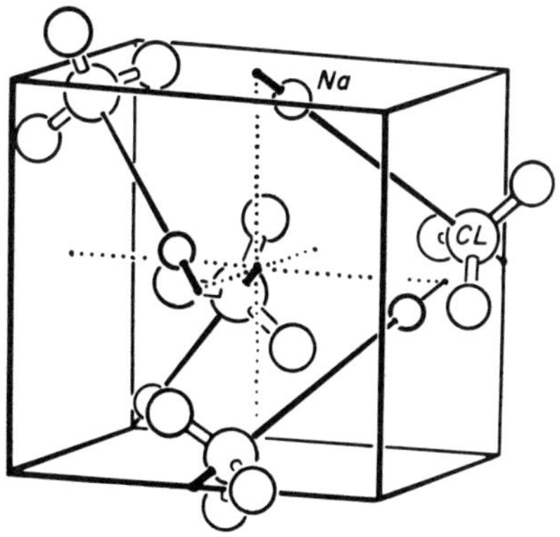

Crystal Structure of Sodium Chlorate

Since both A and E_1 modes are infrared and Raman active, it is possible to observe both the LO and TO frequencies by both techniques (*135,136*). The crystal appears to be an intermediate case between Loudon's case I, $(\nu_{LO}^{\perp} - \nu_{TO}^{\perp}) \gg \nu_{TO}^{\parallel'} - \nu_{TO}^{\perp}$, i.e., when the electrostatic interaction dominates over anisotropic splitting, and case II, $\nu_{LO}^{\parallel'} - \nu_{LO}^{\perp} \gg \nu_{LO}^{\perp} - \nu_{TO}^{\perp}$, where anisotropy dominates over the long-range electrostatic field.

When phonons are created in the xz plane and α_{yy} is measured, the A polarizability tensor component is given, and α_{zy} gives the E_1 polarizability tensor component. Porto (*134*) has found that in the 762–784 cm^{-1} and 814-838 cm^{-1} region there is always a single phonon whose frequency and polarizability tensor changes continuously while going from $\theta = 0°$ (**k** propagating along the z axis) to $\theta = 90°$ (**k** propagating along the x axis). The frequency of the phonons follows the relations

$$\nu_{LO}^2 = (\nu_{LO}^{A})^2 \cos^2\theta + (\nu_{LO}^{E_1})^2 \sin^2\theta$$

$$\nu_{TO}^2 = (\nu_{TO}^{A})^2 \sin^2\theta + (\nu_{TO}^{E_1})^2 \cos^2\theta$$

where θ is the angle formed between the phonon propagation axis and the z axis. Figure 36 shows the comparison between the experimentally measured phonon frequencies and those predicted by the equations above (*135*). These results show that the A_1 and E_1 modes, which originate from different internal normal modes of the IO_3 ion, mix and that the phonon

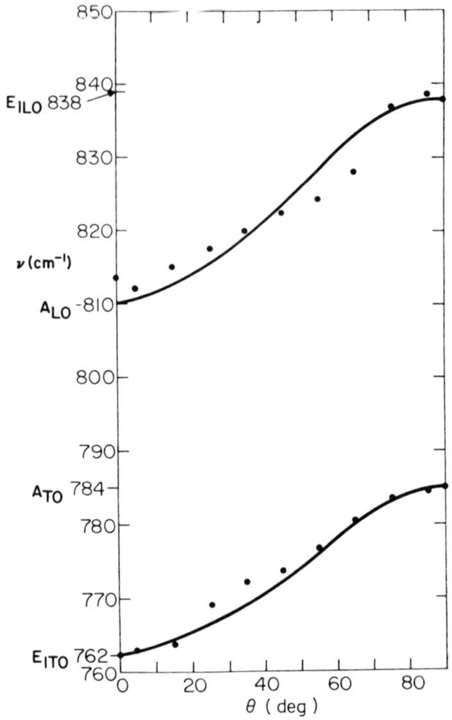

Fig. 36. A and E_1 phonon frequency versus phonon propagation directions for Lithium iodate. The points are the experimental data, and the solid curves are the theoretical curves (*135*).

mechanical polarization is always either transverse or longitudinal, showing the existence of a long-range macroscopic electric field which dominates over all other designations (A_1 or E_1, internal or external modes of the phonons).

e. *Iodic Acid* (α-HIO_3)

Iodic acid crystallizes to give four molecules in an orthorhombic unit cell of space group $D_2^{\,4}$. Hence, there should be fifty seven optical branches to the phonon dispersion curves.

$$\Gamma_{ext} = 6A(R)+5B_1(IR, R)+5B_2(IR, R)+5B_3(IR, R)$$
$$\Gamma_{int} = 9A(R)+9B_1(IR, R)+9B_2(IR, R)+9B_3(IR, R)$$

Thus, all optical modes are Raman active, and for the *B* type modes both *LO* and *TO* components may be observed. Mme. Couture and coworkers (*137*) have carried out careful observations on the variation of frequency of the Raman active *B* modes for different directions of phonon propagation.

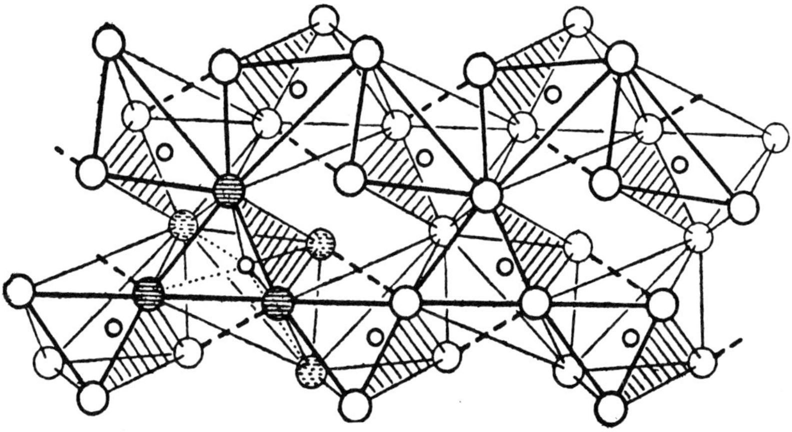

Crystal Structure of Iodic Acid

8. TYPE $A(XY_3)_2$

a. *Strontium Nitrate Structure* [$Sr(NO_3)_2$]

In Sr, Ba, Pb, and Ca nitrates there are four formula units in a cubic cell whose space group is believed to be $T_h^6(Pa3)$. The cations occupy sites of symmetry C_{3i}, and nitrogens C_3.

$$\Gamma_{\text{int}} = 2A_g(R) + 2E_g(R) + 6F_g(IR, R)$$

$$\Gamma_{\text{rot}} = 1A_g(R) + 1E_g(R) + 3F_g(IR, R)$$

$$\Gamma_{\text{trans}} = 1A_g(R) + 1E_g(R) + 3F_g(IR, R)$$

Hence, all optical modes are Raman active (*132*), and in the case of the *F* modes, which are also infrared active, both *LO* and *TO* modes can be obtained from the Raman spectrum. The A_g modes can be distinguished from the B_g modes by the same procedure as was adopted in the study of $NaClO_3$.

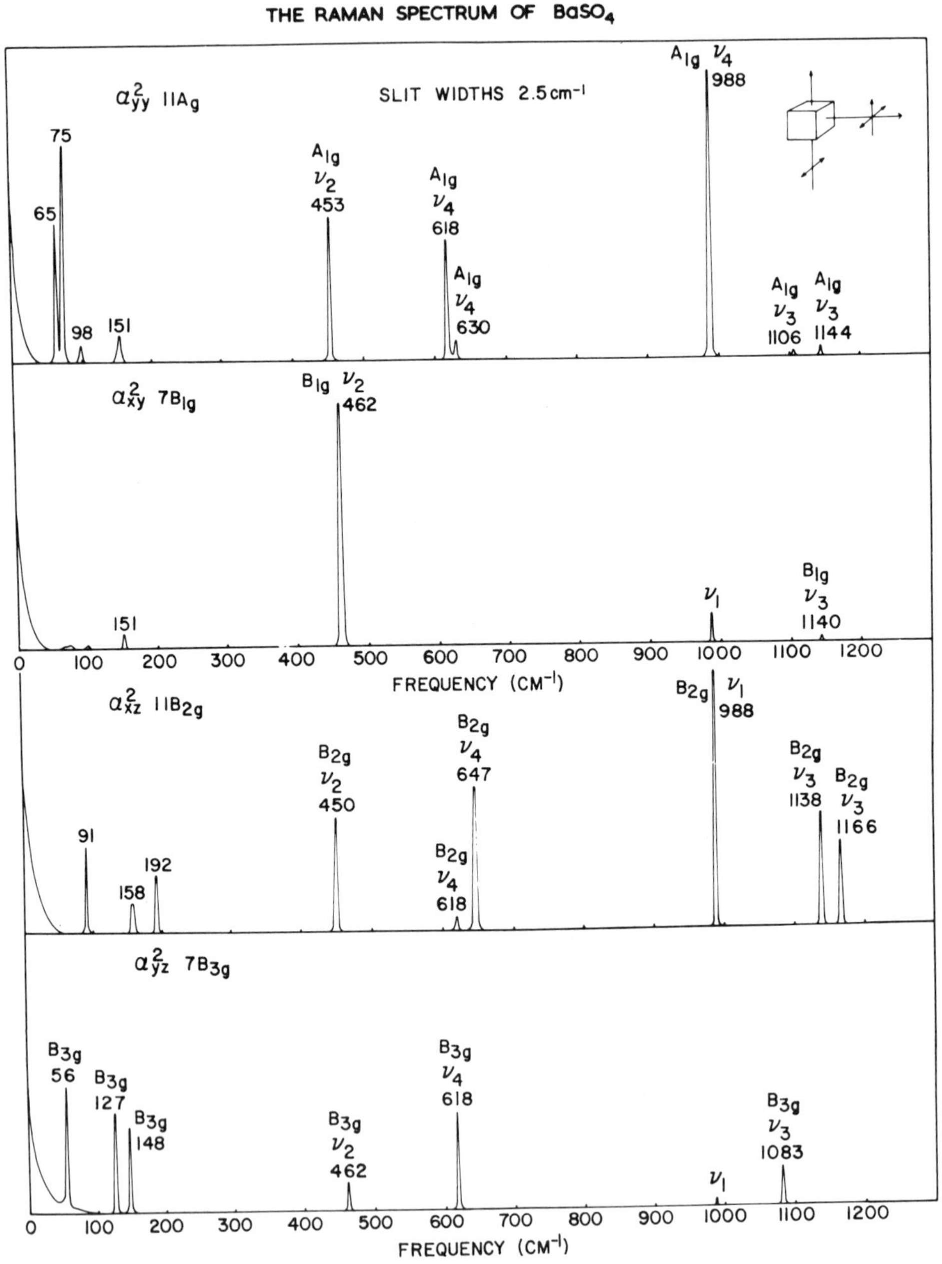

Fig. 37. The polarized Raman spectrum of barium sulphate, $BaSO_4$, obtained with 5145-Å radiation from an ion argon laser. Frequencies below 400 cm^{-1} are associated with external modes and those above with internal vibration of the SO_4^{2-} ion (*115*).

9. Type $A(XY_4)$

a. *Barium Sulfate, etc.* ($BaSO_4$, $SrSO_4$, *and* $PbSO_4$)

All these occur naturally as minerals. The unit cell is orthorhombic and contains four formula units. The space group is D_{2h}^{16}, and as there is a center of symmetry the rule of mutual exclusion holds for the Raman and infrared activity

$$\left.\begin{aligned}\Gamma_{\text{ext}} &= 5A_g+4B_{1g}+5B_{2g}+4B_{3g}\\ \Gamma_{\text{int}} &= 6A_g+3B_{1g}+6B_{2g}+3B_{3g}\end{aligned}\right\}\ \text{Raman active}$$

$$\left.\begin{aligned}\Gamma_{\text{ext}} &= 4B_{1u}(c)+3B_{2u}(b)+4B_{3u}(a)\\ \Gamma_{\text{int}} &= 6B_{1u}(c)+3B_{2u}(b)+6B_{3u}(a)\end{aligned}\right\}\ \text{Infrared active}$$

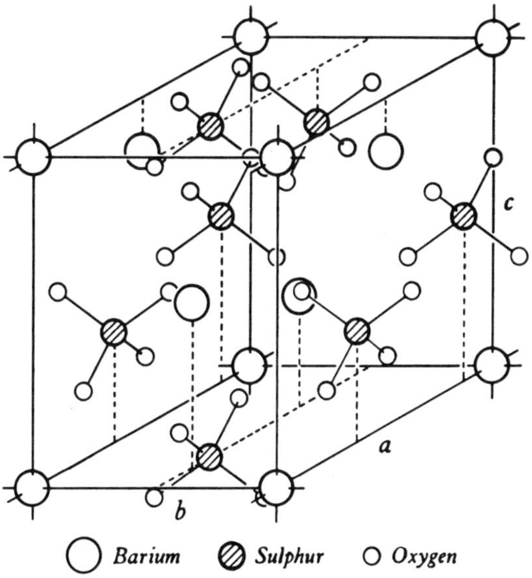

Crystal Structure of Barium Sulphate

This crystal is a good example of one containing molecular ions whose internal modes of vibration have frequencies much higher than the external modes of vibration (See Fig 37). The sulfate ions have site symmetry C_s in the lattice. Halford's method of analysis is particularly appropriate for a consideration of the internal modes as it shows which molecular ion vibrations give rise to which crystal vibrations and the frequencies to be expected for the various modes of vibration. A typical correlation diagram (*115*) is shown in Fig. 38.

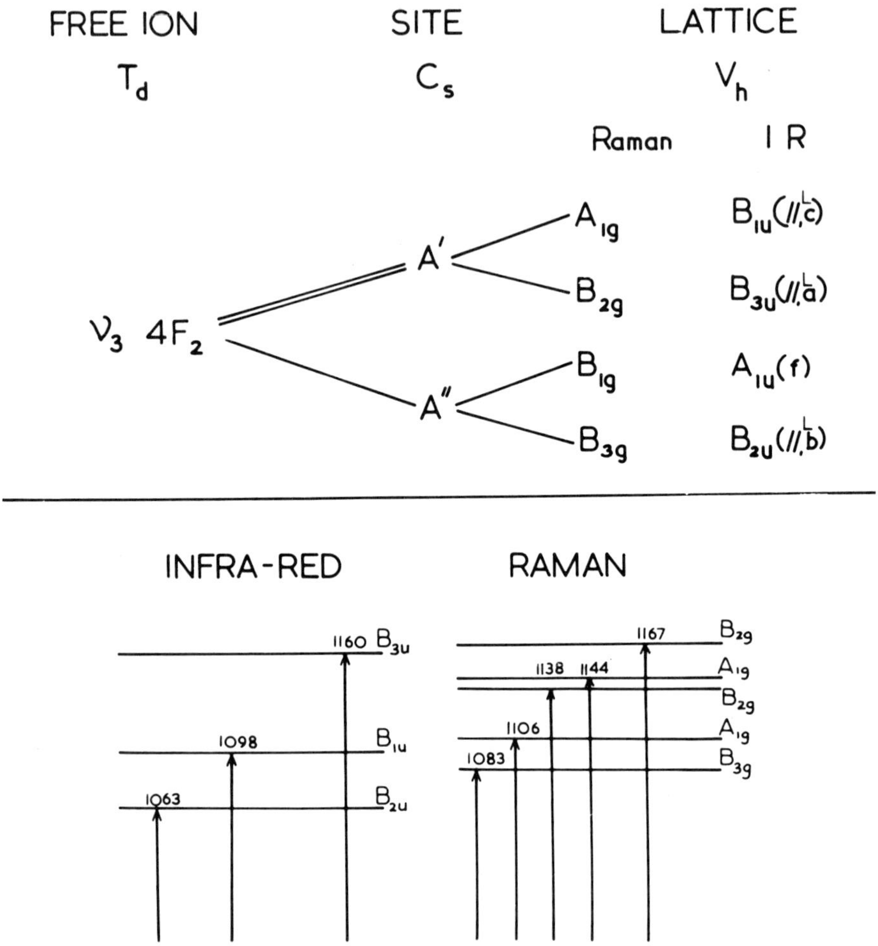

Fig. 38. Correlation diagram for the barytes ($BaSO_4$). Lifting of degeneracies of ν_3 vibrations of SO_4^{--} ions in the crystal field (*115*).

b. *Anhydrite* ($CaSO_4$)

The space group of anhydrite is D_{2h}^{17}, and the primitive orthorhombic unit cell contains two formula units. The axes b and c are very similar in length, and consequently, the structure of anhydrite can be considered as being a slightly distorted tetragonal zircon structure.

$$\Gamma = 6A_g(R)+5B_{1g}(R)+2B_{2g}(R)+5B_{3g}(R)$$
$$+2A_u(F)+4B_{1u}(IR, a)+5B_{2u}(IR, b)+4B_{3u}(IR, c)$$

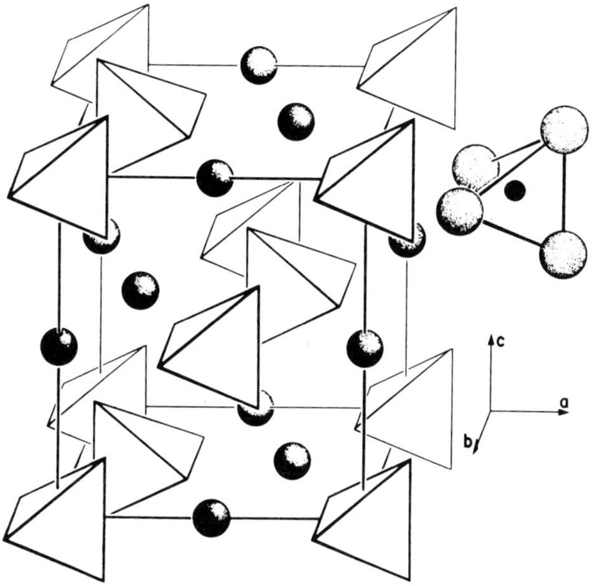

Crystal Structure of Anhydrite

The polarized Raman spectrum has recently been obtained by Berenblut, Dawson, and Wilkinson (*129*).

c. *Scheelite Structure* ($CaWO_4$)

Many examples of crystals with the scheelite structure are known; however, the most frequently studied is calcium tungstate. The centrosymmetric tetragonal unit cell which contains four formula units has space group C_{4h}^6. The tungstate ions occupy sites of S_4 symmetry and cations, C_i sites. Since the ions at the body center are related to those at the corners by simple translations, the number of independent vibrational modes correspond to that of two formula units. Hence,

$$\Gamma = 3A_{1g}(R)+5B_g(F)+5E_g(R)+4A_u(IR, \|^c)+3B_u(F)+4E_u(IR, \perp)$$

Thus, 13 Raman active fundamentals are expected. Examples (*138–140*) that have been studied so far include $CaWO_4$, $SrWO_4$, $PbWO_4$, $BaWO_4$, $ZnWO_4$, $CaMoO_4$, and $PbMoO_4$. Scott (*139*) and Lippincott et al. (*140*) have interpreted the vibrational energy levels in terms of internal modes of the anions split by the crystal field and in terms of translatory and rotatory modes. Figure 39 shows the internal mode frequencies observed in Ba, Sr, Ca, and Zn tungstates as a function of $1/r^6$ where r is the distance

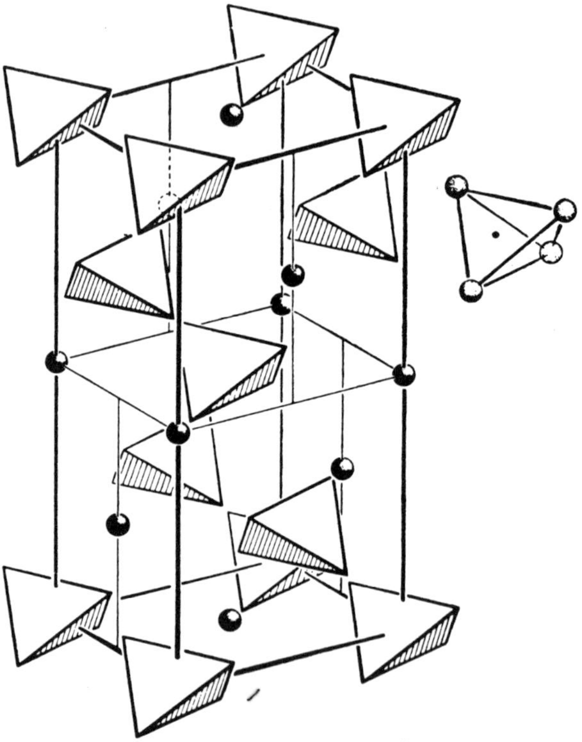

Crystal Structure of Scheelite

between the tungstate ions. The extrapolation to $1/r^6 = 0$ gives an approximation for the vibrational frequency of the WO_4 ion in free space. An r^{-6} dependence is to be expected if the splitting is due to a dipole interaction.

For the external Raman active modes

$$\Gamma = A_g + 2B_g + 3E_g$$

The A_g mode is rotatory in character about the z axis. As there is only one Raman active external mode of this symmetry it is easily identified. The rotatory motions about the x and y axes are E_g-type.

d. *Zircon, etc.* ($ZrSiO_4$, D_yVO_4, D_yAsO_4, *and* $TbVO_4$)

Zircon itself has a tetragonal unit cell containing two formula units $ZrSiO_4$. The space group of the primitive unit cell is D_{4h}^{19}. There are thirty three optical branches to the phonon dispersion curves. Of these

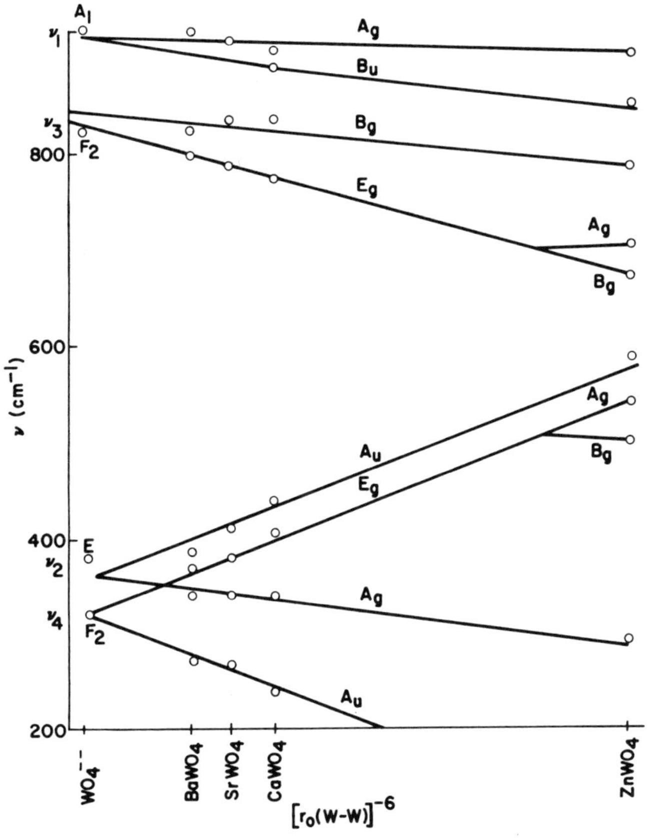

Fig. 39. Tungstate ion level splittings as a function of tungsten-tungsten separation *(139)*.

eighteen branches may be distinguished as essentially internal modes of vibration of the silicate ions and the other fifteen branches as essentially external modes of vibration. The latter may be classified at $\mathbf{k} = 0$ as translatory or rotatory. The silicate ions occupy sites of symmetry D_{2d}, and hence some of the degeneracies are lifted.

$$\Gamma = 2A_{1g}(R) + A_{2g}(F) + 4B_{1g}(R) + B_{2g}(R) + 5E_g(R) + A_{1u}(F) + 3A_{2u}(IR, ||') + B_{1u}(F) + 2B_{2u}(F) + 4E_u(IR, \perp)$$

Figure 40 shows the polarized Raman spectrum *(156)* at room temperature for four orientations. The low intensity of the A_{1g} ν_1 silicon oxygen stretching mode is immediately apparent. However, if the corresponding intensities of ClO_4^{1-}, SO_4^{2-}, and PO_4^{3-} are considered together

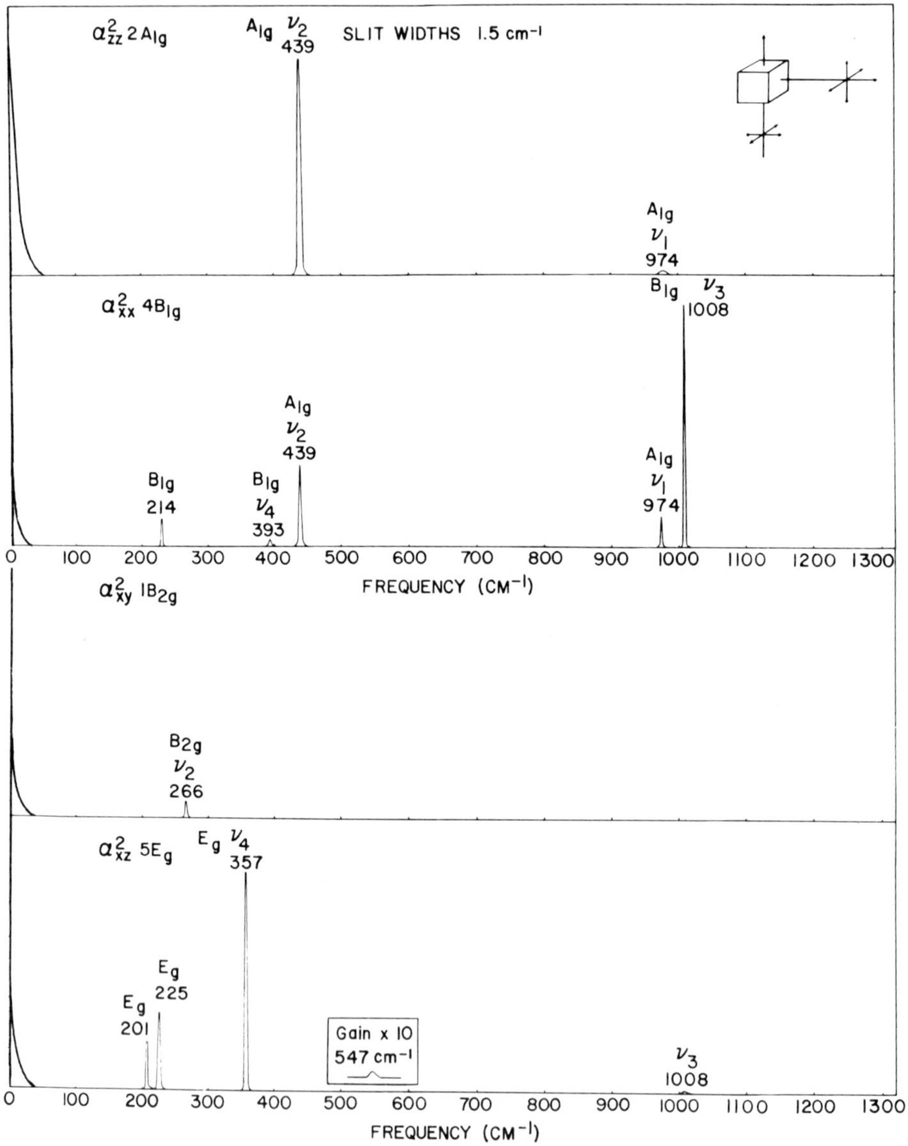

Fig. 40. The Raman spectrum of zircon, $ZrSiO_4$, which has a tetragonal unit cell. Frequencies above 300 cm^{-1} are associated with the internal modes of vibration of the silicate ion SiO_4^{4-}, and those below are due to external modes of vibration (*156*).

with SiO_4^{4-}, it is found that the Raman intensity associated with the symmetric stretching frequencies decreases uniformly as the anion charge is increased for these anions.

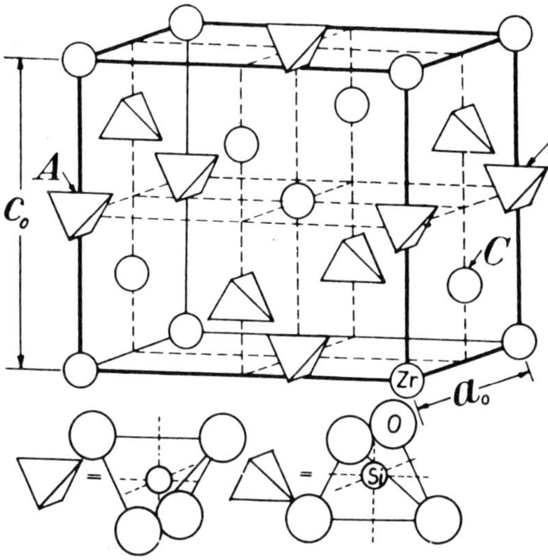

Crystal Structure of Zircon

Figure 41(a) shows the Raman intensity of the ν_3 B_{1g} vibrational mode in zircon as the crystal is rotated about the c axis. The predicted $\cos^2 2\theta$ relationship is well obeyed.

e. *DyVO*$_4$

Above 14°K, dysprosium vanadate has the zircon structure D_{4h}^{19}. However, below this temperature the symmetry is lowered to the orthorhombic structure D_{2h}^{28}. The transition is a manifestation of a cooperative Jahn–Teller effect due to the coupling between lattice displacements and the electronic states of the dysprosium ions, which causes a splitting of the lowest electronic level (*234*, *235*).

Figure 41(b) shows the Raman spectra at 77°K and 4.5°K above and below the transition temperature for the polarizations ZZ and ZX or ZY. The two A_{1g} modes are not affected by the transition, but each of the E_g vibrational modes splits into two components below T_D, showing that the symmetry has been lowered. The splittings are shown in Fig. 41(c).

Similar transitions occur in $DyAsO_4$ and $TbVO_4$ at 12°K and 34°K, respectively. However, for terbium vanadate the orthorhombic structure belongs to space group D_{2h}^{24}.

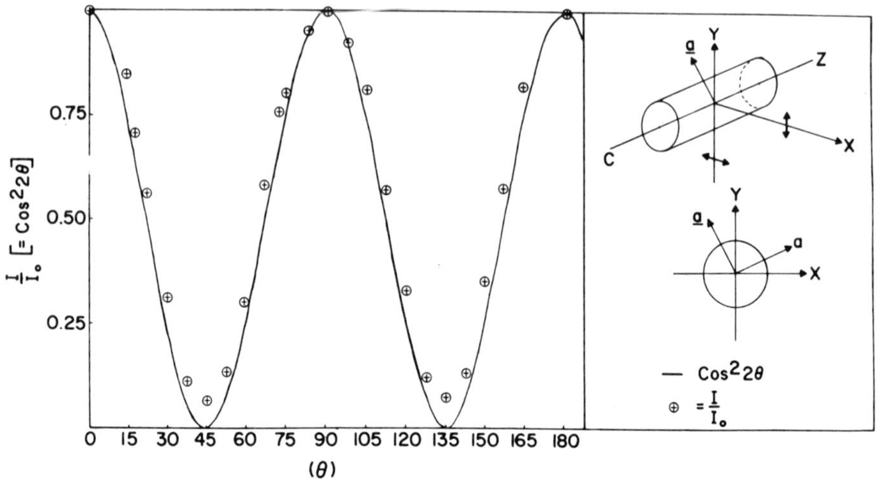

Fig. 41 (a). The Raman intensity of the ν_3 B_{1g} vibration mode at 1008 cm^{-1} in zircon as a function of θ which is the angle between the *a* axis and the excitation direction. Rotation is about the crystal *c* axis. (The predicted $Cos^2 2\theta$ relationship is well obeyed (*156*).)

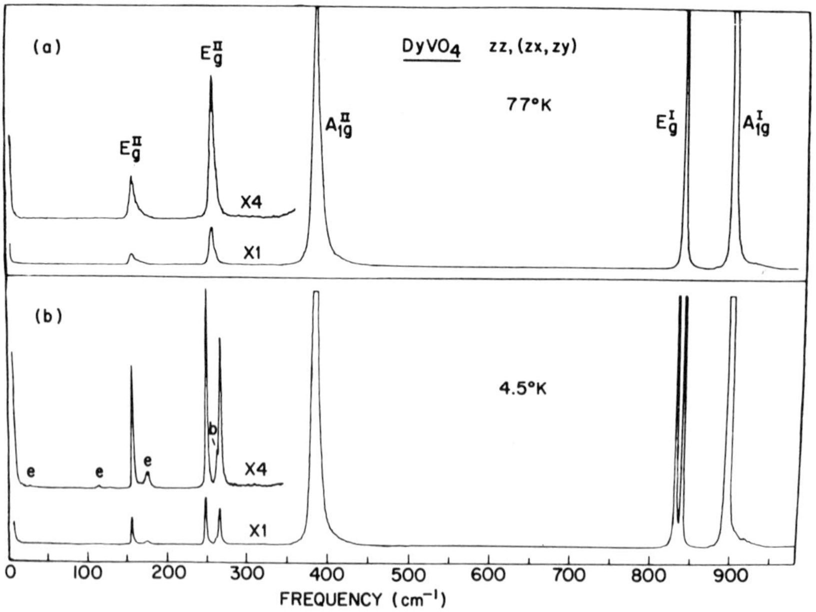

Fig. **41**(b). Raman spectra of $DyVO_4$ at 77°K and 4.5°K (*234*).

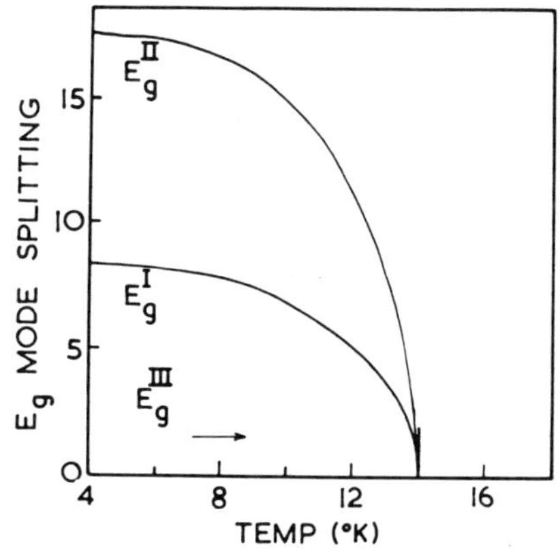

Fig. 41(c). E_g vibrational mode splittings below T_D in D_yVO_4 (*234*).

f. *LiYF*$_4$

Although the structure of $LiYF_4$ is isomorphous with scheelite, its bonding is quite different (*141*). In this crystal the internal binding of the $LiF_4{}^{3-}$ tetrahedra is not significantly different from the other ionic forces in the crystal, and consequently, the separation into internal and external vibrations is not meaningful. On account of the small mass of the lithium ions, they might be expected to vibrate alone at comparatively high frequencies. Experiments with crystals containing different Li^6/Li^7 ratios would be helpful to characterize these normal modes with greater certainty.

g. *Ammonium Halides* (NH_4X)

Ammonium halides crystallize in a number of different structures many of which show disorder. The structures and transition temperatures are summarized below (*142–145*).

Crystal	Phase I	T (°K)	Phase II	T (°K)	Phase III	T (°K)	Phase IV
NH_4Cl	NaCl	458	CsCl	243	$CsCl_{ordered}$		
ND_4Cl	NaCl	349	CsCl	250	CsCl		
NH_4Br	NaCl	411	CsCl	235	Tetrgnl.	78	$CsCl_{ordered}$
ND_4Br	NaCl	405	CsCl	215	CsCl	158	CsCl
NH_4I	NaCl	256	CsCl	232	CsCl		

The NaCl and CsCl type structures (phases I and II) have disordered orientations of the $NH_4{}^+$ ions.

In phase I the space group is $O_h^5(Fm3m)$, a face centered cubic lattice which contains four formula units; however, the primitive unit cell contains only one, and consequently, the selection rules are essentially the same as in the phase II body centered structure of space group $O_h^1(Pm3m)$ which also contains a single molecule. For both structures

$$\Gamma_{\text{ext}} = F_{1u}(IR) + F_{1g}(R)$$

$$\Gamma_{\text{int}} = A_{1g}(R) + E_g(R) + 2F_{1u}(IR)$$

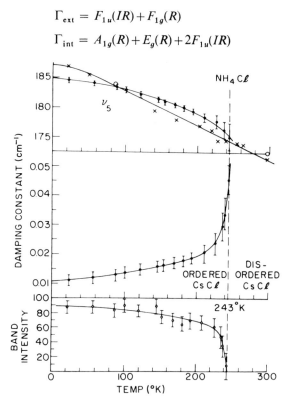

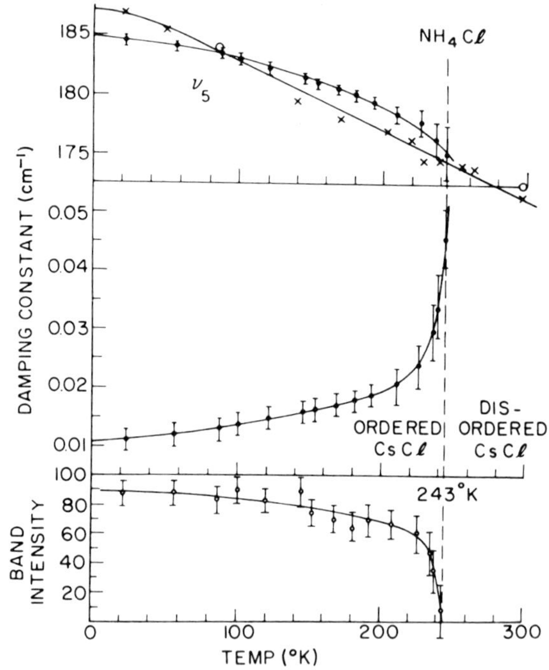

Fig. 42. Variation of ν_5 in NH_4Cl determined from IR (X = thin film; O = reflectivity) and Raman (●) measurements. Plot of the Raman damping constant and band intensity as a function of temperature (*142*).

However, as the structure is disordered, spectroscopic selection rules may be relaxed, and some of the inactive modes may become active. Thus, in phase II in NH_4Br and NH_4Cl (the F_{1u} transverse optic modes which involve the relative motion of the positive and negative ions are Raman active at $\sim 144\ cm^{-1}$ and $\sim 173\ cm^{-1}$, respectively. The rotatory or librational mode of the ammonium is not Raman or infrared active.

However, it is active in the hyper-Raman spectrum and has been observed at approximately 380 cm^{-1} by Maker (private communication) in ammonium chloride.

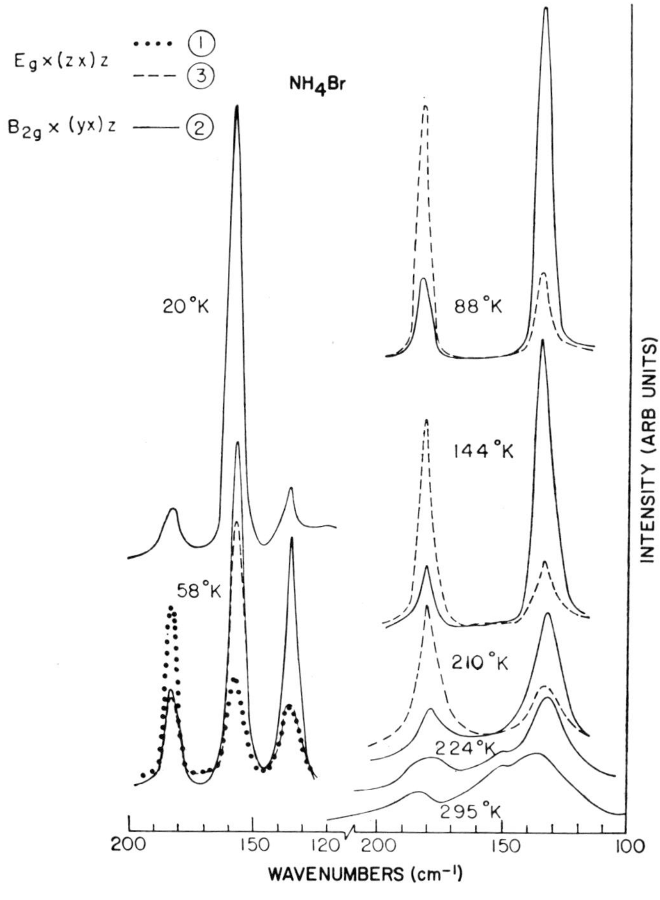

Fig. 43. Raman spectra of NH_4Br single crystal as a function of temperature.

In the ordered CsCl structure which occurs in phase III of NH_4Cl and phase IV of NH_4Br the NH_4 site symmetry is T_d and the crystals are piezoelectric; hence, the F_2 external mode should be infrared and Raman active and both *TO* and *LO* modes should be observed (see Fig. 43).

The Raman spectrum of NH_4Cl in phase III at 150°K has two peaks, at 183 cm^{-1} and 272 cm^{-1}, which can be assigned to these modes.

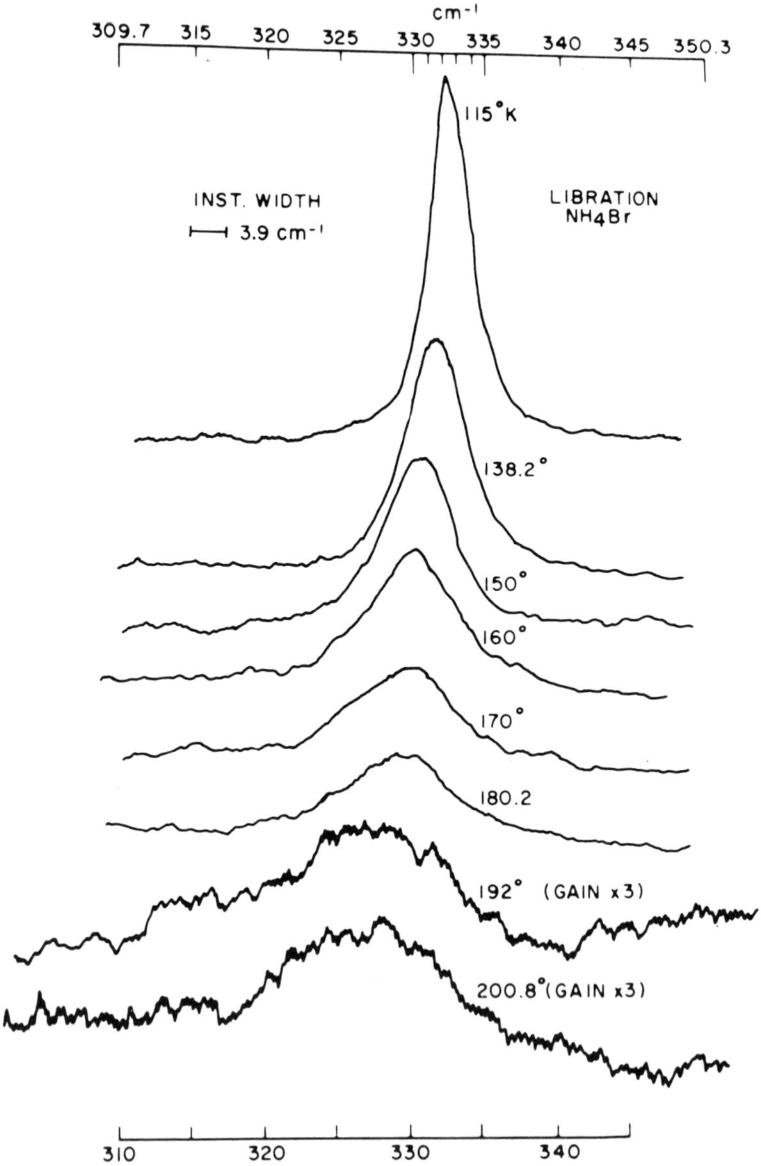

Fig. 44. The E_g librational mode (ν_6) at different temperatures in the ordered phase of NH_4Br (*143*).

The phase III structure of NH_4Br and NH_4I is an ordered tetragonal distortion of the CsCl structure containing two formula units. The space group is $D_{4h}^7(P4nmm)$. The site symmetry of the ammonium ions is D_{2d} and that of the halide ions is C_4.

$$\Gamma_{\text{int}} = 2A_{1g}(R)+B_{1g}(F)+2B_{2g}(R)+2E_g(F)+A_{1u}(F)+2A_{2u}(IR) +2B_{1u}(F)+2E_u(IR)$$

$$\Gamma_{\text{trans}} = A_{1g}(R)+B_{2g}(R)+2E_g(F)+A_{2u}(IR)+E_u(IR)$$

$$\Gamma_{\text{rot}} = A_{2g}(F)+E_g(R)+B_{2u}(F)+E_u(IR)$$

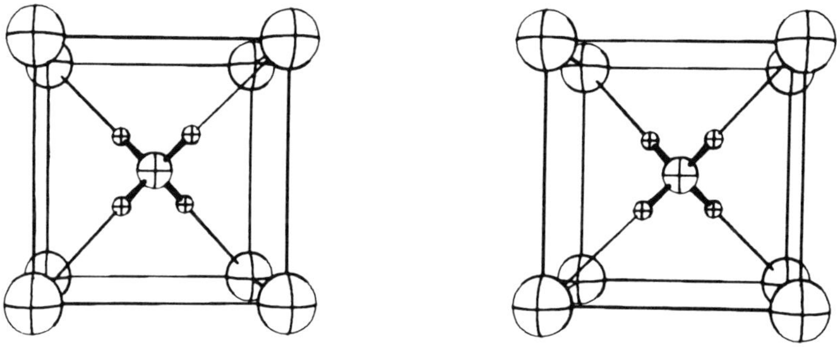

NH4Br-PHASE4 NH4Br-PHASE4

Stereoscopic Crystal Structure of Ammonium Bromide

The A_{1g}, B_{2g}, and E_g modes are Raman active. The rotatory NH_4 motion is observable in the Raman spectrum (*142*), and it occurs at 333 cm^{-1} at 115°K. The variation of frequency and decrease in intensity with temperature is shown in Fig. 44. The corresponding mode in NH_4I occurs at 287 cm^{-1} at 100°K.

Over a wide range of temperature the halfwidth Γ of the rotatory band (*143*) follows the form

$$\Delta\nu = (\Delta\nu_0)\, e^{-V/kT}$$

where $(\Delta\nu_0) = 74\ cm^{-1}$ and $V = 300\ cm^{-1}$. This value of V is very close to the value of 330 cm^{-1} determined for the rotatory mode frequency.

The Raman spectrum of NH_4Cl has been studied at room temperature as a function of pressure to 40 kbar (*145*). The *TO* mode ($\mathbf{k} = 0$) which involves the relative motion of the ammonium and chloride ion has a large pressure dependence of $d\nu/dp = 2.65\ cm^{-1}\ kbar^{-1}$ in the disordered phase up to 10 kbar, while in the ordered phase above 10 kbar the slope is 0.61 $cm^{-1}\ kbar^{-1}$. However, when the frequency at different pressures is plotted as a function of volume, there is no noticeable break in the transition region.

The Raman peak which occurs at 700 cm^{-1} is identified as the overtone of the librational mode. In the disordered phase the pressure dependence is 5.0 $cm^{-1} kbar^{-1}$.

The pressure dependence of NH_4 internal modes of vibration in the disordered phase, measured in $cm^{-1} kbar^{-1}$, are as follows:

ν_1 3052 cm^{-1}	ν_2 1710 cm^{-1}	ν_3 3147 cm^{-1}	$\nu_4(TO)$ 1405 cm^{-1}	$\nu_4(LO)$ 1425 cm^{-1}
−0.1	+0.65	−1.2	−0.35	−0.29

The intensity of the longitudinal mode component is found to increase by a factor of four relative to the transverse optic mode.

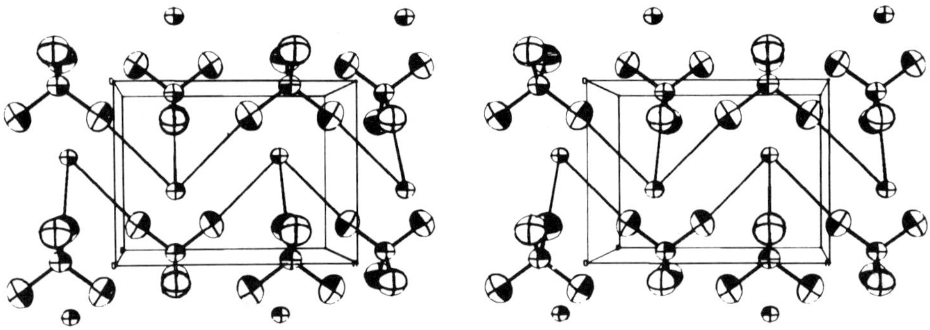

Stereoscopic Crystal Structure of Phosphonium Halides

h. *Phosphonium Halides* (PH_4X)

Phosphonium chloride, bromide, and iodide also crystallize in the tetragonal CsCl structure with space group D_{4h}^7. Here the librational mode has been observed by Raman scattering (*146,147,148*) both in PH_4Cl and PD_4Cl at 370 and 265 cm^{-1}. The ratio 1.40 is very close to $\sqrt{2}$ confirming the assignment. This rotatory mode is also observed in PH_4Br at 343 cm^{-1} and in PH_4I at 326 cm^{-1}.

10. Miscellaneous Crystals

a. *Ammonium Fluorsilicate* $(NH_4)_2SiF_6$

Ammonium fluorsilicate exists in two crystalline modifications: a cubic form and a tetragonal form. The former has space group O_h^5, and the latter D_{3d}^6.

Raman experiments (*149*) on single crystals of ammonium fluorsilicate and the corresponding deuterated samples have shown that the band which shifts from 180 to 165 cm^{-1} on deuteration is a translatory mode involving the ammonium ions.

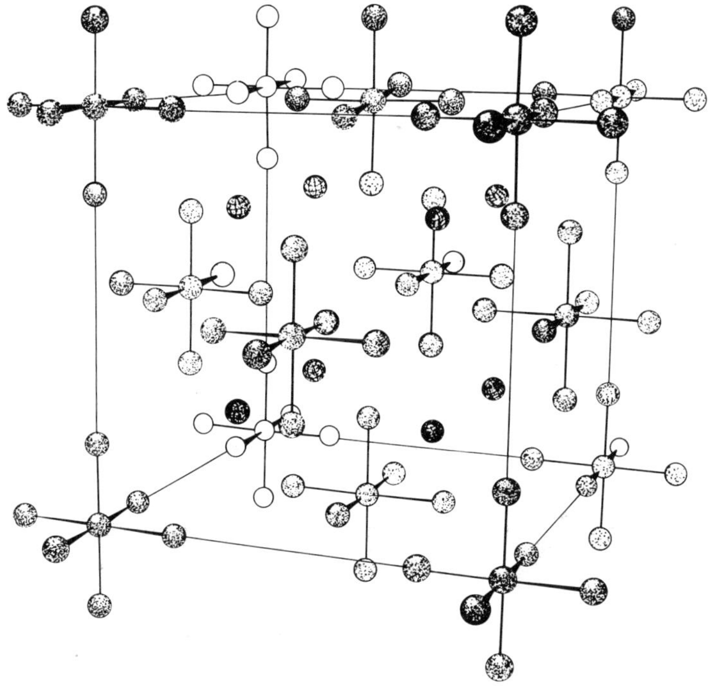

Crystal Structure of Ammonium Fluorsilicate

b. *Ammonium Perchlorate* (NH_4ClO_4)

Ammonium perchlorate which belongs to the space group V_{2h}^{16} has an orthorhombic unit cell.

Raman studies (*149*) have shown that the barrier to rotation of the ammonium ion is low and that at room temperature it may be freely rotating.

c. *Rare Earth (Tb, Dy, Yt), Aluminum Garnets* $[(RE)_3Al_2(AlO_4)_3]$

These rare earth garnets belong to the body centered cubic system with space group symmetry $O_h^{10}(Ia3d)$. There are eight units of the group $(RE)_3\ Al_2\ (AlO_4)_3$ in the body centered unit cell (*131,132*). The rare earth ions are located in closed cubes formed by eight oxygen ions. There are 24 such sites of symmetry D in the unit cell. The site symmetry of the 24 AlO_4^{5-} tetrahedrons is S_4. The Al^{3+} ions occupy 16 equivalent positions of symmetry C_{3i}:

$$\Gamma = 5A_{1u}(F)+3A_{1g}(R)+5A_{2u}(F)+5A_{2g}(F)+10E_u(F)+8E_g(R)$$
$$+14F_{1g}(F)+18F_{1u}(IR)+14F_{2g}(R)+16F_{2u}(F)$$

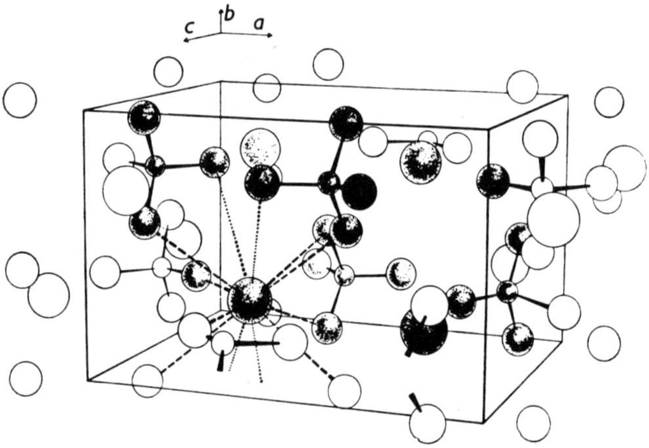

Crystal Structure of Rare Earth Garnet

All the A_{1g} and E_g modes have been identified, but at least three of the $14F_{2g}$ modes are missing from the observed Raman spectra.

d. *Potassium Dithionate* ($K_2S_2O_6$)

Potassium dithionate has a hexagonal unit cell with space group $D_3^2(P321)$ which contains three formula units. All the $S_2O_6{}^{2-}$ molecular ions are oriented parallel to one another with the S—S bond directions coinciding with the crystal c axis.

$$\Gamma_{\text{int}} = 12A_1(R)+6A_2(IR, \|^l)+18E(IR, \perp, R)$$
$$\Gamma_{\text{ext}} = 11A_2(IR, \|^l)+11E(IR, \perp, R)$$

The E modes are both infrared and Raman active and, consequently, both $\mathbf{k} = 0$ longitudinal optic as well as transverse optic phonons should be Raman active; however, experimental studies show that they are comparatively weak (*115*).

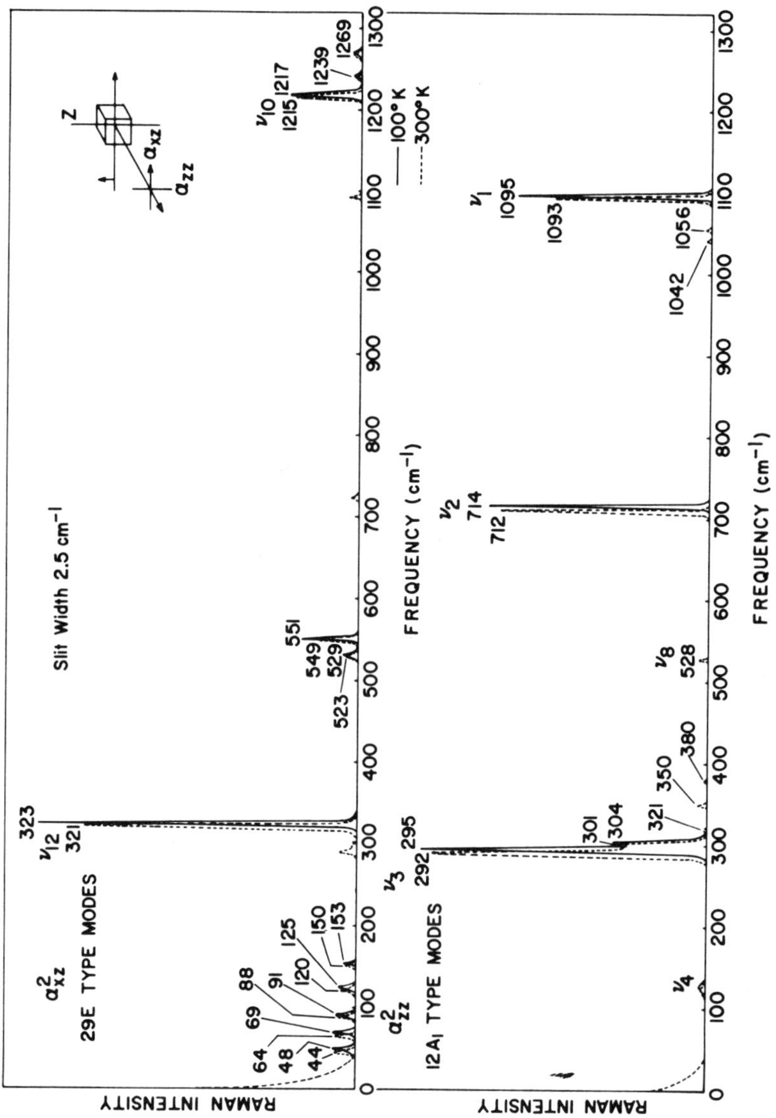

Fig. 45. The Raman spectra of potassium dithionate showing the A_1- and E-type modes. Those above 200 cm^{-1} are due to the internal vibrations of the $S_2O_6{}^{2-}$ ions (*115*).

e. *Sodium Dithionate* ($Na_2S_2O_62H_2O$)

Beattie and coworkers (*150*) have carried out a very thorough Raman study of $Na_2S_2O_62H_2O$ which crystallizes with four formula units in an orthorhombic unit cell of space group $D_{2h}^{16}(Pnma)$. The dithionate ions

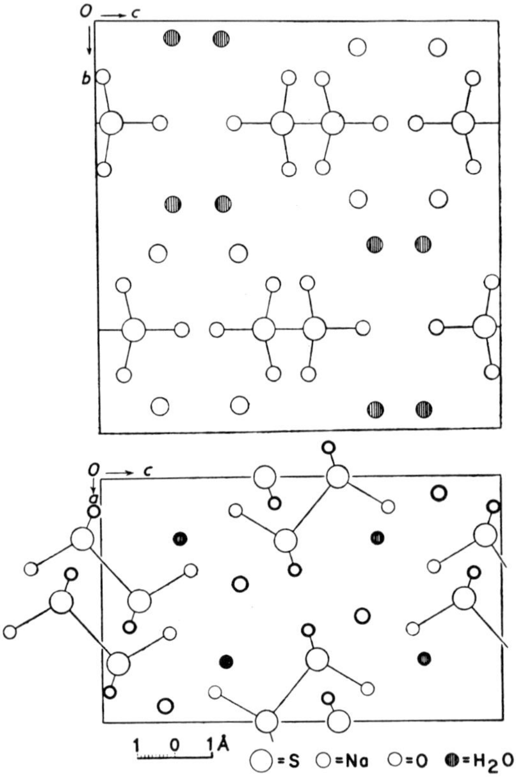

Crystal Structure of Sodium Dithionate

occupy sites with C_3 symmetry. Treating the water molecules as spherically symmetric units,

$$\Gamma = 20A_{1g}(R)+16B_{1g}(R)+20B_{2g}(R)+16B_{3g}(R)+16A_{1u}(IR, ||'c)$$
$$+20B_{1u}(IR)+16B_{2u}(IR)+20B_{3u}(IR)$$

The Raman tensor for the A_{1g} modes contains α_{xx}, α_{yy}, α_{zz} components while only the α_{xy} components are present for B_{1g}, α_{xz} present for B_{2g}, and

α_{yz} for B_{3g}. Using the oriented gas model the crystal Raman scattering intensities may be related to molecular scattering intensities.

$$\alpha_{\text{crystal}} = T\alpha_{\text{mol}}T^{-1}$$

where T is the transformation matrix. To construct the required matrix it is necessary to calculate the direction cosines of the molecular axes in the crystal axes. From measurements of the crystal intensities it is possible to derive a, b, c, and d, the components of the polarizability tensor for various normal modes of vibration of the S_2O_6 ion. For both A_g and E_g modes, ambiguity in sign arises because intensities depend upon α_{ij}^2. However, only one set of values in each mode gives rise to consistent relative intensities. Using the calculated values of a, b, c, and d for the $S_2O_6^{\,-}$, Beattie et al. calculated the relative intensities and depolarization ratios for the different Raman active lines and found excellent agreement with those measured directly for dithionate ions in aqueous solution. They also calculated the molecular force constants and used them to give a set of relative bond polarizability derivatives which appears to be physically reasonable.

f. *Dipotassium Tetrachloroplatinate* $[K_2(PtCl_4^{\,2-})]$

Dipotassium tetrachloroplatinate belongs to the space group D_{4h}^1 (*P4mmm*). The unit cell contains a single formula unit. The $PtCl_4$ ions are all oriented with their planes parallel to one another.

$$\Gamma_{\text{int}} = A_{1g}(R) + B_{1g}(R) + B_{2g}(R) + A_{2u}(IR, \|^l) + B_{1u} + 2E_u(IR, \perp)$$
$$\Gamma_{\text{trans}} = A_{2u}(IR, \|^l) + B_{2u}(F) + 2E_u(IR, \perp)$$
$$\Gamma_{\text{rot}} = A_{2g}(F) + E_g(R)$$

Raman studies (*88*) using polarized radiation have successfully distinguished the A_{1g} and B_{1g} modes from the E_g modes in $K_2(PtCl_4^{\,2-})$, $(NH_4)_2(PtCl_4^{\,2-})$, and in $K_2(PdCl_4^{\,2-})$.

g. *Copper Chloride* $[CuCl_2(H_2O)_2]$

Copper chloride crystallizes with two formula units in a unit cell whose space group is D_{4h}^7(*Pbmn*). Essentially the structure consists (*153*) of square planar units of $CuCl_2(H_2O)_2$ where

$$\Gamma_{\text{int}} = 2A_{1g}(R) + 2B_{2g}(R) + E_g(R) + 2A_{2u}(IR, \|^l) + 2B_{1u}(F) + 4E_u(IR, \perp)$$
$$\Gamma_{\text{trans}} = A_{1g}(R) + A_{2g}(F) + 2B_{1g}(R) + 2A_{2u}(IR, \|^l) + 2B_{1u}(F) + 5E_u(IR, \perp)$$
$$\Gamma_{\text{rot}} = A_{2g}(F) + B_{1g}(R) + 2E_g(R)$$

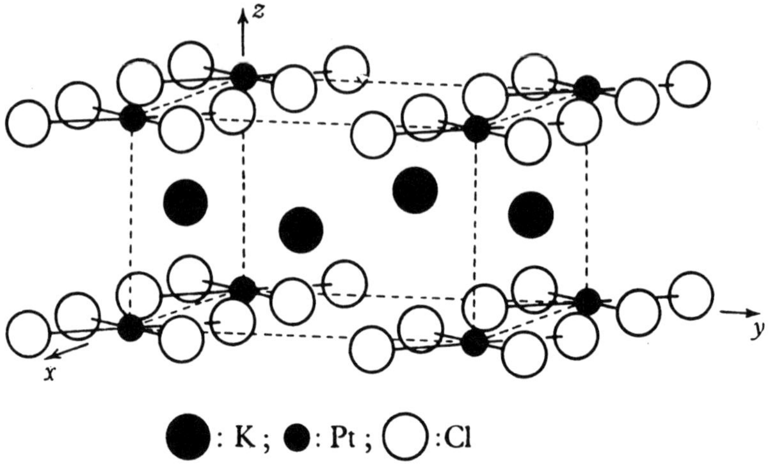

● : K ; **●** : Pt ; **○** :Cl

Crystal Structure of Dipotassium Tetrachloroplatinate

● : Cu; **○** : H$_2$O; **○** : Cl

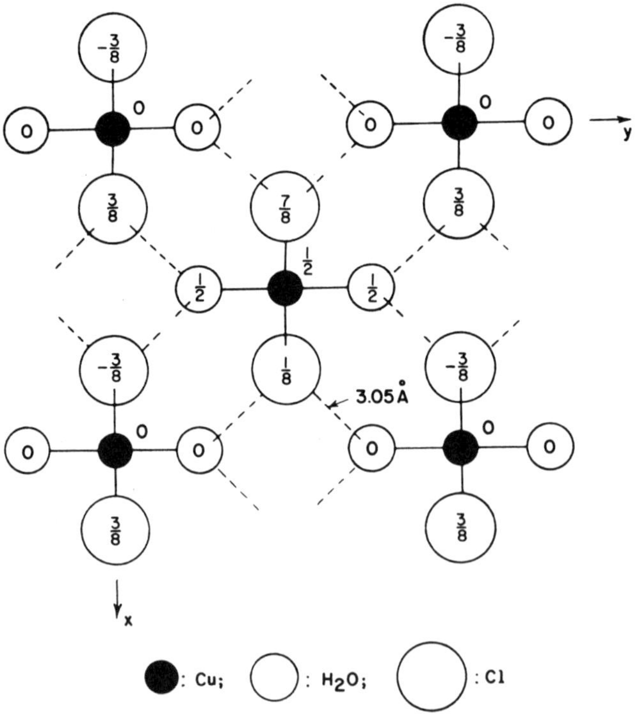

Crystal Structure of Copper Chloride

h. $M_2CuCl_4(H_2O)_2$

These compounds in which M = K, Rb, Cs, or NH_4 all crystallize with two formula units in a tetragonal unit with symmetry $D_{4h}^{14}(P4/mnm)$. The structure of the anions is a distorted coordination octahedron around the copper. Neglecting the presence of hydrogen,

$$\Gamma_{\text{int}} = 3A_{1g}(R)+A_{2g}(F)+B_{1g}(R)+3B_{2g}(R)+2E_g(R) +3A_{2u}(IR, ||^l)+3B_{1u}(F)+6E_u(IR, \perp)$$

$$\Gamma_{\text{trans}} = B_{1g}(R)+B_{2g}(R)+2E_g(F)+A_{2u}(IR, ||^l)+A_{1u}(F)+B_{1u}(F) +3E_u(IR, \perp)$$

$$\Gamma_{\text{rot}} = A_{2g}(F)+B_{1g}(R)+2E_g(R)$$

For H_2O,

$$\Gamma_{\text{rot}} = A_{2g}(F)+B_{1g}(R)+2E_g(R)+A_{1u}(F)+B_{2u}(F)+2E_u(IR, \perp)$$

The single crystal Raman spectra have been reported by Adams and Newton (*241*).

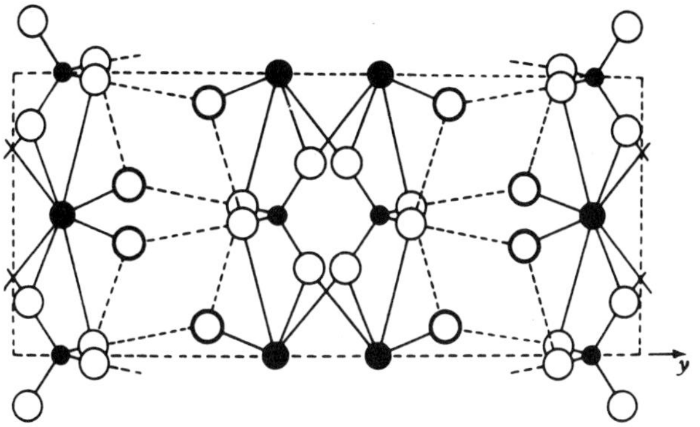

Crystal Structure of Gypsum

i. *Gypsum* $[CaSO_4(H_2O)_2]$

Gypsum has two formula units in a monoclinic unit cell which belongs to space group C_{2h}. There are seventy two branches to the phonon dispersion curves.

$$\Gamma = 17A_g(R)+19B_g(F)+16A_u(IR, ||^lb)+17B_u(IR)$$

To a first approximation the sulfate ion and water molecules may be treated as separate entities located at sites of symmetry C_2 and C_1, respectively. The correlation diagram (*154*) for H_2O together with the experimental Raman and infrared results is shown in Fig. 46. Although water molecules are rather strongly hydrogen bonded, these molecules have Raman lines associated with the O—H stretching vibration whose halfwidths are of the order of 10 cm^{-1}, much less than those usually quoted for such systems.

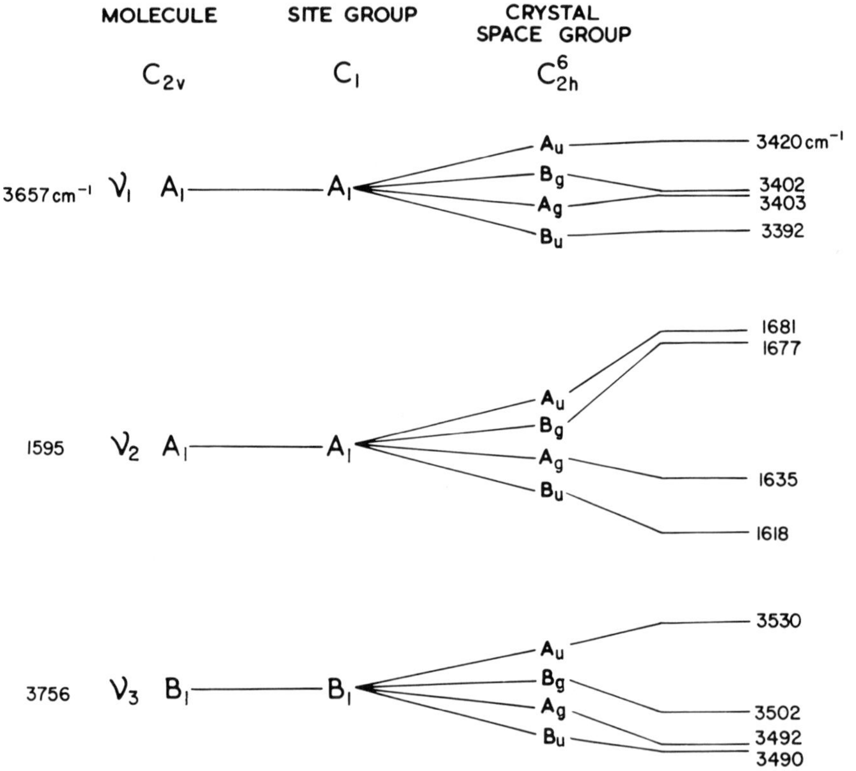

Fig. 46. The correlation diagram for H_2O molecules in gypsum ($CaSO_42H_2O$) showing the experimentally determined frequencies (*154*).

As gypsum is monoclinic it is necessary to excite and observe the Raman scattering with radiation polarized parallel to an indicatrix direction. The twofold *b* axis is an indicatrix axis, but the other two mutually perpendicular indicatrix axes lie in the cleavage plane perpendicular to *b* at an angle θ, which is frequency and temperature dependent to the crystallographic axes *a* and *b*. The similarity transformation which relates the Raman tensor referring to crystal axes to indicatrix directions leaves the pattern of tensors unchanged, and consequently, the A modes are readily distinguished from the B modes of vibration.

$$A^* \quad \begin{bmatrix} A & O & D \\ O & B & O \\ D & O & C \end{bmatrix} \qquad B^* \quad \begin{bmatrix} O & E & O \\ E & O & F \\ O & F & O \end{bmatrix}$$

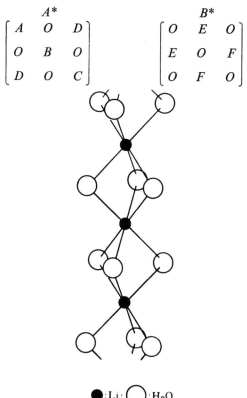

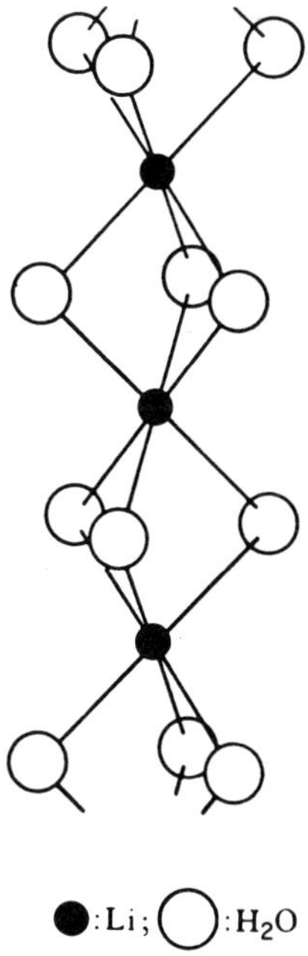

Crystal Structure of Lithium Perchlorate Trihydrate

j. *Lithium Perchlorate Trihydrate* [$LiClO_4(H_2O)_3$]

There are two formula units in a hexagonal unit of space group C_{6v}^4 ($P6mc$). The position of the hydrogen atoms was determined by neutron diffraction.

Mathieu and coworkers have determined the orientation of the water molecules by studying the polarized Raman spectra of a single crystal (*155*).

k. *Amorphous Materials*

The study of the Raman spectra of amorphous materials promises to further our knowledge of the distribution of vibrational modes within them.

In such materials the coherence lengths of the normal modes is probably short compared with optical wavelengths, and consequently, the usual wave vector selection rules break down, and Raman scattering can take

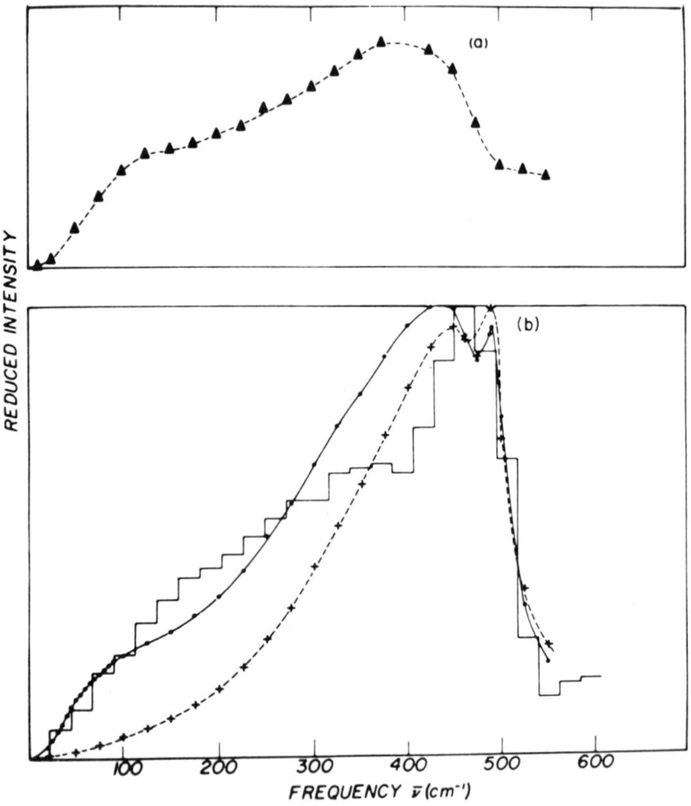

Fig. 47. Fused silica. (a) VH polarized spectrum reduced by $[1+n(\omega)]/\omega$. (b) Dashed line, VV polarized spectrum reduced as in (a); line with dots, VV polarized spectrum reduced by $[1+n(\omega)]$. The histogram is the density of states from the calculations of Bell, Bird, and Dean [Ref. 23C] (*159, 236*).

place from essentially all the normal modes of the material (*159, 236*). However, the intensity depends on a weighting factor composed of an optical coupling tensor. The summation over modes can be replaced by the density of vibrational state $g(v)$ which is the number of modes per unit frequency interval. Shuker and Gammon (*219*) have shown that the Stokes spectrum should be given by

$$I_{\alpha\beta,\gamma\delta}(\nu) = \sum_b C_b^{\alpha\beta,\gamma\delta} \frac{[1+n(\nu)]}{\nu} g_b(\nu)$$

where $n(\nu)$ is the Bose factor and the constants depend on the band interval considered. The tensor components labeled α, β, γ, and δ are selected by the polarization of the incident and scattered light. Thus, the spectrum will in general be very complicated due to overlapping bands and different coupling constants. Figure 47 shows the part of the experimental polarized Raman spectrum for vitreous silica reduced by the factor $[1+n(\nu)]/\nu$ plotted together with the calculated density-of-states histogram for this material. The general features of the density of vibrational states are reflected in the Raman spectra (*159,160*).

V. RAMAN SCATTERING IN MIXED CRYSTALS AND CRYSTALS CONTAINING IMPURITIES

A. Mixed Crystals

Many experiments have been carried out on mixed crystals with a view to understanding the nature of their vibrational spectra (*161*). Raman spectroscopy is proving to be perhaps the most fruitful technique that has been applied so far, and several detailed investigations on simple mixed crystals have been reported.

Experimentally, it is found that two quite different characteristic types of behavior occur in mixed crystals. If the crystal $A_{1-x}B_xC$ is formed as an alloy from AB and BC, which each have one optically active mode ν_A and ν_B, respectively, the two possible forms may be characterized as follows:

One-mode mixed crystals continue to show a single $\mathbf{k} = 0$ optic mode which shifts linearly with concentration x from the frequency of ν_A to ν_B. The linewidth increases and has a maximum for a 1:1 mixture, i.e., $x \approx 0.5$. The intensity of the Raman line does not change appreciably with concentration. Examples of this type include $Ca_{1-x}Sr_xF_2$ (*158*, *162*), $GaAs_{1-x}Sb_x$ (*164*), and $Cd_xZn_{1-x}S$ (*163*).

Two-mode mixed crystals show two modes of vibration whose frequencies are close to ν_A and ν_B of the pure compounds. However, the intensity of the Raman scattering from these modes is proportional to the fraction of each compound present. As the concentration x increases, the intensity of ν_B increases while that of ν_A decreases and both shift slightly. Examples include the mixed crystals $GaP_{1-x}As_x$ (*164*), $CdS_{1-x}Se_x$ (*163*), $ZnS_{1-x}Se_x$ (*166*), and $Si_{1-x}Ge_x$ (*165*).

In some mixed crystals it is possible for different modes to display different behaviors. Chang and Mitra (*161*) have given a theory which is

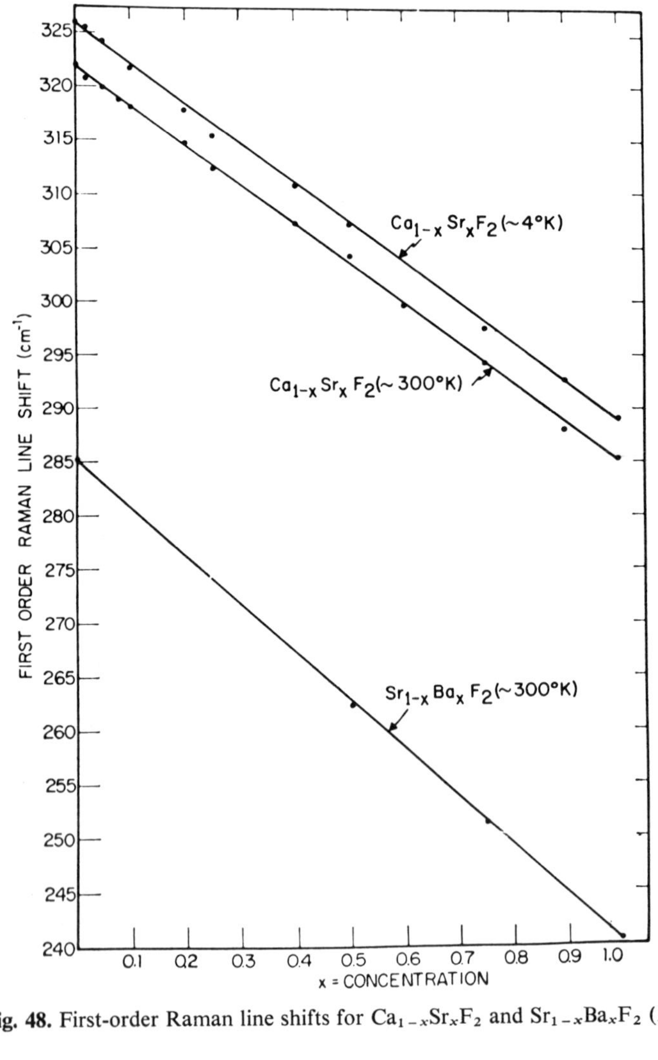

Fig. 48. First-order Raman line shifts for $Ca_{1-x}Sr_xF_2$ and $Sr_{1-x}Ba_xF_2$ (*158*).

able to predict whether a crystal will show one-mode or two-mode behavior as well as the dependence of the optic mode frequencies on the concentration x.

1. One-Mode Type ($Ca_{1-x}Sr_xF_2$ and $Sr_{1-x}Ba_xF_2$)

Figure 48 shows the results for Raman scattering (*158*) and illustrates very clearly the one-mode behavior where the $\mathbf{k} = 0$ line shifts linearly with concentration x, while the linewidth increases and has a maximum for a 1:1 concentration. Pershan (*158*) has carried out calculations of the spectrum expected for CaF_2 with Sr^{++} impurities taking into account the changes in mass and force constants. It provides a clear indication of the difficulty in describing the phonon optical properties of even reasonably simple disordered systems.

2. Two-Mode Type

a. CdS_xSe_{1-x}

Both CdS and CdSe have the wurtzite structure. Figure 49 shows the Raman spectrum of CdS_xSe_{1-x}. The bottom trace shows the *TO* and *LO* modes of CdSe. As the sulphur concentration is increased the frequencies of these two modes converge to the resonant gap mode of Se in CdS. Similarly, the top trace shows the *TO* and *LO* modes, and as the selenium concentration is increased, the frequencies of these two modes converge to the local mode frequency of S in CdSe. In Fig. 50 the Raman shifts (*163*) are plotted against the concentration x and show clearly the convergence to the resonant gap mode frequency of Se in CdS.

With concentration of ZnS the *LO* frequency of $ZnS_{1-x}Se_x$ decreases, and the corresponding *TO* frequency increases. The point of intersection which occurs in pure zinc sulfide may be regarded as the resonant gap mode of Se in ZnS. This occurs at 220 cm^{-1}. The *LO* frequency of ZnS decreases, while the *TO* frequency increases with increasing concentration of ZnSe. The point of intersection of the two lines at 297 cm^{-1} may be identified with the localized modes of S in ZnSe.

b. $GaAs_xP_{1-x}$

$GaAs_xP_{1-x}$ has a zinc blende structure with an absorption edge which varies from 1.43 eV for GaAs to 2.2 eV for GaP; hence, it is necessary to use a NdYAG laser for the arsenic-rich samples (*164*). The spectra

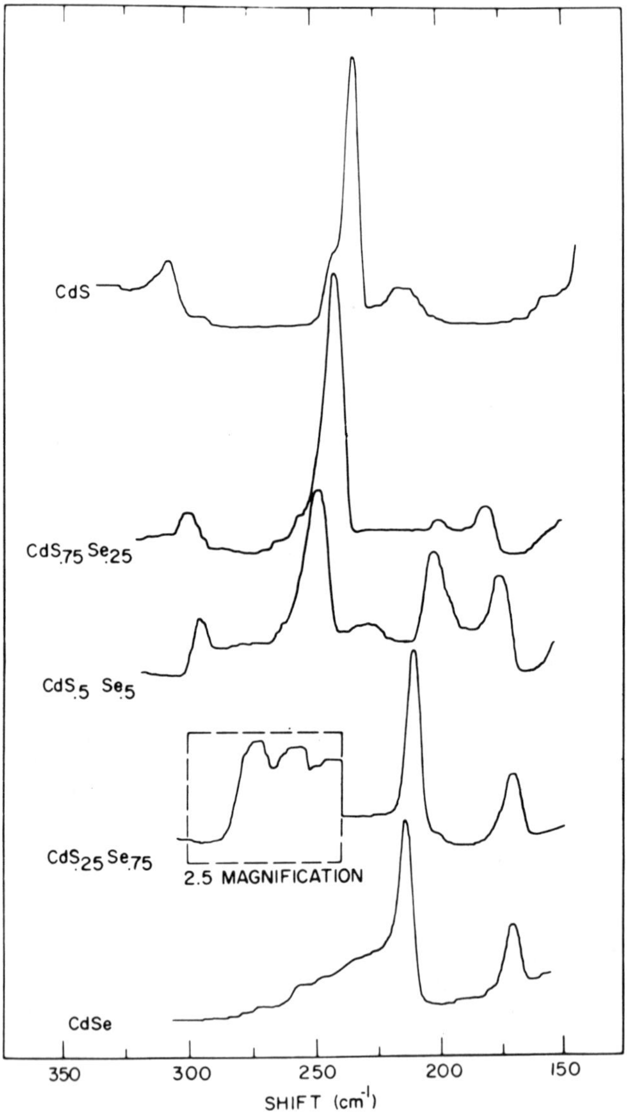

Fig. 49. The Raman spectra of CdS_xSe_{1-x} at 80°K. The bottom trace shows the *LO* and *TO* modes of CdSe. As the S concentration is increased, the two modes converge and diminish in intensity. The top trace shows the *LO* and *TO* modes of CdS. As the Se concentration is increased, the two modes converge and diminish in intensity (*163*).

show bands in two distinct frequency ranges, one of which (345 cm^{-1}–405 cm^{-1}) is identified with GaP and the other (250–295 cm^{-1}) with GaAs. Phosphorus isolated in GaAs gives rise to a localized mode at about 358 cm^{-1}, whereas for arsenic in GaP the two modes at 264 cm^{-1}

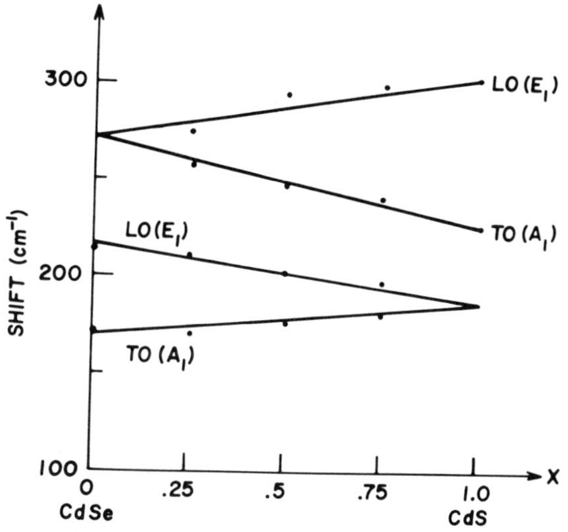

Fig. 50. Frequency of longitudinal and transverse optic modes of CdS_xSe_{1-x} (*163*).

and 271 cm^{-1} are between the acoustical and optical phonon bands. One of the modes is presumably associated with a mode that involves two adjacent arsenic atoms.

c. Si_xGe_{1-x}

Silicon and germanium form mixed crystals in all proportions. Figure 51 shows the Raman spectra of silicon and germanium containing varying percentages of silicon (*165*). The Raman line, whose frequency depends upon a concentration varying from 389 to 402 cm^{-1} (as the silicon concentration increases from 1 to 33%), has been assigned to a local mode involving silicon. Two additional lines appear in the high concentration samples with an intensity ratio of 2:1 at 476 and 448 cm^{-1}. These arise from Raman active A_{1g} and E_g modes of nearest neighbor silicon pairs.

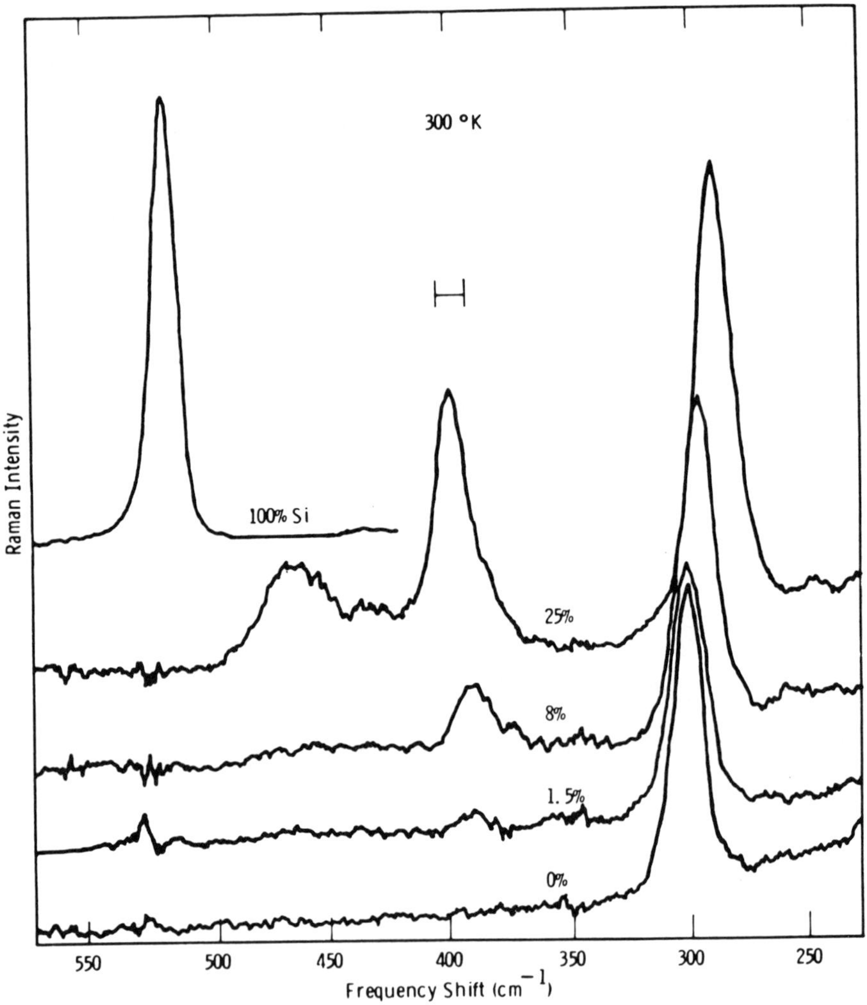

Fig. 51. Raman spectra of germanium-silicon alloys for several compositions. The instrumental resolution is indicated by the vertical lines (*165*).

B. Localized Resonant-Band or Impurity-Induced Raman Scattering in Crystals

An increasing number of observations are being reported on the Raman spectra of alkali halides doped with various cations or anions in an attempt to see localized impurity-induced or resonant-band scattering.

1. Localized Modes of H^- and D^- in CaF_2, SrF_2, and BaF_2

Several studies have been made on the infrared absorption spectra (*168,182*) of hydride ions in alkaline earth fluorides in which they replace fluoride ions and, hence, occupy sites of symmetry T_d. Each H^- ion is surrounded by four metal ions. Corresponding Raman studies have recently been reported (*167*). The energy levels arising from the localized H^- modes have been discussed by Elliott et al. (*182*) who have assumed that the Hamiltonian can be expressed as

$$\hat{H} = \tfrac{1}{2}M\Omega r^2 + A(x^2+y^2+z^2) + Bxyz + C_1(x^4+y^4+z^4) + C_2(x^2y^2+y^2z^2+z^2x^2)$$

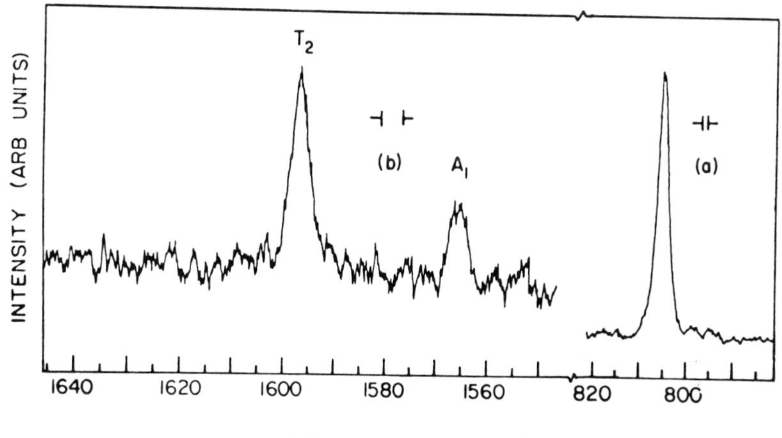

Fig. 52. Raman spectra of BaF_2, H^- at 16°K; (a) fundamental, and (b) second harmonic is of A_1 and T_2 symmetry. (The second harmonic of E symmetry, which is not observed, is predicted to occur at 1617 cm^{-1}.) Instrumental resolution is indicated for each trace (*167*).

where x, y, z, and r are the displacements from equilibrium of the impurity ion. Ω, B, C, and C_2 may be determined from the experimentally determined energy levels. The symmetries of the different vibrational states are listed as follows:

V	Symmetry
0	A_1
1	F_2
2	A_1+E+F_2
3	$A_1+F_1+2F_2$

Hence, $V = 0 \rightarrow 1$ F_2 is both *IR* and Raman active

$V = 0 \rightarrow 2$ A_1, E, and F_2 are Raman active; F_2 is *IR* active

$V = 0 \rightarrow 3$ A_1 and $2F_2$ are Raman active; $2F_2$ is *IR* active

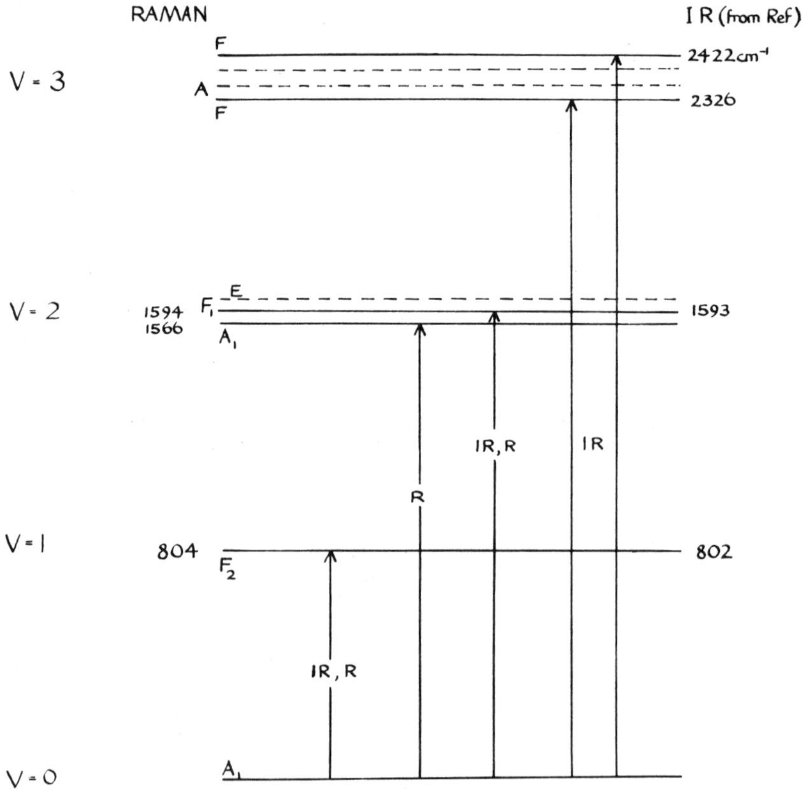

Fig. 53. The observed vibrational energy levels of hydride ions in barium fluoride as determined from Raman and infrared observations (77°K) (*After 182*).

The $V = 0 \rightarrow 1$ and $V = 0 \rightarrow 2$ transitions have been observed in Raman scattering for most of the alkaline earth fluorides for H^- and in some for D^-. Figure 52 shows the Raman scattering in the region corresponding to $V = 0 \rightarrow 1$ and $V = 0 \rightarrow 2$ for hydride ions in BaF_2. Only the A and F_2 components were observed, and the E mode could not be detected. Figure 53 shows the observed levels in BaF_2, H^-. In CaF_2 the observed value of 1895 cm^{-1} for A_1 of $V = 0 \rightarrow 2$ is in excellent agreement with the original calculation of Elliott (*182*) who predicted a value of 1894 cm^{-1}.

The halfwidths of the Raman lines appear to be very similar to the infrared values at the same temperature. While the calculations of Askin (*191*) fail to give the correct ratio of the intensities of the Raman fundamental and overtone, they do predict a ratio of 2:1:0.01 for the F_2, A_1, and E components of $V = 0 \rightarrow 2$, which can be observed from Fig. 52, and this is approximately correct.

2. Localized Modes in GaP

Raman scattering has been observed from GaP doped with impurities (*169*). In general, the lines appear at frequencies greater than that of the longitudinal optic mode and are comparable in intensity to the two-phonon Raman scattering. Two lines at 593.8 cm^{-1} and 569.7 cm^{-1} have been assigned to $^{10}B_{Ga}$ and $^{11}B_{Ga}$, respectively, i.e., to the localized vibration of a boron atom at a gallium site. The intensity ratio ~ 1:4 is approximately equal to that of the natural isotopic abundances of boron. Other lines have been tentatively suggested to be due to the localized modes of Al_{Ga}, Si_{Ga}, and N_P or O_P. The observed depolarization ratio of all the lines was 0.75. This is expected when the site symmetry of the substitutional site is T_d and when, for a F_2 vibration, the derived polarizability tensor has only off-diagonal terms.

3. Doped Alkali Halides

a. *KClTl*$^+$

Raman spectra of Tl^+ doped KCl, KBr, and KI are readily observed as single crystals in which the Tl^+ ion replaces a cation (*170,171*). In the potassium salts the change in force constant appears to be small, and hence, the principal effect of the impurity is to destroy the translational symmetry of the lattice so that the one-phonon spectra become Raman active. In the other alkali halides the change in force constant is larger, but a one-phonon induced Raman spectrum is still expected. A consideration of the impurity induced spectrum in these crystals with symmetry O_h shows that Raman scattering should take place from modes of vibration with symmetry A_g, E_g, and F_{2g}.

If the crystal axes are oriented parallel to X, Y, and Z, then the Raman scattering selection rules are as follows:

$X(YX)Z$ gives F_{2g} modes of vibration

$X(YY)Z$ gives $A_{1g}+E_g$ modes of vibration

$X(Y'Z')Z$ gives E_g modes of vibration

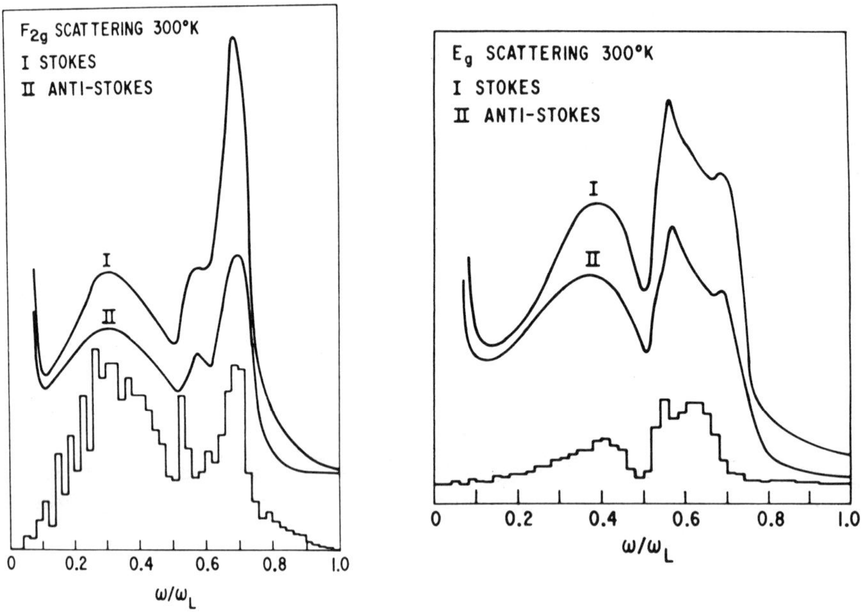

Fig. 54. A comparison of the F_{2g} and E_g Raman spectra with the corresponding theoretical histograms of the perturbed density of vibrational states of Tl^+KCl.

where Y' and Z' correspond to the case where the crystal axes are rotated about the X axis. In general the scattering is strongest from the E_g modes, and the observed spectra are in good agreement with calculated one-phonon spectra. Figure 54 shows the comparison of the Raman spectra for Tl^+KCl with the calculated F_{2g} and E_g histograms.

b. *NaClAg*$^+$

These doped crystals show enhanced Raman scattering in the 100–200 cm^{-1} range due to one-phonon induced scattering in sodium chloride. Peaks at 58 cm^{-1} and 88 cm^{-1} have been assigned by Kaiser (*172*) as being due to the resonant modes of the Ag^+ impurity. Earlier work on the thermal conductivity of this doped crystal had postulated the existence of an E_g resonant mode at 90 cm^{-1}.

c. *KClLi*$^+$

A broad Raman band has been observed at room temperature in this system at 198 cm^{-1} which on cooling to 77°K is considerably narrowed. This peak has been interpreted as a localized mode, although it appears in the optical band of the crystal (*206–208*).

d. *LiFMg*$^{2+}$

The one-phonon spectrum of the host lattice appears with crystals which have been doped in this way (*190*).

4. *F*-CENTERS IN ALKALI HALIDES

F-centers are electrons in anion vacancies in alkali halides. The scattering center has octahedral symmetry; hence, the Raman active perturbed lattice modes should be of symmetry type A_{1g}, E_g, and F_{2g}. The scattering geometries that have been used for their observation are as follows:

$Y(XX)Z$	$A_{1g}+E_g$
$Y(XY)Z$	F_{2g}
$Y(X'X')Z$	$A_{1g}+F_{2g}$
$Y(X'Y')Z$	E_g

where X' and Y' are crystal axes rotated by 45° about the Z axis which is the direction of observation. Although only low concentrations of *F*-centers can be obtained in alkali halides, it is possible to observe an appreciable Raman intensity through resonance enhancement. This is achieved by selecting the laser frequency to coincide with, or to be close to, the frequency of the maximum in the *F*-center visible absorption spectrum. The Raman scattering (*157, 173–175*) occurs chiefly in the crystal one-phonon region, and a defect model whose perturbation extends as far as the fourth neighbors has been used to explain the spectra.

Figure 55 shows the Raman scattering from *F*-centers in NaBr (*175*). This spectrum is dominated by the strong resonance peak at 136 cm^{-1}, which is just greater in frequency than the phonon gap (105–

126 cm^{-1}) between the optical and acoustic branches. The polarization of this peak is as high as 97% at 78°K and is found to be of A_{1g} symmetry. The arrows show the shifts of the line positions due to multiples of the resonance frequency. The relationship of the exciting frequency at 4880 and 5145 Å to the *F*-center absorption band is shown at the right.

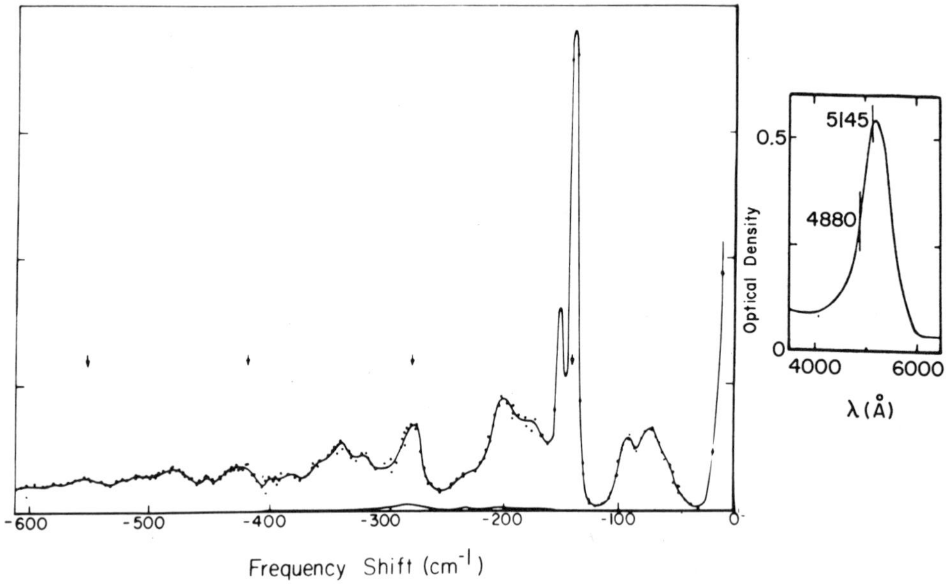

Fig. 55. Unpolarized Raman spectra of NaBr containing *F*-centers (top curve) and of pure NaBr (bottom curve). The relationship of the exciting frequency at 4880 Å and 5145 Å to the *F*-center absorption band is shown at the right (*175*).

It is hoped that the study of the Raman spectrum will provide direct information about the phonon responsible for the *F*-center visible absorption bandwidth.

5. Raman Spectra of Molecular Ions Isolated in Alkali Halides

The infrared absorption spectra of ions in alkali halides have long been studied, and deductions have been drawn on the orientation and motion of the molecular ion and of the crystal field. However, until recently Raman spectrometers had not been sufficiently sensitive to detect the low concentrations of impurities in the alkali halides. Recently, excellent Raman spectra have been obtained which supplement the infrared data and in some cases, allow species, such as the homonuclear diatomic ions O_2^-, S_2^-, and Se_2^-, which cannot be observed by infrared spectroscopy, to be detected.

a. *O_2^-, S_2^-, and Se_2^-*

These ions can be readily incorporated into alkali halides, and their Raman spectra in different host lattices have been reported (*176*). Figure 56

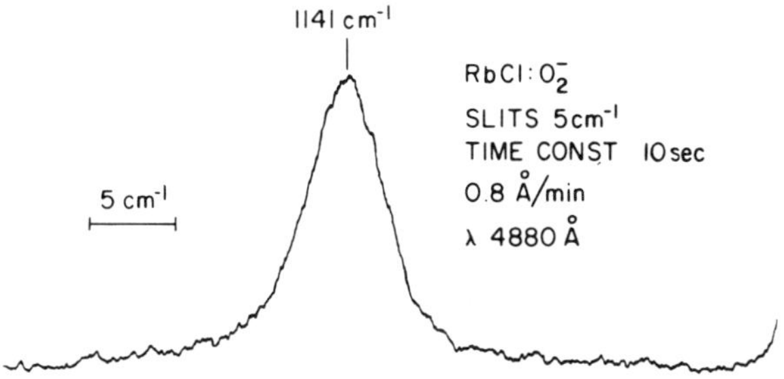

Fig. 56. The vibrational Raman spectrum of O_2^- in RbCl excited with argon ion 4880 Å excitation (Bernstein *et al.*) (*176*).

shows the Raman spectrum of O_2^- in RbCl excited with argon ion 4880 Å excitation. By plotting the O_2^- frequencies, observed in various alkali halides, against the corresponding CN^- frequencies it has been deduced that the ground state vibrational frequency of O_2^- is approximately 1090 cm^{-1}.

Hence, we can make the following comparison:

	O_2^- (cm^{-1})	O_2 (cm^{-1})	O_2^+ (cm^{-1})
ω_e	1106	1580	1876
$x\omega_e$	8	12	16.5

The value for the anharmonicity of O_2^- was obtained from the fluorescence spectrum of O_2^- which is readily excited with the argon ion radiation.

Raman scattering from S_2^- and Se_2^- has been observed in KI at the following frequencies (*177*):

O_2^-	S_2^-	Se_2^-
1123 cm^{-1}	601 cm^{-1}	334 cm^{-1}

The orientation of the S_2^- and Se_2^- ions has been verified by observing the polarization of the Raman radiation with respect to the crystal axes. The calculated and observed Raman intensities for the various arrangements are as follows:

	$X(YY)Z$	$Y(YX)Z$	$X(ZY)Z$	$X(ZX)Z$
(110)	2	1	1	1
(100)	1	0	0	0
(111)	1	1	1	1
Observed	2.3	1.0	0.94	0.85

This confirms that these ions are oriented with their molecular axes in the (110) direction. A series of six lines, whose frequencies with respect to the exciting line can be represented by the expression

$$\Delta\nu = 549.5n - 1.9n^2 \text{ cm}^{-1}$$

were excited in the S_2^- doped sample and appear to be due to fluorescence.

b. *OH^- and CN^-*

Extensive studies have been reported of the infrared absorption spectra of hydroxyl and cyanide ions in alkali halides. The corresponding Raman spectra illustrate the value of complementary studies (*178*). In sodium chloride the hydroxyl ion gives a strong and well-defined peak at $\sim$ 3650 cm^{-1}, which shifts to higher frequencies and narrows slightly on cooling to a liquid helium temperature. This is in marked contrast to the infrared absorption spectrum which is so broad at room temperature to be almost unobservable. OD^- gives a strong Raman line in NaCl at $\sim$2690 cm^{-1}, which has not yet been detected by infrared absorption spectroscopy. A further Raman peak due to the librational motion of the hydroxyl ion is observed at about 300 cm^{-1}. It is believed that the OH^- ions are oriented in the (100) direction and occupy sites of symmetry C. The librational mode is E-type and, consequently, only off-diagonal terms of the derived polarizability tensor should be finite, and this is in fact observed (*179*).

The stretching vibration of the cyanide ion in alkali halides gives rise to Raman lines that are less than 0.3 cm^{-1} wide at 4°K (*180*).

c. *Molecular Motion and Raman Scattering* (*181*, *209*)

Callender and Pershan (*209*) have considered the effect that molecular rotation has on the Raman spectrum of molecules in condensed phases.

For a reference frame that is fixed with respect to the molecule (MF) the polarizability of the molecule can be represented by

$$\alpha(t)^{MF} = \alpha^0 + \sum_{v=1}^{r} \alpha^v Q^v(t)$$

If the orientation of the molecule changes with time, the polarizability in the laboratory frame is obtained by a unitary transformation $U(t)$

$$\alpha(t) = U(t)\alpha^{MF} U(t)^{-1}$$

The Raman spectrum can be expressed by the correlation functions of $\alpha(t)$. Neglecting the rotational contribution the second term can be expressed by fourth rank tensors.

$$I_{kl;ij}(\omega) = (2\pi)^{-1} \int dt \exp(i\omega t)\langle [U(t)\alpha^v U(t)^{-1}]_{ij}[U(O)\alpha^v U(O)^{-1}]_{kl}\rangle$$
$$\times \langle Q^v(t)Q^v\rangle\langle Q^v(t)Q^v\rangle \approx S_{vv^1}\langle (Q^v)^2\rangle \cos\omega_v t$$

Hence,

$$I_{kl;ij}(\omega) = \sum_{v} (I^{v}_{kl;ij} + I^{-v}_{kl;ij})$$

where

$$I^{\pm v}_{kl;ij}(\omega) = (2\pi)^{-1}(Q^v)^2 \int dt \exp[i(\omega \pm \omega_v)t]$$
$$\times \langle [U(t)\alpha^v U(t)^{-1}]_{ij}[U(O)\alpha^v U(O)^{-1}]_{kl}\rangle$$

If the theory is applied to the case of a molecular ion isolated at an anion vacancy in an alkali halide, the site has O_h point group symmetry.

A second rank tensor α^v can be written as $\alpha^v = 3^{-1}(Tr\alpha^v)\mathbf{1} + \beta^v$where $Tr\beta^v = 0$ and $\mathbf{1}$ is the identity matrix.

$$U(t)\alpha^v U(t)^{-1} = 3^{-1}(Tr\alpha^v)\mathbf{1} + U(t)\beta^v U(t)^{-1}$$

and hence,

$$I^{v}_{kl;ij}(\omega) = \langle (Q^v)^2\rangle[3^{-1}Tr\alpha^v]\delta_{ij}\,\delta_{kl}\,\delta(\omega-\omega_v) + \langle (Q^v)^2\rangle K^{v}_{kl;ij}(\omega-\omega_v)$$

where

$$K_{kl;ij}(\omega) = (2\pi)^{-1} \int dt \exp(i\bar{\omega}t)\langle \beta^v(t)_{ij}\beta^v(O)_{kl}\rangle$$

and

$$\beta^v(t) = U(t)\beta^v U(t)^{-1}$$

There are three linearly independent components to the fourth rank tensor

$$K_{ii;ii},\ K_{ii;jj},\ \text{and}\ K_{ij;ij}\ \text{for}\ i \neq j$$

In a site of O_h symmetry the Raman spectrum predicted by the above equation is a sharp line centered at the molecular vibrational frequency ω_v whose intensity is proportional to $[3^{-1}Tr(\alpha^v)]^2$ and two separable sideband spectra that are direct measures of the rotational motion. Figure 57 shows the spectrum of NO_2^- in KBr. The halfwidth of the 1276 cm^{-1} is a direct

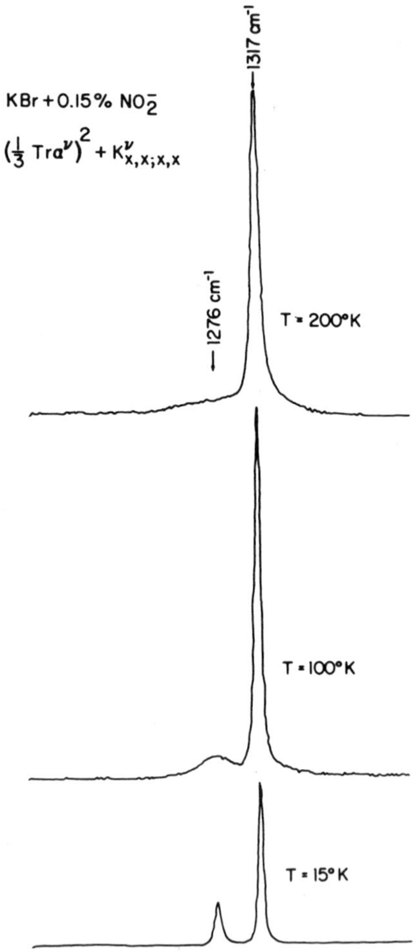

Fig. 57. Raman spectra for two internal modes of the NO_2^- impurity in KBr at three temperatures. The mode responsible for 1317-cm^{-1} line induces a diagonal polarizability tensor for which $Tr\alpha^{MF} \neq 0$. The 1276-cm^{-1} line arises from a mode for which the polarizability tensor is off-diagonal and $Tr\alpha^{MF} = 0$ (*209*).

measure of the correlation time for the NO_2^- rotational motion (1.4×10^{-11} sec at 100°K). For the symmetric N—O stretching mode ν_1, the nonvanishing components of $(\alpha^v)_{ij}$ are diagonal and, hence, $3^{-1}Tr(\alpha^v) \neq 0$ for the asymmetric stretching mode ν_3 only if off-diagonal components are finite and, consequently, $3^{-1}Tr(\alpha^v) = 0$. At room temperature the ν_3 mode gives rise to a very broad Raman band which does not sharpen to give an appreciable peak at ~1276 cm^{-1} until the rotational motion freezes out.

6. Raman Scattering by Radiation Induced Defects

a. *Cl_2^- (V_K Center)*

V_K centers are produced on *X* irradiation at 77°K of KCl that is doped with 0.5% molar Ag (*226*). These give a Raman peak at 235 cm^{-1} due to the excitation of the Cl—Cl vibration. A peak at 265 cm^{-1} has been assigned to the vibration of the Cl_2^- in the Raman spectrum of potassium chloride borate glass. These frequencies are much less than half that found in chlorine gas.

b. *Alkali Azides*

UV irradiation of KN_3 using a mercury arc gives a color center defect that, on illumination with a He/Ne laser, leads to a series of lines that can be represented by the expression (*227*)

$$\Delta\nu = 308n - 1.0n^2 \text{ cm}^{-1}$$

The origin of this spectrum is as yet unknown.

VI. OTHER TYPES OF RAMAN SCATTERING

A. Resonance Raman Effects

It is observed experimentally that as the incident laser photon energy, used for exciting Raman spectra, approaches that of an electronic transition, a marked resonant increase in the intensity of scattering occurs which can be understood in terms of semiclassical theory. Resonant Raman effects have been extensively studied in molecular liquids, and work in this field has been reviewed by Behringer (*210*). More recently, several examples of marked resonant enhancement have been observed in gases (*228*).

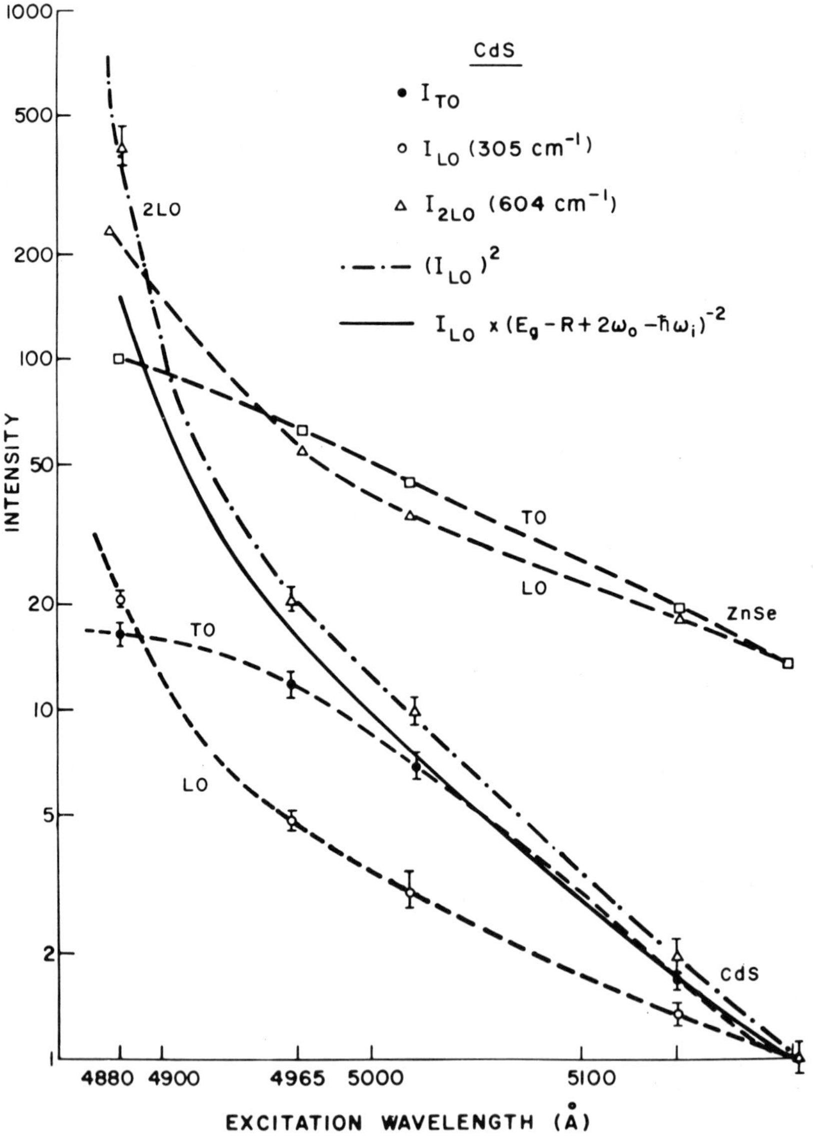

Fig. 58. Percentage enhancement of phonon cross-sections in CdS and ZnSe as a function of photon energy (*184*).

The resonance Raman effect in crystals has been the subject of several studies (*183–189*, *192–194*, *215*) most of which have so far been concentrated on semiconductors whose absorption edges occur in the near infrared, visible, or near ultraviolet regions of the spectrum.

Figure 58 shows the increase in the scattering cross section for CdS and ZnSe as the photon energy of the laser approaches the absorption edge. This behavior can be understood in terms of the theory of Ganguly and Birman which employs excitons as the intermediate state in the scattering process (*229*). These results show clearly that transverse optic cross sections saturate near resonance in marked contrast to longitudinal optic phonon behavior.

TABLE 14

Observed Frequencies (in cm^{-1}) of Raman Active Multiphonon Longitudinal Optic Lines

Line	CdS (*183, 191*)	GaP (*188*)	ZnTe (*187*)	ZnSe (*184*)	InAs (*185*)	ZnO (*194*)
1LO	302–306	403	210	253	241	585
2LO	607	805	421	506	483	1165
3LO	910	1208	632	759	730	1749
4LO	1214		843	1009		2343
5LO	1520		1055	1267		2928
6LO	1819					3520
7LO	2118					4101
8LO	2417					4678
9LO	2716					

When the laser energy is very close to the absorption edge, a series of lines is observed which is due to multiple excitation of the $\mathbf{k} = 0$ longitudinal optic mode. Table 14 lists the Raman frequencies of the multiple excitation lines in several semiconductors. An example is shown in Fig. 59 where CdS was excited with 4579 Å radiation, and nine LO lines are observed with almost equal spacing, confirming that only $\mathbf{k} = 0$ phonons are involved. The number of multiphonon lines observed in III-V and II-VI compounds at resonance is found to vary linearly with the polaron coupling coefficients from $n = 2$ in InSb ($\alpha_e = 0.02$) to $n = 9$ in CdS ($\alpha = 0.71$).

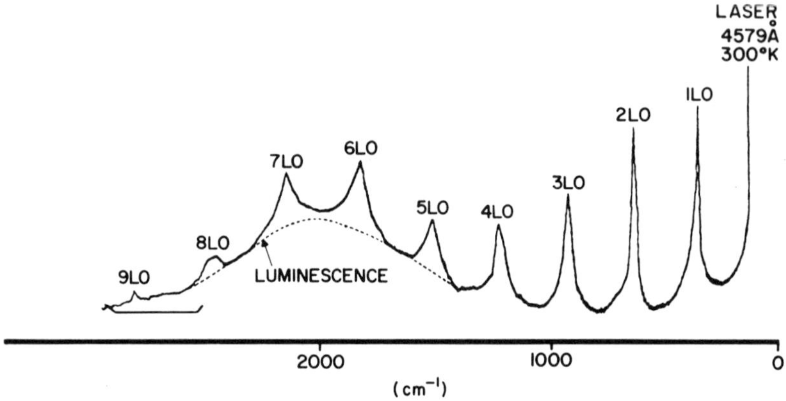

Fig. 59. The Raman spectrum of cadmium sulfide at ~300°K with excitation at 4579 Å (*After Porto, 183*).

B. Polaritons

Transverse optical phonons in polar crystals interact strongly with electromagnetic waves when their energies and momentum wavevectors are nearly equal. The resulting mixed excitations are referred to as polaritons. They may be observed in near forward Raman scattering (*195–202*). The frequency of the allowed polariton is increased as the angle θ from the forward direction is increased, and hence, the dispersion relation of frequency v against polariton wave vector $\mathbf{k}_p$ can be mapped experimentally. From the conservation of energy

$$hv_p = hv_i - hv_s$$

where v_p, v_i, and v_s are the frequencies of the polariton, incident, and scattered radiation, respectively. Similarly, from the conservation of momentum.

$$k_p^2 = (k_i^2 + k_s^2 - 2k_i k_s \cos\theta)$$

For small angles θ, we may set $\cos\theta = 1 - (\theta^2/2)$ and $k_i - k_s = v(\partial k_p/\partial v)$ and $k_i = 2\pi n v/c$, and hence,

$$k_p^2 \approx v^2 \left(\frac{\partial k_p}{\partial_v}\right)^2 + 4\pi^2\theta^2\eta^2 \qquad (1)$$

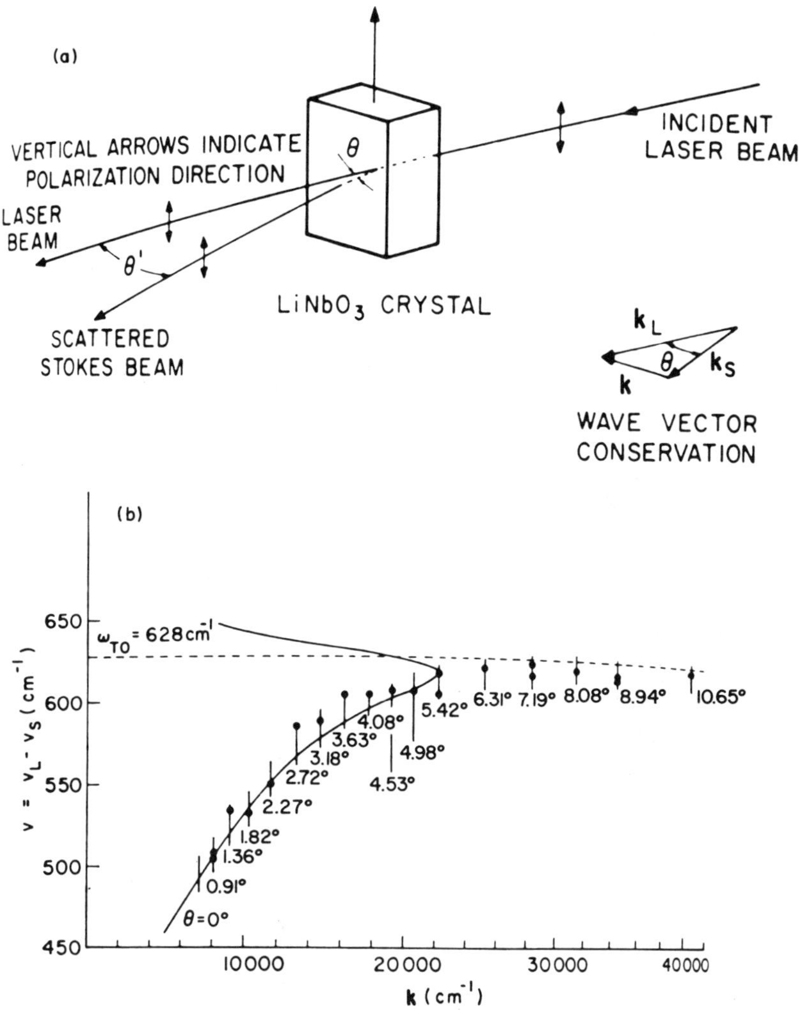

Fig. 60. (a) Vertically-polarized incident laser beam passes through lithium niobate ($LiNbO_3$) crystal as an extraordinary wave ($E \| c$), exciting optical vibration modes in the crystal. Light scattered at the Raman-shifted frequency (Stokes light) at angle θ' is detected to determine the angular dependence of the frequency shift. For the A_1-symmetry mode of interest the scattered Stokes light is also vertically polarized. (b) Comparison of theory and experiment. The solid curve is the theoretical IR dispersion characteristic based on IR reflectivity measurements, the short intersecting vertical lines are frequency-wavevector conservation curves for a given angular separation θ between Stokes and laser beams, and the circles correspond to experimentally observed Stokes frequency shifts. The departure of the experimental points from the theoretical IR dispersion characteristic at larger k values is discussed in the text (*199*).

Now the dielectric parameter ε_ν is equal to

$$\varepsilon_\nu = \frac{k^2}{4\pi^2\nu^2} = \varepsilon_\infty + \sum_i \frac{s_i\nu_i^2}{\nu_i^2 - \nu^2} \tag{2}$$

where the classic oscillator model is used for the real part of the dielectric parameter. Combining these two equations we get the following relation for the polariton dispersion relation:

$$\left(\frac{\partial k_p}{\partial \nu}\right)^2 + \eta^2\theta^2\left(\frac{\nu_i}{\nu}\right)^2 = \varepsilon_\infty + \sum_{i=1} \frac{s_i\nu_i^2}{\nu_i^2 - \nu^2}$$

The terms on the right of the equation may be obtained from infrared spectroscopic studies, and those on the left from near forward Raman scattering. This equation is valid for cubic crystals; however, to obtain really satisfactory agreement with experiment, frequency-dependent damping terms must be included in the resonance equations.

Polariton spectra have been observed in several different crystals including GaP (*195*), ZnO (*196*), α-quartz (*197*), ZnS (*198*), ZnSe (*199*), $LiNbO_3$ (*199*), and $LiIO_3$(*202*). Electric field induced polariton spectra have been reported for the cubic crystal $BaTiO_3$ (*200*).

Figure 60(a) shows the experimental arrangement for the observation of polaritons in $LiNbO_3$. The behavior of the A_1 symmetry mode, which occurs at 628 cm^{-1} for angles θ greater than 10°, is seen in Figs. 60(a) and (b) in which the frequency falls to 492 cm^{-1} for $\theta = 0$. The theoretical dispersion curve has been calculated using known values of the complex dielectric constant ε. The agreement between $\theta = 0$ and $\theta = 5°$ is excellent; however, for $k > 22{,}000\ cm^{-1}$ a phase mismatch between the electric field generated by the phonon and the mechanical vibration occurs. Under these conditions propagation of the vibration as a mixed mode system breaks down, and the dispersion curve then corresponds to a purely mechanical vibration.

C. Hyper-Raman Effect

The assumption that the polarization depends linearly upon the electric field is only a first approximation and is not valid for large field strengths. The polarization may be expressed as

$$P = \alpha E + \tfrac{1}{2}\beta E^2 + \tfrac{1}{6}\gamma E^3 + \ldots$$

where β, the first hyperpolarizability coefficient, plays an important part for large values of E, since it is responsible for the phenomenon of optical harmonic generation using Q switched lasers. Isolated atoms have values of β that are zero, since like μ the dipole moment, it arises from interactions between atoms. A simplified theory of Rayleigh scattering, the Raman effect, harmonic generation, and hyper-Raman scattering due to Long (*242*) is obtained by setting

$$E = E_o \cos \omega_o t$$

$$\alpha = \alpha_o + \left(\frac{\partial \alpha}{\partial \varphi}\right)\varphi$$

$$\beta = \beta_o + \left(\frac{\partial \beta}{\partial \varphi}\right)\varphi$$

$$\varphi = \varphi_o \cos \omega_v t$$

in the equation above where φ is a normal coordinate, ω_v is the corresponding vibrational frequency, and ω_o is the laser frequency.

$$P = \alpha_o E_o \cos \omega_v t + \tfrac{1}{2}\left(\frac{\partial \alpha}{\partial \varphi}\right)\varphi_o E_o \cos \omega_o t \cos \omega_v t$$

$$+ \tfrac{1}{2}\beta_o E_o^{\,2} \cos^2 \omega_o t + \tfrac{1}{2}\left(\frac{\partial \beta}{\partial \varphi}\right)\varphi_o E_o^{\,2} \cos^2 \omega_o t \cos \omega_v t$$

$$P = \underbrace{\alpha_o E_o \cos \omega_v t}_{\text{Rayleigh scattering}} + \underbrace{\tfrac{1}{2}\left(\frac{\partial \alpha}{\partial \varphi}\right)E_o \varphi_o [\cos (\omega - \omega_v)t + \cos (\omega + \omega_v)t]}_{\text{Raman scattering}}$$

$$+ \underbrace{\tfrac{1}{4}\beta_o E_o^{\,2}}_{\text{DC Polarization}} + \underbrace{\frac{\beta_o}{4} E_o^{\,2} \cos 2\omega t}_{\text{Frequency doubling}}$$

$$\underbrace{+ \tfrac{1}{8}\varphi_o E_o^{\,2}\left(\frac{\partial \beta}{\partial \varphi}\right)[\cos (2\omega_o - \omega_v)t + \cos (2\omega_o + \omega_v)t]}_{\text{Hyper-Raman effect}}$$

Thus, the hyper-Raman effect should be observed at large electric field strengths in the vicinity of twice the frequency of the exciting line with separations corresponding to the vibrational frequencies. α and β are actually tensors, and β has components $\beta_{\alpha\beta\gamma}$ which are symmetrical in all suffices. A group theoretical study of selection rules for β has been given by Cyvin et al. (*204*) for the different point groups. They have shown that

1. All infrared active bands are hyper-Raman active.
2. Infrared active bands are always polarized in the hyper-Raman effect.
3. In some cases infrared and Raman inactive modes are *active* in the hyper-Raman effect.

Hyper-Raman scattering has been observed from quartz (*203*) with bands near 450 cm^{-1}, 800 cm^{-1}, and 1200 cm^{-1}, and from NH_4Cl in which the infrared and Raman inactive rotatory mode of the ammonium ion is observed (*205*) at 380 cm^{-1}. Both the $\mathbf{k} = 0$, TO, and LO modes are also observed.

The observation of the weak hyper-Raman lines is carried out using an image-converter detector which permits the simultaneous recording of the whole spectrum excited by a Q switched laser.

D. Electronic Raman Effect

In the electronic Raman effect, which was predicted as long ago as 1934, the quantized energy levels involved in the scattering are low lying electronic levels usually less than 0.5 eV, such as those of lanthanide ions split by a crystal field or impurity levels in semiconductors. (See Chap. 8).

E. Raman Scattering from Landau Levels

When a solid, which contains free electrons, is placed in a magnetic field, the circular trajectories of the electrons are the quantized cyclotron orbits known as Landau levels. If the effective mass of the electron is small in the crystal, the splittings are large enough to be observed by Raman spectroscopy (*230*).

Raman scattering from Landau levels in InSb using a CO_2 laser has assumed considerable importance as it provides a variable frequency source of infrared radiation that can be tuned by changing the magnetic field provided by a superconducting magnet (*231*).

F. Raman Scattering by Plasmons

In this case the scattering takes place from electrons in collective motion. The frequency of such a motion is given by

$$\nu = \left(\frac{\rho e^2}{2\pi\varepsilon m^*}\right)^{1/2}$$

and the wavevector by

$$\mathbf{k} = \left(\frac{4\pi\rho e^2}{kT}\right)^{1/2}$$

where ε is the dielectric constant, ρ is the plasma density, and m^* is the effective mass of the electron. Plasmon scattering has been observed in several semiconductors where the coupling of the longitudinal optic frequency to the plasma frequency is very strongly dependent on the carrier concentration (*232*).

G. Raman Scattering by Magnons

In magnetic systems possessing long-range spin order, the analogous quantum of excitation to the phonon is the magnon. Spin waves of different frequency and wavelength may be propagated in a crystal and can be studied by Raman spectroscopy. Magnon dispersion curves are constructed by plotting the frequency of the magnon as a function of its wave vector. In one-magnon scattering, only zone-center magnons are excited; however, for two-magnon processes all values of k are allowed.

Inelastic light scattering experiments in transparent magnetic materials are providing valuable information about magnons. Types of studies (*211–215*) that have been carried out include the following:

1. Magnon dispersion relations in simply structured antiferromagnetics such as FeF_2 and MnF_2
2. Magnon–magnon interaction effects, e.g., in $RbMnF_3$
3. Paramagnons observed in NiF_2
4. Localized magnons observed in Ni doped MnF_2

1. FeF_2 and MnF_2

These rutile structure antiferromagnetic materials have Neél temperatures of 78 and 67°K. Below this the spins are aligned parallel and antiparallel to the tetragonal axes and are equally divided between the two equivalent sublattices. Figure 61 shows both one- ($52\ cm^{-1}$) and two-magnon ($154\ cm^{-1}$) scattering in FeF_2 at 15°K. Only the zone-center magnon is observed in the first case and, consequently, the line is sharp. The shape of the two-magnon peak depends upon the magnon density of states and on various weighting factors which depend upon the symmetry of the crystal. The similarity of XZ and XY two-phonon peaks indicates

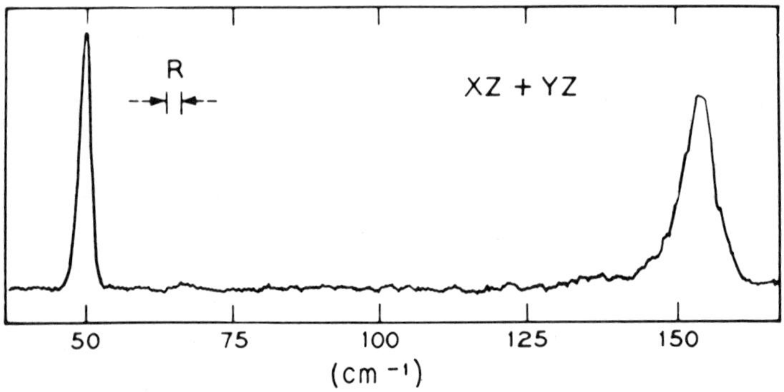

Fig. 61. One-magnon (~ 50 cm^{-1}) and two-magnon (~ 154 cm^{-1}) scattering in FeF_2 at 15°K. The instrumental width *R* precludes measurement of the one-magnon width, but the true shape of the two-magnon peak is observed *(211)*.

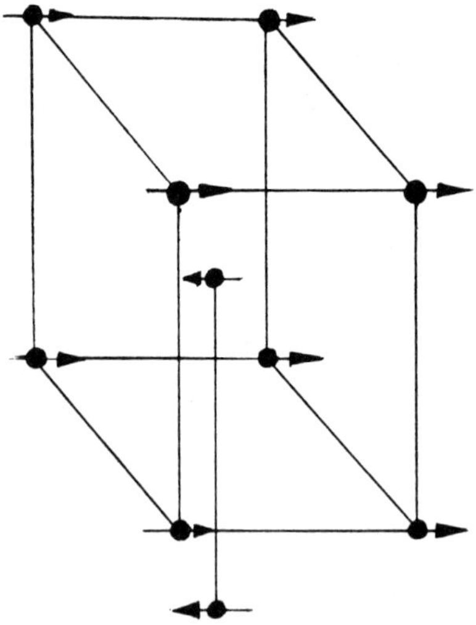

Fig. 62. The orientations of the spins in the anti-ferromagnetic crystal FeF_2 which has the rutile structure. The Fe^{2+} ions are shown as black circles. Eight spins of one sub-lattice and two of the other sub-lattice are shown.

that the exchange interaction between neighbors on the same sublattice in the (001) and (100) directions is negligible (see Fig 62). In MnF_2 this is not the case and the shift in peak frequency has been used to assign values of J_1 and J_2 which are in agreement with results of neutron scattering measurements.

2. $RbMnF_3$

The simple cubic perovskite $RbMnF_3$, which has a Neél temperature of 82.5°K, is a very close approximation to an isotropic Heisenberg antiferromagnet. Figure 30 of Chap. 3 shows the $\Gamma_3{}^+$ component of the two-magnon scattering in $RbMnF_3$ at 10°K compared to the calculated shapes, ignoring magnon–magnon interaction, and the dotted line includes them and provides clear evidence of the importance of magnon interactions on two-magnon spectra.

3. NiF_2

NiF_2, which has the rutile structure, is antiferromagnetic. Below its critical temperature, $T = 73$°K, spins align perpendicular to the C axis such that the spins on the two sublattices are not quite antiparallel. One-magnon transitions have been observed in the far infrared in NiF_2 at 3.3 and 31 cm^{-1}. The latter peak is also observed below the transition temperature in the Raman spectrum shown in Fig. 63. The two-magnon peak at about 200 cm^{-1} decreases in frequency and peak intensity as the temperature is increased but persists above the transition temperature, indicating the existence of spin waves in the paramagnetic phase. These spin waves presumably have very short wavelengths.

4. Ni Doped MnF_2

For Ni doped MnF_2 a localized magnon, which involves the spin deviation of a Ni ion surrounded by 8 Mn second neighbors, has been found at 120 cm^{-1}, while impurity modes involving spin deviations of the second neighbor Mn ions occur near 50 cm^{-1}. Figure 64 shows the Raman spectra (*212a*) for different polarizations. The peak at 167 cm^{-1} is due to the simultaneous excitation of the 120 and 50-cm^{-1} magnons.

VII CONCLUSION

Laser Raman spectroscopy is now providing data on the vibrational frequencies of a very wide range of crystals. Perhaps the most significant

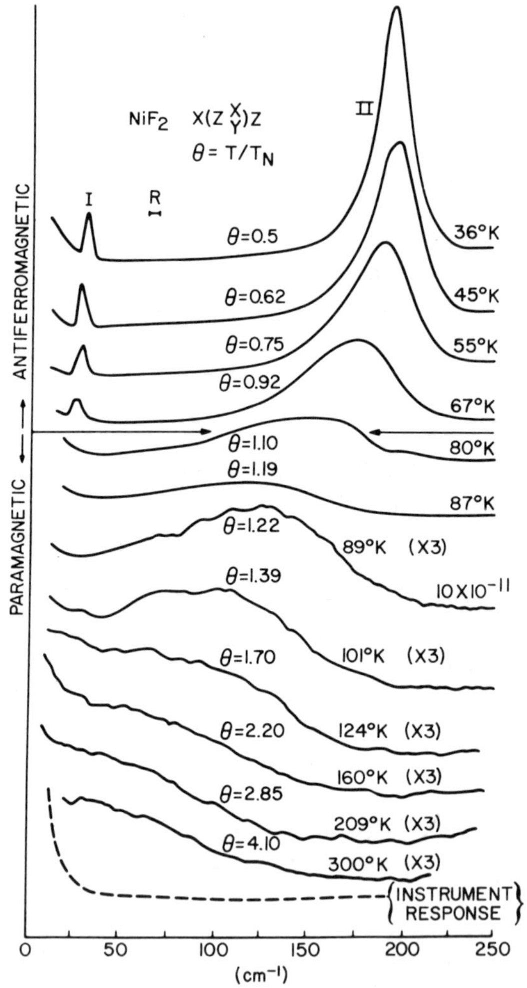

Fig. 63. Magnon spectra of NiF_2 in the anti-ferromagnetic and the paramagnetic phases. The one-magnon peak (I) disappears for $T > T_n$. The two-magnon peak (II) persists, indicating the existence of spin waves in the paramagnetic phase. Note the instrumental response (dashed curve) (*211*).

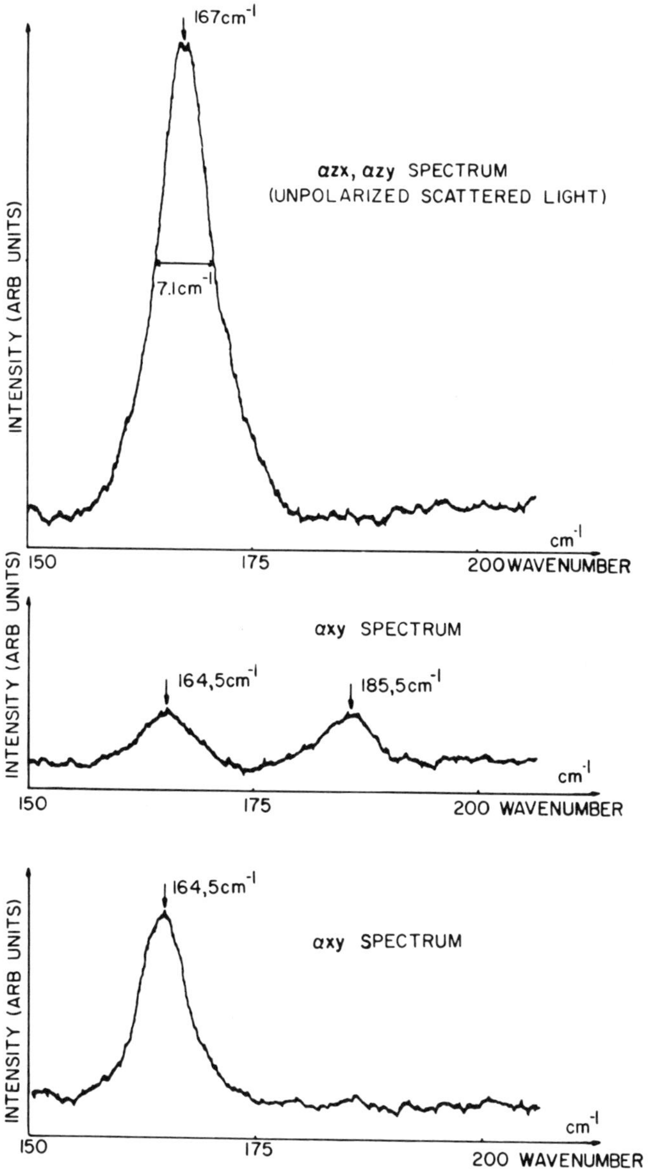

Fig. 64. Experimental Raman scattering spectra in 1% Ni doped MnF_2 at 8°K between 150 and 200 cm^{-1} for different polarizations. Corrections due to instrumental polarization have not been made on the relative intensities of the different polarizations (*212*).

feature is the reliability that can be given to the identification of the symmetry of normal modes of vibration following careful measurement of the anisotropy of the polarizability tensor. Once again, it is emphasized that effort placed into growing suitable crystals for Raman spectroscopy is amply rewarded in the ease of interpretation that it offers, compared to uncertainties in assignments based on powder spectra.

The technique promises to advance considerably our knowledge both of the structure and the dynamics of crystalline solids.

REFERENCES

1. A. Z. Menzies, *Rep. Prog. Phys.*, **16,** 83 (1953).
2. L. A. Woodward, *Quart. Rev. Chem. Soc. London*, **X,** 185 (1956).
3. G. R. Wilkinson, *Mol. Dyn. and Str. Solids* (R. S. Carter and J. J. Rush, eds.), *Nat. Bur. Stand. Special Publication*, 301 (1969).
4. E. B. Wilson, Jr., J. C. Decius, and P. C. Cross, *Molecular Vibrations*, McGraw-Hill, New York, 1955.
5. K. Nakamoto, *Infrared Spectroscopy of Inorganic Co-ordinate Compounds*, Wiley, New York, 1963.
6. M. Born and K. Huang, *Dynamical Theory of Crystal Lattices*, Oxford-Clarendon, 1954.
7. H. Winston and R. S. Halford, *J. Chem. Phys.*, **17,** 607 (1949).
8. S. Bhagavantama and T. Venkataryudu, *Prov. Indian Acad. Sci.*, **9,** 224 (1939).
9. R. S. Halford, *J. Chem. Phys.*, **14,** 8 (1946).
10. D. F. Hornig, *J. Chem. Phys.*, **16,** 1063 (1948).
11. D. M. Adams and D. C. Newton, *Tables of Factor Group and Point Group Analysis*, Beckman, RIIC, London, 1970.
12. D. M. Adams and D. C. Newton, *J. Chem. Soc.* [A], 2822 (1970).
13. R. Hester, *Raman Spectroscopy* (H. Symanski, ed.), Plenum, New York, 1967.
14. R. Loudon, *Adv. Phys.*, **13,** 423 (1964).
15. W. D. Johnston, *Phys. Rev.* [B], **1,** 3494 (1970).
16. M. Krauzman, *Compt. Rend. Acad. Sci.*, **270,** 856 (1970).
17. T. R. Gilson and P. J. Hendra, *Laser Raman Spectroscopy*, Wiley-Interscience, London, 1970.
18. J. P. Mathieu, *Spectre de Vibration et Symmetrie des Molecules et des Cristauz*, Hermann, Paris, 1954.
19. G. Herzberg, *Infra-red and Raman Spectra of Polyatomic Molecules*, Van Nostrand, New York, 1945.
20. G. R. Wilkinson, *Molecular Spectroscopy* (P. Hepple, ed.), p. 43, Elsevier, New York, 1968.
20a. R. H. Lyddane, R. G. Sachs, and E. Teller, *Phys. Rev.* **59,** 673 (1941).
21. W. Cochran and R. A. Cowley, *J. Phys. Chem. Solids*, **23,** 447 (1962).
22. A. K. Wells, *Structural Inorganic Chemistry*, Oxford Univ. Press, 1962.
23. R. C. Evans, *An Introduction to Crystal Chemistry*, Cambridge Univ. Press, 1966.
24. S. A. Solin and A. K. Ramdas, *Phys. Rev.*, **1,** 1687 (1970).

25. F. Stenman, *J. Applied Phys.*, **40,** 4164 (1969).
26. S. S. Mitra, O. Brafman, W. B. Daniels, and R. K. Crawford, *Phys. Rev.*, **186,** 942 (1969).
27. E. Anastassakis and A. Filler, *Light Scattering Spectra of Solids* (G. B. Wright, ed.), Springer-Verlag, New York, 1969.
28. J. H. Parker, Jr., D. W. Feldman, and M. Ashkin, *Phys. Rev.*, **155,** 712 (1967).
29. T. R. Hart, R. L. Aggarwal, and B. Lax, *Phys. Rev.* [B], **1,** 638 (1970).
30. R. K. Chang, J. M. Ralston, and D. E. Keating, *Light Scattering Spectra of Solids*, p. 369 (C. B. Wright, ed.), Springer-Verlag, New York, 1969.
31. E. Anastassakis, A. Pinczuk, E. Burstein, F. H. Pollack, and M. Cardona, *Solid State Comm.*, **8,** 133 (1970).
32. G. W. Chantry, A. Anderson, and H. A. Gebbie, *Spectrochemica Acta*, **20,** 1223 (1964).
33. G. Lucovsky, A. Mooradian, W. Taylor, G. B. Wright, and R. C. Keezer, *Solid State Comm.*, **5,** p. 113 (1967).
34. F. Tuinstra and J. L. Koenig, *J. Chem. Phys.*, **53,** 1126 (1970).
35. L. M. Fraas and S. P. S. Porto, *Solid State Comm.*, **8,** 803 (1970).
36. J. H. Parker, D. W. Feldman, and M. Ashkin, *Light Scattering Spectra of Solids* (G. B. Wright, ed.), p. 389, Springer-Verlag, New York, 1969.
37. O. Brafman and S. S. Mitra, *Phys. Rev.*, **171,** 931 (1968).
38. W. G. Nilsen, *Phys. Rev.*, **182** (1969).
39. S. S. Mitra, *J. Phys. Soc. Japan*, **22,** 61 (1966).
40. M. Krautzman, *Compt. Rend. Acad. Sci.*, **264,** 1117 (1967).
41. T. C. Damen, S. P. S. Porto, and B. Tell, *Phys. Rev.*, **142,** 570 (1966).
42. A. Pinczuk and E. Berstein, *Phys. Rev. Letters*, **21,** 1073 (1968).
43. S. P. S. Porto, B. Tell, and T. C. Damen, *Phys. Rev. Letters*, **16,** 450 (1966).
44. W. G. Nilsen, *Light Scattering Spectra of Solids* (G. B. Wright, ed.), p. 129, Springer-Verlag, New York, 1969.
45. S. Ushioda, A. Pinczuk, E. Burstein, and D. Mills, *Light Scattering Spectra of Solids*, (G. B. Wright, ed.), p. 347, Springer-Verlag, New York, 1969.
46. C. H. Henry and J. J. Hopfield, *Phys. Rev. Letters*, **15,** 964 (1965).
47. J. F. Scott, T. C. Damen, R. C. Leite, and W. T. Silvast, *Solid State Comm.*, **7,** 953 (1969).
48. S. Fray, F. A. Johnson, R. Jones, S. Kay, C. J. Oliver, E. R. Pike, J. Russell, S. Sennett, J. O'Shaughnessy, and C. Smith, *Light Scattering Spectra of Solids* (G. B. Wright, ed.), p. 139, Springer-Verlag, New York, 1969.
49. V. S. Gorlich, V. S. Rjazanov, and M. M. Sushchinskii, *Light Scattering Spectra of Solids* (G. B. Wright, ed.), p. 85, Springer-Verlag, New York, 1969.
50. A. Mooradin and A. L. McWhorter, *Light Scattering Spectra of Solids* (G. B. Wright, ed.), p. 297, Springer-Verlag, New York, 1969.
51. B. Tell, T. C. Damen, and S. P. S. Porto, *Phys. Rev.*, **144,** 771 (1966).
52. S. S. Mitra, O. Brafman, W. B. Daniels, and R. K. Crawford, *Phys. Rev.*, **186,** 942 (1969).
53. J. P. Mon, *Compt. Rend. Acad. Sci.*, **266B,** 244 (1968).
54. E. Loh, *Phys. Rev.*, **116,** 673 (1968).
55. R. C. C. Leite and S. P. S. Porto, *Phys. Rev. Letters*, **17,** 10 (1966).
56. O. Brafman and S. S. Mitra, *Phys. Rev.*, **171,** 931 (1968).

57. C. A. Arguello, D. L. Rousseau, and S. P. S. Porto, *Phys. Rev.*, **181,** 1351 (1969).
58. W. G. Nilsen, *Light Scattering Spectra of Solids* (G. B. Wright, ed.), p. 129, Springer-Verlag, New York, 1969.
59. M. A. Nusimovici, *Compt. Rend. Acad. Sci.*, **268B,** 755 (1969).
60. A. Mooradian and G. B. Wright, *Solid State Comm.*, **4,** 431 (1966).
61. R. C. C. Leite and J. F. Scott, *Phys. Rev. Letters*, **21,** 130 (1968).
62. O. Brafman, G. Lengyel, S. S. Mitra, P. J. Gielisse, J. N. Plendl, and L. C. Mansur, *Solid State Comm.*, **6,** 523 (1968).
63. D. D. Manchon, Jr., A. S. Barker, Jr., P. J. Dean, and R. B. Zetterstrom, *Solid State Comm.*, **8,** 1227 (1970).
64. S. Z. Beer, J. F. Jackovitz, D. W. Feldman, and J. H. Parker, *Phys. Rev. Letters*, **26A,** 331 (1968).
65. D. W. Feldman, J. H. Parker, Jr., W. J. Choyke, and L. Patrick, *Phys. Rev.*, **170,** 698 (1968).
66. D. W. Feldman, J. H. Parker, W. J. Choyke, and L. Patrick, *Phys. Rev.*, **173,** 787 (1968).
67. A. R. Evans an D. B. Fitchen, *Solid State Comm.*, **8,** 537 (1970).
68. M. Krauzman, *Light Scattering Spectra of Solids* (G. B. Wright, ed.), p. 109, Springer-Verlag, New York, 1969.
68a. A. Mooradian and G. B. Wright, *Solid State Research Report*, Lincoln Lab., M.I.T., **1,** 47 (1968).
69. E. F. Steigmeier and G. Harbeke, *Solid State Comm.*, **8,** 1275 (1970).
70. O. Brafman, S. S. Mitra, R. K. Crawford, W. B. Daniels, C. Postmus, and J. R. Ferraro, *Solid State Comm.*, **7,** 449 (1969).
71. R. Zallen, G. Lucovsky, W. Taylor, A. Pinczuk, and E. Burstein, *Phys. Rev.*, **1B,** 4058 (1970).
72. H. Poulet and J. P. Mathieu, *Compt. Rend. Acad. Sci.*, **270B,** 708 (1970).
73. Pamela Denham, R. Field, P. M. Morse, and G. R. Wilkinson, *Proc. Roy. Soc.*, **A317,** 55 (1970).
74. P. G. Marlow, J. P. Russell, and J. R. Hardy, *Phil. Mag.*, 409 (1966).
75. M. Balkanski, M. A. Nusimovici, and J. Reydellet, *Solid State Comm.*, **7,** 815 (1969).
76. M. C. Carabatos, *Compt. Rend. Acad. Sci.*, **270B,** 1289 (1970).
77. S. M. Shapiro, D. C. O'Shea, and H. Z. Cummins, *Phys. Rev. Letters*, **19,** 361, (1967).
78. J. F. Scott and S. P. S. Porto, *Phys. Rev.* **161,** 903 (1967).
79. J. D. Masso, C. Y. She, and D. F. Edwards, *Phys. Rev.*, **B1,** 4179 (1970).
80. A. S. Pine and P. E. Tannewald, *Phys. Rev.*, **178,** 1424 (1969).
81. J. F. Asell and M. Nicol, *J. Chem. Phys.*, **49,** 5395 (1968).
82. S. M. Shapiro, D. C. O'Shea, and H. Z. Cummins, *Phys. Rev. Letters*, **19,** 361 (1967).
83. J. F. Scott, *Phys. Rev. Letters*, **21,** 907 (1968).
84. J. F. Scott, *Phys. Rev.*, **B1,** 3488 (1970).
85. S. P. S. Porto, P. A. Fleury, and T. C. Damen, *Phys. Rev.*, **154,** 522 (1967).
86. R. M. McFarlane and S. Ushioda, *Solid State Comm.*, **8,** 1081 (1970).
87. R. S. Katyar, P. Dawson, M. Hargreave, and G. R. Wilkinson, *J. Physics, C. Solid State Physics*, **4,** 2421 (1971).
88. I. R. Beattie and T. R. Gilson, *Proc. Royal Soc.*, **A 307,** 407 (1968).
89. D. J. Lockwood, *Light Scattering Spectra of Solids* (G. B. Wright, ed.), p. 75, Springer-Verlag, New York, 1969.

90. E. R. Lippincott, *Molecular Spectroscopy* (P. Hepple, ed.), p. 241, Elsevier, New York, 1968.
91. C. H. Perry and D. K. Agrawal, *Solid State Comm.*, **8,** 225 (1970).
92. J. F. Scott, *J. Chem. Phys.*, **49,** 2766 (1968).
93. C. K. Asawa, R. A. Satten, and O. M. Stafsudd, *Phys. Rev.*, **168,** 957 (1968).
94. C. K. Asawa, *Phys. Rev.*, **173,** 869 (1968).
95. R. P. Bauman and S. P. S. Porto, *Phys. Rev.*, **161,** 842 (1967).
96. A. Hadni, C. Henri, J. P. Mathieu, and H. Poulet, *Compt. Rend. Acad. Sci.*, **252,** 1585 (1961).
97. I. P. Kaminow, E. Buehler, and J. H. Wernick, *Phys. Rev.* [B], **2,** 960 (1970).
98. P. Bruesch and C. Schuler, *Brown Boveri Research Rep. KLR*, 1970.
99. S. P. S. Porto and R. S. Krishnan, *J. Chem. Phys.*, **47,** 1009 (1967).
100. I. R. Beattie and T. R. Gilson, *J. Chem. Soc.*, **A5,** 980 (1970).
101. G. Schaack and J. A. Koningstein, *J. Op. Soc. America*, **60,** 1110 (1970).
102. M. DiDomenico, Jr., S. H. Wemple, and S. P. S. Porto, *Phys. Rev.*, **174,** 552 (1968).
103. R. F. Schaufele and M. J. Weber, *J. Chem. Phys.*, **46,** 2859 (1967).
104. C. H. Perry, J. H. Fertel, and T. F. McNelly, *J. Chem. Phys.*, **47,** 1619 (1967).
105. C. H. Perry and N. E. Tornberg, *Light Scattering Spectra of Solids* (G. B. Wright, ed.), p. 467, Springer-Verlag, New York, 1969.
106. J. M. Worlock, J. F. Scott, and P. A. Fleury, *Light Scattering Spectra of Solids* (G. B. Wright, ed.), p. 689, Springer-Verlag, New York, 1969.
107. J. M. Worlock, *Light Scattering Spectra of Solids* (G. B. Wright, ed.), p. 411, Springer-Verlag, New York, 1969.
108. A. S. Barker and R. Loudon, *Phys. Rev.*, **158,** 433 (1967).
109. W. D. Johnston and I. P. Kaminow, *Phys. Rev.*, **168,** 1045 (1968).
110. W. D. Johnston, *Phys. Rev.*, **B1,** 3494 (1970).
111. R. F. Schaufele and M. J. Weber, *Phys. Rev.*, **152,** 705 (1966).
112. S. H. Wemple and M. DiDomenico, *Light Scattering Spectra of Solids* (G. B. Wright, ed.), p. 65, Springer-Verlag, New York, 1969.
113. J. F. Scott, *Phys. Rev.*, **183,** 823 (1969).
114. Y. Marqueton, F. Abba, E. A. Decamps, and M. A. Nusimovici, *C. R. Acad. Science*, **272,** 17, 1014 (1971).
115. P. Dawson, M. Hargreaves, and G. R. Wilkinson (in Press).
116. Z. Iqbal, C. Brown, and S. S. Mitra, *J. Chem. Phys.*, **52,** 4867 (1970).
117. A. Tramer, *Compt. Rend. Acad. Sci.*, **248,** 3546 (1959).
118. E. V. Chisler and M. S. Shur, *Phys. Stat. Sol.*, **17,** 173 (1966); 527 (1967).
119. V. S. Gorelik, M. M. Sushchinskii, and A. E. Novik, *Soviet Physics* (*Solid State*), **11,** 771 (U.S.S.R.) (1966).
120. Y. Lupsin and J. P. Chapelle, *Compt. Rend. Acad. Sci.* **269B,** 263 (1969).
121. Y. Lupsin and J. P. Chapelle, *Compt. Rend. Acad. Sci.* **269B,** 770 (1969).
122. C. K. Asawa and M. K. Bornoski, *Phys. Rev.* **2B,** 205 (1970).
123. S. P. S. Porto, J. A. Giordmaine, and T. C. Damen, *Phys. Rev.*, **147,** 508 (1966).
124. R. E. Miller, R. R. Getty, K. L. Treuil, and G. E. Leroi, *J. Chem. Phys.*, **51,** 1385 (1969).
125. K. Park, *Phys. Letters*, **22,** 39 (1966).
126. G. E. Leroi, D. L. Rousseau, and R. E. Miller, *J. Chem. Phys.*, **48,** 3409 (1968).
127. I. Nakagawa and J. L. Walter, *J. Chem. Phys.*, **51,** 138 (1969).

128. L. Couture, *Compt. Rend. Acad. Sci.*, **218,** 669 (1944).
129. P. Dawson, B. Berunblut, and G. R. Wilkinson (to be published).
130. M. Balkanski, M. K. Teng, and M. Nusimovici, *Light Scattering Spectra of Solids* (C. B. Wright, ed.), p. 731, Springer-Verlag, New York, 1969.
131. R. S. Krishnan, N. Krishnamurthy, T. M. Haridasan, and J. Govindarajan, *Light Scattering Spectra of Solids* (G. B. Wright, ed.), p. 167, Springer-Verlag, New York, 1969.
132. L. D. Vinh and P. Majon, *Compt. Rend. Acad. Sci.*, **270,** 1351 (1970).
133. C. M. Hartwig, D. L. Rousseau, and S. P. S. Porto, *Phys. Rev.*, **188,** 1328 (1969).
134. W. Otaguro, C. A. Arguello, and S. P. S. Porto, *Phys. Rev.* [B], **1,** 2818 (1970).
135. L. Couture, M. Krauzman, and J. P. Mathieu, *Compt. Rend. Acad. Sci.*, **269,** 1278 (1969).
136. R. Claus, H. W. Schrotter, H. H. Hacker, and S. Haussuhl, *Naturforsch*, **24a,** 1733 (1969).
137. L. Couture, M. Krauzman, and J. P. Mathieu, *Compt. Rend. Acad. Sci.*, **270,** 1246 (1970).
138. S. P. S. Porto and J. F. Scott, *Phys. Rev.*, **157,** 716 (1967).
139. J. F. Scott, *J. Chem. Phys.*, **48,** 874 (1968).
140. R. K. Khanna, W. S. Brower, B. R. Guscott, and E. R. Lippincott, *J. Resch. Natl. Bur. Standards*, **A72,** 81 (1968).
141. S. A. Miller, H. E. Rast, and H. H. Caspers, *J. Chem. Phys.*, **52,** 4172 (1970).
142. C. H. Perry and R. P. Lowndes, *J. Chem. Phys.*, **51,** 3648 (1969).
143. C. H. Wang and P. A. Fleury, *Light Scattering Spectra of Solids* (G. B. Wright, ed.), p. 651, Springer-Verlag, New York, 1969.
144. J. R. Durig and D. J. Antion, *J. Chem. Phys.*, **51,** 3639 (1969).
145. Y. Ebisuzaki and M. Nicol, *Chem. Phys. Letters*, **3,** 480 (1969).
146. J. Durig, D. J. Antion, and C. B. Pate, *J. Chem. Phys.*, **52,** 5542 (1970).
147. J. Durig, D. J. Antion, and F. G. Baglin, *J. Chem. Phys.*, **49,** 666 (1968).
148. J. J. Rush, A. J. Melveger, and E. R. Lippincott, *J. Chem. Phys.*, **51,** 2947 (1969).
149. M. Trefler and G. R. Wilkinson, *Disc. Faraday Soc.*, **48,** 108 (1969).
150. I. R. Beattie, M. J. Gall, and G. A. Ozin, *J. Chem. Soc. A Inorg. Phys. Theor.*, 1001 (1969).
151. J. P. Hurrell, S. P. S. Porto, I. F. Chang, S. S. Mitra, and R. P. Bauman, *Phys. Rev.*, **173,** 851 (1968).
152. G. Mace, G. Schaack, T. Ng, and J. A. Koningstein, *Z. Phys.*, **230,** 391 (1970).
153. I. R. Beattie, T. R. Gilson, and G. A. Ozin, *J. Chem. Soc.* [A], 534 (1969).
154. P. Dawson, B. Berunblut, and G. R. Wilkinson, *Spectrochemica Acta*, 27a, 1849 (1971).
155. L. Couture and J. P. Mathieu, *Acta Cryst.*, **5,** 571 (1952).
156. P. Dawson, M. Hargreave, and G. R. Wilkinson, *J. Physics C.*, **4,** 240, (1971).
157. I. Duncan and J. H. Stewart, *Proc. 2nd International Conf. on Light Scattering on Solids*, E. M. Balanski, p. 310 Flammarion Sciences, Paris (1971).
158. W. B. Lacina and P. S. Pershan, *Phys. Rev.* [B], **1,** 1765 (1970).
159. R. Shuker and R. W. Gammon, *Phys. Rev. Letters*, **25,** 222 (1970).
160. M. Hass, *Solid State Comm.*, **7,** 1069 (1969).
161. R. K. Chang and S. S. Mitra, *Phys. Rev.*, **172,** 924 (1968).
162. R. K. Chang, B. Launa, and P. S. Pershan, *Phys. Rev. Letters*, **17,** 755 (1966).

163. R. K. Chang, J. M. Ralston, and D. E. Keating, *Light Scattering Spectra of Solids* (G. B. Wright, ed.), p. 369, Springer-Verlag, New York, 1969.
164. N. D. Strahm and A. L. McWhorter, *Light Scattering Spectra of Solids*, (G. B. Wright, ed.), p. 455, Springer-Verlag, New York, 1969.
165. R. Braustein, *Phys. Rev.*, **130,** 879 (1963).
166. O. Brafman, I. F. Chang, G. Lengyel, S. S. Mitra, and E. Carnall, *Phys. Rev. Letters*, **19,** 1120 (1967).
167. J. A. Harrington, R. T. Horley, and C. T. Walker, *Solid State Comm.*, **8,** 407 (1970).
168. King's College Spectroscopy Group, Report to U.S. Army, 1964–1965.
169. D. T. Hon, W. L. Faust, W. G. Spitzer, and P. E. Williams, *Phys. Rev. Letters*, **25,** 1184 (1970).
170. L. C. Kravitz, *Phys. Rev. Letters*, **24,** 884 (1970).
171. R. T. Hartley, J. B. Paige, and C. T. Walker, *Phys. Rev. Letters*, **23,** 922 (1969).
172. R. Kaiser and W. Moller, *Phys. Lett.*, **28,** 619 (1969).
173. J. M. Worlock and S. P. S. Porto, *Phys. Rev. Letters*, **15,** 697 (1965).
174. S. Radhakrishna and H. K. Sehgal, *Phys. Lett.*, **29A,** 286 (1969).
175. C. J. Buchenauer, D. B. Fitchen, and J. B. Page, *Light Scattering Spectra of Solids* (G. B. Wright, ed.), p. 521, Springer-Verlag, New York, 1969.
176. W. Holzer, W. F. Murphy, H. J. Bernstein, and J. Rolfe, *J. Mol. Spect.*, **26,** 543 (1968).
177. W. C. Holton and M. de Wit, *Solid State Comm.*, **7,** 1101 (1969).
178. W. R. Fenner and M. V. Klein, *Light Scattering Spectra of Solids* (G. B. Wright, ed.), p. 497, Springer-Verlag, New York, 1969.
179. M. V. Klein, B. Wedding, and M. A. Levine, *Phys. Rev.*, **180,** 902 (1969).
180. R. H. Callender and P. S. Pershan, *Light Scattering Spectra of Solids* (G. B. Wright, ed.), p 505, Springer-Verlag, New York, 1969.
181. I. W. Shepherd, A. R. Evans, and D. B. Fitchen, *Phys. Lett.*, **A27,** 171 (1968).
182. R. J. Elliott, W. Hayes, G. D. Jones, H. F. Macdonald, and C. T. Sennett, *Proc. Roy. Soc. A*, **289,** 1 (1967).
183. R. C. C. Leite and S. P. S. Porto, *Phys. Rev. Letters*, **17,** 10 (1966).
184. R. C. C. Leite, T. C. Damen, and J. F. Scott, *Light Scattering Spectra of Solids* (G. B. Wright, ed.), p. 359, Springer-Verlag, New York, 1969.
185. R. C. C. Leite and J. F. Scott, *Phys. Rev. Letters*, **22,** 80 (1969).
186. A. Pinczuk and E. Burstein, *Phys. Rev. Letters*, **21,** 1073 (1968).
187. J. F. Scott, R. C. C. Leite, and T. C. Damen, *Phys. Rev.*, **188,** 1285 (1969).
188. J. F. Scott, T. C. Damen, R. C. Leite, and W. T. Silfvast, *Solid State Comm.*, **7,** 953 (1969).
189. J. F. Scott, T. C. Damen, W. T. Silfvast, R. C. C. Leite, and L. E. Cheeseman, *Opt. Comm.*, **1,** 397 (1970).
190. M. Teng and J. C. Dugautier, *Compt. Rend. Acad. Sci.*, **269,** 1109 (1969).
191. M. Ashkin, *J. de Phys.*, **26,** 709 (1965).
192. B. Bendow, J. L. Birman, A. K. Ganguly, T. C. Damen, and J. F. Scott, *Opt. Comm.*, **1,** 267 (1970).
193. M. V. Klein and S. P. S. Porto, *Phys. Rev. Letters*, **22,** 782 (1969).
194. J. F. Scott, *Phys. Rev.* [B], **2,** 1209 (1970).
195. C. H. Henry and J. J. Hopfield, *Phys. Rev. Letters*, **15,** 964 (1965).
196. S. P. S. Porto, B. Tell, and T. C. Damen, *Phys. Rev. Letters*, **16,** 450 (1966).

197. J. F. Scott, L. E. Cheeseman, and S. P. S. Porto, *Phys. Rev.*, **162,** 834 (1967).
198. S. Ushioda, A. Pinczuk, W. Taylor, and E. Burstein, *Proc. Inatl. Conf. on II–VI Semiconductor Compounds, 1967* (D. G. Thomas, ed.), Benjamin, New York.
199. H. E. Puthoff, R. H. Partell, B. G. Huth, and M. A. Chacon, *J. App. Phys.*, **39,** 2144 (1968).
200. J. F. Scott, P. A. Fleury, and J. M. Worlock, *Phys. Rev.*, **177,** 1288 (1969).
201. E. Burstein, *Comm. Sol. St. Phys.*, **1,** 202 (1969).
202. R. Claus, *Z. Naturforsch*, **25,** 306 (1970).
203. R. W. Terhune, P. D. Maker, and C. M. Savage, *Phys. Rev. Letters*, **14,** 681 (1965).
204. S. J. Cyvin, J. E. Rauch, and J. C. Decius, *J. Chem. Phys.*, **43,** 4083 (1964).
205. P. D. Maker, *Second Inalt. Conf. Raman Spectroscopy*, Oxford, 1970.
206. A. I. Stekhanov and M. B. Eliashberg, *Soviet Phys. (Sol. State)*, **5** (1964).
207. R. Kaiser and P. Mockel, *Phys. Letters* [A], **25,** 749 (1967).
208. R. Kaiser and W. Moller, *Phys. Letters*, **28,** 619 (1969).
209. R. Callender and D. S. Pershan, *Phys. Rev. Letters*, **23,** 947 (1969).
210. J. Behringer, *Raman Spectroscopy* (H. Symanski, ed.), Plenum, New York, 1967.
211. P. A. Fleury, *Light Scattering Spectra of Solids* (G. B. Wright, ed.), p. 185, Springer-Verlag, New York, 1969.
212a. P. Moch, G. Parisot, R. E. Dietz, and H. J. Guggenheim, *Light Scattering Spectra of Solids* (G. B. Wright, ed.), p. 231, Springer-Verlag, New York, 1969.
212. P. A. Fleury, S. P. S. Porto, L. E. Cheeseman, and H. J. Guggenheim, *Phys. Rev. Letters*, **17,** 84 (1966).
213. P. A. Fleury and R. Loudon, *Phys. Rev.*, **166,** 514 (1968).
214. P. A. Fleury, *Phys. Rev. Letters*, **20,** 151 (1968).
215. E. Anastasskis and C. H. Perry, *Proc. of 2nd International Conference on Light Scattering in Solids*, Edited M. Balanski, p. 47, Flammarion Sciences, Paris, (1971).
216. E. R. Lippincott, G. L. Cessae and J. Nestor, *Molecular Spectroscopy*, Edited P. Hepple, p. 313, Applied Science Publishers Ltd. London, (1971).
217. C. H. Perry, D. K. Agrawal, *Phonons*, Edited M. A. Nusimovici, p. 342, Flammarion Sciences, Paris, (1971).
218. D. Hwang, R. Koblinska, S. A. Solin, *Proc. 2nd International Conference on Light Scattering in Solids*, Edited M. Balanski, p. 260, Flammarion Sciences, Paris, (1971).
219. R. Shuker and R. W. Gamon, *Proc. 2nd International Conference on Light Scattering in Solids*, Edited M. Balanski, p. 334, Flammarion Sciences, Paris, (1971).
220. J. F. Asell and M. Nichol, *J. Chem. Phys.*, **49,** 5395 (1968).
221. H. Poulet, *Ann. Phys. (Paris)*, **10,** 908 (1955).
222. R. Lyddane, R. Sachs, and E. Teller, *Phys. Rev.*, **59,** 673 (1941).
223. J. Hougen and S. Singh, *Phys. Rev. Letters*, **10,** 406 (1963).
224. D. Krishnamurti, *Proc. Ind. Acad. Sci.*, **AL,** 223 (1960).
225. N. Q. Dao and G. R. Wilkinson (to be published). *J. Chem. Physics.*
226. A. N. Jette, J. Bohardy, J. C. Murphy, D. C. O'Shea, and C. M. Wilson, *Physics Letters*, **31A,** 449 (1970).
227. I. N. Nair and C. E. Hathaway, *Physics Letters*, **30A,** 253 (1969).
228. W. Holzer, W. F. Murphy, and H. J. Bernstein (to be published).
229. A. K. Ganguly and J. L. Birman, *Phys. Rev.*, **162,** 806 (1967).

230. G. B. Wright, P. L. Kelley, and S. H. Groves, *Light Scattering Spectra of Solids* (G. B. Wright, ed.), p. 335, Springer-Verlag, New York, 1969.

231. R. L. Aggarwal, B. Lax, C. E. Chase, C. R. Ridgeon, D. Limbert, and D. F. Brown, *Applied Physics Letters*, **18,** 383 (1971).

232. P. A. Wolff, *Light Scattering Spectra of Solids* (G. B. Wright, ed.), p. 273, Springer-Verlag, New York, 1969.

233. J. Loader, *Basic Laser Raman Spectroscopy*, Heyden Sadtler, 1970.

234. R. J. Elliott, R. T. Harley, W. Hayes, S. R. P. Smith, *Journ. Phys.* (to be published).

235. P. Brüesch and H. Kalbfleisch, *Phys. Stat. Sol.* (b) **44**, K97 (1971).

236. R. J. Bell, N. F. Bird and P. Dean, *J. Phys. C.*: *Proc. Phys. Soc. London* **1**, 299 (1968).

237. R. Zallen, G. Lucovsky, W. Taylor, A. Pinczuk, E. Burstein, *Phys. Rev.* **1,** 4058 (1970).

238. T. C. Damen, S. P. S. Porto, and B. Tell, *Phys. Rev.* **142,** 570 (1966).

239. T. J. Wieting and J. L. Verble, *Phys. Rev.* **B3**, 4286 (1971).

240. R. Forneris, *Am. Miner.* **54**, 1062 (1969).

241. D. M. Adams and D. C. Newton, *J. Chem. Soc.* **A22**, 3507 (1971).

242. D. A. Long, *Third International Raman Conference*, Rheims, 1972.

Acknowledgments

I wish to thank authors and publishers for permission to reproduce diagrams and especially for the crystal structures which are reproduced from R. C. Evans, *An Introduction to Crystal Chemistry*, Cambridge University Press, and A. K. Wells, *Structural Inorganic Chemistry*, Oxford University Press. The stereographic diagrams of crystal structures are reproduced from W. Hamilton and J. Ibers, *Hydrogen Bonding in Solids*, Benjamin Press.

Crystal Index

The crystals are listed alphabetically by their usual formulas. Structure types and some mineralogical names are also included. Letters in parentheses after a formula represent impurities, e.g., KCl, (Tl^+).

CUMULATIVE AUTHOR INDEX

Numbers in parentheses are reference numbers. Numbers in italics give the page on which the complete reference is listed.

E

F

G

H

L

N

O

P

Q

R

S

T

U

V

W

X

Y

Z

CUMULATIVE SUBJECT INDEX

See also the Compound Index for Chapter 7 (p. 512) and the Crystal Index for Chapter 11 (p. 984).

D

H

I